OXFORD JUNIOR
ENCYCLOPAEDIA

VOLUME VIII
ENGINEERING

OXFORD JUNIOR ENCYCLOPAEDIA

GENERAL EDITORS

LAURA E. SALT AND ROBERT SINCLAIR

ILLUSTRATIONS EDITOR: HELEN MARY PETTER

VOLUME VIII

ENGINEERING

OXFORD UNIVERSITY PRESS

Oxford University Press, Amen House, London E.C.4

GLASGOW NEW YORK TORONTO MELBOURNE WELLINGTON
BOMBAY CALCUTTA MADRAS KARACHI
CAPE TOWN IBADAN NAIROBI ACCRA SINGAPORE

FIRST PUBLISHED 1955
REPRINTED 1956, 1957

PRINTED IN GREAT BRITAIN
AT THE UNIVERSITY PRESS, OXFORD
BY CHARLES BATEY, PRINTER TO THE UNIVERSITY

PREFACE

IN authorizing the preparation of this work the Delegates of the Oxford University Press had foremost in mind the need to provide a basic book of reference for school libraries. In form it was to be a genuine encyclopaedia, in treatment and vocabulary suitable for the young reader. To many children (and indeed to many adults) reading is not a natural activity: they do not turn to books for their own sake. But they can be trained to go to books for information which they want for some particular purpose—and thus, very often, to form a habit which will be of lifelong value. Their capacity to read continuously for any length of time being limited, they can absorb knowledge better if they get it in small quantities: therefore they will often read reference books when they may reject the reading of more extended matter. Again, it is probably true to say of such readers that their approach is from the particular to the general, and from the application to the principle, rather than the reverse, that their main interest is in the modern world around them, and that since they are not very good at conceiving things outside their own experience, their capacity for grasping abstract ideas is limited. On the other hand, once their interest is aroused, they will often pursue a subject to remarkable lengths, so long as its development is logical and the treatment avoids dullness.

But such generalizations can easily be overdone: many children using the books will not be of this type. Moreover, it was evident from the first that a project involving so great an amount of work, however exactly it might meet its principal mark, would be fully justified only if it could be of service to a far wider circle of readers. Even for the age-group first in mind, anything like 'writing-down to children' must plainly be taboo—but clear exposition and simple language are no bad qualities in writing for any audience. Here, then, it seemed, was the opportunity to provide a work of reference suitable for many readers to whom the large, standard encyclopaedias are too heavy and technical, and the popular alternatives for the most part neither sufficiently complete nor authoritative. The fact that the plan allowed for an exceptionally large proportion of illustrations to text (between one-quarter and one-third of the total space) is an advantage to any reader, since pictures may, in many instances, save whole paragraphs of involved explanation. With these secondary aims well in mind, therefore, the General

Editors have ventured to hope that the encyclopaedia may find usefulness
not only among certain younger children, but also among older students in
clubs, libraries, and Young People's Colleges, and even to no small extent
among their parents and other adults who may wish for a simple approach
to some unfamiliar or forgotten subject.

SCOPE AND EMPHASIS. Within certain limits the OXFORD JUNIOR ENCY-
CLOPAEDIA purports to be reasonably comprehensive, though (in common
with all general encyclopaedias) not exhaustive. Chief among these limits is
that matter already easily available in school textbooks is included only so
far as its presence is necessary for the proper understanding of the subject
under discussion. Thus, although an immense field of history is surveyed, it
will be found mainly under headings dealing with its effects, or in the bio-
graphies of those who lived to make it. Purely technical or scientific subjects,
also, are omitted except when they have some general interest. In natural
history and kindred studies the immense variety of forms necessarily led at
times either to their treatment by groups or to their omission on purely
arbitrary decisions as to which species would, in all probability, never be
looked for, or because there was nothing particularly interesting to say of
them. In point of general balance the stress is laid rather on the modern
world, though due space is given to the factors which have shaped it, no less
than to those which are changing it.

ARRANGEMENT. The encyclopaedia is planned to consist of twelve
volumes. Each is arranged alphabetically within itself, and each deals with
a particular range of related subjects. Within its terms of reference, then,
each volume is virtually self-contained, and, owing to the great number of
single-line cross-references, can well be used alone. This arrangement, which
has several incidental advantages (as of production, in difficult times, and of
prompt revision later), arose mainly from one consideration. If articles were
to be kept really short—and, in fact, few approach and almost none exceeds
2,000 words—many subjects could be dealt with comprehensively only by
referring the reader to other relevant articles—itself a desirable thing to do.
It was clearly preferable for these to be under his hand, rather than be dispersed through any of the twelve volumes at the caprice of the alphabet.
This the present arrangement achieves to a great extent. If it has led to a
small amount of overlapping, that again is not without its advantages.

The cross-references play an indispensable part in the make-up of the encyclopaedia. They are of two kinds: references in the text to further articles amplifying the particular point under review, and references at the end of an article to others taking the whole subject farther. Therefore, a reader looking up any wide subject, such as CIVIL ENGINEERING, and following up its cross-references either in the text or at the end of the article, can discover under what main headwords the subject is treated. These, again, will refer him to any subsidiary articles, as also, in many cases, to those of a complementary nature. Thus he may be guided either from the general to the particular or vice versa. It is believed that the titles of the twelve volumes (see p. xii), in conjunction with their sub-titles, will usually lead the reader straight to the volume containing the information he wants. In selecting headwords, the rules generally followed have been to prefer the familiar, or even the colloquial, reserving the technical alternative for a single-line entry, and to group narrow subjects under a headword of wider scope. Thus, for THEODOLITE, *see* SURVEYING INSTRUMENTS; for TEMPERING, *see* HEAT TREATMENT; for EXTRUSION, *see* FORGING AND PRESSING; for WATTS, *see* MEASUREMENT, UNITS OF; and for TIME AND MOTION STUDY, *see* PRODUCTION ENGINEERING.

L. E. S., R. S.

OXFORD, 1955

LIST OF CONTRIBUTORS

EDITORS

F. M. S. HARMAR-BROWN, F. J. M. LAVER,
SIR ALEXANDER GIBB & PARTNERS, A. M. WOOD

PRINCIPAL CONTRIBUTORS

Power and Mechanical Engineering
F. M. S. HARMAR-BROWN, M.A.
PETER TRIPPE, Associate Editor, *The Machinist*.

Civil Engineering
SIR ALEXANDER GIBB & PARTNERS, Consulting Engineers.

Optics
E. H. LINFOOT, M.A., D.Phil., D.Sc. (Oxon), Sc.D. (Cantab.), John Couch Adams Astronomer in the University of Cambridge.

Electrical Engineering
F. J. M. LAVER, B.Sc., A.M.I.E.E.

Metals
MAX DAVIES, B.A., formerly Public Relations Officer, British Iron and Steel Research Association.

LESLIE AITCHISON, D.Met. (Sheffield), M.Sc. (Birmingham), B.Sc. (London), formerly Professor of Industrial Metallurgy in the University of Birmingham.

Nuclear Power
W. J. WHITEHOUSE, M.Sc., of the Atomic Energy Research Establishment, Harwell.

OTHER CONTRIBUTORS

W. F. ATKINS, M.I.E.D., A.M.I.Mech.E., A.M.I.Prod.E., Senior Experimental Officer, National Physical Laboratory.

L. S. ATKINSON, M.I.Mech.E., M.I.E.E., Consulting Engineer, Waygood-Otis Ltd.

LIEUT.-COMMANDER L. M. BATES, R.N.V.R.

J. E. BIALOKOZ, Ph.D., A.M.I.Mech.E.

P. L. BLACKSTONE, T.D., M.A., M.I.E.E., of Messrs. Merz and McLellan, Consulting Engineers.

F. P. BOWDEN, Sc.D., F.R.S., Fellow of Gonville and Caius College, Cambridge.

G. BRADFIELD, of the National Physical Laboratory.

D. J. O. BRANDT, A.R.S.M., B.Sc., A.I.M., Senior Scientific Officer, Steelmaking Division, British Iron and Steel Research Association.

F. H. BURCH, of the National Physical Laboratory.

W. DERYCK CHESTERMAN, B.Sc., F.Inst.P., of the Royal Naval Scientific Service, Admiralty.

A. V. CLEAVER, F.R.Ae.S., Special Projects Engineer, de Havilland Engine Co. Ltd.

WILLIAM COOKSON, M.Inst.Met., M.I.Prod.E., Managing Director, Cookson Sheet Metal Developments Ltd.

A. G. COURSE, Master Mariner, A.M.Inst.T., Dockmaster, Surrey Commercial Docks, Port of London Authority.

H. CREIGHTON, M.A., A.R.I.B.A.

W. DAVIES, Ph.D., B.Sc., A.M.I.Mech.E., Reader in Mining Mechanical Engineering in the University of London; Senior Lecturer, Royal School of Mines.

F. DOLLIN, Chief Turbine Designer, C. A. Parsons & Co. Ltd., Newcastle-upon-Tyne.

E. G. DORMON, M.R.San.I.

F. M. G. DU-PLAT-TAYLOR, M.I.C.E.

SIR ALFRED EGERTON, D.Sc., F.R.S., Emeritus Professor of Chemical Technology in the University of London; formerly Secretary of the Royal Society.

A. J. FERGUSON, A.M.I.Struct.E., Senior Member of Design Staff, Sir Wm. Arrol & Co. Ltd., Glasgow.

D. H. FOLLETT, M.A., Ph.D., F.Inst.P., of the Science Museum, London.

G. R. M. GARRATT, M.A., M.I.E.E., of the Science Museum, London.

H. V. R. GEARY, M.C.

E. W. GOLDING, M.Sc.Tech., M.I.E.E., M.Amer.I.E.E., Head of Rural Electrification and Wind Power Department, Electrical Research Association.

G. G. GOURIET, A.M.I.E.E., of the Research Department, Engineering Division, British Broadcasting Corporation.

CHARLES S. GRAY, B.Sc. (Eng.), A.M.Inst.C.E., A.M.I.Struct.E.

E. M. GREENWOOD.

A. GRIERSON, B.Sc. (Hons.), A.M.I.Min.E., Lecturer in Mining, Royal School of Mines.

P. J. GUY, Assoc.I.E.E., Sub-senior Lecturer, Engineering Training Department, British Broadcasting Corporation.

K. J. HABELL, M.Sc., A.R.C.S., D.I.C., F.Inst.P., Principal Scientific Officer, National Physical Laboratory.

D. HALTON THOMSON, O.B.E., M.I.C.E., formerly Engineer to the Portsmouth Water Company.

S. B. HAMILTON, Ph.D., M.Sc., B.Sc. (Eng.), M.I.C.E., M.I.Struct.E., of the Building Research Station, Department of Scientific and Industrial Research.

GODFREY HARRISON, B.A.

A. H. HAYCOCK, F.I.M.Wood.T., Technical Representative, Drabble & Sanderson Ltd., Sheffield.

HEENAN & FROUDE LTD., Worcester.

H. HEYWOOD, D.Sc., Ph.D., M.I.Mech.E., M.I.Chem.E., Reader in Mechanical Engineering, Imperial College of Science and Technology.

H. J. HINE, B.Sc. (Oxon), of the National Agricultural Advisory Service Unit, National Institute of Agricultural Engineering.

G. R. HOFFMAN, A.C.G.I., B.Sc., A.M.I.C.E.

JOHN HOOPER, Editor, *Sheet Metal Industries*.

J. HOWLETT, Ph.D., of the Atomic Energy Research Establishment, Harwell.

F. G. IRVING, M.Eng., D.I.C., Lecturer, Department of Aeronautics, Imperial College of Science and Technology.

J. W. JENKIN, Ph.D., B.Sc., F.R.I.C., F.I.M., Head of Research Organization, Tube Investments Ltd.

JAMES E. LEE, M.I.C.E., M.Amer.S.C.E., Managing Director, Highways Construction Ltd.

REV. C. J. E. LEFROY, M.A.

C. H. LEWIS, M.Sc., M.Inst.Gas E., of the North Thames Gas Board.

S. LILLEY, M.Sc., Ph.D., Resident Tutor, Department of Extra-Mural Studies, University of Birmingham.

P. R. MARRACK.

J. N. MASKELYNE, A.I.Loco.E., Technical Editor, *The Model Engineer*.

WILLIAM MUCKLE, Ph.D., M.Sc., M.I.N.A., M.I.Mar.E., Senior Lecturer, Department of Naval Architecture, King's College, University of Durham.

L. J. MURDOCK, M.Sc., Ph.D., A.M.I.C.E., Director of Research Department, George Wimpey & Co. Ltd.

T. R. J. OAKLEY, A.M.I.Mech.E., A.M.I.Prod.E., of the National Physical Laboratory.

A. C. PALLOTT, M.B.E., B.Sc. (Eng.), M.I.C.E., M.I.H.V.E., formerly Superintending Engineer, Ministry of Works and Department of Scientific and Industrial Research.

E. A. PALMER, Chief Engineer, Heavy Civil Engineering Department, George Wimpey & Co. Ltd.

T. A. L. PATON, B.Sc., M.I.C.E., Partner of Sir Alexander Gibb & Partners.

J. M. PIRIE, Ph.D., A.M.I.Chem.E.

R. T. PIRIE, D.F.M., B.Sc. (Eng.), of Imperial Chemical Industries Ltd.

WILLIAM RESIDE, Chief Draughtsman, Sir Wm. Arrol & Co. Ltd., Glasgow.

CHARLES E. REYNOLDS, B.Sc. (Eng.) (London), A.M.I.C.E.

J. B. RICHARDSON, A.R.S.M., M.I.M.M., Consulting Mining Engineer.

A. R. ROBBINS, B.Sc., M.A., A.R.I.C.S., Senior Lecturer in Surveying in the University of Oxford.

B. WHEELER ROBINSON, M.A., Ph.D., of the National Physical Laboratory.

S. RODDA, B.Sc., F.Inst.P.

H. R. RUFF, B.Sc., M.I.E.E., Head of the Lamp and Lighting Section, Research Laboratory, British Thomson Houston Co. Ltd., Rugby.

M. Ruhemann, Ph.D., M.I.Chem.E., of Surgas S.p.a., Turin.

L. F. Rydill.

T. Elwen Shaw.

P. A. Sheppard, Professor of Meteorology in the University of London.

Graham A. C. Simpson.

W. O. Skeat, B.Sc. (Eng.), A.M.I.C.E., M.I.Mech.E., M.I.Loco.E.

R. A. Smith, M.A., Ph.D., A.M.I.E.E., Head of Physics Department, Radar Research Establishment, Malvern.

J. Stone & Co. (Charlton) Ltd.

J. W. Sutton, of *The Wire Industry*.

C. W. J. Taffs, M.Sc. (Eng.), M.I.Mech.E.

James Taylor, M.B.E., D.Sc., Ph.D., F.R.I.C., F.Inst.P., M.I.Min.E., Director of Imperial Chemical Industries Ltd.

J. Th. Thijsse, Professor of Hydrology in the Technical University of Delft.

J. D. Todd, M.A., D.Phil., Lecturer and Demonstrator in Engineering Science in the University of Oxford.

Col. C. F. Tumber, O.B.E., T.D., R.A.

Arnold Tustin, Professor of Electrical Engineering in the University of Birmingham.

R. W. Unwin, Photographic Technical Advisor, Philips Electrical Ltd.

F. C. Vokes, B.Sc., M.I.C.E., F.R.San.I., P.P.Inst.S.P., Engineer to the Birmingham Tame and Rea District Drainage Board.

Rex Wailes, F.S.A., M.I.Mech.E., President of the Newcomen Society.

F. A. B. Ward, M.A., Ph.D. (Cantab.), F.B.H.I., F.Inst.P., F.M.A., Keeper of the Department of Physics and Officer-in-charge of the Time Measurement Section, Science Museum, London.

E. B. Watton, A.M.I.E.E., Assoc.A.I.E.E., of Babcock & Wilcox Ltd.

A. A. J. Willitt, of Dowty Equipment Ltd., Cheltenham.

C. A. Wilson, M.Inst.C.E., Divisional Engineer, Docks and Inland Waterways.

S. S. Wilson, M.A., University Demonstrator in Engineering Science in the University of Oxford.

R. E. J. Worth, B.Sc., A.M.I.C.E., Chief Engineer, Planning Department, George Wimpey & Co. Ltd.

Norman Wymer.

J. Yarnell, A.Inst.P., of de Havilland Propellers Ltd.

Assistant General Editor—A. T. G. Pocock.

Assistant Illustrations Editor—Gillian Avery.

ACKNOWLEDGEMENTS

THE EDITORS wish to thank the following for their advice and other help in planning this volume: Sir Edward Bullard, Director, National Physical Laboratory; Willis Jackson, D.Sc., D.Phil., M.I.E.E., F.R.S., Director of Research and Education, Metropolitan-Vickers Electrical Co. Ltd., Manchester; N. F. Mott, M.A., D.Sc., F.R.S., Cavendish Professor of Experimental Physics in the University of Cambridge; J. L. Nayler, Secretary, The Aeronautical Research Council; A. Parker, C.B.E., D.Sc., Director of Fuel Research, Department of Scientific and Industrial Research; J. Foster Petree, M.I.Mech.E., M.Inst.N.A., formerly Editor of *Engineering*; J. A. S. Ritson, D.S.O., M.Inst.M.M., M.Inst.Min.E., formerly Professor of Mining, Imperial College of Science and Technology; F. H. Rolt, O.B.E., D.Sc., formerly Superintendent, Metrology Division, National Physical Laboratory; and A. Thom, M.A., D.Sc., Professor of Engineering Science in the University of Oxford.

The Editors also wish to thank all those who have helped in the compilation of the text and illustrations. They are particularly indebted to the individuals and firms who have generously lent photographs and prepared drawings. The photographs on pp. 385 and 386 are reproduced by courtesy of the Birmingham Tame and Rea District Drainage Board.

They wish to make special acknowledgement to Major H. V. R. Geary, M.C., for help in the early planning of this volume, in particular, in the establishing of boundaries between it and Vol. VII.

COLOUR PLATES

PLAN OF VOLUMES

HOW TO USE THIS BOOK

THIS VOLUME is one of twelve, each on a separate subject, the whole set forming what is called an encyclopaedia, or work from which you can find out almost anything you want to know. (The word comes originally from the Greek *enkuklios*, circular or complete, and *paideia*, education.) Each of the twelve volumes is arranged alphabetically within itself, as twelve dictionaries would be.

The difference between a dictionary and an encyclopaedia is that, while the first gives you no more than the meanings and derivations of words, the second tells you a very great deal more about their subjects. For instance, from a dictionary you would find that a DAM was an artificial barrier built across a stream to obstruct its flow and raise its level, and you would learn little more; but an encyclopaedia will tell you why dams are built and how they help to provide a regular water supply, for example, or hydro-electric power; it will tell you something about the earliest dams, and will describe how a modern dam is built and what materials are used. Then a dictionary contains nearly every word in the language; but an encyclopaedia deals only with words and subjects about which there is something interesting to be said, beyond their bare meanings. So you should not expect to find every word in an encyclopaedia—every subject is there, but not every word.

To find any subject, you have first to decide in which of the twelve volumes it comes. Each of these has a title as well as a number, and also a list of general subjects to make the title clearer. All these are set out in the Plan of Volumes on the opposite page. Very often you will be able to tell from the title alone which volume contains the information you need; but if not, the list of sub-headings in the plan opposite will help to direct you. For example, if you want to read about people, the way they have lived at different times and places, and the things they have believed and worshipped, you would turn to Volume I. If, however, you want to find out about an animal or plant, you would look it up in Volume II, Natural History; but if you wanted to know how that animal or plant is used in something like farming, fishing, or trapping, you would find it in Volume VI. If your subject were something in nature that does not have life—such as the sun, or a particular country or river, or a kind of stone—you would find it in Volume III, with tides, earthquakes, the weather, and many other things.

Matters connected with communication of any kind—of people, or goods, or even of ideas—are in Volume IV. So you would look there for languages and printing and broadcasting, as well as for ships and trains and roads. Business and trade are in Volume VII. Recreations are in Volume IX, which includes games and sports, entertainment, clubs, animal pets, and sporting animals. How we are governed and protected by the State, the law, and the armed forces is told in Volume X. Volume XI deals with almost everything connected with our homes, from the design and furnishing of the house to the clothes and health of those who live in it. The titles of Volumes V and XII, Great Lives and The Arts, explain themselves; and a rather fuller account of the volume you are now reading, on Engineering, is given on page xv opposite.

To find your subject, think of its ordinary name, and then look it up just as though you were using a dictionary—the As on the first page and the Zs (if there are any) on the last. If you cannot find it, try a more general word. For instance, if you want to read about Neutrons, and cannot find it under that name (as you cannot), try either NUCLEAR POWER in this volume or ATOM in Volume III—either of which will lead you to it. As you read any article, you will probably come across the titles of other articles in some way connected with what you are reading. You will know that they are titles of other articles because they will be printed in capital letters. Either they will be followed by (q.v.) in brackets (this is short for the Latin *quod vide*, and means 'which see'), or else they themselves will be in brackets, with the word *see* in front of them. You can look up these other articles at once if you want to know more about the particular point dealt with, or you can save them up until you have finished the article you are reading. At the end of any article you may find the words 'See also', followed by one or more titles in small capital letters. If you look these titles up, they will tell you still more about the subject that interests you. These last 'cross-references' are very useful if you want to look up a particularly wide subject (such as METALLURGY or ENGINES, HISTORY OF), because they show you at once the titles of all the main articles dealing with it. You can then decide for yourself which to read.

WHAT YOU WILL FIND IN THIS VOLUME

THIS VOLUME TELLS HOW MAN USES NATURE'S RESOURCES BY FORGING TOOLS, CONSTRUCTING MACHINERY, HARNESSING POWER, AND ERECTING GREAT ENGINEERING WORKS

POWER. More than 2,000 years ago man discovered how to make WIND POWER and WATER POWER work for him, and the idea that there were enormous stores of potential ENERGY in FUELS has also been recognized at least for some hundreds of years. But only within the last 250 years has man discovered how to exploit this energy by using first STEAM ENGINES and then various forms of INTERNAL COMBUSTION ENGINES, STEAM and GAS TURBINES, as well as ELECTRIC MOTORS. The use of NUCLEAR POWER is now also being explored.

MECHANICAL ENGINEERING. This branch of engineering is concerned with the actual making of things. It makes use of both the traditional skill of the craftsman in FITTING and the speed and precision of MACHINE TOOLS, such as DRILLING MACHINES, LATHES, and PRESSES, in construction. The mechanical engineer must study the properties of METALS and ALLOYS and must have an understanding of their behaviour under STRESS AND STRAIN, EXPANSION AND CONTRACTION, and FRICTION, and the ways in which they can be changed by HEAT TREATMENT.

ELECTRICAL ENGINEERING. The development of ELECTRIC CURRENT as the means of providing power for the ELECTRIC MOTOR, HEATING, and ILLUMINATION is one of the great engineering contributions of the early 20th century. This volume describes how electricity is generated in POWER STATIONS and distributed by the GRID SYSTEM and through electric CABLES. It also describes how a study of ELECTRONICS has provided our generation with RADIO, RADAR, and TELEVISION.

CIVIL ENGINEERING. The civil engineer makes use not only of the skill of the mechanical engineer but also of his own special knowledge of SURVEYING and the principles of BUILDING to construct large public works, such as DAMS, DOCKS AND HARBOURS, as well as ROADS, RAILWAYS, and BRIDGES, and to carry out schemes of LAND RECLAMATION. To do this he must understand such techniques as CONCRETE CONSTRUCTION and STRUCTURAL STEELWORK and the uses of traditional BRICKWORK.

SCIENCE AND MATHEMATICS. In modern engineering so high a degree of accuracy in measurement is required that a knowledge of mathematics, in particular of GEOMETRY, TRIGONOMETRY, and CALCULUS, and of its application to MECHANICS, is essential. Modern LENGTH-MEASURING INSTRUMENTS, WEIGHING INSTRUMENTS, THERMOMETERS, and TIMEKEEPERS can measure to a degree of accuracy which would have seemed incredible 100 years ago. INSTRUMENTATION has also made possible the AUTOMATIC CONTROL of whole processes, especially in CHEMICAL ENGINEERING.

SPECIAL BRANCHES OF ENGINEERING. The skills described above are drawn upon to carry out particular tasks, such as SHIPBUILDING, AERONAUTICAL, MINING, and RAILWAY ENGINEERING, and the making of CAMERAS, TELESCOPES, and MICROSCOPES, SOUND RECORDING instruments, and REFRIGERATORS.

The words in capitals are the titles of some of the general articles

A

ACCOUNTING MACHINES, *see* CALCULAT-
ING MACHINES. *See also* Vol. VII: ACCOUNTING,
MACHINE.

ACCUMULATOR, ELECTRIC, *see* BATTERY,
ELECTRIC.

ACOUSTICS. This is the study of SOUND (q.v.
Vol. III) from the Greek 'to hear'. The subject
covers both the response of the ear and the behaviour of sound waves in rooms such as concert
halls, churches, cinemas, and broadcasting
studios. Acoustics also helps to explain how
MUSICAL INSTRUMENTS (q.v. Vol. IX) work.

The designer of a concert hall, theatre, or
church tries to ensure that people in all parts will
hear clearly and without distortion. With music
perfection is especially important. The acoustic
properties of several well-known buildings are
far from good. Many of these were built at a time
when large orchestras were becoming fashion-
able, and little was known about the acoustic
properties of large auditoria. The architects
thought more of size than of clear hearing, and
consequently in such halls it is possible to hear
properly only from certain parts. In contrast, the
Royal Festival Hall, built for the 1951 Festival of
Britain, has so embodied all the advanced techniques of acoustic engineering that it is possible
to hear clearly from all parts of the hall (*see*
SOUND INSULATION).

The acoustics engineer must be able to make
accurate measurements. There are three things
to measure: frequency, intensity, and loudness.
Frequency is a matter of pitch—the difference
between any two notes in the musical SCALE (q.v.
Vol. XII); engineers measure this by recording
the number of vibrations in the sound per second.
Intensity is the measure of the degree of physical
energy in the sound. It is distinct from loudness:

the human ear estimates loudness not by intensity alone but by a combination of pitch and intensity, middle-pitched sounds seeming louder
than either bass or treble sounds of equal intensity. Intensity itself is measured in 'decibels': this
is not a fixed unit, such as a 'foot' or a 'pound',
but expresses the proportion by which the intensity of a sound differs from that of another. Loudness is measured in 'phons': there are 130 even
steps of loudness, or phons, between the softest
sound the ear can detect and the loudest sound
the ear can bear. The loudness of a sound, in
phons, corresponds to the ratio of intensity of an
equally loud sound of standard pitch (1,000 vibrations per second) expressed in decibels above
the threshold of hearing.

The human ear can detect differences between
slight sounds better than between loud ones, so
that any scale which measures sound must progress by bigger steps as the sound grows louder.
The steps on a scale of decibels and phons, therefore, instead of being marked on the basis of 1, 2,
3, 4, and so on, are marked on the basis of 1, 10,
100, 1000.

The size, shape, and surface materials of a
building can greatly alter the nature of a sound.
This can be tested by singing a note or two in
a tiled bathroom and then singing the same
notes in a living room. The fact that the voice
sounds richer and fuller in the bathroom is due to
reverberation—the hard tiles reflect the sound
and produce multiple echoes that prolong and
enrich it.

Sound is reflected in much the same way as
light (*see* WAVE MOTION, Vol. III). When a light
or sound wave strikes a reflecting surface at an
angle, the wave is reflected at an equal but opposite angle (Fig. 1). The amount of the reflection
depends upon the nature of the surface: light,
for example, is totally reflected from a mirror,

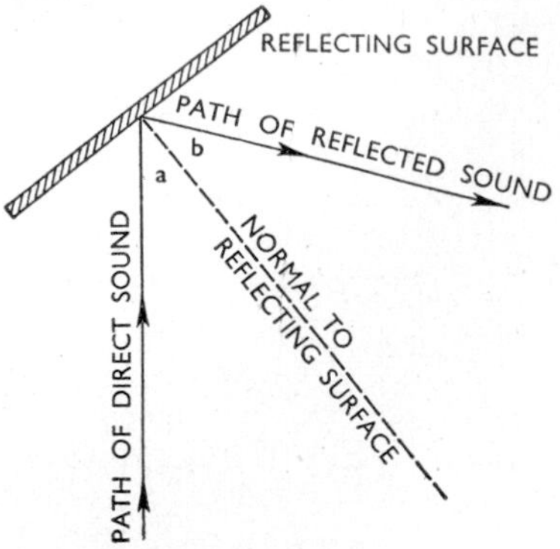

FIG. 1. REFLECTION OF SOUND

Angle *a* equals angle *b*. The 'normal' is at right angles to the reflecting surface

but is absorbed and hardly reflected at all from a black, matt surface. Similarly some materials reflect sound easily, while others absorb it. A performer in a reverberant room is surrounded by hundreds of reflecting surfaces each producing an echo of his music.

When a sound is made it travels away from its source in all directions, and only some of it travels directly towards an individual listener in a room. The rest sooner or later is reflected back to his ear, though some of it may be reflected several times, and the time it takes to reach him depends on the distance it has to travel. Moreover each time it is reflected some of the sound is absorbed. Because of this reflection and absorption the sound appears prolonged and dies away gradually instead of ceasing abruptly when the sound source stops. The time that it takes a sound to die away is called the 'reverberation time'.

Any sound in a very reverberant room produces so many echoes that the original sound is confused. On the other hand, a room with no reverberation produces a very flat, dull sound. When the B.B.C. acoustics engineer, for example, designed a talks studio in the early days of broadcasting, he draped the walls and even the ceilings with thick curtains and covered the floor with thick pile carpet so that the sound of the speaker's voice was hardly reflected at all. The result was so drab and dull a sound that now a talks studio is designed with a reasonable amount of reverberation.

The acoustics engineer, therefore, has to find a type of material for walls, floor, and ceiling, which will allow enough but not too much sound to be reflected. A complication is that no material absorbs high-pitched and low-pitched sounds

equally. Cotton wool, glass wool (made of fine glass fibres), velvet curtains, and pile carpets are excellent absorbers of high-pitched sounds; but since none of them absorbs low-pitched sounds so well, these have to be absorbed by devices such as vibrating absorbers and box 'resonators'. A typical low-pitch sound absorber is a wooden panel tightly clamped at its edges. The sound sets the wood in vibration, and in so doing wastes, in heat, some of the sound energy which could otherwise be reflected.

But, even when the acoustics engineer has designed the building with what he believes to be the right proportion of high-pitch to low-pitch absorbers to suit the building's particular purpose, the result is not always satisfactory. Even a difference of $\frac{1}{16}$th inch in the thickness of the cushion of air behind a resonant panel may alter the pitch to which the panel will respond, and even a slight difference in the texture of the water-paint applied to walls and ceilings may alter the reflecting qualities of a surface.

Elaborate testing techniques, therefore, have to be used. For one of these, called 'pulsing', a loud-speaker is installed in the space to be tested and fed with very short bursts of musical notes of varying pitch—just a few vibrations at each pitch —called pulses. The sound is picked up by a microphone and recorded, as shown in Fig. 2. In this way the actual variations in the loudness of the sound and the time and manner in which it dies away can be studied. Examination of Fig. 2*b* shows that, in this case, after the initial pulse ended, the sound picked up by the microphone actually increased momentarily, and that there were two pronounced echoes during the time the sound was dying away. These are bad features. By making many such tests from different parts

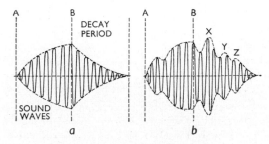

FIG. 2. RECORDS OF SOUND PULSES

a. Sound pulse with smooth decay recorded in a good studio. *b.* Sound pulse recorded in a faulty studio. The reinforcement of sound at x and the pronounced echoes at y and z are all bad features. The sound begins at A and is shut off at B

of the building the engineer can tell exactly how the building reflects sound and what correctives must be applied.

See also SOUND RECORDING; SOUND INSULATION.
See also Vol. III: SOUND.

AERODYNAMICS, *see* HYDRODYNAMICS.

AERONAUTICAL ENGINEERING. Unless all the components of an aircraft are very strong and very efficient for their weight, it may not be capable of flight at all, or at least may not be economical in operation. Also, unless the components are very reliable, the aircraft will not be safe, for the consequences of any failure are usually serious. Consequently, aeronautical engineering is in general characterized by a greater application of science than other and older forms of engineering. A larger technical staff is usually employed for each job; greater use is made of mathematical analysis in design, and of large and expensive equipment for research and testing; more elaborate organizations for inspection of manufacturing processes are employed, and more careful control exercised over the materials used. The establishment of all these facilities in the AIRCRAFT INDUSTRY (q.v. Vol. VII) has in the past been aided by the large sums of money officially expended on aeronautics, because of its military importance.

1. DESIGN. The aeronautical engineer uses a branch of the science of HYDRODYNAMICS (q.v.) known as aerodynamics, which is concerned with the flow of air over wings and bodies, in order to ensure that all parts of the aircraft contribute towards offering the least possible air resistance (drag) for a maximum lift, in normal flight. This has led towards the evolution of smoother and more graceful shapes (better streamlining); the elimination of all possible external excrescences and the stowage inside the main form of engines, wheels, bracing struts, and wires; the improvement of wing sections (aerofoils); and the development of aircraft with the various parts (wings, tail, fin, control surfaces) of such size and relative disposition that the craft is stable and controllable in all attitudes and any conditions of flight.

The tendency has been for wing loadings (weight of aircraft—including payload—per sq. ft. of wing area) to increase as aircraft have become more efficient; in fact, one of the main reasons why performance has improved has been the increase in this quantity (since smaller wings have lower drag), together with a corresponding reduction in the power loading (weight of aircraft per engine horse-power). This has made the difficulties of take-off and landing greater, since these have to be done at higher speeds, demanding better and longer runways. Devices such as slots and flaps have been developed to produce increased lift for landing and take-off at a given speed, and also to increase drag at landing to provide an 'air-brake' effect (*see* AIRCRAFT TAKE-OFF, Vol. IV).

As soon as flight speeds exceeded about 400 miles per hour, the effects of compressibility of the air began to be felt. Below this speed, the air flows round wings and streamlined bodies with substantially no alteration to its density, for gentle pressure and velocity changes occur interchangeably around the contours. At the higher speeds, however, violent changes in air DENSITY, as well as PRESSURE (qq.v. Vol. III), do occur, causing 'shock' waves, and leading to sudden large increases in drag, and shifting centres of pressure on the various wing, tail, and control surfaces, which cause difficulties in control and stability (*see* SUPERSONIC FLIGHT, Vol. IV). These effects are at their worst in the 'trans-sonic' region, that is, near to the speed of sound (about 760 m.p.h.).

It has been found that all these compressibility effects are less serious if the wings are not thick in relation to their chord, with the maximum thickness about half-way back along the chord (Fig. 1*b*), and also if the wings are swept back from the direction of flight. A special form of the swept-back wing is the 'Delta', which has the further obvious advantage of providing a large internal stowage space for fuel, engines, or

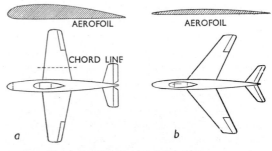

FIG. 1. SHAPES OF AIRCRAFT WINGS

a. Short, broad wing for low-speed flight. The aerofoil (section at chord line) has the maximum thickness well forward. *b.* Swept back wings for supersonic flight. The aerofoil is thin and the maximum thickness is well back about the centre of the wing payload (Fig. 2*a*). For very high supersonic speeds, straight wings are used again, but it becomes even more important to use thin sections. One of

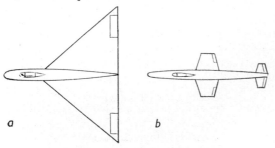

FIG. 2. HIGH-SPEED AIRCRAFT
a. Delta wings. *b*. Stubby straight wings for very high speed

the designer's most serious problems arises from the fact that his aircraft must operate over a wide range of conditions; even a supersonic aircraft must take off, climb, and land at fairly low speeds and, as in all engineering design, some compromise is therefore necessary.

2. PROPULSION. For fixed-wing aircraft (aeroplanes) the varying requirements of speed, altitude, and range affect the choice of engine even more than they do the shape of the aircraft. The various types of aircraft engines from which the designer can choose are fully described in the article AIRCRAFT ENGINES in Volume IV. The choice, in short, lies between the reciprocating (or piston) engine and the gas turbine engine which drive a PROPELLER (q.v.), the jet propulsion engine of either the turbojet or ramjet types, and the rocket engine. All propeller engines give thrust which decreases with flight speed; the thrust of all turbojet and rocket engines is unaffected by flight speed; while the thrust of the ramjet, which is inefficient at low speeds, increases with flight speed. All these engines except the rocket give decreasing thrust with height; the thrust of the rocket actually increases slightly. In general the piston and gas turbine propeller-driving engines are most efficient for relatively low speeds and the jet propulsion and rocket engines for high speeds.

3. STRUCTURAL DESIGN. Nearly all modern aircraft are built of metal, though wood is still used for some of the smaller types, and experiments are being made with moulded plastic construction. Early aircraft had fabric covering, but now it is usual to arrange for the skin-covering to carry at least a proportion of the main structural loads, supporting it where necessary by a frame

structure underneath, and by stiffening members ('stringers') attached to the inside of the skin.

A true 'stressed-skin' structure, in which the skin carries all the load, is called a 'monocoque' (the kind of structure to be seen in a lobster's claw), but in practice (especially on smaller aircraft), the presence of so many cut-outs in the skin (doors, windows, air intakes, jet pipes, wheel wells, &c.) demands a great deal of supporting structure. The main (spanwise) members of the wing are called 'spars', with 'ribs' running chordwise; in the body, or fuselage, the main longitudinal members are the 'longerons' joining the different fuselage 'frames'. All these members, and the skin, are usually riveted together, though some use is made of electric spot welding and metal-to-metal adhesives.

Air frames are usually made of aluminium and magnesium alloys as being the strongest for their weight. High-tensile steels are used for certain

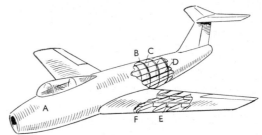

FIG. 3. THE STRUCTURAL PARTS OF AN AIRCRAFT
A. Skin covering. B. Frame. C. Stringer. D. Longeron.
E. Spar. F. Rib

structural fittings (such as wing-fuselage or undercarriage attachment points), and are the main material in the engines. The recently developed metal titanium, whose alloys are nearly as strong as high-tensile steel but only half its weight, is coming gradually into wider use as production expands. Special heat-resistant steels and nickel alloys are essential for the construction of, especially, GAS TURBINE engines (q.v.). Very careful design calculations and structural testing are demanded for modern aircraft because the stresses imposed by high-speed flight are so much greater.

4. AUXILIARY SERVICES. Apart from its outward form and basic internal structure, the modern aircraft is a mass of complicated engineering mechanisms. Its undercarriage and flaps must be raised and lowered, and for high-speed flight the control surfaces are also usually power-operated. Electric, hydraulic, or pneumatic machinery is used for such auxiliary services.

De Havilland

THE AIRCRAFT ASSEMBLY LINE AT THE DE HAVILLAND FACTORY AT CHESTER
'Dove' light transports are in the foreground and 'Vampire' jet trainers behind

Electrical circuits and many small motors and other devices are installed to provide heating and lighting and to operate various instruments.

For HIGH-ALTITUDE FLIGHT (q.v. Vol. IV), the cabin must be pressurized and air-conditioned, either by separate blowers or by air taken from the main turbine-engine air compressors, in either case needing complicated control gear. For bad-weather flying, the wings, tail, engine air intakes, and propellers must be de-iced, using either electrical, pneumatic, chemical, or hot-air devices.

5. PRODUCTION. The specification for a new aircraft is usually drawn up by the military service or airline which requires it. Sometimes, however, it originates as a 'private venture' in an aircraft firm. Armed with a knowledge of the requirements, the project design office then examines various possible layouts. Finally, one is selected, and the preparation of thousands of detail design drawings for it begins. Even before these are finished, the construction of one or two prototypes of the aircraft is begun in the experimental shops.

If the flight tests of the prototypes are successful, the main production shops of the factory begin to provide the large number of jigs, tools, and other equipment necessary for manufacture of the aircraft in quantity. Very few, if any, aircraft types are built in sufficient quantities to justify what could be described as mass-production methods. Nevertheless, the production aircraft is built by rather different methods, nearer to those of a mass-production line, than are used for the prototypes, which are largely hand-built. Some design changes may be made at this stage, as the result of practical experience gained in the building of the prototypes, to simplify manufacture or to improve ease of servicing and maintenance. It is, of course, vital that all these practical points should be given consideration at as early a stage as possible, particularly since arrangements for quantity production are sometimes made even before the prototype has flown, in order to save time.

See also HYDRODYNAMICS; Colour Plate, opp. p. 272.
See also Vol. IV: AERÓPLANE.
See also Vol. VII: AIRCRAFT INDUSTRY.

AIR-CONDITIONING, *see* VENTILATION.

AIRCRAFT ENGINES, *see* AERONAUTICAL ENGINEERING. *See also* Vol. IV: AIRCRAFT ENGINES.

ALGEBRA. This is a form of ARITHMETIC (q.v.) in which letters (such as a, b, x, y) are used as symbols to represent numbers, in order to assist calculation where some wanted number is either unknown or not immediately clear. The basic idea of Algebra is explained in MATHEMATICAL NOTATION (q.v. Vol. IV).

Algebra is best thought of as a mathematical shorthand, and that is how it developed historically. The most important mathematical statement is the 'equation', using the word 'equals' (symbol =). Let us consider this practical example: it takes 3 hours at a certain speed to travel an unknown distance. We want to find the unknown distance; all we know is that by travelling 10 miles per hour faster it would take 1 hour less. Let us call the unknown distance x miles. If it takes 3 hours to travel x miles, the average speed must be $\dfrac{x}{3}$ miles per hour. So a speed 10 miles per hour faster is $\left(\dfrac{x}{3}+10\right)$ miles per hour. But to go x miles in 2 hours by this faster speed implies a speed of $\dfrac{x}{2}$ miles per hour. So we have now found two ways of expressing this faster speed: these are $\dfrac{x}{2}$ and $\dfrac{x}{3}+10$, and each is the same number. We can therefore set this out as an 'equation'—a mathematical statement which balances two equal parts, including an unknown quantity (or quantities):

$$\frac{x}{2} = \frac{x}{3}+10.$$

Since the fractions on both sides are of a different kind, the one cannot easily be subtracted from the other unless they are converted into fractions having the same denominator (*see* ARITHMETIC, Section 5). If two equal quantities are multiplied by the same number, whatsoever number that is, they still remain equal. Therefore, since the denominators 2 and 3 are both factors of 6, let us multiply the entire equation by 6:

$$6\times\frac{x}{2} = \left(6\times\frac{x}{3}\right)+(6\times 10)$$

therefore
$$\frac{6x}{2} = \frac{6x}{3}+60$$

therefore $\qquad 3x = 2x+60$

therefore $\quad 2x+x = 2x+60$

therefore $\qquad\quad x = 60.$

So the unknown distance is 60 miles.

An equation is, as it were, an algebraic pair of scales. And if we alter each side in the same way the equation remains balanced or true.

Many of the laws of nature can be expressed very simply in algebraic language, in which case the statement is known as a formula. It is known, for instance, in electrical theory that the potential difference across the ends of a conductor is proportional to the electric current flowing (Ohm's Law) (*see* ELECTRIC CURRENT, Section 7). If we call the potential difference measured in volts V, the current in amperes I, and the resistance of the conductor measured in ohms R, then the formula becomes $V = IR$. Thus, supposing a current of $7\frac{1}{2}$ amperes is flowing through a resistance of 30 ohms, the potential difference across the resistance is $V = 7\frac{1}{2}\times 30 = 225$ volts.

See also CALCULUS; GEOMETRY; GRAPHS.
See also Vol. IV: MATHEMATICAL NOTATION.

ALLOYS. An alloy is an intimate blend of a METAL (q.v.), usually with one or more other metals, but sometimes with a non-metal or with both metals and non-metals. The ingredients are generally blended while molten.

Every alloy contains a very large proportion of one metal, called the 'parent metal'; for example, bronze contains about 90 per cent. of copper, and most ordinary steels contain about 99 per cent. of iron. Bronze and various types of brasses are examples of alloys containing two metals: bronze contains about 10 per cent. of tin, and different kinds of brass between 10 per cent. and 40 per cent. of zinc—copper in both cases being the parent metal. Ordinary steels and cast irons are examples of alloys containing a metal blended with a non-metal; to the parent-metal, iron, is added carbon, which is not a metal. Printers' type-metal is an alloy in which two metals, antimony and tin, and sometimes, also, about 0·8 per cent. of copper, have been added to the parent metal, lead. Duralumin, an alloy used especially in aircraft building, contains 94 per cent. of aluminium, the parent metal, and also manganese, copper, magnesium, iron, and silicon. White metals used for anti-friction BEARINGS (q.v.) contain tin, copper, and antimony, and sometimes lead also. Certain alloy steels based on iron and carbon contain also nickel and chromium, tungsten and chromium, or manganese and molybdenum.

Most metals can be made to alloy with most others, and since the proportion of any metal in the alloy may vary from, say, 1 per cent. to 99 per cent. the number of possible alloys is extremely great. Alloys already proved of practical value amount to several thousands. Excluding those based on iron (see IRON AND STEEL), the following are among the most common alloys and have roughly the compositions shown (in percentage):

High-grade brass: copper 70, zinc 30.
Common brass: copper 58, zinc 40, lead 2.
Gun-metal: copper 88, tin 10, zinc 2.
Phosphor-bronze: copper 90, tin 10, phosphorus ¼
Tinman's solder: tin 67, lead 33.
Type-metal: lead 76, antimony 16, tin 8.
Duralumin: aluminium 94, copper 4, magnesium ½, manganese ½, iron ½, silicon ½.
Elektron: magnesium 92, aluminium 7, zinc 1.
Coinage bronze: copper 97, tin ½, zinc 2½.
'Silver' coins: silver 50, copper 40, nickel 5, zinc 5.
Nickel-silver: copper 60, zinc 25, nickel 15.
Cupro-nickel: nickel 80, copper 20; or nickel 70, copper 30.
Resistance wire: nickel 75, chromium 15, iron 10.

The usual method of making an alloy is to mix the ingredient metals in the proportions required and to melt them all together. Another method is to melt the parent metal first, and to add the other ingredients—as solids—to the molten metal. When the mixture of metals has melted completely, it is thoroughly stirred and then poured into the shape chosen for it (see METAL-LURGY, Section 3). The great majority of metals mix perfectly in this way, but certain pairs of metals, such as iron and lead, will not do so. When iron and lead are melted together, the iron floats on top of the lead and the metals never blend.

Though an alloy is made by mixing together two, or more, molten metals, it is no longer a simple mixture like salt and sugar by the time it has solidified. When all its ingredients are molten the alloy is a liquid solution like salt in water, the parent metal having dissolved the subsidiary ones. In this condition any small quantity of the alloy is exactly the same in composition as any other part. Since it is impossible to distinguish one small portion from another, the alloy is said to consist of only one 'phase'—it is homogeneous and is called 'monophase'.

Many alloys, particularly—though not exclusively—those containing only small proportions of subsidiary metals, solidify in such a way that the ingredient metals are distributed just as evenly and uniformly as in the liquid, and the solid alloy remains monophase or homogeneous (Fig. 1a). Brasses containing not more than 33 per cent. of zinc behave in this way, as do all the alloys consisting only of copper and nickel, in any proportions.

Other alloys, however, when they solidify, change internally so that, when looked at through a microscope, they show small crystals of more than one type of composition, or 'phase', some containing more of the parent metal than others (Fig. 1b). Such an alloy is said to be 'polyphase'. Brasses containing more than 36 per cent. of zinc behave in this way. Polyphase alloys are the only alloys able to respond to HEAT TREAT-MENT (q.v.) for hardening and other purposes; neither a pure metal nor a monophase alloy can do so.

A solid, pure metal consists of crystals in which the atoms are arranged in a definite pattern characteristic for that metal, forming unit cells (see METALS). Alloys are constituted from similar cells—atoms of the subsidiary metal replacing atoms of the parent metal in some of the cells and so altering their size. Introducing these new atoms naturally alters the properties of the parent metal and makes something new—indeed, that is why alloys are made.

One obvious effect is to change the melting-point: for example, if pure lead, which melts at 327° C., is mixed with twice its weight of pure tin, which melts at 232° C., the resulting alloy—tinman's solder—melts at 180° C. By mixing

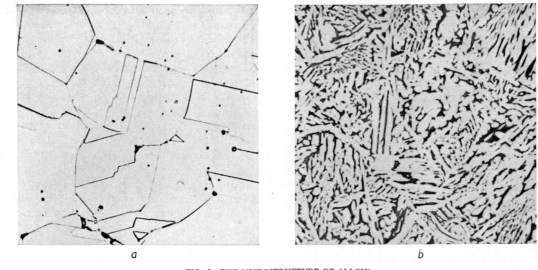

FIG. I. THE MICROSTRUCTURE OF ALLOYS

a. Stainless steel, a monophase alloy: *b*. Common brass, a two-phase (binary) alloy. The magnification of *a* is greater than *b*

together 4 parts of bismuth, 2 parts of lead, 1 part of tin, and 1 of cadmium, an alloy may be produced which melts at about 70° C.—so low a melting-point that teaspoons made of such an alloy would melt in a cup of hot tea. A material of such a low melting-point is useful for the construction of automatic fire alarms or safety plugs for boilers. Pure iron melts at 1,500° C., but when 4 per cent. of carbon is added to it the resulting alloy, cast iron, melts at 1,150° C., and so can be more easily poured into shaped moulds (*see* CASTING).

The electrical conductivity (*see* ELECTRIC CURRENT) of a pure metal may be vastly altered by alloying. Compared with a conductivity of 100 for pure copper, that of an alloy containing 60 per cent. copper and 40 per cent. nickel is only 3·6. If 20 per cent. of chromium is added to 80 per cent. of nickel the conductivity of the alloy is only one-fifteenth as good as that of nickel, the parent metal. Compared with copper (100) the electrical conductivity of pure aluminium is 60: but if aluminium is alloyed with a little magnesium, copper, and manganese, its conductivity is reduced to 23. The heat conductivity of pure metals is affected by alloying in a similar way and by approximately the same amounts. Thus it is possible to make a teapot or saucepan with a cool handle.

Many pure metals are relatively soft, ductile (able to be drawn out thinly), and malleable (able to be moulded under pressure). By alloying,

these attributes may be greatly altered. The strength of forged commercially pure iron is 19 tons per square inch, but if an iron alloy containing 4 per cent. of nickel, 1¼ per cent. of chromium, and ⅛ per cent. of carbon is cast, forged, and then cooled in air, its strength is greater than 100 tons per square inch. If commercially pure aluminium, with a strength of only 4½ tons per square inch, is alloyed with 5 per cent. of zinc, 3 per cent. of magnesium, 2½ per cent. of copper, and 1 per cent. of nickel, its strength after heat treatment is greater than 35 tons per square inch. The strength of pure copper is 14 tons, but when copper is alloyed with 40 per cent. of zinc and 1 per cent. of tin its strength is more than doubled. Almost always the introduction of another metal (or metals) raises the strength and therefore the hardness of the parent metal.

Though the hardness of a metal is increased by alloying, its ductility and malleability fall, almost proportionately. It also becomes more brittle. At some stage of alloying the material produced is too brittle to be of any practical use, and no good purpose is served by introducing more of the subsidiary ingredients. Sometimes the limiting brittleness is reached when very small proportions of the subsidiary element are present. As little as one-ten-thousandth part of bismuth may make copper, and some brasses, quite brittle. Steel loses much of its toughness if it contains so small a proportion of phosphorus as one part in a thousand. In many alloys the brittleness is caused by the presence of an inter-metallic compound lying between the grains which compose the alloy. The compound itself is brittle, and its occurrence in this situation destroys the toughness of the whole alloy.

See also METALS; METALLURGY; HEAT TREATMENT.
See also Vol. III: METAL ORES; MATTER.

ALTERNATING CURRENT. This is an ELECTRIC CURRENT (q.v.) that reverses its direction of flow at regular intervals. When an alternating current flows through a metal wire, the electrons that carry the current do not drift smoothly along the wire in one direction, as they do for a direct current, but surge backwards and forwards regularly. One complete to-and-fro motion is called a cycle, and the number of cycles occurring in one second is called the frequency. Most public electricity supplies provide alternating current (A.C.) with a frequency of 50 cycles per second. Fig. 1 shows some complete cycles of this frequency, arranged to represent a current with a peak strength of 10 amperes. The diagram shows

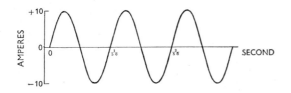

FIG. I. ALTERNATING CURRENT WITH A FREQUENCY OF 50 CYCLES PER SECOND

how the current changes its strength and its direction of flow according to a regular wavelike pattern. These alternating currents are produced by ELECTRIC GENERATORS (q.v.) of a kind called alternators. The strengths of alternating currents and voltages are not normally measured by their peak strengths, but by the rather lower amounts that show their heating power. These are known as the r.m.s. (root mean square) values, and a current with a peak strength of 10 amperes has an r.m.s. strength of 7 amperes. Again, an A.C. of r.m.s. 230 volts has a peak voltage of 325 volts.

The heat that is produced when an electric current overcomes the resistance of a conducting wire (see ELECTRIC CURRENT, Section 3) is the same whatever the direction of the current, and so A.C. can be used for heating and lighting just as well as direct current (D.C.). The strength of

the current that flows through ordinary conductors is the same for A.C. and D.C.; but D.C. and A.C. behave differently when the electric circuit contains 'choke coils', that is, appliances with an iron core round which are wound many turns of insulated copper wire to increase the magnetic effect of its current. When D.C. is flowing through a choke coil, the pressure (volts) between the connecting wires simply depends on the resistance (ohms) of the copper wire and the strength (amperes) of the current opposed to the resistance, according to Ohm's Law (see ELECTRIC CURRENT, Section 7). But when A.C. flows through the coil, the continual changes of the current set up a magnetic influence or 'field' that changes in sympathy with every reversal, and this changing magnetic 'field' causes an alternating voltage to act in the coil by electromagnetic induction (see INDUCTION, ELECTRIC).

This induced voltage depends initially on the current passing through the wire and the number of turns in the coil. But it is acting against the applied voltage, and is trying to get up a current of its own, flowing in the opposite direction. The net result is that a much smaller current actually flows through the coil than would flow through a non-inductive coil of the same resistance in ohms. The forward current is reduced, or choked, and so a coil used in this way is often called a choke-coil.

Again, D.C. will not pass through the insulating material that separates the plates of an electric CONDENSER (q.v.), but the continual ebb and flow of A.C. makes the circuit act as if A.C. were in fact flowing through the condenser. The strength of the A.C. which thus flows as though through a condenser depends on the voltage of the generator and upon the capacity of the condenser.

The induced voltage produced when A.C. flows through a choke coil is put to good use in the electric TRANSFORMER (q.v.), which is used to alter the voltages of A.C. supplies. It is possible to generate A.C. at 22,000 volts and transform it up to 132,000 volts for transmission over long distances; at the distant end the A.C. supply can be transformed down to 230 volts for distribution and use in private houses (see GRID SYSTEM). In this way the best voltage for each different purpose—easy generation, efficient transmission, and safe domestic use—can be easily produced. It is not possible to change voltages easily with D.C. supplies, and this is why A.C.

has so largely replaced D.C. for electric power supplies.

For long-distance transmission A.C. has the further advantage that, when sent along a wire

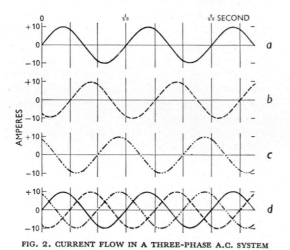

FIG. 2. CURRENT FLOW IN A THREE-PHASE A.C. SYSTEM

a, b, c. Currents of equal strength with their courses following each other at equal intervals of time. *d.* Resultant pattern of waves which cancel each other out so that no current is produced

or cable, the alternations of current are like waves of electricity passing along the wire. It happens that three equal waves (Figs. 2*a, b, c*) can be added together in such a way that they cancel each other out (as shown in Fig. 2*d*). The three waves must be timed so that their crests are equally spaced from each other. When three equal alternating currents are handled in this way and applied to a wire or cable, no current flows in it.

Fig. 3 shows how use is made of this fact. In Fig. 3, three A.C. generators, A, B, and C, are

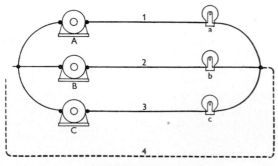

FIG. 3. THREE-PHASE A.C. SYSTEM

Generators A, B, C supply lamps *a, b, c* through wires 1, 2, 3. No current flows through wire 4 which is therefore left out

joined to the three lamps *a, b,* and *c,* by the wires numbered 1, 2, 3, and 4. The current for lamp *a* comes from generator A through wires 1 and 4. Lamp *b* is supplied from generator B through wires 2 and 4, and lamp *c* from generator C through wires 3 and 4. Wire 4 is intended to complete the circuit by carrying the 'return' current from each lamp. But in wire 4 the alternating currents for all three lamps add together, and when the three generators are timed properly, these three currents cancel each other out (as in Fig. 2) and no electric current flows. It follows that if wire 4 carries no current it need not be there at all; and it is in fact left out altogether. Such an arrangement is called a three-phase A.C. system, each current being one phase, and the three currents are produced by one three-phase generator which has three separate armature windings (*see* ELECTRIC GENERATORS). As return wires do not have to be provided in a three-phase system, less wire is needed, which greatly reduces the cost of long-distance distribution compared with D.C. or single-phase A.C. systems.

A.C. cannot be used for charging batteries, for ELECTROPLATING (q.v.), or for certain other purposes. It has to be converted to D.C. for these uses by a process called rectification (*see* RECTIFIERS), or the A.C. can be used to drive a motor that drives a D.C. generator.

See also ELECTRICAL ENGINEERING; ELECTRIC CURRENT.

AMMETER, *see* ELECTRICAL INSTRUMENTS.

AMPERES, *see* MEASUREMENT, UNITS OF, Section 3.

AMPLIFIER, *see* THERMIONIC VALVES.

AMPLITUDE MODULATION, *see* RADIO ENGINEERING.

ANCHORS. These important pieces of equipment are carried by ships or craft of any size. When lowered to the bed of the sea or river they hold the vessel steady either by their own weight or by hooking themselves to the bottom. In this way a ship keeps its position, for example, when waiting outside a harbour until the tide is suitable for entering. By anchoring, a disabled ship can be prevented from drifting on to rocks or shoals.

The earliest anchors were simply large stones

National Maritime Museum

FIG. I. ANCHOR WITH WOODEN STOCK

Behind is an anchor with a moveable iron stock. A number
of different designs were used in the 19th century. Etching
by E. W. Cooke, 1830

attached to a rope cable; but soon hook-shaped anchors were developed which would dig into the ground and were less easy for the cable to drag. Such anchors, still used by many small craft, consist of two 'flukes', or arms (similar in shape to the head of a pickaxe), fitted to a 'shank' (corresponding to the pickaxe handle), with a ring at the end to which the cable is attached. To ensure that one of the flukes always points vertically downwards to bite into the ground, a 'stock' is fitted, which projects from the ring end of the shank at right angles to the flukes (Fig. 1). In whatever position the anchor falls, either one of the flukes or one end of the stock sticks into the bottom. If the stock touches the bottom first, the anchor rolls over when the ship pulls on the cable until the stock is horizontal and one of the flukes is in position to dig into the bottom. For large fighting ships, such as H.M.S. VICTORY (q.v. Vol. IV), the anchor-stocks were made of wood; later, they were made of iron and could be removed so that the anchors could be stowed more neatly when on board.

This type of anchor remained practically unaltered for all classes of ships until 1852. Of the several new designs then brought out, the Admiralty adopted that of a Frenchman named Martin. This had the stock set on the shank parallel to the flukes, which were hinged and could turn together until they lay at an angle of about 30° to the shank, and so dug into the bottom when dragged by the cable. These anchors had such excellent holding power that they could be made lighter; and, as the upper fluke did not project when the lower one had

taken hold, there was no danger either of the ship resting on the upturned fluke at low tide nor of the cable being fouled, or entangled, with it. The anchors, however, still had to be hoisted on board by a tackle and were awkward to stow.

Early in this century it was found that the anchor's holding power was very little affected if the stock was removed altogether. Stockless anchors are now used for all modern ships (except small craft), and are stowed by heaving them up by the cable into the 'hawse pipe', the hole in the ship's bows through which the anchor cable runs out (Fig. 2).

Most ships over 325 tons carry three main anchors, called 'bower' anchors, two in the hawse pipes on each side of the bows and an emergency anchor, formerly called the 'sheet anchor', in reserve on the foredeck. Smaller ships carry only two. In addition, all ships carry a 'stream' anchor, often fitted in the stern, which is used to prevent the ship swinging violently when at anchor. Ships also carry a 'kedge' anchor, used to move a ship a short distance if other forms of power break down. The anchor is dropped from the ship's boat into the sea some distance from the ship; then, when the anchor cable is hauled in from the ship, the ship is pulled forward towards the anchor.

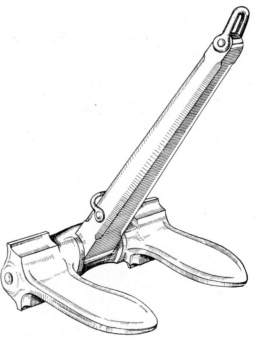

FIG. 2. STOCKLESS ANCHOR

All anchor cables used to be made of hemp, and there was always a danger that these would be cut or worn through on rocky bottoms. Today chain cables of great strength are used, the sheer weight of which helps to hold the ship steady so that lighter anchors can be used. A modern 9-ton anchor with its chain cable can hold a ship of as much as 35,000 tons.

FIG. 3. C.Q.R. ANCHOR

An anchor with great holding power, the C.Q.R. anchor, is now used by many small craft. It is stockless and instead of flukes has a fitting like a ploughshare (Fig. 3). It is used with a long cable so that its pull is almost horizontal. The more the ship tugs the more firmly will the ploughshare dig into the bottom.

A ship in very heavy seas, in waters too deep for her anchor cable to reach the bottom, sometimes uses a 'sea anchor'. This can be of any shape or material provided it remains relatively steady in the water and is large enough to act as a drag on the ship. A type carried by small craft is similar in shape to the wind sock used on airfields (Fig. 4).

See also Vol. IV: Ship; Sailing Ships.

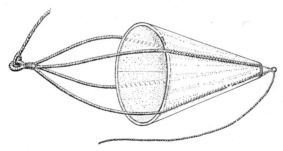

FIG. 4. SEA ANCHOR

ANEMOMETER, see Meteorological Instruments.

ANNEALING, see Heat Treatment, Section 2.

ANODE, see Thermionic Valves.

ANODIZING, see Electroplating; Surface Treatment.

AQUEDUCT, see Water Supply. See also Vol. XI: Water Supply, History of.

ARITHMETIC. This is the science of numbers, the art of calculation.

1. Addition. The fundamental number is unity or 'one', represented by the symbol 1. All the other whole numbers, or 'integers', are produced by successively adding 1 to itself: $2 = 1+1$; $3 = 2+1$; $4 = 3+1$; and so on. This is the same process as counting (see Counting, History of, Vol. IV), and in this process we employ certain symbols such as 'plus' and 'minus' (see Mathematical Notation, Vol. IV). To sum, or add together, two numbers they are split into their component units and the number of separate units counted:

$$5+3 = (1+1+1+1+1)+(1+1+1) = 8.$$

2. Subtraction. Subtraction is the opposite of addition and answers the question: 'What must be added to one definite number (say 8) to give another definite number (say 11)?' The answer is the difference, which written in symbols appears as $11-8 = 3$. But if we have to answer the question 'What is $8-11$?' (that is, 'What must be added to 11 to give 8?'), the answer is 'Less than nothing', and we use negative numbers to answer it, saying that $8-11 = -3$. A familiar example of a negative number is on the scale of a Centigrade Thermometer (q.v.), where all temperatures below the freezing-point of water are expressed in these numbers. Again, in a newspaper list of gains and losses in the values of shares on the Stock Exchange, a negative number indicates a decrease in value.

3. Multiplication. Repeated addition of the same number is known as multiplication. $3+3+3+3$ is written as 4×3. The multiplication tables from 1 to 12 are the basis of the calculation of larger multiplication sums. When two numbers are multiplied, each is a factor of the answer, and the result is the product.

4. DIVISION. The opposite operation, called division, answers the question: 'By what number must one number (say 3) be multiplied to give another number (say 15)?' The answer is the quotient (in this case, 5). The operation has the effect of splitting 15 into 3 equal parts, and is written $15 \div 3$ or usually $\frac{15}{3}$ or 15/3.

5. FRACTIONS. It is not always possible to split up a number exactly, for example, $16 \div 3$. The answer can be expressed $16 \div 3 = 5$ and 1 over (the remainder), or to give a more complete answer, the remainder 1 can also be divided into three equal parts. These parts are no longer whole numbers but fractional numbers—in this example one-third of 1, written as $\frac{1}{3}$. The lower number or denominator, 3, means that unity is divided into three parts and the upper number or numerator, 1, means that only one of these parts is taken. For instance, $\frac{4}{7}$ inch means that the unit (an inch) is divided into 7 equal parts, of which 4 are taken. So $16 \div 3 = 5\frac{1}{3}$.

Integers which are exactly divisible by 2 are called even numbers; and those which, when divided by 2, leave a remainder of 1, are called odd numbers.

6. PRIME NUMBERS. If a number (such as 13 or 17 or 23) can be exactly divided by no other number except itself or by 1, it is called a prime number. Otherwise, a number can be split up or 'factorized' into the product of prime numbers—that is, the result of multiplying prime numbers together. For instance, 60 equals $2 \times 2 \times 3 \times 5$, so that 2, 2, 3, 5 are the prime factors of 60.

7. DECIMALS. Our notation for counting is based on the number 10. The position of the numerical symbol or figure determines the value of that figure—that is, whether it is worth so many units, tens, tens of tens (hundreds), tens of hundreds (thousands), and so on. The symbol 0, or zero, is used to show that there is none of a particular set of values involved. So 3107 means three thousands, one hundred, no tens, and seven units, or $3 \times (10 \times 10 \times 10)$, added to $1 \times (10 \times 10)$, added to 0×10, added to 7×1; the basis of tens is clearly seen. In dealing with mixed numbers—that is, a set of figures containing both whole numbers and fractions—this convenient system can be extended by means of decimal fractions. A dot is placed to the right of the number in the units position, and the numbers to the right of the dot are taken as the numerators of fractions of which the denominator is ten, a hundred, a thousand, and so on. So 37·401 means

$$3 \times 10 + 7 + \frac{4}{10} + \frac{0}{100} + \frac{1}{1000}.$$

Again the basis of tens is clearly seen, both in the whole numbers on the left of the dot or 'decimal point' and in the fractions on the right. One of the advantages of this system is that numbers in it can be added, subtracted, multiplied, and divided in the same way as whole numbers, so long as the position of the decimal point is observed. Another advantage is that all that is needed to multiply or divide a number by 10 is to move the position of the point one place to the right or left. For example, $37·12 \times 10 = 371·2$, or $37·12 \div 10 = 3·712$.

For addition or subtraction the numbers must be set out so that the decimal points are beneath one another. Multiplication and division are carried out in the ordinary way as if no decimal points were involved, and then a rough check is made with approximate numbers to decide where the decimal point should be put in the answer.

Addition	Subtraction
470·2	72·360
115	0·012
0·03	72·348
585·23	

Multiplication	Rough check
17·32	17
3·7	4
51960	68
12124	
64084	*Answer* 64·084

There is another form of check in multiplication. In the two numbers to be multiplied together there are, in all, three figures to the right of the decimal point (·32 and ·7); the answer also contains three figures (·084) to the right of the decimal point. This rule always holds good, whether the figures after the point are few or many.

Division	Rough check
324	7)230
7·1)230·04	
213	32 and 6 over
170	
142	*Answer* 32·4
284	
284	

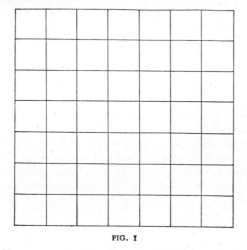

FIG. 1

To convert a fraction, say $\frac{3}{8}$, into a decimal we must remember that $\frac{3}{8}$ means $3 \div 8$. In decimal form, the 3 is really 3·000... so that if we divided 3·000 by 8 in the usual manner we get 0·375, which is the decimal equivalent of $\frac{3}{8}$. Sometimes the division does not come to an end, but the last figure or figures continue to repeat in regular order. The result is then called a recurring decimal. Thus $\frac{3}{7} = 0\cdot4285714285...$, and however long we continue dividing, the sequence 428571 cannot be got rid of. In such cases the result is usually confined to the first few figures; thus $\frac{3}{7} = 0\cdot42857$ is the answer to the fifth decimal place. If an even more accurate answer is needed, dots are placed over the first and last figures of the series to indicate recurrence; thus $\frac{3}{7} = 0\cdot\dot{4}2857\dot{1}$.

8. SIGNIFICANT FIGURES. Very few measurements are performed with complete accuracy, apart from the counting of whole units (as at a census or election). A signpost which reads '$6\frac{1}{4}$ miles' means only that the distance is nearer to $6\frac{1}{4}$ miles than to 6 or $6\frac{1}{2}$. No one expects the signpost to be accurate to a foot. But even scientific instruments are able to measure to only a limited degree of accuracy, and this limits the number of figures needed in a calculation. Suppose that a rod, measured to an accuracy of one-hundredth of an inch, is 6·47 inches long. Then one-third of that rod is $6\cdot47 \div 3 = 2\cdot1566...$ inches. But it would be unreasonable to expect a greater degree of accuracy in measuring part of the rod than in measuring the whole. So we simply say that the third part of 6·47 is 2·16 inches 'to three significant figures', meaning that three figures are enough for our purpose. The third

figure in this case is altered from 5 to 6 because, since we must choose between 2·15 and 2·16, the latter is nearer the truth. On the same principle, measurements of 5173·2 yards and 0·07196 inches would become 5170 yards and 0·0720 inches to three significant figures. In calculations the degree of accuracy is usually reduced by one significant figure for every operation carried out, because any errors will accumulate. Let us calculate, as an example, the area of a rectangular field which is actually 2,178 feet by 3,142 feet, but where the original measurement was made to an accuracy of only three significant figures.

Exact figures	3 significant figures
2,178	2,180
3,142	3,140
6,534,000	6,540,000
217,800	218,000
87,120	87,200
4,356	
	6,845,200 Answer
Exact answer 6,843,276	
6,840,000 to 3 significant figures	6,850,000 to 3 significant figures (*note* error)
6,800,000 to 2 significant figures	6,800,000 to 2 significant figures (*note* error no longer shows)

Thus the answer can be relied upon to only two significant figures.

9. INDEX AND INDICES. When a number is multiplied by itself, the product is called the square of the number; thus the square of 7 is 49. The reason for this is that the area of a square (*see* GEOMETRY) which has sides 7 units long is 49 square units (Fig. 1). 7×7 is sometimes written as 7^2 for short, the small 2 being an index number (plural: indices) which stands for the number of times 7 is written down for self-multiplication. In the same way $15 \times 15 \times 15 \times 15$ can be written 15^4. There are many other uses for an index number (*see* LOGARITHMS).

10. SQUARE ROOT. Just as 49 is called the square of 7, so 7 is called the square root of 49, because it is the length of the side of a square the area of which is 49 square units. We write it in symbols as $\sqrt{49}$ (or sometimes $\sqrt[2]{49}$). Numbers such as 1, 4, 9, 16, 25, and so on are called perfect squares, because they have an exact square root: 1, 2, 3, 4, 5, and so on—thus the prime factors of 25 are 5×5. But numbers such as 14, or 2 which is a prime number, have not got exact square roots (although it is possible to calculate an approximate root by a lengthy process). The square root of 2, for example, is 1·4139..., a number which continues as a never-ending decimal.

For that reason a number such as √2 is called an 'irrational' number because it can never be exactly expressed by a given number. We can only say that it lies between 1·4 and 1·5 (two significant figures), or 1·41 and 1·42 (three significant figures), or 1·413 and 1·414 (four significant figures), and so on.

11. OTHER ROOTS. A square root, since it concerns a number which is to be multiplied by itself once, is a comparatively simple affair. Other roots can be worked out which represent multiplication repeated over and over again. For instance, the tenth root ($^{10}\sqrt{}$) of 1,024 is 2 (*see* LOGARITHMS).

See also ALGEBRA; GEOMETRY; TRIGONOMETRY; LOGARITHMS; GRAPHS; CALCULUS.

See also Vol. IV: COUNTING, HISTORY OF; MEASUREMENT, HISTORY OF; MATHEMATICAL NOTATION.

ARMAMENTS, *see* Vol. X: ARTILLERY; WEAPONS, HAND.

ASWAN DAM. EGYPT, which has virtually no rainfall, has always depended for its existence on water brought by the NILE (qq.v. Vol. III) from the distant uplands of Abyssinia and Central Africa. At the end of the 19th century, when the country was nearly bankrupt, it was vitally necessary to increase crops of cotton—Egypt's only considerable export—and of food grains. But this could be done only if there was an adequate supply of water all the year round, for during the summer the flow of the Nile is reduced to one-fifth of its average. It was therefore decided to build a DAM (q.v.) across the Nile, forming a reservoir in which the winter flood waters could be stored and then released to the fields during the summer by a system of IRRIGATION canals (q.v. Vol. VI). The Aswan dam was planned and built by British engineers for this purpose, between 1899 and 1902, about 570 miles south of Cairo.

Archaeologists protested against the original scheme because the water in the reservoir would submerge the ancient temple on the island of Philae, with its shrines to Egyptian gods and Roman emperors; so the height of the dam was lowered by 10 feet to 71 feet, just halving its capacity. But the land needed more and more water, and within 5 years the dam had to be raised, submerging the temple. For the original construction 14,000 men and women excavated the ground by hand, carrying baskets loaded with materials to and from the site; but when the dam was later heightened, more machinery was used.

The demand for water in Egypt, however, still continued to increase as the population grew; so after detailed research into the HYDROGRAPHY (q.v.) of the Nile, it was decided again to heighten the dam, and this was carried out between 1929 and 1933. The cost of the original construction and successive additions totalled just under £9¾ millions. The dam, which is of the gravity type, holds over 1 million million gallons in its reservoir, and is now 116 feet high and 1⅓ miles long. It is an impressive sight, especially when viewed from downstream with its sluices under full discharge.

The reservoir is empty early in July. The first spates of flood water from the mountains arrive the same month, reaching a peak in September;

ASWAN DAM AFTER THE SECOND HEIGHTENING

Ransomes & Rapier Ltd.

but 'impounding', or storing, is seldom started until November. Between February and July a steady supply is released to the land, either flowing by gravity or being pumped through a network of canals. Though the flow of the Nile varies greatly from year to year, the main banks have been so carefully maintained that no serious flooding has occurred during the past 50 years (*see* FLOOD CONTROL). A scheme is now in hand to build a HYDRO-ELECTRIC POWER station (q.v.) near the dam.

Though the temple of Philae disappears each winter beneath the rising waters of the reservoir, each spring it re-emerges for the pleasure of archaeologists and sightseers. Careful underpinning of its foundations and special treatment of the stonework has kept it undamaged (*see* Vol. V, p. 373).

See also DAMS.
See also Vol. VI: IRRIGATION.

ATOMIC ENERGY, *see* NUCLEAR ENERGY.

AUTOMATIC CONTROLS. In many modern machines and engineering processes certain quantities have to be controlled, such as, for example, temperatures, rates of speed, and so on. This is often done by automatic devices. The various highly ingenious means for doing this are known, in general, as control systems.

Simple examples of control apparatus are found in the STEAM ENGINE (q.v.), where a governor enables the speed to be controlled; and in the petrol engine, where the carburettor and throttle control the mixture of air and petrol vapour and its flow to the cylinders (*see* INTERNAL COMBUSTION ENGINE). ELECTRIC MOTORS (q.v.) have control arrangements made up of switches or contacts operated in the correct order at the correct rate, often in very complicated combinations. Gas and electric stoves and boilers, electric irons and kettles, and many other pieces of domestic equipment have automatic devices for controlling temperature.

1. AUTOMATIC ERROR CORRECTION. A very simple example of automatic control is the one which controls the temperature in the ordinary domestic gas oven. In fact, even the most complicated automatic controllers, such as the automatic pilot for aircraft or the controls of a petrol refining plant, work on much the same simple principle as the gas-oven regulator. The principle is that of 'automatic error correction'. When

the temperature in the oven rises above a fixed limit, the gas supply to the burners is automatically decreased. When the temperature drops below this limit, the gas supply is automatically increased.

Many regulators for measuring the temperature and causing the flow of gas to vary according to the temperature make use of the fact that some metals expand more than others as they are heated (*see* THERMOSTAT). Fig. I shows one way in which this is used to control the flow of gas. The metal part that expands is the brass tube, A, which is fixed inside the oven. Inside the tube is a rod made of a special alloy, invar, that hardly changes at all in length when heated. As the oven is heated, the brass tube increases in length, carrying the rod with it, so that the plate B at the end of the rod closes a gap G through

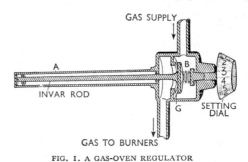

FIG. I. A GAS-OVEN REGULATOR

A. Brass tube. B. Plate at end of invar rod. C. Gap through which gas flows

which gas is flowing. Thus as the oven gets hotter the flow of gas is reduced. When the oven cools, and the brass tube contracts and pulls back the rod, the gap becomes open again and lets through the gas.

When the regulator dial is turned up, it moves the plate so as to increase the gap and consequently increase the supply of gas. When the temperature has reached a new higher level, the gas supply is reduced to maintain this. In this way the heat of the oven is controlled.

2. AUTOMATIC PILOT. This device in an aircraft is expected to do the same things that the human pilot would do. For instance, a pilot keeps his aeroplane on its course by setting his compass to the course required, and then keeping the needle against the point marked N. Now, an automatic pilot also works by the compass, and is so devised that it moves the rudder in the proper direction to correct the error whenever the compass points to right or left of the mark N.

Thus, in this case, the compass is the measuring instrument or error detector, corresponding with

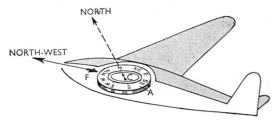

FIG. 2. NAVIGATING AN AEROPLANE BY COMPASS

To fly north-west the course-setting ring (A) round the compass (C) is set with NW opposite the arrow F. The automatic pilot operates the rudder to keep the compass on N

the expanding rod in the oven temperature regulator (Fig. 2).

The rudder cannot be operated directly by the compass because this is too sensitive an instrument to be able to exert so large a force. Therefore, a separate motor with its own source of power is used to move the rudder. The movements of the compass merely control this rudder motor, which then imparts the necessary power.

There are various ways of obtaining such power-amplifying controls, generally known as 'servo-controls'. Fig. 3 shows, in bare principle only, how such a control can work. In this case compressed air is the power used. Other types of servo-controls use electrical power, and many control systems use hydraulic power. The arrangement shown in the diagram makes use

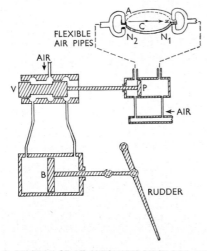

FIG. 3. DIAGRAM OF AN AUTOMATIC PILOT FOR AIRCRAFT

B. Piston in main rudder servo-motor cylinder. V. Slide valve. C. Compass card. A. Projection on compass card. P. Piston controlling valve. N_1, N_2. Air nozzles

of a piston, B, operated by compressed air to move the rudder. The air to operate this piston is controlled by a valve, V, and it is this valve that is controlled by the movement of the compass.

The compass card itself has a projection, A, extending half-way round its edge. When the card turns, one end of this projection moves into the gap between two air nozzles N_1, while the other edge moves out from between two other nozzles N_2. Air under pressure is supplied to these nozzles, and if one pair is less blocked than the other, this reduces the pressure in the pipe to this pair of nozzles and increases the pressure on the other pipe. The difference between the pressure in the two pipes causes a small piston, P, to be displaced. Thus if the card turns in one direction from the point N, the pressure difference between the two sides of the piston, P, is in one direction; but if the card turns in the other direction, the pressure difference is reversed. The piston, therefore, moves in the direction of the error of the compass needle and controls the valve, V, which in its turn controls the rudder piston. The final result is that a movement of the compass from the mark, N, causes a corresponding movement of the rudder.

Similar controls are provided, worked from the GYROSCOPE (q.v.) of the gyro compass, in order to operate the elevator fins on the tail, and so to keep the aircraft flying level. A third control works the ailerons on the wings to keep the aircraft from rolling. These are not shown on the diagram, but they work on the same principle.

3. AUTOMATIC CONTROL IN INDUSTRY. Some of the most important applications of automatic control are in the chemical industry. Chemical processes such as the manufacture of NYLON or certain stages of OIL REFINING (qq.v. Vol. VII) require very close control, to the proper values, of quantities such as temperatures, rates of flow, pressures, acidity, proportions of materials, and so on. Chemical works used to have to employ many people to watch various meters and measuring instruments and to move control handles. Now, more and more, such operations are being done by automatic control systems. Such apparatus is costly, but much labour is saved, and also, in many cases, the automatic controls work faster and more uniformly than even the most skilled operator can.

Automatic controls are also used to control the thickness in rolling steel plate, or to obtain the precise amount of stretch of the wet paper in paper-making machines; they are used to control the work of many MACHINE TOOLS (q.v.). Automatic controls are also very important in warfare. All countries use automatic gun layers, and also automatic radar trackers which will track aircraft in darkness or fog as well as in daylight. Flying bombs are guided by automatic controls rather like the automatic pilot, and so on (*see* GUIDED MISSILES, Vol. X).

All these controls are based on the same fundamental principle of continuous detection and correction of error that has been described in the cases of the oven control and the automatic pilot. The details and appearance of the apparatus are of course quite different in the different applications.

See also THERMOSTAT; INSTRUMENTATION.

AUTOMATIC PILOT, *see* AUTOMATIC CONTROLS, Section 2.

AUTOMOBILE ENGINEERING, *see* INTERNAL COMBUSTION ENGINE. *See also* Vol. VII: MOTOR INDUSTRY.

AXLES. A shaft or spindle is known as an axle when it supports or drives a wheel (*see* Fig.). As used in engineering, the term is a general one covering any pin, bar, or shaft on which a wheel revolves. It can either be locked solid with the wheel and rotate with it, or it can remain stationary, simply supporting the revolving wheel.

In many cases, particularly in the motor-car industry, the axle itself is associated with a number of other parts, all of which form part of the whole axle assembly. Because of these complexities in modern transport design, it is now usual to refer to the entire axle assembly as the axle, although this is not strictly correct. For instance, a manufacturer refers to 'rear driving axles',

which include the axle housing, axle shafts, and differential and driving gear. The front axle is normally understood to include the whole unit

TYPES OF AXLE

a. Fixed axle which rotates with wheels. *b.* Axle which remains stationary when the wheel revolves. A. Hub

which supports the front end of the car, even including part of the steering mechanism.

Because of the various loads which axles have to carry and the strain which is imposed on them, their correct design is very important, and it has been necessary to develop special very tough steels for axle shafts.

All axles are associated with BEARINGS (q.v.) of some kind. Where the wheels revolve on a fixed axle, there must be a bearing surface on the axle. Where the axle revolves with the wheel, the axle itself must run in bearings which support the load carried by the wheels. Bearings of the plain or roller type are used according to need.

See BEARINGS.
See also Vol. IV: WHEEL; MOTOR-CAR.

B

BALANCES, *see* WEIGHING INSTRUMENTS.

BALL AND ROLLER BEARINGS, *see* BEARINGS.

BALLISTICS. This is the science of the movement of projectiles—such as shells, bombs, or bullets. It is now closely related to the science of aerodynamics (*see* HYDRODYNAMICS). We can consider it under three main headings: internal ballistics, external ballistics, and terminal ballistics.

(*a*) *Internal ballistics* deals with the motion of projectiles in guns and the related subject of the burning of propellant charges in ROCKETS (q.v.). The speed of the projectile as it leaves the gun, or that of the rocket when the charge has burnt, can be calculated from a knowledge of the nature of the propellant (*see* EXPLOSIVES), the quantity used, the weight of the projectile, and the dimensions and characteristics of the gun or rocket motor. Since internal ballistics deals largely with the pressure variations in the gun or the rocket motor, it forms the basis of the design of these weapons and of all the components in the projectiles.

(*b*) *External ballistics* deals with the flight of the projectile and is mainly concerned with the effect of air resistance. In a vacuum, the flight of a projectile is a simple parabola. The friction of the air, however, against the sides of the projectile slows down and alters the course of the flight to an extent depending on its shape and stability. To lessen air resistance, shells and rockets are to some extent streamlined. To make them stable in flight, they may either be given spin or fitted with fins. Shells and bullets, for example, are caused to spin rapidly when fired by spiral-like grooving inside the barrel of the gun or rifle, and the gyroscopic effect of this spin tends to make the projectile hold a steady flight. Rockets are normally stabilized with fins, which serve the same purpose as the fins of a dart (*see* p. 376). Fins are useless, of course, on a rocket travelling outside the earth's atmosphere.

(*c*) *Terminal ballistics* deals with the behaviour of projectiles on impact with targets and is almost entirely experimental, although some formulae have been developed which enable performance to be predicted between fairly narrow limits.

Experiments are of the utmost importance in ballistics. The problem of measuring projectile velocities has been solved in very great measure by the use of photo-electrically controlled electronic clocks (*see* ELECTRONICS). The behaviour of projectiles can be investigated by direct and shadow photography; while the CATHODE-RAY TUBE (q.v.) can be used to show the behaviour of the burning propellant under different pressures in the gun chamber or rocket motor. The great advances in these techniques have emphasized the need to know more accurately the structure of the ATMOSPHERE (q.v. Vol. III) through which projectiles have to pass, and useful experiments have been carried out in WIND TUNNELS (q.v.), which make it possible to study the behaviour of projectiles over a wide range of air speeds and air PRESSURE (q.v. Vol. III).

See also EXPLOSIVES; WIND TUNNEL.
See also Vol. IX: SPORTING GUNS AND RIFLES.
See also Vol. X: ARTILLERY; NAVAL GUNS; BOMBS AND MINES; WEAPONS, HAND.

BAROGRAPH and **BAROMETER,** *see* METEOROLOGICAL INSTRUMENTS, Section 2b.

BATTERY, ELECTRIC. This is used to produce ELECTRIC CURRENT (q.v.), and is made up of a number of separate 'cells' joined together. Each cell is a small box containing substances that act on each other chemically to produce the electric current. Although many different kinds of cell have been invented, actually only a few kinds are much used nowadays.

1. DRY CELLS. The most common electric cells are those used in the dry batteries of electric torches. These are called primary or 'Leclanché' cells after their inventor. One is shown cut in half in Fig. 1. The cell is contained in a small zinc pot, which is also the negative connexion, or terminal. The positive terminal, a carbon rod, is surrounded by a wet mixture of granulated carbon and black oxide of manganese held together

by a piece of sacking. The zinc pot is filled with a paste of water and white crystals of sal-ammoniac (ammonium chloride), and the cell is sealed with pitch. The sal-ammoniac slowly

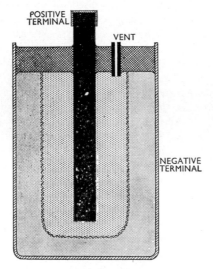

FIG. I. SECTION OF A DRY CELL

dissolves the zinc, an action which produces an electric current, and the oxide of manganese acts on the hydrogen gas that collects on the carbon rod, turning it immediately into water. Each cell produces a voltage of $1\frac{1}{2}$ volts, and the two cells joined end-to-end or 'in series' in an electric torch battery light a 3-volt bulb. The voltage of a cell depends only on the kinds of materials used and

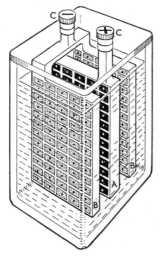

FIG. 2. DIAGRAM OF AN ACCUMULATOR

A. Positive plate. B. Negative plates. C. Positive and negative terminals

not on the size of the cell, but larger cells can provide a larger current (amps) for a longer time. When the zinc or the sal-ammoniac is used up, the cell can make no more electric current. Dry batteries can be used only to give small electric currents for short periods.

2. ACCUMULATORS. Large electric currents can be produced by an accumulator or secondary cell (Fig. 2). This is a glass box containing a mixture of sulphuric acid and distilled water, with one positive and two negative 'plates' dipping into the acid. The plates are hollow lead boxes with a large number of holes so that the acid can pass freely inside. The positive plate is filled with a paste of sulphuric acid and peroxide of lead, and the negative plate is filled with spongy lead. These cells have a voltage of 2 volts, and can produce quite large electric currents for several hours at a time. When they are exhausted they can be recharged by joining them to an ELECTRIC GENERATOR or RECTIFIER (qq.v.) for a few hours. They are therefore sometimes called accumulators or storage batteries, since they accumulate or store electricity when they are being recharged. Accumulators which meet with rough usage are not cased in glass but in containers made of various strong plastics.

The lead-acid cells just described are the most common kind of storage battery—the kind, for instance, used in an ordinary motor-car; but there are other kinds in use. One useful type is filled with a solution of caustic potash, which is a strong alkali, and has plates of nickel and iron; this is often used to provide current for small electric trucks. High-voltage electric supplies can be obtained by connecting a large number of cells in series.

Certain ELECTRIC FISHES (q.v. Vol. II)—electric eels and electric rays, for example—possess what amount to batteries of cells in series which are able to generate a certain amount of electricity (in some cases enough to give a man a severe shock).

See also ELECTRIC CURRENT; ELECTRICAL ENGINEERING.

BEARINGS. Any mechanism that moves, from the smallest spindle in a wrist watch to the huge propeller shafts of modern liners, has to be supported in such a way that it is held securely in position while yet being free to make its movement. The devices used to give this support are known as 'bearings'. Nowadays, because of the great variety of modern machinery and the high speed at which much of it runs, the design and manufacture of bearings has become a highly specialized branch of engineering.

The commonest type of moving part is the rotating shaft; so the majority of bearings are designed for this application. Firstly, the shaft must be supported along its length, and for this 'journal bearings' are used, so called because any supported portion of a shaft is known as a 'journal'. There may be one or more of these bearings according to the length of the shaft and its size and weight. If the shaft is a horizontal one, the bearings hold it in the horizontal position in which it is required to work—that is, they restrict its movement in a radial direction; but they do not prevent its moving lengthwise. A vertical shaft, therefore, or any shaft having a thrust on its ends, must have bearings which prevent this lengthwise, or axial, movement. These are known as 'thrust bearings'.

The earliest-known bearings, perhaps as early as 4000–3000 B.C., were probably of wood, allowing the wooden hub of a chariot wheel to run on a wooden axle (*see* WHEEL, Vol. IV). Iron, the first metal to be used for bearings, did not appear until comparatively recently. With the invention of the steam engine and modern machinery, bearings able to carry vastly increased loads and to support moving parts operating at much higher speeds were needed. The first problem was to reduce the friction between shaft and bearing that eventually caused the bearing to become so hot that it seized to the shaft. In the mid-19th century it was discovered that if a plain bearing—that is, a bearing which is simply a cylinder surrounding the shaft it supports (*see* Fig. 1*a*)—was flooded with oil, friction was much reduced. This lubrication causes a very thin film of oil to separate the bearing from the shaft so that the two are not, in fact, in actual contact. Many different devices are now used to ensure that the bearing receives and retains sufficient oil.

About 1875 an American, named Babbitt, introduced a special soft ALLOY (q.v.) called 'white metal', which provided greatly improved bearing surfaces because of its anti-frictional properties. This metal, which has been named after Babbitt, consisted originally of tin, copper, and antimony; but as the high percentage of tin made it expensive, more practical types of 'babbitt' have now been developed. White metal, however, is not strong enough to be used for the whole bearing, so a stronger material is used with a lining of white metal on which the shaft runs.

A more recent development, introduced about 1920, is the porous metal bearing, which is made

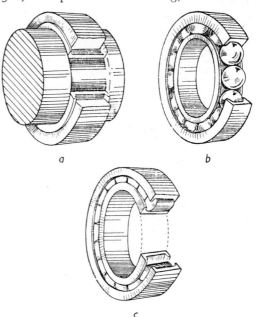

FIG. 1. TYPES OF BEARING

a. Plain bearing. The babbit can be seen between the two surfaces. *b.* Ball-bearing. *c.* Roller bearing

from powdered metal bonded together under pressure and heat. This metal not only has a good bearing surface, but can absorb lubricant like a sponge, thus acting as its own oil reservoir. Many watch bearings are made of 'jewels'—fused mineral powders containing a large proportion of precious stone such as sapphire, agate, or ruby.

The plain bearing is in use wherever rotating mechanisms are employed, and can be designed for almost any kind of work, from very heavy applications such as steam-engine driving axles, to shafts and spindles on high-speed machinery. For many modern applications, however, particularly those involving exceptionally high-speed operation, the plain bearing is not adequate, and the ball-bearing and other such types have been developed. The friction, or resistance, of a plain bearing is a sliding action, the surface of the shaft actually sliding on the bearing surface. By substituting balls, this action becomes a resistance to rolling instead of sliding, and the friction is considerably reduced. Such bearings, however, are much more complicated. In general, they consist of a ring of balls running between grooves in an inner and outer ring, known as 'races' (Fig. 1b). The whole bearing is a complete unit on its own and is fitted to the turning shaft by being forced tightly on to it. Thus, the inner race turns with the shaft, while the outer race remains stationary and is held in a housing as required. A light metal casing called a cage spins round with the balls to keep them spaced out evenly. The balls, which must be manufactured to a high degree of precision, are of special steels, normally one of the high-carbon chromium alloys, and are hardened.

The development of the ball-bearing led to other types using rolling parts, and designed for specific purposes. For instance, rollers are often used instead of balls for carrying very heavy loads, the rollers being small cylinders lying horizontally and distributed evenly round the ring (the race) in the same way as the balls in ball-bearings (Fig. 1c). For one type of bearing the rollers are actually tapered to form cones and run in races which also form cones to accommodate them. These tapered rollers lie at an angle to the rotating part and have the advantage that, as well as taking the horizontal, or radial, load, they can also take a thrust, or axial, load.

A great variety of types of bearings in which rolling components of one kind or another are used is available for the many requirements of modern machinery. Miniature ball-bearings have been made as small as $\frac{1}{8}$-inch overall diameter.

When an instrument has to be suspended so that it always remains in the same position irrespective of outside movements, such as a ship's COMPASS (q.v. Vol. IV), a special suspension known as a 'gimbal' is used. This usually consists of a pair of rings moving on pivots in such a way as to move freely in two directions and so counteract the motion of the ship. The bearings in which the gimbals move are called gimbal bearings.

Not all bearings are designed to contain rotating mechanisms; for many purposes a non-rotating sliding action is needed. For example, the runners of a sledge on snow become bearings for the sliding action of the sledge. More complicated examples are found, for instance, in the saddle of a LATHE (q.v.) which must slide along the bed, and in the various slides and cross-slides on the saddle which must be able to move in the appropriate directions. In the same way, DRILLING MACHINES (q.v.) must have bearings and bearing surfaces to allow the head to be raised and lowered on the column to bring it up and down in relation to the work being drilled.

See also FRICTION AND LUBRICATION.

BELT AND CHAIN DRIVE. To drive a piece of rotating mechanism a method has to be found of transmitting the power from the driving source in such a way that it will rotate the part required, which may be some distance away from it. For instance, when the pedals of a bicycle are pushed, they are producing power which has to be transmitted to the rear wheel in order to make the bicycle move. This is done by linking the shaft rotated by the pedals to the hub of the rear wheel by a continuous chain (*see* Fig. 7c). For driving machinery, a belt running over pulleys, or wheels, is often used, an arrangement known as 'belt drive'. Some pulleys are driving pulleys—that is, they impart movement to the belt; others are driven pulleys which are rotated by the belt. Apart from direct drive (that is, where the driving source and the driven part are directly connected by a shaft) or the use of GEARING (q.v.), the chain or belt drive is one of the commonest methods of transmitting rotary motion used in engineering.

The belts which have to transmit the power from one rotating part to another must be strong enough to deal with the power transmitted, which may often be considerable. They must not only be made of very strong materials but must also be so designed that they will stretch as little as possible and will not slip on their pulleys.

The belts may be of various shapes, the simplest being a flat, flexible band, passing round pulleys at the driving and the driven ends (Fig. 1). Where a large amount of power is to be transmitted, the belt may be made up of several layers or plies.

A flat belt on a pulley with a flat face tends to ride over to one side if the driving and the driven pulleys are not exactly in line. Thus, in practice, pulleys for flat belt drive are generally rounded a little on the face so that the middle of the surface over which the belt runs is higher than the edges; consequently, as a belt always tends to climb to the highest part of the rim, the belt is kept riding centrally on the pulley without any tendency to move over to the sides or to come off the pulley.

To prevent slipping, there must be a high degree of FRICTION (q.v.) between the belt and the pulley. Leather possesses this property, and

N.I.A.E.

FIG. I. BELT DRIVES ON THRESHING MACHINE

One belt is crossed to change direction of the driving
pulley and improve the grip

therefore transmission belts are sometimes made of leather. The grain or hair side of the leather is run in contact with the pulley, and the leather kept pliable by regular oiling. Another type of belting is made by sewing together several layers of cotton canvas, in various thickness from 3-ply to 8-ply and more. The canvas is treated with a special oil to give protection to its fibres, and sometimes with a gum known as balata to make the belt waterproof. Rubber belting is also used —not pure rubber, since this would stretch too much, but several thicknesses of cotton duck or canvas impregnated with rubber compound. Rubber and balata belting can be used in moist places where leather is not suitable. For certain purposes, plastics, such as nylon, may also be used.

As belts form an endless loop, means must be found, once the belt has been cut to length, of joining the ends together so strongly that they will stand the considerable strain put upon them. Sometimes they are spliced and laced with raw-hide leather thongs, but more often the ends are

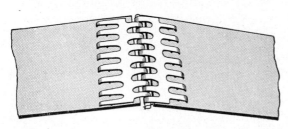

FIG. 2. JOIN IN FLAT BELTING

fastened together by a hinge joint consisting of two rows of spaced steel rings. The rings on one end of the belt fit between the spaces on the other end, and a metal rod, inserted as a peg through the rings, holds the ends of the belt together while still providing the necessary flexibility to allow it to run over the pulleys (Fig. 2).

Whatever the kind of belting, the relative speeds of driving and driven pulleys connected by the same belt depend on their relative sizes, the speeds being inversely proportional to the diameters. If the driven pulley is twice the size of the pulley that drives it, for example, it will revolve at only half the speed; if it were one-third the size, it would revolve at three times the speed (*see* GEARS). This makes it possible for the mechanism being driven to operate at a different speed from the driving shaft, and also to provide a range of speeds. In the case of flat belting, a stepped pulley can be provided, comprising in effect a number of pulleys of different diameters all made as one (Fig. 3). To change speed, the belt is simply moved from one step on the pulley

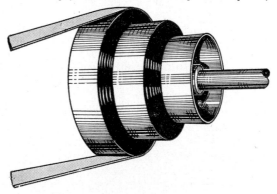

FIG. 3. STEPPED PULLEY

to another; the lower the step, the higher the speed obtained, and vice versa.

Rope belts made of hemp are sometimes used for large machines in mining and other industries; but a more common form of drive for such machines now consists of V-section belts made of rubber and cotton, which run in pulleys with corresponding V-section grooves (Fig. 4). The heavier the load, the more tightly the belt is wedged against the sides of the groove, and the firmer is its grip. This arrangement can be used successfully on quite small pulleys as in motor radiator fans, for example.

When large amounts of power are to be transmitted, several V-belts side by side on one pulley

FIG. 4. MULTIPLE V-ROPE DRIVE

G. King

(as shown at *b*), and the V has been widened, the belt settles down nearer the centre of the pulley. The effective diameter on which the belt is operating, d_2, is now clearly much smaller than when the two pulley halves were close together and the effective diameter was d_1; and, assuming that the pulley is at the driven end, the speed would be increased accordingly.

An advantage of this type of speed variation is that, unlike the stepped pulley, where the speed can be varied only in steps, here it can be varied smoothly throughout the entire range provided.

It is difficult to make a perfectly level joint in a V-belt, and usually the cotton core for high-speed belts of this type is woven all in one piece and then coated with rubber. Since these ready-made belts have no join, the only way of altering

are used, each belt having its own groove. This 'multiple V-rope drive' is widely used in driving modern MACHINE TOOLS (q.v.).

V-section belts and pulleys can also be used to provide another method of varying speed. The pulley is made in two halves, which can be moved nearer to each other or farther apart (Fig. 5). When they are close together (as shown at *a*), and the V-groove in the pulley is at its narrowest, the belt rides towards the top of the groove. When the two halves are farther apart

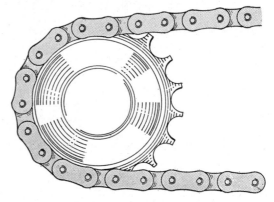

FIG. 6. CHAIN AND SPROCKET WHEEL

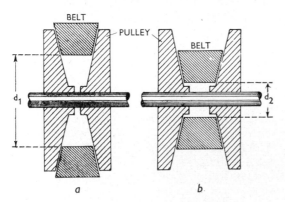

FIG. 5. SPEED VARIATION WITH V-BELT

a. When the two halves of the pulley are close together the effective diameter on which the belt is operating is d_1. *b*. When the two pulley halves are farther apart the effective diameter is d_2

tension (to take up slack, for instance, if the belt stretches) is to change the distance between the pulleys; and devices for doing this have to be provided. There is, too, a type of V-belt called the Whittle belt made up of hinged links, usually of leather, and all independent and alike, so that one of them can be taken out to shorten the belt or one added to lengthen it.

In spite of all precautions, belts for transmitting drive still have a tendency to slip in certain circumstances; therefore, when a drive with no possibility of slip is required, some form of chain drive is often used.

Chains for transmitting power have, in fact, developed from belts and were once known as link belts. They are made up of a number of rigid links, each one hinged to its neighbour. The chain runs on sprocket wheels which have teeth to engage in openings in the links (Fig. 6). Since

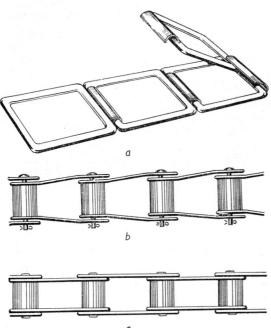

FIG. 7. TYPES OF CHAIN

Square link chain. One link is partially removed.
b. Pintle chain. *c*. Bicycle chain

these teeth, as it were, are in mesh with the chain, the chain cannot possibly slip.

The first kind of transmission chain to be in general use was the wrought-iron square-link chain. All the links in this chain are exactly alike, each having a curved tongue or hook which joins up with the next link, and so on throughout the chain (Fig. 7*a*). The links remain interlocked while the chain is in its working position, but it can be opened by being bent back in the opposite curve to the one it takes travelling round the sprockets. Similar chains are now made in pressed steel, though the wrought-iron type is still much used.

The 'pintle' chain is also made from wrought iron. In this, the links are roughly in the shape of a 'U' (Fig. 7*b*), the top of the 'U' of one link fitting over the base of the 'U' of the next. A hole is drilled right through both links where they meet in this way, and a pin is inserted and secured in the hole to join the links together.

The type of chain used for the chain drive on bicycles also consists of links held together by pins, but, in this case, a hardened steel 'sleeve' is fitted over each pin to make a roller; this forms the surface that comes into contact with the sprocket teeth (Fig. 7*c*). Chains like this, which

are also made in very large sizes for driving industrial machinery, have a number of advantages over the simple pintle chain. It is possible to make them short in pitch, and they will run satisfactorily over small diameter sprocket wheels. They can be thus used for producing a great reduction in speed ratio without the need for a very large driven sprocket.

When wear begins to occur in driving chains, the same effect is noticed as in belting—the chain appears to stretch, due to wear in the pins joining the links; the links then become out of pitch with the sprocket and cannot fit down properly between the teeth. The slope of the sprocket teeth has to be exactly the correct shape in order to ensure proper meshing with the links of the chain, and thus an efficient drive.

BIMETALLIC STRIP, *see* THERMOMETER; THERMOSTAT.

BLAST FURNACE. Iron is smelted—that is, it is manufactured from IRON ORE (q.v. Vol. VII) —in blast furnaces. In the heat of the furnace the metallic iron is separated from iron oxide (iron plus oxygen) which is the form in which iron is found in the earth. The oxygen is freed by the chemical action of the furnace and is discharged as gas. The heat of the furnace also melts the earthy and sandy constituents of the ore into a 'slag' or scum which can be discharged from the furnace quite separately from the iron. This slag, however, has a useful function in the furnace. The iron maker 'works' his slag by additions of limestone into a condition in which it will react chemically with some of the chemical impurities in the ore, particularly sulphur, drawing them into itself. When the slag, therefore, is tapped, it takes a large part of the sulphur with it. Thus, the blast furnace has three products: gas, slag, and iron. Slag and iron are both drawn from the furnace as liquids, and harden as they cool.

The blast furnace is a vertical tube or stack, usually from 80 to 100 feet high, or as high as three two-storey houses on top of one another. It is lined with fire-resisting brick (*see* FIRECLAYS AND REFRACTORIES), and across the inside it measures from 13 to 20 feet at the top, and from about 15 to nearly 30 feet at the bottom, in the well or 'hearth' where the liquid iron collects.

Into the top are 'charged' or fed the iron ore, coke, and limestone, the raw materials of the iron-making process. Hot air is blown in violently through nozzles or 'tuyères' (twee-yers), which encircle the furnace, usually about 8 feet from the bottom and about 5 feet or so apart. The air, which comes to the tuyeres from the 'bustle pipe', is blown into the furnace at a pressure of about 12 lb. per square inch, at a speed far greater than the fiercest natural gale, and at a temperature of about 600° C. to 700° C.

The pressure is supplied by blowing engines, which may be steam driven and which often use gas from the furnace itself as a fuel. In most modern installations each furnace has a separate blowing engine. The air is heated by pairs of Cowper stoves, tall, brickwork towers to which gas from the blast furnace is carried as fuel. While the gas is heating the brickwork in one stove of the pair, the air on its way to the furnace is heated by passing over the already heated brickwork in the second stove. At intervals of about half an hour the stoves are 'reversed' and

the air is blown through the one which has just been heated up by burning gas, while the other is regenerated (reheated) by burning gas.

The gale of hot air blown into the furnace keeps the coke in the charge burning furiously, just as a pair of bellows provides a draught to keep a domestic fire ablaze. In the great heat thus generated, the oxygen in the air combines with some of the carbon in the coke to form the gas carbon monoxide. This chemical reaction sets off a whole series of other reactions which do the iron-maker's work of freeing oxygen from the iron oxide. The carbon monoxide gas has the property of attracting to itself any available oxygen at high temperatures to make a different gas, carbon dioxide. This it does by drawing oxygen from the iron oxide of the ore; and the molten iron is left to trickle down the furnace and gather in the hearth, while the carbon dioxide travels up the stack. Carbon dioxide then attracts to itself more carbon from the hot coke,

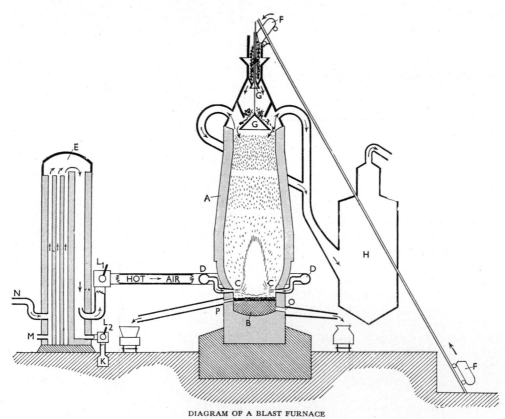

DIAGRAM OF A BLAST FURNACE

A. Stack. B. Hearth. C. Tuyères. D. Bustle pipe encircling furnace. E. Cowper stove. F. Skips. G. Large and small bells. H. Dustcatcher. J. Clean gas outlet. K. Hot gas from J. L_1. Air valve (open). L_2. Gas valve (closed). M. Gas outlet. N. Air inlet. O. Iron taphole. P. Slag taphole

and becomes carbon monoxide again. Then the process is repeated—the carbon monoxide once more reacts with the oxygen in the ore and passes on up the furnace as carbon dioxide; this in turn attracts carbon from the coke and again becomes carbon monoxide—and so on and on to the top of the stack, where in the lower temperature the reactions do not occur with such ease.

The liquid iron as it trickles down soaks up a certain amount of carbon from the hot coke, and by the time it gathers in the hearth, it contains about 3 per cent. to $3\frac{1}{2}$ per cent. of carbon. A lump of ore takes about 8 hours to reach the bottom of the stack from the time it is put in at the top. During the course of its journey while the oxygen is being drawn off, the earth and other constituents, known as the 'gangue', have been melted, and the slag also trickles down the furnace to gather in the hearth. There it floats on top of the iron as cream floats on milk. The function of the limestone in the charge is to combine with the ash in the coke and the liquid slag as it passes down the furnace and to make a liquid which will react with the sulphur in the iron and extract it from the iron. Too much limestone makes the slag liquid but incapable of removing sulphur; too little limestone removes sulphur but forms a sticky, gummy slag that will not run freely from the furnace.

The liquid slag and iron are 'tapped' or run out from the furnace separately at different levels at regular intervals throughout the day and night, all days in the week, all weeks in the year. Iron is tapped out every 5 or 6 hours; slag in smaller quantities every 2 hours or so. Raw materials are constantly fed in at the top of the furnace to keep it full.

The raw materials are charged from wheeled trucks or 'skips' running up inclined tracks at the side of the furnace. A system of conical hoods ensures that gas is not wastefully blown out of the top of the furnace when this is open for the raw materials to be charged. The gas is a valuable fuel, once it has been cleaned of the heavy burden of dust and ash that it carries. As well as being used for raising steam and heating the stoves, it often also heats the COKE OVENS (q.v.) from which the blast furnace gets its solid fuel. The blast furnace is thus practically self-contained for its heat and energy requirements.

The iron tapped from the furnace is dealt with in two ways. If the blast furnaces are linked to adjacent steelworks, the liquid iron may be sent

Steel Company of Wales

THE TOP OF A BLAST FURNACE

there directly in great heat-insulated containers, and charged to the steel furnaces with a minimum loss of heat. In the steelworks it is usually stored until wanted in a liquid state in huge 'mixers' holding as much as 1,000 or 1,500 tons. The mixers take iron from different furnaces at different times and mix the different qualities to produce a consistent raw material for the steel maker (*see* STEEL-MAKING).

If the steelworks is a long way away, or if the iron is not intended for steel making but for iron founding (*see* CASTING) or for a wrought-iron puddling furnace, it is cast into solid 'pigs' on a pig-casting machine. This consists of an endless chain carrying metal moulds. The moulds are filled with molten iron from the ladle—the container into which the iron has been poured on being tapped from the blast furnace—and then move slowly up an incline, being sprayed as they go with water to cool them. As each mould passes over the top of the endless chain the now cool and solid bar of iron is tipped into a railway truck.

A modern furnace may make well over 700 tons of iron a day, using 2 to 3 tons of raw materials for every ton of pig iron produced. Thus a plant with two large blast furnaces will use 2 million tons of raw materials a year. In the United Kingdom about half the iron, which amounts altogether to about 10 million tons a year, is made from imported ore; and many works on the coast unload the ore into their stockyards or storage bunkers direct from ships from Sweden, Newfoundland, North or West Africa, or from the many other overseas sources of ore (*see* IRON AND STEEL INDUSTRY).

The firebrick lining of a blast furnace usually lasts long enough for 2 or 3 million tons of iron to be made before the furnace has to be relined. This usually takes rather over a month to do, though in 1952 a team of workers at Scunthorpe, Lincolnshire, relined a furnace with a 25-foot hearth in 24 days, and thus set up a world record.

See also IRON AND STEEL; COKE OVEN; STEEL-MAKING; CASTING.

BLASTING. This is the operation of separating by means of EXPLOSIVES (q.v.) a quantity of stone, coal, metallic ore, or whatever it may be from the main mass of rock in a tunnel, mine, or quarry (*see* STONE QUARRYING, Section 2, Vol. VII).

Drill holes for blasting are arranged systematically in patterns so that the explosive charges will break the rock between the inner end of the drill holes and the exposed face. The distance between the inner ends of the holes is known as the 'burden', and the charges are calculated to secure the breaking of the rock efficiently with as little explosive as possible.

The explosive is usually in the form of long cylinders called cartridges, and these are packed tightly in the hole, each cartridge being in close contact with the preceding one. One of the cartridges, the 'primer', which may be the first, second, or last in the hole according to circumstances, has in it a detonator (*see* FUZE), in which is crimped a length of safety fuze or, if it is an electric detonator, two thin wires.

In mining, when groups of holes in a set pattern have been charged with explosive and the primers placed in position, the rest of each hole is packed tightly with dry, gritty, fine material, called 'stemming'. This is 'tamped' into position with a wooden tamping rod to keep the charge closely confined and to make the explosive fully effective. Usually, the mining engineer wants his charges to go off in a certain order; the first few to go off are the ones that break out the 'cut', usually a central wedge; while the others, going off a fraction of a second later, break off adjacent wedges in succession until the whole excavation is complete. The whole system is therefore set off from a central point a safe distance off, the order in which the charges fire being fixed by the

THE SIDE OF A QUARRY IMMEDIATELY AFTER FIRING AN EXPLOSIVE CHARGE

I.C.I.

lengths of the various fuzes, if these are used, or by the delay period of the detonators, if electric detonators are used. In the latter case, the electricity is provided by a specially safe kind of hand-operated generator called an exploder, which can be worked only by a key in the charge of the man responsible for the blasting.

Before the actual firing takes place warning is given, and all men in mine or quarry that are working in the vicinity stop work and withdraw to a safe place to protect themselves from 'fly' rock—small fragments that are ejected at high speed. In underground work, moreover, no workmen may return to the scene of the blast until sufficient time has elapsed for the dispersal of dust and fumes from the combustion of the explosives.

In quarries that are near towns or buildings, the ground vibrations set up may be sufficient to damage property in the neighbourhood. To reduce vibration, the individual charges are fired with very short delay periods between them. Special detonators are now available with delays of from $\frac{1}{40}$th to $\frac{1}{20}$th of a second.

See also QUARRYING MACHINERY.

BLUEPRINT, *see* DRAWING, REPRODUCTION OF.

BOAT BUILDING. For some 2,000 years, until the development of wrought iron in the middle of the last century, nearly every type of vessel, from PRIMITIVE SHIPS to the great SAILING SHIPS (qq.v. Vol. IV) of the 15th to the 19th centuries, was built of timber in one of two ways. These two main methods of construction, called 'carvel' and 'clinker', are still used for building small wooden craft today. Carvel boats, which now include most yachts, CANOES (q.v. Vol. IV), and light rowing boats used for boat races (*see* ROWING, Vol. IX), consist of wooden planks laid edge to edge on a frame of timbers to form either a single or double 'skin' of wood according to the weight of the vessel. Clinker boats, which include most LIFEBOATS (q.v. Vol. IV), heavy dinghies, and some SAILING BOATS (q.v. Vol. IX) of the 18- to 20-foot class, consist of overlapping wooden planks. Other small vessels, such as landing craft, some motor launches, and tugs, usually have steel hulls and are built in the same way as large ships (*see* SHIPBUILDING).

When building a carvel boat, the keel, which comprises its backbone, is made first. This used to be fashioned out of a single tree, usually oak,

Norman Wymer

BUILDING A CARVEL BOAT
Above: Fixing the timbers to the ribbons
Below: Fixing the second set of planks in a double skin yacht

which was left to season for one year for every inch of its thickness and was then steamed and bent to shape. Though this is still done in many building yards, it is now more usual to laminate the keel—that is, several strips of oak are 'scarfed', or jointed, together to provide three separate units, known as the 'stem', 'keel', and

Norman Wymer

BUILDING A CLINKER BOAT

Top: The keel and moulds of a lifeboat
Centre: Riveting together two planks
Bottom: Setting a timber in position after steaming it into a plastic condition

'stern-post'. These are joined and strengthened by copper fastenings.

The completed keel is set on low trestles in the building bay or shed, and held upright by strips of wood linking both stem and stern-post to

beams in the ceiling. Temporary U-shaped 'moulds' of various sizes are fixed at right angles to the keel, the largest in the centre and the smallest at either end, with their tops attached to the ceiling.

The moulds are linked together by a series of wooden 'ribbons', arranged at equal distances up each side and extending the whole length of the boat. They are set in grooves cut into the edges of the moulds, and secured to the stem and stern-post to provide a temporary framework upon which to build.

The all-important oak 'timbers', which extend across the inside of the boat like the ribs of a whale, are steamed until they are sufficiently pliable and are then set in position. One man stands on the keel to push each timber into place, a second bolts it to the keel, and a third fixes it to each of the ribbons.

The planks which form the outer 'skin' are usually made from mahogany; because the boat is curved and because no two planks are alike, they have to be sawn and placed with the greatest skill. If the boat has only a single skin, the planks are laid to run the entire length of the vessel. Beginning at the keel, the boat builder gradually works his way upwards, setting each plank edge to edge above the one before, and fixing them by copper rivets to each timber and to either end of the keel. As the planks rise higher the ribbons are removed, and when the builder has filled in both sides he also takes out the moulds. If the boat has a double skin, the first set of planks is covered with oiled calico, and a second set is fixed diagonally above the calico at an angle of about 45° to the first. The inside of the skin is strengthened by adding 'stringers', lengths of light wood extending the length of the boat.

When the 'gunwales', the strong top edge of the boat which carries the rowlocks for oars, and various fittings to the inside of the boat have been added, the craft is complete structurally. But to ensure that it is absolutely seaworthy, every seam and join is 'caulked'—that is, each joint is wedged open to half the thickness of the plank, and layers of special cotton are driven in with a blunt chisel and mallet.

The keel of a clinker boat is made in exactly the same way, and the same temporary U-shaped moulds, but without ribbons, are used for building the hull. The planks, however, are laid first, the cross-timbers being set in place after the planks have been laid and the moulds removed. The boat builder lays his first plank along the keel and rivets it in position; then he lays the second plank so that it overlaps the outside of the first to a depth of ¾ inch to 1 inch, and then rivets the two edges together, and secures the ends to the stem and stern-post. The moulds keep the planks firm as the boat builder places them, and guide the shape. To ensure that each plank overlaps the next adequately a step is cut in the outside upper edge of each. When both sides of the craft are ready, the moulds are removed and the timbers set in place. Because of the overlap of the planks, clinker boats need very little caulking.

See also Vol. IV: PRIMITIVE SHIPS; SAILING SHIPS.
See also Vol. IX: SAILING BOATS.

BOILERS. STEAM (q.v.), which is a source of power, is produced by heating water in a boiler. Steam boilers were known to the Egyptians and Romans: when the priest kindled a fire on the temple altar, it might heat a concealed boiler, and the consequent mixture of steam and hot air would perform a variety of 'miracles', such as causing serpents to hiss or statues to blow horns or pour libations of wine from goblets. Water-heating vessels of water-tube construction have been found in the ruins of POMPEII (q.v. Vol. XII). Little practical use was found for boilers, however, until the advent of the STEAM ENGINE in the 18th century, when containers like brewers' coppers fitted with domed lids were first introduced to generate STEAM (qq.v.). From these evolved the 'haystack' boiler, a beehive-shaped vessel of hammered iron plates, and, later, the 'wagon' boiler as used by James Watt. In the 19th century Trevithick, realizing that with the increasingly high pressure of steam only a circular section would provide sufficient strength, evolved a cylindrical boiler with domed ends.

All these were what are called 'pot' boilers, the heating being entirely from outside. Trevithick evolved the first boiler with a firebox inside the water-space to increase the heating surface. His 'Cornish boiler' had an internal circular flue. By adding another flue, Sir William Fairbairn in 1844 evolved the 'Lancashire boiler', which is still widely used (Fig. 1). This consists of a cylindrical steel shell (A) up to about 30 feet long and 10 feet diameter, with two cylindrical furnace flues (B) running right through it. Since the gases leaving the flues are very hot, and the whole object of an efficient boiler is to extract as much heat as possible from the fire, the boiler is set in brickwork so that the gases from both flues combine and return underneath the boiler, heating a portion of the outside surface. At the front end the gases divide and pass along the sides of the boiler, thus making use of more of their heat before they flow up the chimney.

In the 'Economic' boiler, a variation on the Lancashire, the flue gases return through a number of small tubes set in the water space, and leave at the front end of the boiler (Fig. 2). In the 'Super-Economic', they make a third pass to the back end of the boiler through a second series of small tubes. All these boilers are known as 'shell' or 'fire-tube' types, and are still widely used for generating steam on land for pressures

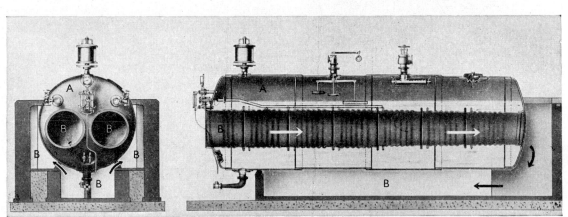

Edwin Danks & Co.

FIG. I. END VIEW AND SECTION OF A 'LANCASHIRE' BOILER
A. Shell containing water. B. Flues. Arrows show direction of flow of gases from fire

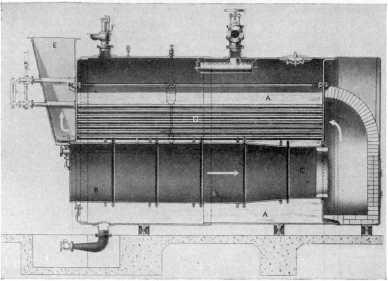

FIG. 2. SECTION OF AN 'ECONOMIC' BOILER

Edwin Danks & Co.

A. Water space. B. Fire. C. Flue. D. Tubes for hot gases. E. Exit to chimney

a number of small tubes set in the water-space of the boiler before passing up the chimney.

The 'water-tube' boiler reverses the fire-tube principle, the water being inside the tubes, and the fire outside. This is done because small tubes can be more easily built to withstand high pressures than large shells. A simple form of water-tube boiler consists of a number of tubes connected at both ends to a vessel full of water and having a flame applied to it. As the heated water expands and becomes less dense than the cold water, it rises, and so sets up a continuous circulation; cooler water comes down the unheated tube, and a mixture of hot water and steam bubbles rises up the heated tube to the vessel above, where the steam separates from the water. By replacing this simple vessel with a heavy steel drum and using a large number of tubes, we have a practical working boiler (Fig. 3). The tubes instead of being inclined are often vertical, with their lower ends fixed into another drum; this drum is fed with cooler water by 'downcomer' tubes placed either outside the furnace or in a cooler part of it. So long as there is a temperature difference between the 'generating' and 'downcomer' tubes, there will be a continuous circulation of water—and this is the principle of all so-called 'natural-circulation' boilers. Successful boilers have been built in which the circulation is forced by pumps; but natural circulation boilers are by far the more numerous.

up to about 250 lb. per square inch and for capacities up to around 20,000 lb. of steam per hour.

The 'locomotive boiler', another example of the fire-tube type of boiler and the type used in locomotives since Stephenson's 'Rocket', has a fire-box at one end and the chimney at the other so that the furnace gases make one pass through

The advent of the STEAM TURBINE for POWER STATION work (qq.v.) caused a demand for larger and larger boilers. Water-tube boilers with capacities of more than a million pounds of steam per hour and as large as a ten or twelve-storey block of flats are now built. They use 'pulverized-fuel firing', the coal being ground to a fine powder in mills and carried by a stream of heated air to burners where it is burned like gas (Fig. 4). Their consumption may be as much as a ton of coal per minute. Smaller boilers are fired by

Babcox & Wilcox Ltd.

FIG. 3. DIAGRAM OF A WATER-TUBE BOILER

A. Drum. B. Water tubes. C. Mechanical stoker with endless chain grate

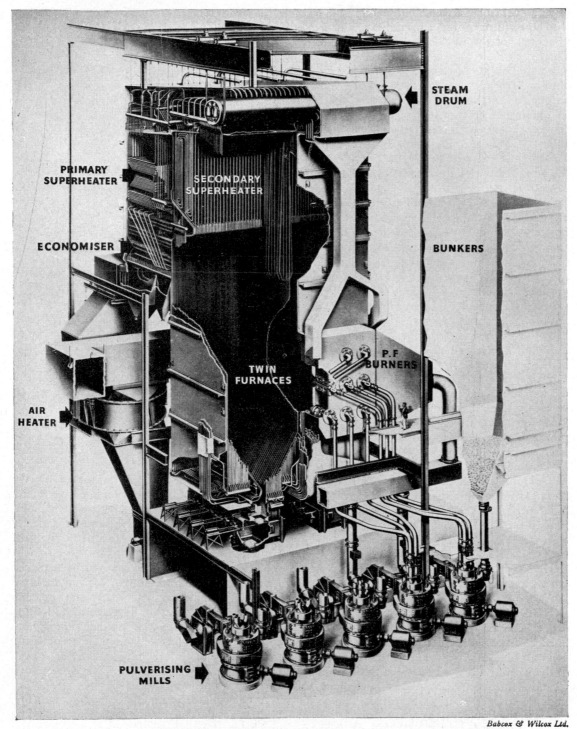

FIG. 4. DIAGRAM OF A 'RADIATION' BOILER FOR EVAPORATIONS OF 800,000 TO 1,000,000 LB. PER HOUR

The scale of this huge boiler is given by the figure beneath the P.F. Burners

mechanical stokers, which either carry the coal
into the furnace on an endless-chain grate
(Fig. 3c), or throw it in by revolving paddles.
Only the smallest are still fired by hand.

Steam is heated to a temperature higher than
the boiling-point of water by being passed
through a superheater—usually a system of tubes
in a high-temperature zone of the furnace. The
limit of superheat is set by the ability of the steel
tubes to withstand intensely high temperatures
for long periods; at present about 1,060° F.
(corresponding to a dull red heat) is the highest
in normal use.

As the furnace gases leaving the boiler tubes
are always at a higher temperature than the
boiler water, much useful heat would be lost if
they were allowed to escape directly up the
chimney. For this reason economizers have been
used since early days: the hot gases are passed
around nests of tubes through which the feed
water is pumped on its way to the boiler. Any
additional heat in the gases is often used to pre-
heat the air used for combustion in the furnace
in an 'air heater', which follows the same broad
principles.

The steam boiler, so important a part of
modern methods of generating power, ranges in
its use from small heating boilers in factories and
business premises to the giants used in modern
power stations. Even in the atomic age it is still
likely to play an important part, though boilers
for atomic power, instead of having furnaces,
will obtain their heat from nuclear fission (*see*
NUCLEAR POWER). Though their design may be
different, their fundamental principles will
remain the same.

See also STEAM; STEAM ENGINE; STEAM TURBINE.

BORING MACHINES, *see* DRILLING AND BOR-
ING MACHINES.

BOULDER DAM. This DAM (q.v.), which spans
a deep canyon on the Colorado River, on the
border of the southern American States of Ari-
zona and Nevada, will remain the highest dam
in the world until work has been finished on La
Grande Dixence and Mauvoisin—two dams still
under construction in Switzerland. The water
stored in the Boulder dam's vast reservoir is used
for IRRIGATION (q.v. Vol. VI), WATER SUPPLY,
and the generation of HYDRO-ELECTRIC POWER
(qq.v.). The dam itself also controls the flood
waters of the river (*see* FLOOD CONTROL).

U.S.I.S.

BOULDER DAM

Surplus water from the reservoir is discharged below the
dam on either side of the gorge

At the beginning of the 20th century many
plans for controlling the Colorado, the flow of
which varies greatly from season to season, were
considered by the United States Government.
Eventually a scheme was prepared which included the construction of a dam of unprece-
dented height in Boulder Canyon; in 1930 the
plant needed for its construction began to be
assembled. Meanwhile orders had been placed
for a special road and railway to bring the great
quantity of building materials to the site, and
for a special transmission line 222 miles long to
supply the electric power needed during construction. All designs were tested for strength and
performance on a number of scale models; even
the effects of possible earthquakes were calculated and allowed for.

A COFFERDAM (q.v.), 90 feet high, was first
built across the canyon above the site of the dam
and below the entrances to four tunnels, through
which the river water was diverted. These
tunnels, which were 56 feet in diameter before
lining and over 3 miles long, were cut through

the solid rock. The rock proved to be so sound that no timbering or roof supports were needed, though the tunnels were lined with concrete to reduce resistance to fast-flowing water.

The foundations for the dam were then excavated and later 'grouted' (the cracks or fissures filled with liquid mortar) to minimize leakage. The dam, which is of the arch-gravity type, 660 feet thick at the base and 726 feet above its deepest foundations, was formed of concrete cast in position in large blocks, which were 'keyed' together horizontally and vertically, the joints being grouted. A special cement, made to generate as little heat as possible during setting, was used for the concrete, which was further cooled by refrigerated water circulated through 1-inch pipes embedded in it. This greatly reduced the setting temperature and therefore the shrinkage of the concrete and its tendency to crack (*see* CONCRETE CONSTRUCTION).

The diversion tunnels, when they had served their original purpose, were converted to permanent use. The two outer tunnels form 'spillways' to conduct surplus water past the dam to the river downstream. The inner tunnels carry the water which is used to generate electricity. This water enters through four reinforced concrete intake towers nearly 400 feet high, built up on the rocky sides of the reservoir just above the dam, and flows through steel tubes, called 'penstocks'. The penstocks run inside the tunnels and then branch out to feed the rows of turbines in the POWER STATION (q.v.) immediately below the dam. The turbines and generators, which are grouped in two banks on either side of the gorge, form several large generating stations, each supplying power to a separate system. Their total capacity is nearly 1½ million horse-power.

In 1935, after nearly 4 years, the dam was sufficiently advanced for the reservoir to start collecting water. When the last 'lift' of concrete was in place, the storage capacity of the reservoir, now known as Mead Lake, was more than 1¼ million million cubic feet. The project had cost nearly 52 million dollars.

Besides supplying vast quantities of electric power, the dam has made possible the irrigation of 2 million acres of land; it has prevented any serious flooding of the Colorado basin, and has greatly improved navigation on the river.

See also DAMS; FLOOD CONTROL; HYDRO-ELECTRIC POWER.
See also Vol. VI: IRRIGATION.

BRAKES AND BRAKING. In order to control any moving mechanism it must be possible not only to set it in motion and keep it moving at the speed required but also to stop it without difficulty. Since the FRICTION (q.v.) of a moving mechanism is kept as low as possible to slow down or stop a machine, some way of increasing the friction artificially or of increasing the load so that the machine does not keep on running under its own momentum has to be found. This is normally done by a brake.

There are two points common to all the various types of brake in use; firstly, the brake must be capable of providing the artificial load required and of operating quickly and reliably; and secondly, since the energy absorbed by the brake is converted into heat, some means must be provided for getting rid of this heat. The heat can be calculated, since there is an exact equivalent between the energy absorbed and the heat produced: 778 foot-pounds of energy (1 ft. lb. is the work done in raising 1 lb. weight through 1 ft.) are equivalent to 1 British Thermal Unit (1 B.Th.U. is the heat required to raise 1 lb. of water through 1° F.).

The simplest type of brake consists of a block, known as a 'brake shoe', pressed against the rim of a wheel (Fig. 1). It is the type used on trains and, in a more elementary form, on old horse-drawn carts, the pressure of the shoe against the

FIG. 1. BRAKE SHOE ON A LOCOMOTIVE WHEEL
A. Brake shoe. B. Vacuum cylinder. C. Train pipe by which vacuum cylinder is exhausted to apply brake

wheel providing an artificial load which slows the wheel down. In the 'band brake' (Fig. 2) the shoe is replaced by a band which passes round the wheel and is tightened on to it. This type of brake is difficult to cool, and a better arrangement is the 'drum brake' (Fig. 3) in which two shoes are forced apart in a variety of ways against the inner surface of a drum. Motor-car brakes are usually of this type. The braking effect of each shoe is different, since they tend to rotate slightly under the drag of the brake drum, the

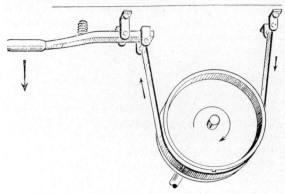

FIG. 2. BAND BRAKE

The brake is applied by pushing down the lever

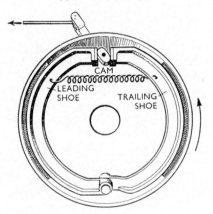

FIG. 3. DRUM BRAKE

When the lever is moved the cam forces the shoes against the inside of the brake drum. The spring keeps the shoes away from the drum when the brake is off

'leading shoe' being forced harder against the drum than the 'trailing shoe'. To overcome this disadvantage the 'two leading shoe' system has been developed, in which the trailing shoe consists of an outer shoe carrying the brake lining sliding on inclined grooves in the inner shoe. Under the drag of the brake drum the outer shoe is forced harder against the drum, thus acting as a second leading shoe. The drum brake is often kept cool by fitting fins to the outside of the drum, and directing air on to it. The latest type of brake is the 'disk brake' (Fig. 4), in which the shoes clamp together on either side of a disk.

Special brake lining material is used for the rubbing surface of brake shoes. It consists of asbestos with a binder of synthetic resin, both materials which will stand high temperatures without melting or burning.

With electrical machinery, it is possible to brake without using the mechanical methods of the type described. This takes advantage of the fact that an electric generator has to overcome a large load in order to generate electric current (see ELECTRIC MOTORS). An electric driving motor, for example, can be switched, when it is required to brake, so that instead of drawing current from the supply and acting as a motor, the reverse procedure applies—the motor becomes a generator and consequently produces the artificial load required for braking. This type of action, known as regenerative braking, has the advantage that no mechanical power is needed to apply the brake. The motor, while braking, is actually generating current and returning it to the line from which it normally gets its supply.

Apart from vehicles, brakes are very widely used throughout industry. Many machines have to be started and stopped hundreds or even thousands of times an hour in order to carry out automatic processes (see MACHINE TOOLS), and others, such as large presses (see FORGING AND PRESSING), may incorporate enormous flywheels which would run on their own momentum for a considerable time if they were not braked. For all these, special types of brakes have been developed, some able to control very large and heavy equipment, others capable of braking very fast and very often, and so on. These, however, do not involve any different general principles.

In addition to stopping moving mechanisms, brakes are also used to provide an artificial load

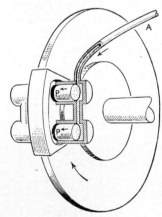

FIG. 4. HYDRAULICALLY OPERATED DISK BRAKE

The pressure of the oil from the pipe A forces the pistons P on to the rotating disk

on an engine or motor for the purpose of measuring output—its brake horse-power (b.h.p.). Such brakes are called absorption DYNAMO-METERS (q.v.), and they measure the output of energy of a machine by measuring how much b.h.p. is needed to oppose it.

See also HYDRAULIC POWER TRANSMISSION.

BRICKWORK. 1. Various kinds of BRICKS AND TILES (q.v. Vol. VII) have been used for building for over 6,000 years; in Britain, brickwork has been widely used since Tudor times. Bricks have many advantages over other building materials: any size or shape of wall, for example, can be built from bricks of one standard size; they are light and easy to handle; they give walls variety of colour and texture; they need little or no maintenance—their appearance often improving with age; and the clay or brick earth from which most bricks are made is found in most places.

A standard size British brick measures $8\frac{5}{8}$ inches by $4\frac{1}{8}$ inches, and is $2\frac{5}{8}$ inches deep. The varieties most used in Britain are:

Flettons. Mass-produced, machine-made bricks, suitable for all general purposes.

Red facings. Red bricks used only for the outside, or face, of walls.

London stock. Yellow bricks with which many of the plainer buildings in London have been built.

Engineering bricks. Dense, heavy bricks of great strength. These are used for pillars carrying heavy loads, and for corners of walls or gates that may be knocked by passing traffic.

Firebricks. These give good resistance to heat, and are used for lining furnaces, retorts, and factory chimneys.

Glazed bricks. These usually have white surfaces which reflect the light, and are easily cleaned. They are used in such buildings as hospitals and swimming baths.

As brickwork is used mainly for walls and arches, it must be strong enough to carry the load of floors and roofs. Average quality bricks in ordinary lime mortar can usually carry a load of about 4 tons per square foot; heavy engineering bricks in cement mortar, however, can carry up to 30 tons per square foot (*see* BUILDING, PRINCIPLES OF).

2. BONDS. There are several ways of arranging, or 'bonding', bricks to give strength and an attractive appearance, the most common arrangements being English, Flemish, and Dutch bonds. A brick laid along the length of the wall is called a 'stretcher', and one laid across the width is called a 'header'. English bond consists of alternate courses, or layers, of headers and stretchers (Fig. 1a); Flemish bond has headers and stretchers laid alternately in each course (Fig. 1b); and Dutch bond is similar to English bond but with every other course of stretchers moved along $4\frac{1}{2}$ inches and with modified arrangements at the end of the wall (Fig. 1c). English bond is the simplest and is used for most general purposes, while Flemish and Dutch bonds are rather more attractive in appearance. For walls $4\frac{1}{2}$ inches thick, however, all the bricks have to be laid along the length of the wall, and this arrangement is known as 'stretcher' bond (Fig. 1d). With this exception the thickness of the wall has no effect on the appearance of the bond

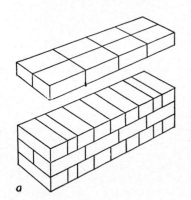 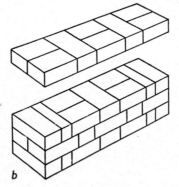 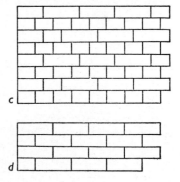

FIG. 1. BRICK BONDS
a. English bond. *b.* Flemish bond. *c.* Dutch bond. *d.* Stretcher bond for $4\frac{1}{2}$-inch walls

3. BUILDING A WALL. The two ends of a wall are always built first, as these control the construction of the main body of the wall. They are

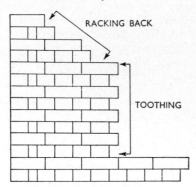

FIG. 2. METHOD OF BUILDING A BRICK WALL

continually tested with a 'plumb line' to ensure that they are vertical, and, when every fourth course has been laid, they are measured with a gauge rod to ensure that the four courses with their joints measure 12 inches. (In northern England and Scotland the bricks are often slightly thicker, the four courses with their joints measuring 13 inches.) So that the two ends of the wall may interlock with the rest of the wall when it is built they are 'toothed', that is, a stretcher in every other course is left projecting $2\frac{1}{4}$ inches, or 'racked back', that is, the bricks are set back one above another like a flight of steps. Racking back is preferable to toothing as it is then easier to ensure that the mortar joints are filled solid when the main body of the wall is connected to the ends. Often, however, a combination of both methods is used (Fig. 2).

When the ends of the wall have been built to a height of a few feet, the body of the wall is laid a course at a time. A thin cord is stretched taut between the ends and level with the top edge of the course, the bricks being laid along the line of the cord.

The bricks are bonded together with mortar, spread about $\frac{3}{8}$ inch thick. Mortar is usually made from a mixture of lime and sand (in the proportion 1:3), cement and sand (1:4), or cement, lime, and sand (1:2:9). Sufficient mortar to bed about eight headers or four stretchers horizontally is usually spread at one time.

Cavity walls are often used instead of solid brick walls for the outside of houses. These consist of two distinct walls, each $4\frac{1}{2}$ inches thick, separated by a 2-inch cavity, and connected at intervals by metal ties. Cavity walls prevent moisture seeping into the building and increase the insulation of heat and sound (*see* SOUND INSULATION), particularly if the cavity is unventilated.

Sometimes the joints between the bricks are raked out to a depth of $\frac{3}{4}$ inch, and then filled with a stronger or differently textured mortar. This is known as 'pointing', and is used for old or new brickwork, either to increase the resistance of mortar joints to the weather, to replace decayed mortar in old walls, or to improve the appearance of a wall by using tinted mortar.

About 6 inches from the ground, and wherever it is necessary to prevent moisture from the ground soaking up into the brickwork, damp-proof courses are introduced into the wall. Various materials are used for these, the most common and effective being two courses of slate bedded in cement mortar. An alternative is a thin layer of some non-rusting metal, such as lead, sandwiched between two layers of bitumen-impregnated felt. To prevent water seeping through at the base of chimney stacks or at the junction of a slate roof with a vertical brick wall, the joint is sealed with 'flashings'—that is, one or more layers of lead, zinc, copper, aluminium, or bituminous felt.

All brick arches consist of a number of mutually supporting wedges (*see* BUILDING, PRINCIPLES OF). Some, known as 'axed arches', are built of bricks specially cut to a wedge shape to form a curve. For others, called 'plain' or 'rough' arches, ordinary rectangular bricks are used, with the mortar joints between forming a wedge. For plain arches, the bricks are laid in a series of

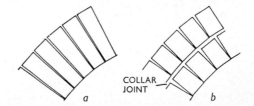

FIG. 3. CONSTRUCTION OF BRICKWORK ARCHES
a. Axed arch with bricks cut to wedge shape. *b.* Plain arch with uncut bricks and wedge-shaped joints

curved courses, each $4\frac{1}{2}$ inches deep, with a 'collar' joint separating each course (Fig. 3).

4. TOOLS. The most important tools used for brickwork include a trowel for laying and spreading the mortar and for rough-cutting the bricks;

a club hammer; a 'bolster' or wide-bladed steel chisel; a 'scutch' or brick hammer for cutting and trimming the bricks; lines and pins for the alignment, during construction, of each course; a 'spirit level' for ensuring that the wall is level and a 'plumb rule' or 'vertical level' to see that it is vertical; and, during 'pointing', a flat board called a 'hawk' for holding the mortar (Fig. 4).

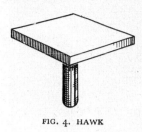

FIG. 4. HAWK

Various machines are used to carry the bricks during big building operations. Bricks can be passed up to the bricklayers' SCAFFOLDING (q.v.) either by an elevator, working on the endless belt principle, or by a platform or pulley hoist (*see* CRANES) fitted with a special clamp holding about ten bricks. They can be carried for fairly short distances by a CONVEYOR (q.v.), or over greater distances by a power-driven wheelbarrow or special brick-barrow or truck. These trucks pick up a small stack of bricks and carry it where it is needed without further handling.

See also BUILDING CONSTRUCTION; BUILDING, PRINCIPLES OF; MASONRY.

See also Vol. VII: BRICKS AND TILES.

BRIDGE BUILDING.

For hundreds of years men have built BRIDGES (q.v. Vol. IV) over fast-flowing rivers or deep and rocky crevasses. Primitive bridges consisted simply of beams supported by brackets of wood or stone embedded in either bank. By the middle of the 19th century, as great roads and railways were developed, huge bridges with a span of hundreds of feet were being built to carry the new traffic routes over otherwise impassable barriers (*see* BRIDGES, RAILWAY, Vol. IV). After 1877 new materials such as steel (*see* STRUCTURAL STEELWORK) and reinforced CONCRETE (q.v.) were brought into use. These materials, stronger than any previously used, made possible the construction of the great bridges we see today.

Modern bridge building probably demands greater ingenuity from designer and builder than any other CIVIL ENGINEERING project (q.v.). Many things have to be taken into consideration, and these may vary widely according to local conditions. In deciding what type of bridge (arch, cantilever, suspension, and so on) is most suitable, the designer has to allow for the type and weight of the traffic, the width and depth of the gap to be bridged, the nature of the foundations, and the method of erecting the bridge. It is also often necessary, in very exposed localities, to take into account the effect of violent gales on the bridge. The designer has to calculate carefully how the various loads will be distributed, and to decide which building materials are most suitable for carrying these loads (*see* BUILDING, PRINCIPLES OF). Several different types of structure and materials may be used for the same bridge. For example, a bridge may have a large central span of the cantilever type, similar to that of the FORTH or QUEBEC BRIDGES (qq.v. Vol. IV), constructed in high-tensile steel, with lattice or plate girder spans of mild steel on either side, and with a floor of reinforced concrete. Such variation may be caused by the fact that the water is very deep in the centre of the river which would make supporting piers and foundations costly to construct. It would therefore be cheaper to adopt large spans with few piers for this section of the bridge. As the water shallows towards the shore, shorter spans would be used since they would be easier to erect and less expensive materials would be needed. For a bridge over a wide river of practically constant depth, however, it may be cheaper to build the piers at regular intervals, so that the bridge would consist of a large number of spans of equal size.

Whatever the type of bridge, the piers or abutments—solid masses of masonry or concrete which support the weight of a bridge and the traffic on it—must be firmly founded on good ground or rock. When bridging a waterway, the piers often have to be sunk to a great depth before reaching good foundations. With large bridges this is done by a method known as 'caisson sinking'. The caisson consists of an inverted box, made of steel or reinforced concrete, with holes in the roof to provide access from above. At first the caisson rests on the river bed, and part of the pier is built on its roof, with open shafts leading to the access holes. The earth inside the caisson is then excavated, being removed through the access holes and shafts, and as the excavation proceeds, the caisson gradually sinks into the ground until it reaches the required depth. The building of the pier is then completed, and finally the caisson and shafts are filled with concrete. When sinking very large caissons in a river bed,

Cement and Concrete Assn.

PRE-STRESSED CONCRETE BRIDGE IN VENEZUELA

Above: Central formwork to support arch being lifted into position. *Below*: The bridge complete except for the parapets

or wherever water may be encountered, it is sometimes necessary for men to work inside the bottom of the caisson in order to excavate the earth. To keep the water out, air is forced into the caisson, the pressure of the air being just sufficient to overcome the water pressure.

Very often, especially when bridging a fairly shallow river, the piers and abutments are constructed inside a COFFERDAM (q.v.). For small bridges, where the surface soil is poor, piles, made

of reinforced concrete, timber, or steel, may be driven down to firmer ground (*see* BUILDING CONSTRUCTION), the solid pier being supported on the piles.

There are various methods of actually building a bridge on its foundations, and a system which is satisfactory in one case may be totally unsuited where the conditions are different; in many cases the type of bridge is determined by the most convenient and cheapest method of

Dorman Long & Co. Ltd.

SYDNEY HARBOUR BRIDGE NEARING COMPLETION

erection. When building a bridge of masonry arches, or of reinforced concrete, some temporary staging is needed to support the materials. This temporary staging, usually of timber or steel, can often be built up from the ground below; but sometimes openings have to be left for traffic below the new bridge, or sometimes the ground is for some reason unsuitable and specially designed staging is needed. This often means building a temporary timber or steel bridge to support the masonry or concrete, the temporary bridge being erected in the same way as a permanent bridge.

When building a small steel bridge it is often possible to place the individual parts directly in position by CRANES (q.v.), so that little more is involved than connecting these pieces together. With larger spans, however, the girders may be too heavy to lift in one piece; a number of temporary, intermediate supports have then to be built so that the girders can be put in place in sections. As soon as the sections have been connected, the girder becomes self-supporting, and the temporary supports are removed.

In many cases, where it is not practicable to provide temporary supports, the bridge is built out from each abutment towards the centre of the span, the girders acting as large brackets, or 'cantilevers'. The girders must be tied back at the piers to prevent them falling forward, just as a bracket falls if it is not firmly fixed to a wall. The Forth and Quebec bridges were both built in this way, but as they were designed as cantilever bridges the anchoring arrangements formed permanent parts of the structure. On the other hand, the SYDNEY HARBOUR BRIDGE (q.v.

Vol. IV) is an arch design, and the ties and anchorages were removed after the bridge had been joined at the centre.

Sometimes a bridge, or part of a bridge, may be completely built in a convenient place and then moved bodily into position on its final supports. For instance, the centre span of the Quebec bridge was erected on barges some distance away and floated down to the bridge site; there it was lifted into position on its supports at the ends of the cantilevers.

The construction of a suspension bridge involves rather different problems. The piers or towers at either end of the bridge are built first, often to a considerable height above the level of the bridge 'deck'. The great chains or cables that help to support the bridge are then hauled into place. These cables are built up from wire ropes or, in the case of large bridges, from a very great number of single wires, which are bound together to form one large cable, sometimes more than 3 feet in diameter. They are hauled across the tops of the towers which support them, and have their ends firmly anchored, either to rock or to large blocks of concrete bedded in the ground. After the cables are in place, vertical steel suspenders are fixed to them, and these support the bridge deck.

Military bridges, which often have to be built quickly, are usually made up of a number of standard parts. The Bailey bridge is a well-known example. The parts are designed so that they can be connected together in the field to form bridges of varying sizes; and if any part of the bridge is destroyed by enemy action it can be replaced easily by a duplicate part. These bridges are either built complete on one bank and rolled into place; or, if the span is big, temporary staging may be used; or the bridge may be supported, temporarily or permanently, on floating pontoons.

See also CONCRETE CONSTRUCTION.

See also Vol. IV: BRIDGES; BRIDGES, RAILWAY; FORTH BRIDGE; QUEBEC BRIDGE; SYDNEY HARBOUR BRIDGE; GOLDEN GATE BRIDGE.

BUILDING CONSTRUCTION. 1. ORGANIZATION.

The planning and organization of a large building project begins long before the workmen appear on the site. The ground is first surveyed (*see* SURVEYING), and a soils test carried out (*see* SOIL MECHANICS). Preliminary designs and estimates are drawn up, either by an architect or an engineer, or sometimes by the two together. Permission to build is obtained from the TOWN AND COUNTRY PLANNING authority (q.v. Vol. X), and inquiries are made to ensure that the building can be connected to the main drainage, gas, water, and other services. When the designer has made certain that each part of the building will be strong enough to withstand the loads placed upon it (*see* BUILDING), final drawings and calculations are submitted to the local

John Laing & Son Ltd.

A 60-FT. PILE (ON THE LEFT) BEING DRIVEN INTO THE GROUND BY A STEAM-OPERATED HAMMER

authority to ensure that all building BY-LAWS (q.v. Vol. X) are complied with. A specification is then prepared showing what materials are to be used for each part, and how they are to be fixed. This specification, with the drawings, is sent to a 'quantity surveyor', who draws up a 'bill of quantities' showing in detail how much of each material and how much labour is needed for every part of the building (*see* BUILDING INDUSTRY, ORGANIZATION, Vol. VII). Selected building contractors are then asked to submit tenders of the cost of building.

The contractor who is subsequently appointed has much preparatory work to do. With the designer he prepares a building programme for the whole job, and places orders for all the materials to be delivered in certain quantities at certain times. He decides what EARTH-MOVING EQUIPMENT and CRANES (qq.v.) may be necessary, how many lorries and how many men are needed at each stage, and what temporary offices, canteens, and so on will be needed at the site. In the country, he may have to build special roads to the site, and organize buses to take men to and from their homes. A weighbridge may also be required to check the delivery of every lorry-load of material.

2. CONSTRUCTION. When the designer has completed his detailed drawings, the positions of certain key points of the building, such as the lines of the outer walls, are calculated and marked out on the site. Heavy earth-moving equipment is used to level the site and to dig down to a firm layer of earth or rock on which to lay concrete foundations; if there is a big depth of loose soil, piles, solid lengths of timber, steel, or reinforced concrete, may be driven deep down into the earth by a heavy hammer, or 'monkey', to take the weight of the building. The pile is hoisted into a vertical position by ropes passing over pulleys at the top of the pile 'frame'; at the base of the frame the ropes are connected to an electric or steam winch which works the hammer. The hammer, which may weigh up to 5 tons, drives the pile down until it reaches a solid layer of ground or until the penetration for each blow is very small. Trenches, which carry the house drains, the gas and water pipes, and other services beneath the building, are then excavated across the site. These trenches may be made into permanent channels by lining them with brick or concrete, with strong slabs of concrete laid over them to carry the weight of the building.

THE CONSTRUCTION OF AN ELECTRICITY GENERATING STATION
Steelwork is being erected for boilers and concrete foundations for turbines

If a factory is being built, other slabs may be laid at this time to form beds for the heavier machines.

If the building is steel framed, large girders, stanchions (uprights), and other parts are delivered to the site and erected to form a lattice-work skeleton (*see* STRUCTURAL STEELWORK). This skeleton, or frame, will carry the main loads of the building. If the frame is of reinforced concrete, temporary moulds of wood or steel, called 'shuttering', are fixed in place, with steel rods to provide reinforcement. Concrete is poured in between the shutters, engulfing the steel reinforcement; the concrete is then consolidated and left to set, while more shuttering is fixed in place for the storey above (*see* CONCRETE CONSTRUCTION).

The walls (sometimes called 'cladding' in framed buildings) are then built. These may be of BRICKWORK or MASONRY (qq.v.), or of light prefabricated panels of wood or concrete attached to the framework. Spaces are left for windows and doors which are put in place later. To enable the builders to work above ground SCAFFOLDING (q.v.) is erected, rising higher and

higher as the work proceeds, the materials being lifted up by cranes or hoists. If the walls themselves carry the main loads of the building, they are more stoutly constructed of masonry, brick, or concrete.

While the upper storeys are being built, door and window frames in the lower storeys are fixed in the spaces left for them. The window frames are usually of metal, made in a factory to certain standard sizes which will exactly fit the wall spaces.

Meanwhile the cross-walls inside the building are being built in the same way as the load-bearing outer walls, but are lighter, and though preferably sound-proof, they need not be heat-proof. Spaces are left for staircases, lifts, water-pipes, and electric wiring.

The floors, which may be of concrete or wood, are supported by horizontal beams, the ends of which rest in spaces left for them in the outer walls and cross-walls. Concrete, though more fire-proof and a better barrier than wood against air-borne sound, transmits impact noises more easily. Therefore, where sound insulation is important, in blocks of flats and offices, for example, the floors, whether of wood or concrete, must be separated from the supporting framework by a 'quilt' of soft, springy material, such as glass wool (*see* SOUND INSULATION).

Roofs, for which various materials can be used, may be flat or pitched. The construction of flat roofs, now often used in large buildings, is similar to that of floors, the roof being laid on a framework of horizontal beams. As roofs carry less load, they can be lighter than floors, but must be weatherproof. A flat concrete roof, for example, may have a weatherproof covering of asphalt, bitumen felt, or tarred felt, with some form of heat insulation beneath. Allowance must be made for EXPANSION AND CONTRACTION (q.v.) of concrete due to changes of temperature.

Pitched roofs are generally covered with tiles, slates, or sheets of asbestos-cement or various metals, such as steel, aluminium, copper, or lead, laid on a sloping framework of steel or timber. If steel is used as a covering, it must be protected from corrosion either by a coating of bituminous paint or by being galvanized with zinc.

Some modern factories are roofed with a series of slopes, ridges, and 'valleys', the north-facing slopes consisting almost entirely of glass in order to admit as much indirect daylight as possible to every part of the building. Such roofs must be as light and strong as possible; if the building is on a single level, the roof is supported by widely spaced vertical stanchions (uprights) carrying beams or open-frame girders to which the roof 'trusses' are fixed (*see* STRUCTURAL STEELWORK). As much floor space as possible is left free for machines and materials.

3. PROGRESS PLANNING. Though the building contractor is responsible for the main construction, many special jobs—the installation of heating and air-conditioning plant, for example, or the erection of structural steelwork—are given to specialist sub-contractors. In addition, the work of plumbers, joiners, painters, and other craftsmen has to be properly organized, and telephone conduits and other public services have to be installed at the right time. The main contractor is responsible for co-ordinating the work of all these people so that they start only when everything is ready for them and do not get in each others' way.

Expert timing is essential in building in order to avoid waste of time and money and a feeling of frustration because materials have failed to arrive, or because someone has not finished his job at the right time. Great judgement and experience are needed to estimate the number of days and hours required for so many different operations, and to fit them all into a practical and efficient time-table.

As construction proceeds, the 'clerk of the works', the designer's representative, regularly checks the amount of work done against the building programme. If any alterations are made to the original plan, or if special difficulties arise which are not covered by the contract, such as delays due to very bad weather, the contractor's payments have to be adjusted. In all these matters the quantity surveyor, who produced the initial bill of quantities, helps the designer, clerk of works, and contractor until the last job is done, checked, and paid for.

See also BUILDING, PRINCIPLES OF; CONCRETE CONSTRUCTION; STRUCTURAL STEELWORK; BRICKWORK; MASONRY; SOUND INSULATION; Colour Plate, opp. p. 176.
See also Vol. VII: BUILDING INDUSTRY, HISTORY OF; BUILDING INDUSTRY, ORGANIZATION.
See also Vol. XI: HOUSES, HISTORY OF; WALLS; ROOFS.

BUILDING, PRINCIPLES OF. 1. The art of building consists in designing and erecting as economically and attractively as possible the kind of structure which its owner wants. The design will be affected chiefly by the purpose of the building and its site. A railway station, a warehouse, or a cinema, for example, must each be planned quite differently, and in a town where land is costly and where there may be other buildings on every side, the design has to fit in with the limitations of the site.

Whatever the purpose of the building it must be designed so that it is strong enough to stand. This involves three main factors, all of which have to be considered in relation to each other: the foundations, the loads to be carried by each part of the structure and by the foundations, and the materials to be used for building each part.

2. FOUNDATIONS. In modern BUILDING CONSTRUCTION (q.v.) these are usually of concrete, and must be carried down to a layer of earth or rock strong enough to bear the weight of the building and its contents and to withstand the force of the wind blowing on the surfaces of the building. The nature of the ground has to be studied and the weight it can safely carry has to be calculated most carefully (*see* SOIL MECHANICS), for if too great a load is applied the ground will sink, or 'settle', causing the building to crack. In the 1930's, for example, it was discovered that the supporting power of the ground beneath St. Paul's Cathedral, in London, was becoming seriously reduced by the pumping of water from neighbouring sites, and a special Act of Parliament was passed to restrict any more building or excavations in that area. In some countries the special stresses caused by earthquakes must also be allowed for. Rock, coarse sand, and gravels normally provide good support, but finer soils, such as clays, may present considerable problems. The clay subsoil of London, for example, is one of the factors that limits the height and size of buildings there; whereas in New York, where the ground consists of solid rock, towering skyscrapers can be built.

building to 'float' as a whole, where separate, independent foundations might sink by unequal amounts (Fig. 1c). Piles are used to take the weight of a building when it is impossible to dig down to a solid layer of earth, either because the ground is waterlogged or because there is a very great depth of poor soil. Piles are solid lengths of timber, steel, or reinforced concrete, generally from 20 to 80 feet long, driven into the ground by a heavy steam hammer. Sometimes hollow steel tubes are used, being driven into the ground in the same way as solid piles and afterwards filled with concrete. Before the concrete hardens, the tubes are withdrawn and can be used again.

3. LOADS. The weight of the building and

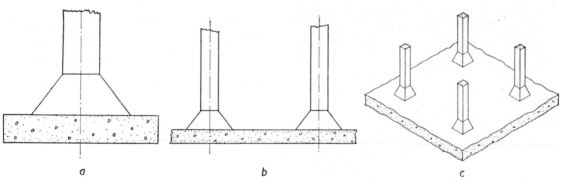

a   b   c

FIG. 1. DIAGRAM OF FOUNDATIONS
a. Independent. b. Strip. c. Raft

The main types of concrete foundations are 'independent', 'strip', 'raft', and 'pile'. For BRIDGE BUILDING (q.v.) and other heavy engineering structures 'caisson' foundations are used. Independent foundations are used to support columns or piers which are unevenly spaced and unequally loaded. A pad of concrete, plain or reinforced, is placed under each column or pier, the base of the pad extending far enough in all directions to spread the load evenly over the ground (Fig. 1a). Strip foundations are used when a row of columns is so closely spaced that independent foundations would nearly meet (Fig. 1b). When the columns are both near together and regularly spaced, and carry nearly equal loads, raft (sometimes called 'slab') foundations, extending the whole length and breadth of a building, are used instead of strip foundations. The raft may be a thick slab of mass concrete, or a thin slab of reinforced concrete, laid between lines of concrete beams joining the feet of the columns. A raft foundation is often suitable in very soft ground, for it enables the

everything in it must be carried by walls, or pillars, or both, so that every part is strong enough to withstand the loads imposed on it. There are three kinds of load: 'dead', 'live', and 'wind' loads.

Dead loads consist of the permanent weight of the whole building and of each part of it. The designer has to calculate how these loads will be distributed, and their effect on each part of the building. Live loads, which arise only when the building is in use, include the people using it, the furniture and goods stored in it, and possibly the volume of snow which may lie on the roof after a storm. In most factories machinery represents a large part of the live load, and the VIBRATION (q.v.) the running machinery is likely to cause must also be carefully considered. In a warehouse the goods stored there form the chief load, and the strength of each floor must be in proportion to the maximum amount to be stacked on it. Building By-Laws (q.v. Vol. X), to which designers have to work, give lists, based on surveys of existing buildings, of weights appropriate for heavy storage, light storage, public buildings, offices, flats, and so on. The total load, both dead and live, increases towards the bottom of the building, and the thickness of load-carrying walls or columns must be increased accordingly.

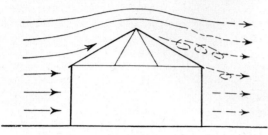

FIG. 2. WIND FORCES ON A BUILDING

Wind produces pressure against the outside walls of a building on the windward side, but it also produces suction on the walls on the opposite, or leeward, side. In other words, the air pressure on the outside of the leeward wall becomes less than the pressure inside the building, and there is a tendency for this wall to fall outwards. Wind may also exert pressure on a steep roof, but if the roof is low pitched or flat, the air stream is forced up and over it, again causing suction which tends to pull the roof off the building (Fig. 2). The wind may be strong enough, especially on high ground or near the coast, to overturn a building, or even to lift a very light building off its foundations if it is not securely anchored. Wind pressure is greater on a flat surface than on a rounded one: for example, it is half as much again on a square chimney with one face to the wind as on a round chimney of the same width.

The end-walls and cross-walls, that is, the outer and inner walls of a building, take most of the force of wind. If there are no cross-walls, and the outside walls consist only of light panels or glass between columns, the columns on the windward side would have to resist most of this force, but they are helped by the floors, which pass on some of the force to the columns on the other side.

4. MATERIALS. The most important building materials are steel (see STRUCTURAL STEELWORK), CONCRETE, BRICKWORK, MASONRY (qq.v.), and timber. Each has its own special characteristics and greater or less resistance to various kinds of load. A material can fail in three ways when a load is applied: it may be crushed, or torn apart, or bent. But a material which can be easily bent

or torn apart may have great resistance to a crushing load, and so on (see STRESS AND STRAIN).

Which material can be used to the best advantage for a particular part of the building depends, therefore, on the kind of load to which it is to be subjected and on the shape of the part. Materials such as wood, steel, and reinforced concrete, which can resist both crushing and tensile (or tearing) loads, are most suitable for columns, beams, and girders; while masonry, brickwork, and plain concrete, which resist crushing but are weak in tension, are used for building walls and arches. The way in which beams and arches respectively carry their loads, and the forces which they have to resist, are shown in Fig. 3.

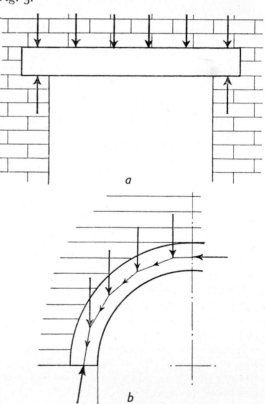

FIG. 3. FORCES ON OPENINGS IN WALLS
a. Lintel. b. Arch

No material in a building is subjected to a load nearly as great as that at which it is known to fail. There are several reasons for this: most materials can be cracked or distorted by loads lower than those which produce complete failure, and allowance must be made for variations in the quality of materials and in the care and skill with which they are fixed. The various strengths usually allowed for in building are shown in the accompanying table. The crushing strengths shown are for short columns only; long columns tend to bend instead of being crushed, and the designer has to allow for this.

fix machinery, cranes, and all kinds of fixtures to steel columns than to concrete ones. On the other hand, for some structures, such as hotels and schools, especially if they are in the country, it may be better and cheaper to build in concrete.

The function of the walls of a frame building is only to keep out the rain and wind, to keep in

TABLE OF STRENGTHS OF BUILDING MATERIALS

Strengths are given in either tons (T.) or pounds (lb.) (1 ton = 2,240 lb.) per square inch of the cross-section. The strength of materials such as stone and wood varies, and the stresses of all materials are dependent on the shapes, sizes, and lengths of the members. The figures given in this table, therefore, are average values. The margin between the working stress and breaking stress is the Factor of Safety and this also varies with circumstances.

Material		Wt. in lb. per cu. ft.	Strength			
			In tension		In compression	
			Breaking stress	Working stress	Breaking stress	Working stress
Timber	Oak	50	4 to 8 T.	Up to 2 T.	2 to 4 T.	1,000 lb.
	Pine	40	2 to 6 T.	Up to 1·5 T.	2 T.	800 lb.
	Teak	50	2 to 7 T.	Up to 1·5 T.	5 T.	1,000 lb.
Bricks	Ordinary	120	..	..	1,500 lb.	60 lb.
	Hard Engineering	140	..	..	10,000 lb.	350 lb.
Concrete	Plain	144	..	..	2,000 lb.	600 lb.
	Reinforced	150	..	18,000 lb.*	2,000 lb.	750 lb.
Stone	Sandstone	140	..	..	3·5 T.	450 lb.
	Granite	170	..	..	7·5 T.	600 lb.
	Slate	170	..	..	7·0 T.	600 lb.
Steel (Structural)		490	28 to 32 T.	Up to 10 T.	28 to 32 T.	Up to 8 T.
Iron	Wrought Iron	480	20 to 24 T.	Up to 7 T.	16 to 28 T.	Up to 6 T.
	Cast Iron	450	7 to 10 T.	1·5 T.	40 T.	10 T.
Aluminium Alloy		160	25 T.	6 T.	25 T.	6 T.

* This figure represents the value for steel only since it is the steel embedded in the concrete which takes up all tensile stresses.

5. STRUCTURE. In any structure the main loads are carried either by the walls or by a steel or reinforced concrete framework of columns and beams. In frame construction, which is usually more economical for buildings of more than three storeys, the walls support only their own weight or are simply attached to the framework.

A steel framework can be put up more quickly than a concrete one because the concrete for one storey must be allowed to harden before the weight of the next is placed upon it; concrete, however, has higher resistance than steel to fire, water, and corrosion by the atmosphere. Steel is generally favoured in cities and towns, where land is expensive and owners want their buildings in use quickly, and where building operations may be a nuisance to inhabitants and cause traffic congestion. Steel may also be chosen for workshops and factories for it is much easier to

heat, and to provide privacy. They may be of brick, often in two thicknesses with an air space between for insulation; of factory-made wooden panels, with a weather-proof outer skin, a decorative inner surface, and a layer of insulating material between; of aluminium; or even of glass. There must, of course, be glass windows to admit light.

Load-bearing walls are generally of brick, stone, or concrete, and are usually of the 'cavity' type, with a space between the outer and inner surface to keep out damp and cold (*see* BRICK-WORK, Section 3). The openings for doors and windows in load-bearing walls have to be carefully constructed so that the walls are not weakened, and are now usually made by spanning the opening with a steel or reinforced concrete beam, which has sufficient strength to carry the weight of the wall above. Alternatively, the openings can be formed by arches. In these, wedge-shaped stones or bricks ('voussoirs') are so arranged that the weight of the wall above is directed downwards and outwards, to either side of the arch. The 'keystone' in the centre of the arch locks the voussoirs together so that the more pressure they have to bear the more

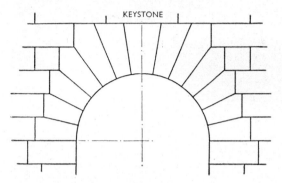

FIG. 4. THE CONSTRUCTION OF AN ARCH

strongly are they wedged together (Fig. 4). Sometimes a 'relieving arch' is built in the wall above a weak point to divert the thrust away from it. As an arch needs greater height than an opening of beam construction it is not often used in modern commercial buildings, except where a very large opening is appropriate, as in the front of a cinema or railway station.

The floors and cross-walls of a building must as far as possible keep out sound (see SOUND IN-SULATION), while roofs must not only be weather-proof but must also keep the building as warm as possible in winter. Where much daylight is essential the roof may be designed to include a number of glass panels facing away from the sun. Such considerations, as well as actual methods of building, are discussed in the article BUILDING CONSTRUCTION (q.v.).

See also BUILDING CONSTRUCTION; CONCRETE CONSTRUC-TION; STRUCTURAL STEELWORK; MASONRY; BRICKWORK; SOUND INSULATION.
See also Vol. XII: ARCHITECTURE.

BULLDOZER, see TRACK MECHANISM; EARTH-MOVING EQUIPMENT.

BUOYANCY. This is the upward pressure of water that supports a ship at sea and enables it to float. When a ship is launched it pushes aside the water to make room for itself; and the dis-placed water, trying to get back into the space occupied by the vessel, pushes upwards against the ship. This upthrust increases as the vessel sinks deeper until, when it equals the weight of the ship, the ship sinks no farther but floats in 'equilibrium'. ARCHIMEDES (q.v. Vol. V), in the 3rd century B.C., realized that this upthrust, or buoyancy, equals the weight of water displaced by the ship, called the ship's 'displacement', which in turn equals the weight of the ship. This principle is very important in NAVAL ARCHITEC-TURE (q.v.) because, if the designer can calculate the weight of water displaced by a ship of certain dimensions, he knows the total load (that is, the weight of the vessel and of all fittings and cargo) that the ship can safely carry.

The designer calculates a ship's displacement by multiplying the underwater volume of the vessel by the DENSITY (q.v. Vol. III) of the water in which the ship will float. The density of water, that is, its weight compared with its volume, varies in different parts of the world, between summer and winter, and between fresh water and salt water. As water will not support any-thing with a density higher than its own, these changes have to be calculated carefully when deciding the safe-loading of a ship (see SAFETY AT SEA, Vol. IV). The density of the salt water in the Bitter Lakes in the Suez Canal, for ex-ample, is high and will easily support a heavily loaded ship. But some of the cargo would have to be removed before the same ship could float at the same draught in the fresh water of Surrey Docks, London, where the density is lower.

The density of water is measured with a 'hydrometer', a glass cylinder weighted with small pieces of lead to hold it down and with a thin glass stem at the upper end which is marked with a scale reading from 0 at the top to 40 at the bottom. This scale is translated into measurements of density. When the hydrometer is placed in the water it sinks until its weight is equalled by the weight of water it displaces. This varies according to the density of the water, and so with different densities more or less of the glass scale will be above the water-line. In fresh water, which has the lowest density, the instrument will be almost submerged and the reading will be 0; in sea water it will be 25; and in the Bitter Lakes, which have the highest density, it will be 40. Accurate tables covering all these changes in density have been prepared for all parts of the world.

The designer, having calculated the total load,

THE LAUNCHING OF R.M.S. *ORCADES* AT BARROW-IN-FURNESS IN 1947

that his ship can carry in safety, must distribute that load in such a way that the vessel will remain 'stable', that is, will not turn over or be swamped when rolling or pitching in heavy seas. The weight of a ship floating upright in still water acts downwards, and is concentrated at G, the centre of gravity (Fig. 1a). The buoyancy

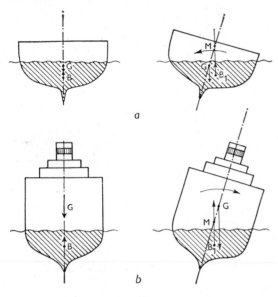

FIG. I. THE STABILITY OF A SHIP

a. When the centre of gravity G is below the metacentre M the ship is stable. *b.* When G is above M the ship is unstable. B, B₁. Centres of buoyancy

acts vertically upwards and is concentrated at B, the centre of buoyancy. When the ship is upright, the centre of gravity and the centre of buoyancy are in the same vertical straight line.

When the ship rolls, the centre of gravity, which depends · only on the distribution of weights in the ship, does not move relative to the ship, unless some of the weights (such as cargo) move. The position of the centre of buoyancy, however, depends upon the shape of all the parts of the ship which happen to be submerged, and these alter from second to second as the ship rolls. Thus, the centre of buoyancy moves from B to B_1, and if a vertical line is drawn through B_1 it will intersect the original vertical through B and G at a point M—called the 'metacentre'. The position of the metacentre relative to the centre of gravity affects the stability of the ship. When

the ship rolls its weight acts vertically downwards through the centre of gravity and the buoyancy force acts upwards through the metacentre in its new position. If the metacentre is above the centre of gravity, as in Fig. 1a, then the 'couple' (*see* LEVERS) produced by the two forces tends to turn the ship back again and it remains stable. If the metacentre is below the centre of gravity, however, as in Fig. 1b, the couple tends to turn the ship still farther in the direction of the roll and it may then be unable to recover. Ships are always designed, and their cargoes always stowed, with enough weight low down to ensure that the centre of gravity is always below the metacentre.

The parts of a ship that are usually above water provide what is known as 'reserve buoyancy'. For example, a ship moving through heavy waves will at intervals sink deeper than when floating in equilibrium in still water. Because more of the ship is then submerged, the buoyancy is greater than the weight and forces the ship up again, thus preventing it from being swamped. Again, if a ship is damaged and water enters the hull, the ship will lose some of its buoyancy and begin to sink. As it sinks, however, this lost buoyancy is compensated to some extent by other parts of the ship becoming submerged. If too much water enters the hull, however, the reserve buoyancy cannot compensate, and the ship goes to the bottom. To prevent this happening, the ship is divided into a number of watertight compartments by steel bulkheads; if only one compartment is damaged, flooding is restricted, and sufficient reserve buoyancy is left to keep the ship afloat. In large passenger ships two or even three compartments can be flooded without the ship sinking.

When a SUBMARINE (q.v. Vol. X) is to dive beneath the surface, its buoyancy is reduced by allowing water to enter large tanks, called buoyancy tanks, which are carried inside the hull. When it is to rise, the water is forced out from the tanks, and the buoyancy is increased. The calculations must be accurate or the submarine will sink to the bottom or stay only partly submerged. To remain submerged the weight of the submarine must as nearly as possible equal the weight of the water it displaces.

See also NAVAL ARCHITECTURE.

C

CABLES, ELECTRICAL. These carry ELEC-TRIC CURRENT (q.v.) from the place where it is generated to the place where the electric power is used. The electricity is carried along copper wires that have been wrapped in insulating material and enclosed inside a sheath to protect them from damage. They are usually placed underground, sometimes directly in the soil, and sometimes inside earthenware pipes called cable ducts. Electric power can also be carried along overhead lines suspended from steel towers (*see* GRID SYSTEM). The various kinds of electric cable can be conveniently divided into power cables, and those used for telephones, telegraphs, and television.

1. POWER CABLES. These range from small cables bringing the 230-volt electric supply into ordinary houses to very large cables carrying the entire output of a 132,000-volt POWER STATION (q.v.). The medium-sized 11,000-volt power cable shown in Fig. 1a has copper wire conductors composed of many thin strands for flexibility. Three conductors are used because the cable is for carrying three-phase A.C. power (*see* ALTER-NATING CURRENT). Each conductor is separately

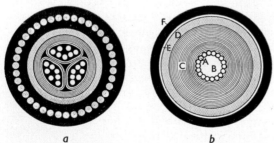

a   b

FIG. 1. SECTIONS OF ELECTRIC CABLES

a. 11,000-volt power cable for carrying three-phase A.C. power. *b.* 132,000-volt power cable. A. Stranded copper conductor. B. Hollow filled with oil. C. Oiled paper and wood pulp. D. Lead sheath. E. Steel tape. F. Tarred hessian

wrapped in paper that has been soaked in a special oil to make it a better insulator; then, before being bound together by oiled paper, all three are packed with oiled jute string to pre-vent any of the insulating oil seeping out and ruining the cable. The bundle of conductors is enclosed in a lead sheath to keep moisture out of the cable, and this sheath, which is rather soft, is protected by wrappings of steel wire and tarred jute.

The insulation of the cable shown in Fig. 1a is not strong enough to withstand very high vol-tages. The cable used for voltages as high as 132,000 volts, as shown in Fig. 1b, contains only one hollow, stranded, copper conductor, which is insulated with paper and wood pulp impreg-nated with oil. The cable has a lead sheath pro-tected with steel-tape armouring, and a tarred hessian outer covering, and the whole cable inside the lead sheath is filled with an insulating oil which is supplied to the cable from a reser-voir and keeps the insulation in good order. The cable is in sections about 1 mile long, each sec-tion having its own oil reservoir. A high-power cable capable of withstanding voltages up to 250,000 volts is now made. It is arranged like the cable in Fig. 1a, but the part inside the lead sheath is filled with non-inflammable nitrogen gas, at the high pressure of 200 lb. to the square inch, which permeates the oiled paper insulation. Steel cylinders filled with high-pressure nitrogen gas are connected to the cable at intervals, and an automatic alarm is given if a leak causes the gas pressure to drop.

These large underground electric power cables are used to avoid the unsightliness or danger of overhead lines, for instance, in large cities, and when crossing rivers. A large underwater power cable has been tested for use across the English Channel to connect the British and European grid systems.

2. TELEGRAPH, TELEPHONE, AND TELEVISION CABLES. These work at quite low voltages, and so need much less insulating material than do the power cables. They also have many more separate conductors. Two wires are needed for a complete electric circuit, and some of the cables that connect telephones to the exchange have as many as 1,800 separate pairs of wires in a cable less than 3 inches in diameter, each pair being used to connect one telephone. The copper conductors in such a cable, which are only about $\frac{1}{80}$ inch in diameter, are wrapped in paper to

B. I. Callenders

SINGLE-CORE CABLES FROM TRANSFORMERS TO SWITCH-GEAR

a special code, and up to eighteen separate tele-graph messages can be sent in place of one tele-phone conversation by using different notes for each. Thus a trunk cable able to carry 288 tele-phone conversations could instead at the same time carry more than 5,000 telegraph messages.

Another kind of trunk telephone cable consists of a single copper wire fixed by means of disks of a hard, waxy, insulating substance at the centre of a $\frac{3}{8}$-inch diameter copper tube. With these cables, called coaxial cables, the 'carrier' method can be used to pass 660 separate tele-phone conversations over a single cable. Ther-mionic valve amplifiers have to be placed every 6 miles along the cable to increase the strength of the signals, but a single amplifier can handle all 660 conversations at once. Coaxial cables are also used to carry the B.B.C.'s television pro-grammes from the studios in London to the network of transmitters in other parts of the country. A special kind of coaxial cable is laid on the sea bed and carries many telephone conver-sations between England, Holland, France, and Ireland. These submarine cables have to resist the pressure of the water and stand up to possible damage, so they are equipped with thermionic valve amplifiers in heavy steel cases, which rest on the sea bed.

The very long submarine cables that cross the Atlantic Ocean and link all parts of the world are also coaxial cables; but until these can be fitted with amplifiers they cannot be used for telephony, and can carry only one telegraph message at a time. There are plans for laying two new transatlantic cables, with amplifiers every 40 miles, which will be able to carry thirty-six telephone messages simultaneously. One of the problems is to design amplifiers made well enough to rest on the bed of the ocean and work for, say, 20 years without needing any attention

See also GRID SYSTEM; TELEPHONE ENGINEERING.
See also Vol. IV: CABLE.

insulate them from each other, and the wrap-pings are specially marked so that the telephone engineers can recognize each separate pair (*see* TELEPHONE ENGINEERING).

Although thin copper wires are satisfactory for short-distance telephone calls, for long-dis-tance trunk calls they would not provide clear enough speech, and thick wires must be used. Even with thick wires the speech signals become too faint after about 24 miles, and THERMIONIC VALVES (q.v.) have to be used as amplifiers to increase the strength of the signals. The high cost of cables and amplifiers for trunk routes has led to the invention of ways for sending several separate telephone conversations over the same pair of wires. Each conversation is carried over the cable on a separate 'carrier' wavelength by using at each end small transmitters and receivers similar to those used for RADIO (q.v.). Separate pairs of wires are used for the 'go' and the 'return' signals—that is, for each of the two people talk-ing. There are now several thousands of miles of trunk telephone cables using this 'carrier' method to carry twenty-four separate conversations on each pair of wires, enough wires being provided in each cable for 288 conversations.

Telegraph signals are sent nowadays by switching a musical note on and off according to

CALCULATING MACHINES. 1. This name usually refers to those instruments which can perform all the four operations of arithmetic (addition, subtraction, multiplication, and divi-sion); they are in general use in banks and large offices. Practically all devices of this sort are really elaborate kinds of counting instruments. There are other calculating devices such as the SLIDE RULE (q.v.) in which numbers are repre-sented by lengths, but these are essentially measuring instruments. The history of calculating machines is outlined in the article COUNTING INSTRUMENTS (q.v. Vol. IV), and their use in commerce and industry is described in the article ACCOUNTING, MACHINE (q.v. Vol. VII). Here we are concerned with the way they actually make calculations.

The first true calculating machines, built by PASCAL (1642) and LEIBNITZ (1671) (qq.v. Vol. V), although they never worked satisfactorily, embodied most of the principles of the modern machines. As engineering skill developed in the late 19th century it became possible to produce more reliable calculators; and since the development of ELECTRONICS (q.v.), automatic machines able to carry out long series of calculations at very great speed—the popularly misnamed 'electronic brains'—have been invented. This ability to work out difficult arithmetical calculations speedily and accurately is of great value in modern science and engineering. For example, the Nautical Almanac Office, a branch of the Royal Observatory which produces all the information about the movements of stars and planets needed for navigation, issues each year about 3,000 pages of tables. The design of high-speed aircraft involves long and complicated calculations concerning the flow of air around the wings and the stresses in the structures; whilst the new subject of NUCLEAR POWER engineering (q.v.) is continually producing involved mathematical problems which can be solved only by laborious calculation.

A digital machine is made up of identical units each dealing with a separate digit of the numbers used; so the difference between a machine which can add 3 digit numbers and one which can add 6 is simply that the second has 3 units more than the first; it is no more difficult

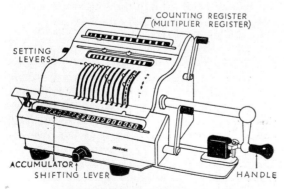

FIG. 1. HAND CALCULATING MACHINE

Labels on figure: COUNTING REGISTER (MULTIPLIER REGISTER); SETTING LEVERS; ACCUMULATOR; SHIFTING LEVER; HANDLE

Monroe Calculating Machine Co.

FIG. 2. ELECTRICALLY DRIVEN DESK CALCULATING MACHINE
Numbers with up to 10 figures are set on the keyboard, and the machine can be made to add, subtract, multiply, or divide by means of the control keys. The 20-figure product of two 10-figure numbers is formed in about 10 seconds

to make—indeed, 10-figure machines are quite common.

2. *Desk machines.* These are about the size of a typewriter. Fig. 1 shows a hand-operated machine; Fig. 2 one of the more elaborate electrically operated models.

Suppose that, with the hand-operated machine, we wish to add 187 to 324. We 'set' 187 by moving the three right-hand levers to positions 1, 8, 7 and give the handle one clockwise turn; 187 then appears in the accumulator and a 1 in the counting register to show that we have added one number into the accumulator. Then we change the setting to 324 and make another turn; the sum 511 appears in the accumulator, and 2 (because two numbers have been added) in the counting register. Subtraction is simply addition done backwards, the handle being given an anticlockwise turn.

Before starting a second sum we 'clear' all the registers to zero by means of the handles provided.

Multiplication is merely a series of additions, and division a series of subtractions; but now the ability to 'shift' the accumulator relative to the setting mechanism becomes important. To multiply 187 by 324 we set 187 and make 3 positive (clockwise) turns, forming $187 \times 300 = 56100$ in the accumulator and 3 in the counting register; we then shift the accumulator one place to the left and make 2 turns, and lastly shift once more and make 4 turns; the products 187×20 and 187×4 are added into the accumulator in their right positions:

$$187 \times 300 = 56100$$
$$187 \times 20 = 3740$$
$$187 \times 4 = 748$$
$$\overline{}$$
$$187 \times 324 60588$$

The process is exactly that of long multiplication. The counting register shows 324, and so checks that the correct multiplier has been used.

To divide 60588 by 187, we first set 60588, add it to the accumulator, and clear the '1' from the counting register; then we set 187, shift the carriage so that the '1' of 187 is in line with the '6' of 60588, and subtract until a further turn of the handle would give a negative remainder. This takes 3 turns, leaving 4488. We then shift the carriage one place to the left and continue subtracting; 2 turns reduce this to 748, and a third turn would give a negative result, so we shift again; after 4 turns the remainder is zero. The steps are

$$60588 - (187 \times 300) = 4488$$
$$4488 - (187 \times 20) = 748$$
$$748 - (187 \times 4) = 0$$
$$\therefore 60588 = 187 \times 324, \text{ or } 60588 \div 187 = 324.$$

Decimals are dealt with by 'pointing' the numbers, that is, by setting the moveable markers to show the position of the decimal point. To multiply $1 \cdot 87 \times 3 \cdot 24$ we mark the point two places from the right in the setting and counting registers and, since the product of two 2-decimal numbers is a 4-decimal number (*see* ARITHMETIC, Section 7), four places from the right in the accumulator. This gives the correct result, $6 \cdot 0588$; the same pointing will be correct for any pair of 2-decimal numbers.

In electrically driven machines a motor takes the place of the handle and is operated by touching a control bar. These machines are always built with a keyboard instead of setting-levers, and many models have automatic multiplication and division, so that the operator has only to set the numbers and press the 'multiply' or 'divide' key.

Fig. 3 shows the mechanism of a typical calculator. If a key—5 for example—is pressed, one or both selector gears A slide on a splined shaft B, so that the correct number of teeth—that is, 5— are placed ready to mesh with the 10-tooth inter-

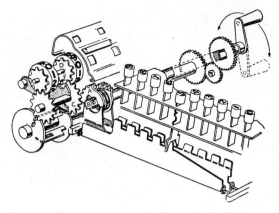

FIG. 3. MECHANISM OF A CALCULATING MACHINE

A. Selector gear. B. Splined shaft. C. Intermediate gear. D. Counting wheel. E. Driving shaft. F. Stud on counting wheel

mediate gear C, which is itself in mesh with a 10-tooth gear carrying one of the counting-wheels D of the accumulator. When the driving shaft E makes one turn, the accumulator wheel is driven through $\frac{5}{10}$th of a revolution, and so records the addition of 5 into the accumulator. Whenever a counting wheel makes a complete turn (that is, 10 has been added to it), a stud F which it carries engages with the wheel immediately to the left and gives it $\frac{1}{10}$th of a turn, recording the carrying of 1 to the next place. When the first wheel has made ten whole revolutions and has consequently caused the next wheel to make one whole revolution, the stud on this wheel will give $\frac{1}{10}$th of a turn to the third wheel, recording the carrying of 1 to the third place—and so on. The stud is really a signal, by which a counting-wheel can, as it were, tell the rest of the machine that it has passed its zero position. In electrical machines it is used to operate levers and clutches which control all the automatic movements in multiplication and division.

3. *Larger machines.* More elaborate calculators, particularly machines which print their results, are needed for large-scale work—in large offices and banks, for example. The method of making the machine print a result is very simple in principle, although the actual mechanism may be complicated. The counting-wheels of a register are geared to a second set of wheels carrying printing type round their circumferences. The depressing of a 'print' key causes this type to strike the paper.

An interesting machine of this class is the

Ferranti Ltd.

FIG. 4. ELECTRONIC COMPUTER AT MANCHESTER UNIVERSITY

On either side of the control desk are tape readers (the input unit), behind the right-hand one a teleprinter (output unit), and in the centre switches and cathode ray tubes on which the progress of the calculation can be watched. The store and arithmetical unit are in the racks on the left

'multi-register printing-adding machine'. This machine has several accumulator registers (ten in some models). A number set on the keyboard can be added to or subtracted from any one of these, or into any group of these simultaneously, and the number in any one register can be added to, or subtracted from, any other register or combination of registers, and the contents printed. The machine was designed for commercial accounting, but has been widely used in scientific computation.

The most elaborate of all the mechanical calculators are the 'punched-card machines', first produced in 1886, to aid the analysis of the U.S.A. census returns. These are entirely automatic and are the forerunners of electronic machines. Numbers are represented by groups of small holes punched in cards (*see* Vol. VII, p. 2) according to a code which can be interpreted by the reading mechanism, and the apparatus controlling the calculator can be set

so that the machine will carry out a sequence of different operations on the numbers on each card and print the results, or totals of results, from any group of cards as required. These machines are large and expensive. One of the most striking activities of punched-card machines is the calculation of the motion of the moon from the year 1935 to 2000, made at the Nautical Almanac Office in 1929—a calculation which was completed in about 6 months, a tenth of the time estimated for hand computation.

4. *Electronic calculators.* In all the machines described so far the arithmetic is done by moving mechanical parts, usually wheels, and this sets a limit to the speed of the machine. A more severe limitation is set for all except the punched-card machines by the need for an operator. Recently, however, entirely new machines have been designed which can perform long and intricate calculations and print the results entirely automatically. The article ELECTRONICS (q.v.)

describes how in these machines numbers are represented as trains of electrical pulses travelling along wires, and these are counted and sorted by groups of THERMIONIC VALVES (q.v.). It is possible with these to count accurately pulses lasting for 1/1,000,000 second and following one another at intervals of 1/100,000 second. Machines have been built in which pairs of 10-figure numbers are added at the rate of 10,000 per second, or multiplied at the rate of 1,000 per second.

A machine of this kind must have five main parts: an 'input unit' for receiving information (that is, numbers and instructions about the calculation); a 'store' or set of registers for holding this information; an 'arithmetical unit' for doing the actual arithmetic; an 'output unit' for recording its results; and a 'control unit' for linking all these together.

The store might be described as a large collection of counters, each identified by a number called the 'address' or 'location', and the control unit as a very elaborate set of switches—a kind of automatic telephone exchange—by means of which numbers are selected from the store and manipulated in the way required by the calculation. Every calculation has to be stated so that the instructions or 'orders' are a series of simple steps each specifying a single arithmetical operation, for instance, 'add the number in address 53 to that in address 87'. The instructions are given by means of patterns of holes punched in paper tape. This is sent through the input mechanism which, either by mechanical contacts or light-beams operating PHOTOCELLS (q.v.), detects where the holes have been punched and sends suitable trains of pulses to perform the required arithmetical operation. The whole calculation, including the typing of the result, is completed in a hundredth or even a thousandth of the time taken to do the work with a desk machine.

These high-speed machines are exceedingly complicated and delicate, and still very difficult to construct. The first to be built was the 'Eniac' (Electronic Numerical Integrator And Computer), at the University of Pennsylvania in 1944; it contains about 18,000 thermionic valves, consumes about 100 kilowatts of power, and fills a large room. Much more compact and less extravagant machines have now been made— for example, the Ferranti machine at Manchester University, which contains about 4,000 valves and yet has much greater capacity (Fig. 4).

CALCULUS. This is a mathematical method of calculating how one quantity varies with respect to another. Many problems, such as the working out of the orbits of stars and comets, the flight of bullets, or the strength of foundations of new blocks of flats, are beyond the reach of arithmetic, algebra, and geometry. The branch of mathematics invented by NEWTON and LEIBNITZ (qq.v. Vol. V) that deals with problems of this sort is called calculus.

There are two branches of calculus. Differential calculus finds out the rates of change of variable quantities, such as the speed of a motorbus which has just started off from a bus stop. Integral calculus carries out the complementary task; it calculates variable quantities, such as the area of cross-sections of a propeller blade or of a field with a curved boundary. Both branches solve their problems by calculating with infinitely small quantities, that is, quantities that can, at least in theory, be made smaller and smaller forever. For example, if you halve something, then halve the result, then halve that again, and so on, you will never, in theory, reach zero, since from every halving there will always be something left. The full name of this study is, therefore, the 'infinitesimal calculus'.

1. DIFFERENTIAL CALCULUS. If a quantity depends on another quantity—say, the volume of water in a reservoir depends on the depth at some point—we say mathematically that the first quantity is a 'function' of the second. The relationship between them can be shown by the curve of a GRAPH (q.v.) in which one coordinate represents, say, the depth and the other, say, the volume (Fig. 1). Differential calculus enables us to find the rate at which the volume is changing as the depth increases. If at the depth p the volume were v (shown at A), then at a slightly greater depth $(p+\delta p)$ the volume would also be slightly

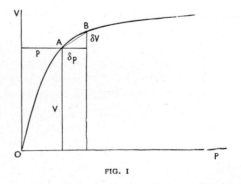

FIG. 1

greater $(v+\delta v)$ (shown at B). If δp gets smaller δv also gets smaller. If δv and δp tend to zero, B gets closer to A and the straight line between A and B touches the curve A. The ratio $\dfrac{\delta v}{\delta p}$ is the 'gradient' of AB, and so as δp tends to zero, the ratio is the gradient of the curve at the point A. This is written $\dfrac{dv}{dp}$, and is called the differential coefficient of v with respect to p. This can be calculated for all depths of water if the algebraic equation that connects v and p is known. The actual manipulation of the algebra is, however, beyond the scope of this article.

2. INTEGRAL CALCULUS. Suppose we want to find the area of a shape, ABDC (Fig. 2), bounded by a curve AB and three straight lines CA, DB, and CD. The curve can be plotted on a graph if the relationship between the coordinates y and x

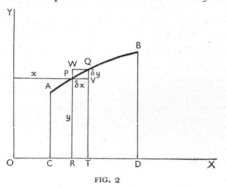

FIG. 2

is known. The distance of the point P on AB from the x-axis is y, and from the y-axis is x. Suppose there is a point Q near P, and let us call PV 'δx' and QV 'δy'. Then the area PVTR $= y \times \delta x$. This is slightly less than the area PQTR, which in turn is less than the area of the rectangle WQTR which equals $(y+\delta y) \times \delta x$. The whole area of ABDC can be thought of as being made up of slices similar to PQTR and its extent lies between the sum of all the rectangles like PVTR and the sum of all the rectangles like WQTR. If the size of δx is reduced so that it is infinitesimally small and the number of rectangles is increased until there is an infinitely great number of them, the area of ABDC equals the sum or 'integral' of all these rectangles. This area is written $\int_{r_1}^{r_2} y\,\delta x$, where $r_1 = $ OC and $r_2 = $ OD. If the relation between y and x is known the integral can usually be calculated.

CAMERA. 1. PINHOLE CAMERAS. A simple form of camera can be made by piercing a small hole near the centre of one end of a wooden box, and supporting with clips a photographic plate flat against the other end (Fig. 1), the gelatine-coated

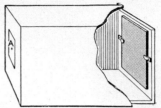

FIG. 1. PINHOLE CAMERA. A. Pinhole

side of the plate being towards the pinhole. The inside of the box should be painted with photographer's 'dead black' paint to absorb stray light, and no light must be allowed to leak in round the edges of the lid. To make the pinhole, a fine sewing needle is pushed through a sheet of copper foil or tinfoil, and this is then fixed with drawing pins over a larger hole cut through the wood of the box. The box is 'loaded' in the dark, and the pinhole covered up.

The loaded 'pinhole camera' is then set on a firm stand pointing at the object to be photographed—perhaps the view out of the window—and the pinhole is uncovered for 5 to 10 minutes, the length of exposure depending on the size of the pinhole, the length of the box, the brightness of the day, and the 'speed' of the photographic plate. At the end of the exposure, the pinhole is covered up again, and the plate taken out in a darkroom and developed and printed in the usual way. The result is a 'pinhole photograph'.

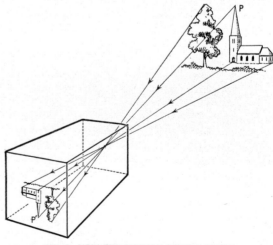

FIG. 2. HOW THE PINHOLE CAMERA WORKS

Fig. 2 shows how the picture is formed in the pinhole camera. From each point of the object, rays of light travel out in all directions as straight lines. Those rays which happen to pass through the pinhole continue on their way until they strike the photographic plate, where they form the picture which is later developed (*see* PHOTO-GRAPHIC EMULSION).

The pinhole camera, however, is unsuitable for ordinary photography because the exposure time needed is too long to make it possible to photograph moving objects, and because the image is not very sharp. If we enlarge the pinhole, the image becomes brighter, but more indistinct. If we make the pinhole smaller, the image becomes fainter and its sharpness increases down to a certain point, below which its sharpness decreases again. This is because the effects of the wave-nature of LIGHT (q.v. Vol. III) become relatively more important as the pinhole-size is reduced, until with a sufficiently small pinhole they visibly reduce the sharpness of the image.

2. CAMERA LENSES. The image can be made several thousand times brighter, and at the same time more distinct, by using a well-designed camera LENS (q.v.), or 'objective', in place of a pinhole. The lens refracts the rays from each point P of the object (*see* Fig. 3) so that they come together, almost exactly, in a single point P' which lies in the gelatine-coated surface of the photographic plate. P' is called the image of P by the lens. The set of image-points P' builds up the 'image' formed by the lens. This image must be flat if the camera is to give pictures in sharp

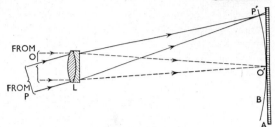

FIG. 4. OBJECTIVE WITH CURVED FIELD SURFACE

O'P'. Images formed of object O and P on photographic plate A. B. Curved image surface. L. Achromatic doublet lens

focus all over a flat photographic plate. If we try to use a simple achromatic doublet lens (*see* Fig. 5c) as a camera objective, the image which the lens forms of a distant landscape lies on a curved surface (as in Fig. 4), and the picture obtained on a flat photographic plate adjusted to the focus O' will be sharp only near the centre

FIG. 5. CAMERA OBJECTIVES

a. Taylor triplet (F/3·5) *b*. Tessar (F/3·5) using four kinds of glass. *a*. and *b* are 'fast' (anastigmatic) lenses. *c*. Inexpensive achromatic doublet lens (F/11) A. Crown glass. B. Flint glass. C. Stop

of the field of view. The objective suffers from 'field curvature'.

To produce sharp, flat, and brilliant images, a camera objective needs to be made up of at least three component lenses (*see* Fig. 5*a*, *b*). Such objectives, commercially known as 'anastigmats', are expensive because not only the lenses themselves but also the metal mountings which hold them in position have to be made with great accuracy. Much 'slower' and less expensive lenses can be used successfully for ordinary snapshot photography; most of those usually sold in box cameras consist of an achromatic doublet provided with a stop (a metal ring which acts as a screen and limits the effective diameter of the lens) in a special position (*see* Fig. 5*c*). The presence of the stop makes it possible to redesign the doublet so as to give better image quality in the outer parts of the picture. Such a lens, working at F/11 (*see* LENS, Section 5), is about ten times slower than an F/3·5 anastigmat—that is, it requires ten times as long an exposure time.

In anastigmats, the stop is used to improve the

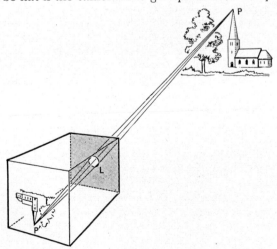

FIG. 3. BOX CAMERA FITTED WITH OBJECTIVE LENS (L)

images in a different way. The brilliant, flat images produced by these lenses are rather liable to suffer from 'pincushion' or 'barrel' distortion (*see* Fig. 6). The inclusion of a suitably placed

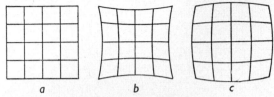

FIG. 6. DISTORTION OF THE IMAGE

a. Object. *b*. Image with pincushion distortion. *c*. Image with barrel distortion

stop in the design makes it possible to keep down the distortion to a harmlessly small amount, about $\frac{1}{70}$th of that shown in Fig. 6.

3. THE IRIS DIAPHRAGM. In most cameras the stop takes the form of an iris diaphragm, in which thin, overlapping, metal fins (*see* Fig. 7*a*) provide a clear aperture which is very nearly circular and of adjustable size. Each fin is attached by a pivot at one end to a ring which can be turned in its own plane, and by a slot-and-pin at the other end to a fixed ring. As the movable ring is turned, the size of the aperture alters. Most lenses give sharper images with the iris partly closed. A pointer moving against a scale, usually on the edge of the shutter-mounting, indicates the F-number to which the lens has been 'stopped down'. Exposure-meters are on sale which enable the correct exposure times under different lighting conditions and at different F-numbers to be calculated easily and quickly. A correct exposure is one of the most important factors in getting a good photograph.

4. CAMERA SHUTTERS. Close to the diaphragm is the shutter consisting of three thin metal leaves (*see* Fig. 7*b*) which rapidly move out and back when a trigger is pressed. The better shutters, which usually allow for exposures of 1, $\frac{1}{2}$,

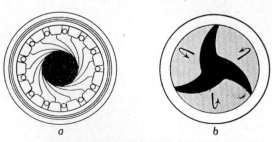

FIG. 7. *a*. IRIS DIAPHRAGM STOP PARTLY CLOSED. *b*. SHUTTER PARTLY OPEN

$\frac{1}{5}$, $\frac{1}{10}$, $\frac{1}{50}$, $\frac{1}{100}$, and $\frac{1}{250}$ second, are 'set' beforehand by pressing down a separate trigger. These shutters can also be set to remain open while the firing trigger is held down and to close when it is released ('bulb'), or to open at the first pressing down of the trigger and to remain open until it is pressed down again ('time').

5. FOLDING CAMERAS. The construction of a typical modern folding camera is shown in Fig. 8. The front of the case hinges forwards, and is held firmly in position by diagonal struts to form a base. Then the lens mounting is pulled forward and locked into position on its supporting slide. A 'bellows' of soft leather unfolds as the lens comes forward and forms a light-tight enclosure between the lens and the case. Focusing

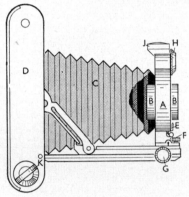

FIG. 8. A FOLDING CAMERA

A. Shutter and iris diaphragm. B. Lens. C. Bellows. D. Case. E. Shutter trigger. F. Diaphragm control. G. Focusing-knob. H. Shutter speed control. J. Finder. K. Film spool winding handle

is done by means of a knurled head operating a rack and pinion motion which moves the slide carrying the lens mounting. A pointer and scale (not visible in Fig. 8) indicates the correct focal setting for objects at various distances from about 6 feet to infinity, and a coupled RANGE-FINDER (q.v.) is sometimes fitted as well.

The camera is loaded by removing the back of the case and inserting a spool of film into the socket at the upper end. On the spool is a long roll of thick paper, to the middle part of which is attached a length of photographic film sufficient for six or eight pictures. The side of the paper next to the film is blackened, and the paper itself is usually dyed red. The spool is unwound until the end of the paper roll can be threaded through a slit in the spindle of an empty spool at the lower end of the case. (This can be done without exposing any of the photographic film to the light.) Then the back of the case is replaced, and the winding continued until the first part of the film is in position. A figure 1, printed on the red paper, becomes visible through a small, red-tinted window in the back of the case when the spool has been turned far enough. After each exposure, the film is turned on to bring a fresh surface into position. After the last exposure, the handle is turned on until the roll is all wound on to the lower spool; and the photographic emulsion having been well shielded from the light by layers of paper, the roll can be removed from the camera in daylight.

6. FINDERS. These are attached to the side of a camera to show which part of the view will appear in the picture. Various types of finders are in common use; one design consists of a simple biconvex lens, behind which are mounted a diagonal flat mirror and a field lens (Fig. 9). A rectangular stop, placed just above the field lens, makes the field of view of the finder, as shown in the mirror, agree with that which the camera will photograph. The picture seen in the finder appears reversed from left to right.

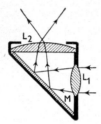

FIG. 9. VIEW-FINDER
L₁. Biconvex lens.
L₂. Field lens. M.
    Mirror

See also LENS; PHOTOGRAPHIC EMULSION; CINE-CAMERAS AND PROJECTORS.
See also Vol. IX: PHOTOGRAPHY.

CAMERA, MINIATURE. 1.

This name correctly applies only to a high-precision CAMERA (q.v.) which takes pictures on a spool of film of the same width as standard cine-film—35 millimetres. As the film has holes along both sides for winding, the picture is only 24 mm. wide, a little less than an inch, so that all prints have to be made by enlargement with the help of a projector.

Miniature cameras were developed in Germany in the 1920's and 1930's. In contrast to the traditional folding cameras, they slide open and shut on a strong steel tube, like a telescope, perfectly rigid and light-proof.

The miniature camera is so small that it and enough films for hundreds of pictures can be carried in a pocket; furthermore, the 36-picture film saves time and trouble in reloading. But the camera's chief attraction lies in the fact that the lenses are very large compared with the tiny picture taken, and consequently a larger 'aperture' (in other words, a lower F-number) can be used; this makes it possible to take photographs successfully in very dim light—street scenes at night, or snapshots of a theatre audience.

It is possible to use different lenses according to the type of photograph to be taken—lenses of large aperture for dim lights, those of smaller aperture for getting clearer defined backgrounds in good light, and also telephoto lenses to magnify very distant scenes, and wide-angle lenses to give a broader field of view when that is needed. The lenses are easily slipped on and off. The small negative of the miniature, however, cannot be enlarged to more than a certain extent without losing both clearness of outline and delicacy of gradation. A fine-grain film yields the best enlargements (*see* PHOTOGRAPHIC EMULSION), but this grain lowers the 'speed' of the film, thus limiting one advantage of miniature cameras, their capacity for fast work.

Miniature cameras were the first to incorporate RANGE-FINDERS (q.v.), and to link these mechanically with the lens so that focusing was automatic.

2. FOCAL-PLANE SHUTTERS. In most amateur cameras the shutter forms part of the actual lens system. But a camera cannot be fitted with interchangeable lenses unless its lens system is entirely independent of the shutter mechanism. The shutter of the miniature camera, therefore, is placed far back in the body of the camera, in what is called the 'focal plane', in front of and almost touching the film, so that no light can reach the film while the lenses are being changed.

In cameras of normal size, the focal-plane shutter (used largely by press-photographers) consists of a strip of fine but light-proof fabric completely covering the film or plate at the back of the camera, and wound on a spindle on one side. On the part of the fabric which is rolled up there is an open slit. When the photographer presses a button, a coiled spring causes the fabric blind to wind very rapidly off the spindle on one side on to a spindle on the other, and, as it does so, the open slit passes across the film or plate, causing the necessary exposure to take place. The duration (or 'speed') of the exposure is governed by altering the width of the slit or the tension of the coiled spring. During the period of exposure, however short it may be, the film or

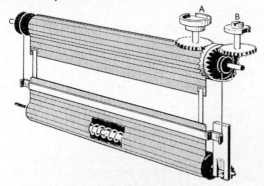

FOCAL-PLANE SHUTTER

A, B. Connexions to controls of reels of upper and lower blinds. C. Springs in roller (visible where section has been cut away in lower roller)

plate receives illumination equal to the full aperture of the lens. With the ordinary diaphragm lens which, in simpler cameras, opens and shuts more in the manner of an eye with eyelids, there is an appreciable proportion of the period of exposure during which the segments or 'lids' are only partly open, and the light passing through is less than the aperture-number denotes.

The miniature cameras, instead of using the full roller-blind principle, use a metal shutter in the 'focal plane'. The mechanism for setting and releasing the shutter is at the back of the camera, as well as a dial to show the number of exposures made, and a device to prevent the shutter being opened until the area of film last exposed has been moved forward.

See also CAMERA; LENS.
See also Vol. IX: PHOTOGRAPHY.

CAMERA, REFLEX. This is a camera of any size or pattern which incorporates a mirror

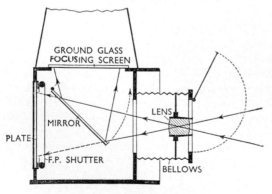

DIAGRAM OF A REFLEX CAMERA

giving an exact and full-size view of the picture to be taken. The true reflex camera, now almost obsolete, contained a large tilting mirror (*see* Fig.) interposed between the lens and the film or plate. The photographer looked down at a ground-glass screen in the roof of the camera, and saw a reflection of the scene, which reached the mirror by being focused through the camera's actual lens. When he pressed a button, a mechanism tilted the mirror upward, allowing the focused rays from the lens to reach the plate at the back of the camera, which was simultaneously exposed by a focal-plane shutter (*see* CAMERA, MINIATURE, Section 2).

The modern reflex camera, which is smaller and less clumsy, consists of two optical compartments, one on top of the other. The lower one is the true camera, with a lens, a shutter, and plate or film. The upper compartment has a duplicate (though rather simpler) lens, a fixed inclined mirror, and a ground-glass screen in the roof. The photographer looks down at the screen, moves the focusing device (which operates both 'viewing' and 'taking' lenses at once) until the objects he sees are 'sharp', and releases the shutter when he is satisfied with the composition of the picture.

See also CAMERA; CAMERA, MINIATURE.
See also Vol. IX: PHOTOGRAPHY.

CANAL BUILDING. Most English CANALS (q.v. Vol. IV) were built before heavy mechanical aids had been invented. They were laboriously constructed by men with picks, shovels, and wheel-barrows; the word 'navvy', for example, is derived from 'navigator', the workmen who built the early waterways or 'navigations'. The great engineer James Brindley (*see* CANALS, BRITISH, Vol. IV), in the 18th century, was the first to devise more rapid methods of canal construction: for instance, he started the plan of opening each section of a canal as it was completed, so that it could be used for bringing the earth for embankments and other materials in specially constructed boats to the men working on the new sections. He also introduced floating workshops for his carpenters and masons. Today, canal builders use many different kinds of heavy machinery—for example, great excavators with buckets holding sometimes as much as 11 cubic yards of earth (*see* EARTH-MOVING EQUIPMENT), and miles of railway track carrying special trucks to be unloaded by mechanical unloaders are common sights when a large canal is being built.

The first step in planning a canal is to decide the route it is to follow. This involves problems of SURVEYING and reconnaissance which are in many ways similar to those in ROAD BUILDING (qq.v.); in addition, the canal builder has many special problems to consider. For example, a route is selected which will give the canal a level water surface throughout as much of its length as possible. But if the canal has to travel over rising or falling ground, the water-level must be made to rise or fall in a series of steps, the 'tread' of each step being known as a 'reach'. The water in each reach has to be kept at the required level by means of gates, which when constructed in pairs form a lock in which ships and BARGES (q.v. Vol. IV) can be raised or lowered as they travel along the canal. If the difference of levels is greater than the normal height of a lock gate, a lift is often constructed instead of a series of locks (*see* LOCKS AND WEIRS, Vol. IV). To reduce to a minimum the number of locks and embankments and the amount of excavation, the route is made to follow as far as possible the contours of the ground, or, in special cases, is made to travel in a tunnel through a range of hills or to cross a valley by a specially constructed aqueduct. Another important factor which the engineer has to consider is that a canal needs a dependable supply of water: where the flow of rivers or streams is uncertain, reservoirs have to be built to maintain the supply during dry weather, and overflow weirs and sluices have to be provided to prevent the water overtopping the banks during wet weather. The stability of the soil, too, must be thoroughly tested so as to avoid as far as possible any route that lies through soft or wet ground.

The width and depth of a canal must, of course, be considerably greater than the width and depth of a loaded barge below the water-line: in other words, there must be sufficient

Docks & Inland Waterways

BARGES CROSSING WOLVERTON AQUEDUCT ON THE GRAND UNION CANAL
The aqueduct crosses the River Ouse which can just be seen on the right

'clearance', and the greater the clearance the less effort will be needed to propel the barge. Generally the minimum bottom width of the canal should be at least twice the width of the barge plus 4 feet, and its depth $1\frac{1}{2}$ feet more than the greatest depth of the barge below the water-line. Narrower canals must be widened at intervals to allow barges travelling in opposite directions to pass each other. The top width of the canal varies according to the slope of the banks. Some canals on the Continent have side slopes of $1\frac{1}{2}$ or 2 to 1; if they are 10 feet deep this means that they will be 34 feet greater than double the width of the barge. The speed of barges also affects the clearance. The width of many old canals was designed for barges towed by horses, and on such canals the speed of modern mechanically propelled barges has to be restricted to 3 or 4 miles an hour. For greater speeds the clearance must be considerably increased; otherwise the banks are damaged by wash.

Once the route and dimensions of the canal have been decided, the ground has to be cleared and the channel excavated by special heavy machinery such as bulldozers, mechanical excavators, and scrapers; embankments and towing

Docks & Inland Waterways

NEWARK LOCK FROM THE INNER END LOOKING DOWNSTREAM

paths have to be built, and locks constructed. Once the channel has been formed, the bed of the canal itself must be made watertight. This is done by lining the bed with a layer of clay, mixed with water, called 'puddle clay', with reinforced concrete, or with asphalt.

As canal embankments have to bear a considerable weight of water, they must be carefully built in layers of clean earth, well consolidated by ramming or rolling. Their outer surfaces are protected against the weather by grass, or occasionally by carefully packed stone, to prevent slips of earth which might release the water and cause serious flooding. As some barges are hauled by tractors (developed from the small, rubber-tyred agricultural tractor and fitted with hooks to release the tow in emergency), a towing path 10 feet wide is built on one side of the canal, wide enough for two tractors to pass; a bank at least 5 feet wide is provided on the other, the height being at least 12 inches above the top water level. The banks are protected against erosion caused by the wash of barges and boats by mass concrete walls or reinforced concrete or steel piles. Sometimes a wall of timber and brushwood is used.

Lock walls are generally built of brick, concrete, steel, or timber. The floor of the lock must be strong enough to withstand any upward thrust of the subsoil, especially of a clay subsoil. The only lock to be built recently in England is the new Newark lock, on the river Trent, opened in 1952. This lock is 193 feet long, 30 feet wide, and can pass four barges carrying 500 tons of cargo or a large single craft of 200 to 250 tons. Its construction presented many difficulties, and had to be carried out without interfering with the working of the old lock, which ran alongside the new one. A special bridge had to be built over the river to divert traffic. After the steel sheet piles (*see* BUILDING CONSTRUCTION), which form the sides of the lock, had been driven down, the water-level had to be lowered before any ground could be excavated; to do this a system of wells was sunk along the length of the lock, the water from the lock being withdrawn by a centrifugal PUMP (q.v.). Another difficulty was that the marl and silt on which the concrete foundations of the lock were built were likely to exert a considerable upward thrust. To relieve this pressure on the concrete, therefore, a number of porous concrete pipes, 2 feet in diameter, had to be sunk through the lock bottom to act as vent holes.

James Brindley, when asked of what use were rivers, is reported to have said, 'to fill canals'. Modern ideas tend to support this view and, except in very large navigable rivers, it is usual to construct a canal alongside a river rather than canalize the river itself. Canals do not suffer from fluctuations in the level of the water due to flood or drought; a steady rate of transit can be maintained either with or against the flow; and natural drainage is not interfered with. Canals, however, do tend to silt up because of erosion, or with sand and silt brought in by rivers and streams, and dredging is frequently necessary. In larger canals the ladder or bucket DREDGER (q.v. Vol. IV) is used; for smaller canals spoon dredgers or grab dredgers discharging into boats, or drag-line caterpillar cranes working from the bank, are more usual.

See also EARTH-MOVING EQUIPMENT; SOIL MECHANICS.

See also Vol. IV: CANALS; CANALS, BRITISH; WELLAND CANAL; RUSSIAN CANALS; PANAMA CANAL; SUEZ CANAL; LOCKS AND WEIRS.

CASTING. 1. This method of shaping metal consists of melting it and pouring it into shaped moulds. Other methods of shaping metals are by cutting or machining them (see MACHINE TOOLS and FITTING) or by pressing or squeezing them when solid (see FORGING AND PRESSING).

Toy soldiers of a soft metal such as lead are a typical example of casting. Common examples of cast iron are lamp-posts, garden rollers, frames and bedplates for machinery, road drain grids and manhole covers, domestic cookers and radiators. There is an enormous number of differ-

ent steel castings, varying from alloy steel components weighing an ounce or two for aero-engines and aircraft, to frames for locomotives, liners, and warships, some of which weigh over 100 tons.

Castings are made in foundries, of which there are nearly 3,000 in Britain alone. There are two main groups of castings—ferrous, in which the metal contains iron, and non-ferrous, in which other metals are used, such as aluminium or bronze.

There are four parts to a founder's task: making the mould, melting the metal, pouring the metal, then removing the mould from the solidified metal. The general principle of melting is the same for all metals, though the details vary with the composition of each.

In making cast iron, solid lumps of pig iron (see IRON AND STEEL, Section 2) are melted in a device known as a cupola (Fig. 1), a metal tube 15 to 20 feet high and about 4 feet in diameter, lined with firebrick to retain heat (see FIRECLAYS AND REFRACTORIES). It is like a small BLAST FURNACE (q.v.) and is heated by coke. Pig iron, together with scrap iron, is charged into the cupola through a door near the top; at the foot, air is

Ruston & Hornsby

FIG. 1. MOLTEN METAL BEING TAPPED FROM A CUPOLA INTO A DRUM-TYPE LADLE

Nuffield Organization

FIG. 2. ASSEMBLING A MOULD OF AN INTERNAL COMBUSTION
ENGINE CYLINDER BLOCK AND PLACING THE CORES IN POSITION

blown through nozzles to keep the coke burning furiously. As the iron melts, it trickles down and collects at the bottom of the cupola, to be poured out through a tap-hole into large buckets called ladles. The top of the cupola is usually open, and the glow and flames from it are a common and impressive sight in most industrial towns. The process is fast, the iron passing through a cupola in an hour or less. The output from a normal cupola is about 8 tons an hour.

Steel for casting is made either by refining pig iron by the open-hearth process or in a Bessemer or similar converter, or by melting steel scrap in electric furnaces (*see* STEEL-MAKING). As the steel founder generally wants only small quantities of molten steel at a time, he uses small, fast furnaces.

2. MOULDS. These are made in many ways, and of many materials. The commonest method is to make a mould by packing stiff, damp sand round a wooden 'pattern' (*see* PATTERN MAKING), which has the shape of the finished casting. The pattern is then removed, leaving its impression on the sand, and the molten metal is poured into this impression.

Moulds are made in moulding boxes which are in two halves (Fig. 2). The procedure is rather like removing the skin from an orange by cutting it round and then lifting off the top and bottom halves, leaving the orange complete. If the two halves of the skin are now put together again and filled with some material, this material would reproduce the shape of the orange. The two halves are the equivalent of the two half-moulds, and the orange underneath the skin represents the wooden pattern. The split along the two halves of the mould is arranged so that, when they are separated, the pattern can be lifted out. The box is then put together again, and the molten metal poured in through small holes. The pattern can be used to make a very large number of moulds.

Making moulds by hand is a skilled task. If the sand is rammed too hard round the pattern, the gases which emerge from the molten metal cannot escape, and the casting may be disfigured by scabs and blow-holes. On the other hand, if the mould is packed too softly, it will not be able to withstand the pressure of the molten metal when it is poured in.

To meet these difficulties, many foundries are highly mechanized, especially where many castings of the same sort are manufactured. The equipment includes moulding machines which automatically ram the sand round the two halves of each pattern separately; the halves are then matched together and held securely to provide a complete mould while the metal is poured in (Fig. 3). The machine works not only much more quickly than the hand moulder, but also more accurately.

When a large number of castings is to be made, a metal mould or permanent 'die' may be used. Such a die is much more expensive than making a mould from sand, but in the long run is more economical since it can be used over and over again. Recently another method known as shell moulding has become popular; the mould is a thin shell made of a mixture of sand and plastic material. It is much lighter than a sand mould and gives a very fine finish to the casting.

Other types of mould and moulding materials, such as plaster of paris, can also be used for special tasks (*see* BRONZE SCULPTURE, Vol. XII).

If the metal casting is to be hollow, a core must be inserted in the mould to prevent its filling up with solid metal (*see* p. 323). The core, like the main part of the mould, is moulded to a pattern in sand, which is then baked to make it stiff. One

Nuffield Organization

FIG. 3. CASTING A CYLINDER BLOCK
The metal is being poured into the mould from a ladle of a different type from that in Fig. 1

or more cores, as required, are placed in the main mould in such positions that they will produce the correct cavities when the mould is filled. The cores are placed in the mould in marked positions, known as core prints, and, if necessary, are wedged in position with small pieces of metal which look like collar studs and are known as 'chaplets'.

To allow the molten metal to enter the mould, channels, called 'runners', are cut in the sand, leading to the main cavity of the mould. The place where the metal enters the mould is known as the 'gate'. Some moulds are provided with exits or overflows ('risers') connected to the highest part of the cavity, which allow gas and floating dirt to pass out when the metal is being poured, and ensure that the mould is completely filled with metal.

In modern foundries, CONVEYORS (q.v.) carry the moulds to the pouring bay near the cupola, and, when the moulds have been filled, carry them on to the 'stripping' section—travelling slowly to allow them to cool on the way. There the sand moulds are knocked out on to a grid,

and the castings are left to cool further. Finally, the castings are 'fettled' with wire brushes, grinding wheels, pneumatic chisels, and other tools to remove runners, risers, fins of metal round the joint line, and any adhering sand and cores, until only the clean, finished casting is left (Fig. 4). When an exceptionally good finish is needed the castings may be cleaned by shot-blasting (*see* SURFACE TREATMENT).

3. OTHER FORMS OF CASTING. Special forms have been developed for special purposes. For instance, pipes or tubes and other hollow parts, both in iron and steel, can be made by 'centrifugal casting'. In this method, the mould itself spins round so that the molten metal, as it flows into it, is thrown against the walls of the mould, where it solidifies. Thus, no core is needed to produce the hollow, tubular form, and also a higher tensile strength is obtained. Centrifugally cast pipes, for instance, have a tensile strength of 16 to 20 tons per square inch compared with 10 tons per square inch obtained by sand casting. This means they can be made thinner and lighter for the same strength. Centrifugal steel castings

Nuffield Organization

FIG. 4. 'FETTLING' CASTINGS OF CYLINDER BLOCKS BEFORE
THEY ARE SENT AWAY FOR MACHINING

are used in jet engines, and castings are made in the same way for petrol-engine piston-rings and cylinder liners (the actual lining fitted into the cylinder bore in which the piston runs).

A 'lost wax' process is used for making small alloy steel castings such as gas-turbine blades, which are wanted in large quantities and which have to be highly accurate with a fine finish. The pattern is made of wax instead of wood, and has itself been cast in a very accurate metal mould. A soft, heat-resisting substance is then put on the wax pattern, completely surrounding it, and is allowed to harden into a rigid coating in which a small hole is left. When the whole thing is heated, the wax melts and runs out of the mould, thus leaving the heat-resisting shell surrounding a cavity which reproduces the exact form of the original pattern. Molten steel is poured into this mould through the hole, and when the steel has cooled, the mould is broken away, leaving an accurate casting.

Pressure die-casting, in which a machine is used to force molten metal into a die under pressure, is another method often used for making small, complex, non-ferrous parts in large quantities.

See also BLAST FURNACE; FORGING AND PRESSING; IRON AND STEEL; MACHINE TOOLS; PATTERN MAKING.

CATERPILLAR TRACKS, *see* TRACK MECHANISM.

CATHODE, *see* PHOTOCELL; THERMIONIC VALVES.

CATHODE RAY TUBE. This is a device by which pictures and diagrams are produced electrically on a luminous screen. The screen is familiar as that on which TELEVISION pictures (q.v. Vol. IX) are seen in the home. Cathode ray tubes are used in RADAR (q.v.) for air and sea navigation, and also in cathode ray oscilloscopes used by engineers and scientists to study the shapes of electrical vibrations and waves.

A cathode ray tube consists essentially of an 'electron gun' and a specially coated screen enclosed inside a glass bulb from which the air has been extracted. The electron gun (Fig. 1) provides a narrow beam of quickly moving electrons—that is, very small particles of negative electricity—which are obtained by thermionic emission from a heated cathode (*see* THERMIONIC VALVES). The cathode is a small nickel cylinder coated with strontium and barium oxides. Another nickel cylinder, called a 'control electrode', completely surrounds it except for a hole in one end so small that only a narrow pencil-like beam of electrons can pass through it. The electrons are attracted away from the cathode through the hole in the control electrode by yet another nickel cylinder, called the 'anode', which is joined to the positive end of a high-voltage supply. Inside the anode is a metal plate with a small hole in it, through which some of the electrons fly, attracted towards the anode at high speed, and so pass on as a narrow beam towards the coated screen in the glass bulb.

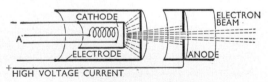

FIG. 1. SECTION OF AN ELECTRON GUN
A. Current to cathode heater

The screen is actually the flat end of the glass bulb (Fig. 2). It is specially coated with a thin film of a substance which is 'fluorescent'—that is, it gives out a bright light from any spot on which electrons fall. (A commonly used fluorescent substance is the mineral willemite, containing zinc, silicon, and oxygen.) As the electrons strike the atoms of the fluorescent substance they cause them to vibrate, and it is the vibrating atoms which give out the waves of light. Whenever the electron beam is cut off, the vibrations die away, and the spot of light quickly fades. A television picture or a diagram for radar or other purposes is formed on the glass screen as the beam is moved about and varied in intensity.

After passing through the hole in the anode the electron beam passes through a fourth hollow nickel cylinder, known as the 'focusing electrode'. This is connected to a variable voltage supply, which is adjusted to focus the narrow electron beam, or bring it to a single point on the fluorescent screen. From the focusing electrode the beam passes between four small oblong metal plates or, in television sets, coils which can bend the beam up or down, left or right. In the diagram (Fig. 2), the four metal plates are marked

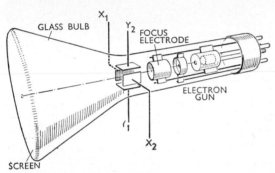

FIG. 2. CATHODE RAY TUBE

x_1, x_2, y_1, y_2. If one of these plates, say y_2, is joined to the positive terminal of a battery and the plate opposite it, y_1, is joined to the negative terminal, then y_2 will attract the electron beam and y_1 will repel it, which has the effect of deflecting the beam so that it will strike the screen at a spot higher up than the centre. Plates y_1 and y_2 can thus be used to control the level (higher or lower) of the spot at which the electrons strike the screen, and by varying the voltages connected to y_1 and y_2 the beam, and consequently the spot, can be moved up or down from the centre. Similarly the plates x_1 and x_2 can be used to move the beam and spot to the left or right of the screen.

Suppose that the spot is resting at the middle of the screen on the left-hand side, and that a steadily increasing positive voltage is connected to x_2. The electron beam will be attracted, and

the spot will move steadily across the screen from left to right, tracing out as it goes a straight bright line (Fig. 3a). Suppose that at the same

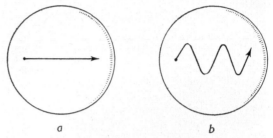

FIG. 3. SCREEN OF CATHODE RAY TUBE

a. Path of beam when positive voltage is connected to one plate. *b.* Path of beam when alternating voltage is also connected to other plates

time an alternating voltage (*see* p. 9) is applied to plates y_1 and y_2; this varying voltage will deflect the beam up and down (Fig. 3b). Therefore, with the beam pulled to the right by an x plate, and at the same time pulled rapidly up and down by the two y plates, the spot will trace a wavy pattern. This is obviously similar in shape to the voltage wave, and this method, by which a visible spot expresses a voltage, forms the basis of the cathode ray oscilloscope.

The electron beam can also be moved about by the magnetic field (*see* INDUCTION, ELECTRIC) of a coil of wire carrying an electric current, and two pairs of coils are usually used instead of plates in television sets. Each point on the surface of the fluorescent screen of a television set receives the beam of electrons at just the right moment (*see* TELEVISION ENGINEERING). All that remains is to ensure that at each point the light is of the right intensity, so that it can indicate the right degree of light or shadow for that particular part of the complete picture. The number of electrons in the beam can be varied, and the electron beam can even be cut off completely, by changing the voltage of the electric supply connected to the control electrode surrounding the cathode. The more electrons there are in the beam the brighter is the spot of light on the screen. The incoming television signals are connected to the control electrode and so produce the variations in light and shade.

CELL, ELECTRIC, see BATTERY, ELECTRIC.

CENTRAL HEATING, see HEATING. *See also* Vol. XI: HEATING SYSTEMS.

SHASTA DAM WHEN NEARING COMPLETION

CENTRAL VALLEY PROJECT (California).

This is an outstanding example of the way in which the water resources of a large agricultural area can be harnessed by CIVIL ENGINEERING (q.v.). The area covered by the project is about 500 miles long and 40 miles wide, forming part of the catchment of two great rivers, the Sacra-mento and the San Joaquin, which run through the south-western United States.

The scheme, which now irrigates 8 million acres, was planned in 1938, when the Central Valley had been highly developed, containing about 59,000 farms and 1 million people. Three million acres of land depended on IRRIGATION

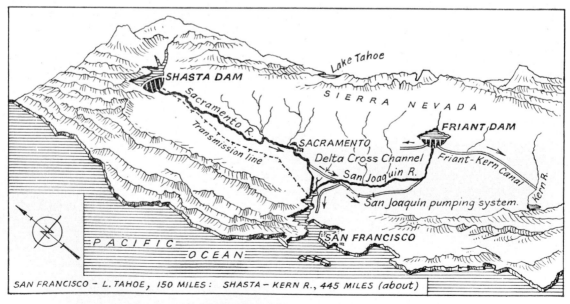

SAN FRANCISCO – L. TAHOE, 150 MILES: SHASTA – KERN R., 445 MILES (about)

MAP OF THE CENTRAL VALLEY

(q.v. Vol. VI) to produce crops, but there was not enough water to keep this up; the water reserves deep under the soil had been falling for 10 years as more and more was taken from wells. And there were other problems: most of the water came from the Sacramento and only a small proportion from the San Joaquin, where the need for irrigation was much greater; the irregular flow of both rivers caused serious floods; and, in addition, farmers used so much water from the rivers that the sea invaded the estuaries and its salty water made large areas unfit for agriculture (*see* FLOOD CONTROL). Much land had to be abandoned, and farmers were faced with ruin.

This important area was saved by building a vast DAM (q.v.) on the upper Sacramento, forming a reservoir to hold 196,000 million cubic feet of water. This dam, called the Shasta, is a curved gravity dam, 602 feet high and stretching 3,500 feet along its crest. Water turbines, with a capacity of 300,000 horse-power, are built into the dam to generate HYDRO-ELECTRIC POWER (q.v.). Work on the Shasta dam took 4 years, and the whole scheme, which was not in full operation until 1951, cost 36 million dollars.

The Shasta reservoir holds enough water to irrigate farms and to supply factories and towns throughout the Sacramento and the lower San Joaquin valleys. A canal 50 miles long connects the two rivers and then continues for a further 100 miles through the San Joaquin valley, the water being pumped in successive stages to a height of about 160 feet above sea-level.

Another dam, 250 feet high, was built on the San Joaquin, to hold nearly 20,000 million cubic feet of water; this reservoir, called the Friant reservoir, feeds two large irrigation canals, one running northwards for 35 miles, and the other 165 miles to the south; these feed a network of smaller irrigation canals. In this way all the San Joaquin water was made available for use in its upper valley, where irrigation is most needed.

See also DAMS; CIVIL ENGINEERING.
See also Vol. VI: IRRIGATION.

CHAINS, *see* BELT AND CHAIN DRIVE; WELDING.

CHEMICAL ENGINEERING. 1. This is the special branch of engineering concerned with the design and building of large-scale plants for manufacturing chemicals (*see* CHEMISTRY, INDUSTRIAL, Vol. VII). The term 'chemicals' includes all products that are manufactured by chemical changes or reactions, such as NYLON and RAYON, DYES, SOAP, or GLASS (qq.v. Vol. VII). Most products of this kind have been discovered or developed within the last 100 years—many within the last 25. Chemical engineering has, therefore, only recently emerged as a special branch of engineering.

Such things as soap, glass, and soda have been made on quite a large scale by simple chemical methods for centuries. The methods were fairly straightforward, and the necessary apparatus and furnaces could be constructed by metal workers and builders under the direction of chemists who understood the process, the best kind of equipment for each process being gradually worked out by trial and error.

When more complicated chemicals were needed, it became more and more difficult to plan the equipment in which to make them. It was soon realized that the work of making almost any kind of chemical on a large scale could be divided into a series of steps, that there were only a few such steps, and that each could be applied to several different kinds of manufacturing. When he thoroughly understood each step, the chemical engineer could fit the right ones together, and so more easily plan the best kind of equipment to make new chemicals in large amounts. The steps are of two kinds. First, there are 'operations' such as boiling, distilling, filtering, pumping from one place to another, freezing, pulverizing, mixing, stirring, evaporating, and so on. Second, there are 'processes', that is, steps in manufacture during which actual chemical changes or reactions take place between the materials being handled. These reactions can be classified, the standard types of reaction being called 'unit processes' and those of operations, 'unit operations'.

2. UNIT OPERATIONS. When a chemical is made, the different substances to be reacted, whether solid, liquid, or gas, have to be brought together and mixed. After the reaction is over, the chemical that is wanted must be separated from the rest of the mixture. In a laboratory, all this can usually be done by pouring liquids from one beaker into another, by stirring solids and liquids in a beaker, or by blowing in gas through a glass tube. Afterwards, the wanted chemical can be separated by pouring the product through a filter paper, or perhaps by distilling it from a glass flask.

Shell Photographic Unit

A MODERN CHEMICAL PLANT WITH NEARLY ALL THE EQUIPMENT OUT OF DOORS

Various products which are solvents and other organic chemicals made from petroleum gases are separated and purified by distillation in the tall columns. There are also storage tanks for the finished products and a network of pipes for carrying liquids and gases about the plant

But when chemicals have to be brought together, mixed, and separated on a large scale, the task becomes much more difficult, and the equipment requires skilful designing. The designer probably has to allow for many effects that hardly appear in the laboratory—such as heating or cooling during the reaction. A tablespoonful of salt, for example, can be dissolved in water simply by stirring the salt in water in a glass beaker; but if a ton of salt has to be dissolved in water, big mixers are needed. In order to plan mixers which will do the job without waste of power, the engineer must know how the solids and liquids will behave when stirred together. In fact, the engineer is studying that part of the unit operation known as 'mixing and agitation'.

Nearly always in a chemical process, some of the materials brought together or the products taken away are liquids or gases. These are usually pumped along through large metal pipes. In the unit operation called 'fluid flow', the engineer must understand how a particular liquid or gas will flow along under different conditions, so that he can calculate what size of pipe must be used,

how much pressure must be applied, and what is the best type of pump.

Almost without exception in a chemical process there has to be heating up or cooling down. The rules governing the way in which heat can be put into or taken out of a material are brought together in the unit operation of 'heat transmission'.

Equally important is the unit operation 'fractional distillation', by means of which a mixture of liquids that boil at different temperatures can be separated (*see* DISTILLATION, Vol. VII). The first reaction in one method of making synthetic RUBBER (q.v. Vol. VII), for example, starting from alcohol, gives a liquid containing at least a dozen different substances dissolved together, some of them with almost the same boiling-points. Each one of these has to be separated for further treatment. In order to do this a plant with nearly fifty separate distillation towers is used, some of them giants nearly 100 feet high, like those shown in the photograph.

If the material that we want is mixed with water but not dissolved, it can be recovered by 'filtration'; if it is dissolved, the water can be driven off by 'evaporation'. Often the operation of drying must also be carried out.

3. UNIT PROCESSES. The chemical steps necessary in the large-scale manufacture of chemicals are called 'unit processes', each one being based on a particular chemical reaction. To know what happens when chemicals react, and what reactions may be used to make a particular substance, is the work of chemists. Chemical engineers must then decide the best way to carry out each reaction on the full scale. All this information is collected and classified under the names of the unit processes.

4. THE CHEMICAL ENGINEER AT WORK. Probably the best way of understanding the work of a chemical engineer would be to follow through the production of a particular substance.

One chemical of which millions of gallons are wanted nowadays is called ethylene glycol, best known as the 'anti-freeze' that prevents water in the radiators of cars and lorries from freezing in winter. It is made from ethylene, a gas obtained in large quantities when certain kinds of oil are 'cracked' at high temperature—that is, when the oil molecules are broken up so that the atoms regroup into different substances (*see* OIL REFINING, Vol. VII). The usual method of making ethylene glycol starts by bubbling a mixture of ethylene and chlorine through water. The three react together to give ethylene chlorhydrin. This is the unit process of 'chlorhydrination'.

The ethylene chlorhydrin is then reacted with slaked lime (calcium hydroxide) to give ethylene oxide. This reaction comprises the unit process of 'saponification', that is, an alkali (calcium hydroxide) has been used to split the ethylene chlorhydrin molecule in a similar manner to the way in which a different alkali (sodium hydroxide) is used to split a complex organic molecule in soap manufacture.

The ethylene oxide is then dissolved in water at high temperature and pressure, whereupon the hydrogen and oxygen atoms in the water combine

with the ethylene oxide molecule to give a solution of ethylene glycol in water. A chemist would describe the whole process in the language of chemical formulae:

1. Chlorhydrination:
$$C_2H_4 + Cl_2 + H_2O \text{ [ethylene+chlorine+water]}$$
$$\rightarrow Cl(C_2H_4)OH + HCl \text{ [ethylene chlorhydrin+}$$
$$\text{hydrochloric acid]}$$

2. Saponification:
$$2Cl(C_2H_4)OH + Ca(OH)_2 \text{ [ethylene chlorhydrin+}$$
$$\text{slaked lime]}$$
$$\rightarrow 2(C_2H_4)O + CaCl_2 + 2H_2O \text{ [ethylene oxide+cal-}$$
$$\text{cium chloride+water]}$$

3. Hydration:
$$C_2H_4O + H_2O \text{ [ethylene oxide+water]}$$
$$\rightarrow C_2H_4(OH)_2 (+\text{excess water}) \text{ [ethylene glycol solution}$$
$$\text{in water]}$$

After these three unit processes, there still remains the unit operation of 'low-pressure distillation' whereby the ethylene glycol is separated from the water.

Suppose a factory is to be built to make 10 tons of ethylene glycol a week. Chemists, having first found out by experimenting with small quantities the proper pressures and temperatures to use, and what impurities will be formed, then pass on to the chemical engineers full information about the properties of all the chemicals and any peculiarities in the reactions. From this in-

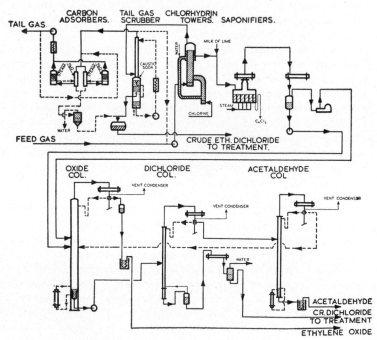

FLOW DIAGRAM FOR A FACTORY TO MAKE ETHYLENE GLYCOL

Even for a comparatively simple chemical process, very complicated plant is necessary to purify and separate the products

formation the chemical engineers work out a flow diagram in which each piece of equipment to be used is represented (see Fig.). At this stage, this equipment is shown by symbols, with single lines to represent all the elaborate piping.

In the diagram for this particular job, out of all the items of equipment only two are required for unit processes—in this case reaction (1) and reactions (2) and (3) together. Nearly all the rest are needed for the unit operations by which the products are separated and purified. This is quite characteristic of modern chemical plants.

After working out the flow diagram, the engineer calculates separately the shape and size of each piece of equipment so that each item is in the proper relationship to the whole plant. The sizes of all the piping—often miles of it in a single large plant—and the power needed for pumping are calculated by means of the principles of HYDRAULICS (q.v.). Studies of heat transmission are used to design the many heating coils and the condensers. When all this work has been done, the designs are passed on to the mechanical and structural engineers, who work out in detail the exact way to construct each piece, and design the concrete foundations and the steel girders on which all the parts are to be mounted.

As we are supposing this to be a new process, it will be necessary to build a pilot plant—a plant built just as the final plant is to be, but on a much smaller scale. Unexpected things often happen when a new chemical process is 'scaled-up'; and the operating of the pilot plant, although it may take some time, makes it possible to check all the predictions and calculations and to build the final plant more efficiently and probably more simply than had at first been planned. This may in the long run save both money and time. It may be as long as 10 years after the first successful laboratory experiment that the chemical engineers can start up and measure the performance of the final plant.

5. TRAINING OF CHEMICAL ENGINEERS. As we have seen, chemical engineers hardly ever work on their own; chemists supply them with process information; after they have made their designs, mechanical engineers construct the equipment. But chemical engineers must know enough CHEMISTRY (q.v. Vol. III) to understand what the chemists tell them, and enough about MECHANICS (q.v.) to produce practical designs.

At one time, most chemical engineers began as chemists or mechanical engineers and studied chemical engineering afterwards. Nowadays some take degrees at universities in chemical engineering, while others obtain their knowledge by practical work in a factory or drawing office, combined with evening study in technical schools. Most chemical engineers in this country belong to the Institution of Chemical Engineers, an Institution which holds qualifying examinations and ensures that standards of training and proficiency are maintained. Well-trained chemical engineers are in great demand for a wide variety of work.

See also Vol. III: CHEMISTRY.
See also Vol. VII: CHEMISTRY, INDUSTRIAL.

CHROMIUM-PLATING, see ELECTROPLATING; SURFACE TREATMENT.

CHRONOMETER, see Vol. IV: CHRONOMETER.

CINE-CAMERAS AND PROJECTORS.
1. Cine-cameras (35 mm.) for professional movie-making are of varied types. The smaller models can be held in the hand; there are intermediate types such as those used for newsreel work; whilst the studio models, even without the tripods or trucks, weigh as much as 180 lb.

Lenses vary in focal length and range from 1 in. to 20 in. (see LENS, Section 5). Some cameras are fitted with single interchangeable mounts, and others with rotating turret heads holding 3, 4, or 6 lenses. There is also the 'zoom lens', the focal length of which can be changed instantly so that long shots can become close-ups without the necessity of 'tracking' the camera forward. Adjustable view-finders are often included, but many cameras have a combined viewing and focusing system which makes it possible to look directly through the taking lens whilst filming. This may be done by a reflex device or by mirrors mounted on the front of the shutter blade at an angle of $45°$, in which case the image is seen from the side of the camera. The shutter used to mask the movement of the film is a half-circle, which, at sound speed, that is, at twenty-four 'frames' or pictures per second, gives an exposure of $\frac{1}{48}$th second, the moving forward of the strip of film occupying the other $\frac{1}{48}$th. Some cameras, however, have shutter blades adjustable from $10°$ to $200°$, which make it possible to reduce the exposure time when photographing fast-moving objects, and so to minimize image blurring.

The film capacity of the camera differs according to the size and usage. The standard film, 35 mm. (1⅜ in.) wide and perforated along each edge, is supplied in rolls of varying lengths. 100-ft. rolls are loaded into the camera body, but the bigger rolls up to 1,000 ft. (11 min. running time) are loaded into external magazines and mounted on to the camera.

The film is worked in the camera by cam-operated claws which enter the film perforations, pull down the film for exactly the depth of a picture, and then withdraw, lifting clear of the film, and re-enter the perforations to repeat the cycle. Register pins are fitted to ensure that the film is accurately placed in the 'gate' (the aperture through which the light comes) and also to steady it. These pins move in as the claw moves out (*see* Fig. 1). The normal taking speed is twenty-four frames per second, but most cameras can vary this, usually between eight and sixty-four frames per second.

Some cameras are normally driven by spring motors, but sometimes an external motor drive may also be fitted as an alternative. Others use ELECTRIC MOTORS (q.v.), either battery-operated or run from a mains supply; in the latter case a synchronous type of motor is usual. Whatever type of drive is used, the essential requirement is constant driving speed.

There are two ways of photographing in

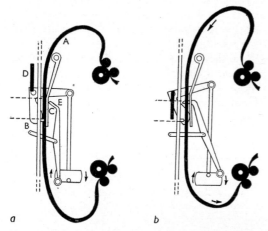

FIG. 1. THE MOVEMENT OF THE FILM IN A CINE-CAMERA

a. The film A held in place during exposure. The register pin B is engaged in a perforation, the pressure plate C presses the film against the gate, and the shutter D is open. *b.* The film being moved forward. The pressure on the film is released so that it leaves the register pin, the claw E engages in a perforation and pulls the film down, and the shutter is closed. (From R. Spottiswoode: *Film and its Techniques,* University of California Press)

colour. One way is to have a single colour film, which has three separate emulsion layers on one film base, and can be used in any ordinary camera. The other way is to use special beam-splitting cameras, which produce three separate negatives, one recording green light, another blue, and the third red. The light rays from the lens fall on a semi-reflecting prism block which allows some to pass on to the green recording film, but which at the same time deflects others on to a blue recording film, and through this on to the red record which is behind in direct contact. The three negatives are used to produce a single coloured positive.

2. CINE-PROJECTORS. The 35-mm. cine-projector as used in cinemas projects positive images on to large screens, which may be 20 ft. in width. Satisfactory screen illumination of pictures this size needs an extremely bright and, for optical reasons, compact light source, the most satisfactory undoubtedly being the carbon arc lamp. This consists of carbon rods each connected to an electricity supply. The electric current causes the ends to burn with an intense glow, and as the carbons burn away, the gap is maintained at its correct distance by holding the rods together, either by hand or by motor. The efficiency of the arc lamp is considerably increased by using a curved mirror reflector, the two together being called a 'mirror arc'. The light passes through a glass lens called a condenser, which concentrates it evenly on to the gate, where it travels through the film and then through the projection lens, and so on to the screen.

The projection lens is of wide aperture, generally F/1·9, so that it passes the maximum amount of light and at the same time ensures even definition of the projected image. In cinema projection, the focal length of the lens is very important as it governs the relation between the size of the picture and the distance from the screen. Thus a 3-in. lens gives a picture 20 ft. 7 in. wide at a distance of 75 ft., but if a picture of the same width is required at double the distance from the projector, then a lens of 6-in. focal length is needed. A 6-in. lens would give a picture width of only 10 ft. 4 in. at a distance of 75 ft.

As the film passes the 'gate', which holds the film flat during projection and acts as a brake at the end of each picture change, the changes are made by a mechanism known as a Maltese cross (Fig. 2). The cross is rotated, and at the completion of every quarter turn, the film is pulled forward exactly one frame. The solid blade of the rotating shutter masks the movement of the film and then moves on to allow the light to pass. During the visible period, the constant changes of light could easily cause flicker and eyestrain; but this is avoided by rotating a single-bladed shutter several times.

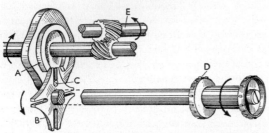

FIG. 2. DIAGRAM OF THE MECHANISM FOR MOVING THE FILM IN A PROJECTOR

At each revolution of the cam A one arm of the Maltese cross B engages the pin C and makes a quarter turn, moving the film on the sprocket D forward one frame. The cam is driven from the driving shaft E which also drives the shutter to move in correct time with the film

The shutter must be precisely placed so that it completely masks the film during movement, as otherwise streaks over the light portions of the picture, known as 'travel ghosts', may be seen. Top streaking or bottom streaking occur if the shutter is too late or too soon in moving.

The film is passed to the sound head. At this point, to prevent any uneven speed which might cause variations of pitch in the sound reproduction, the film is passed over rollers and slides both before and after the sound head. The sound is, in itself, a miniature projector, which sends a beam of light through the sound track, and on to a PHOTOCELL (q.v.). This has the property of changing the light alterations into electrical variations which, after amplification, are reproduced through loud-speakers as sound (see SOUND RECORDING).

Finally the film passes on to a take-up spool, which has a compensating drive to allow for the increase in diameter of the roll as the film is wound on. Films are mounted on spools holding 1,000 ft. (1 reel, running for 11 minutes) or 2,000 ft. Until the universal introduction of safety base film (cellulose acetate) in 1951, this was the maximum permitted by law, but up to 4,000 ft. can now be normally used. The introduction of this safety film has now made unnecessary the safety shutter, fireproof projection boxes, and separate rewinding rooms, all of which used to be compulsory.

Three-dimensional (3D) pictures in the cinema are stereoscopic, the left and right images corresponding to what would be seen by the right and left eye (see STEREOSCOPE). The first experiments were made for use with lantern slides, the left and right images being printed in red and blue-green. Viewing these images through spectacles with blue-green and red eye-pieces results in an impression of a black-and-white picture in relief, the eye with the red spectacle viewing the blue-green image and vice versa.

The POLARIZED LIGHT (q.v.) method produces better results. One image is photographed through a polarizer so that the intercepted light waves all lie in a vertical plane, while the other is photographed through a polarizer which passes the light waves in a horizontal plane. If the images are viewed through spectacles of polarizers passing light in vertical and horizontal planes, each eye will see only one image.

The cine-cameras are usually set up in pairs with distances varying from 2 in. to 11 in. between their lenses. In this way the camera-man can control the depth of field and ensure that near objects appear close to the viewing plane of the screen. As it is generally not practicable to mount cameras as close as 2 in., it is usual to photograph the images through mirrors or prisms (see Fig. 3). The projector screen has a metallic surface in order not to depolarize the light which is reflected.

At present 3D films have to be viewed through polarizer spectacles. There are various suggestions for doing away with the need for spectacles, but there are many serious difficulties to overcome.

See also CINEMATOGRAPHY; SOUND RECORDING; LENS.
See also Vol. IX: CINEMA, HISTORY OF.

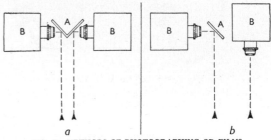

FIG. 3. METHODS OF PHOTOGRAPHING 3D FILMS
a. With two mirrors. *b.* With one mirror
A. Mirror.   B. Camera

Gaumont British News

CUTS FROM A FILM OF ROGER BANNISTER RUNNING THE MILE FOR THE FIRST TIME IN UNDER FOUR MINUTES

CINEMATOGRAPHY. 1. Principle. The cinematograph depends for its illusion of continuous movement on the screen on a property of the eye known as 'persistence of vision'. The retina of the eye retains an image for a small fraction of a second after it has disappeared from view. Thus, if the eye views a succession of still pictures, each showing a slightly later stage in a movement than the previous picture and following each other in sufficiently rapid succession, the illusion of continuous movement results. In the cinema, what the eye really sees is a series of still pictures, each moving object occupying a different position from one picture to the next. For example, if several photographs are taken of a man raising an arm, each showing the arm in the position it occupied when the exposure was made, and the pictures are shown quickly, one after another, an impression of continuous movement results. Furthermore, if the pictures are shown at the rate at which they were taken, the movement will appear to be natural. If the pictures are projected slower or faster than they were taken, the apparent speed of movement can be slowed down or speeded up. That is why, when old silent films designed to be projected at sixteen frames per second are projected on a modern sound projector at twenty-four frames per second, the 'custard pie' comedians and other characters of the era appear to be moving ludicrously fast.

2. History. Scientists began to investigate 'persistence of vision' in relation to the viewing of moving objects early in the 19th century. Then experimenters began to mount pictures of objects in progressive stages of motion on to the edge of a disk. These pictures viewed through corresponding slots revolving on a similar disk produced good results. The pictures used for these experiments were drawings; the next important advance came with the development of photography. This enabled the pictures, made as glass-plate transparencies, to be projected one by one on to the screen, using a ratchet and pawl mechanism (*see* Ratchet).

The final and perhaps the most important advance towards cinematography was made possible by Eastman of the U.S.A., who provided a flexible film of cellulose nitrate base coated with a Photographic Emulsion (q.v.). The value of this was quickly realized, and Cine-cameras (q.v.) using this material were produced almost simultaneously in Great Britain, the U.S.A., and France.

The first camera, made by Friese-Greene, photographed seven or eight pictures per second. The apparatus made by the French Lumière brothers was designed to take pictures at the rate of twenty-six per second, and Friese-Greene made one capable of operating at a rate of fifty per second. Sixteen changes per second, however, being just frequent enough to make the changes unnoticeable, remained the standard rate until the advent of 'sound on film' pictures. Good sound reproduction needs a passage of film at least half as fast again (*see* SOUND RECORDING), and so twenty-four frames (pictures) per second became, and is today, the accepted standard running speed of sound film.

Today, the essentials of any cine-camera or projector are the film transport mechanism, which moves the film forward one 'frame' and holds it stationary for an instant ($\frac{1}{48}$th second) every $\frac{1}{24}$th second; the shutter, which cuts off the light or the exposure whilst the film is moving; and the LENS (q.v.) system, to project the object being photographed on to the film, or to project the image on the film on to the cinema screen. These features are described in further detail in the article CINE-CAMERAS AND PROJECTORS.

See also Vol. IX: CINEMA, HISTORY OF; CINEMATOGRAPHY.

CIRCUIT, ELECTRIC, *see* ELECTRIC CURRENT, Section 2.

CIVIL ENGINEERING. This is concerned with designing and building large-scale structures which are intended to stand for a long time and to be useful to large numbers of people. The part played by civil engineering in opening up and developing new parts of the world has been and is enormous. The life of Canada, for example, has been transformed by the civil engineers who have exploited the river ST. LAWRENCE (q.v. Vol. III), which flows from Lake Ontario, through deep forests, by cataracts and rapids, and then widens out to the Gulf of St. Lawrence. Today, a series of canals, such as the WELLAND CANAL (q.v. Vol. IV), bypasses the cataracts and rapids and links the GREAT LAKES (q.v. Vol. III) and the river into a chain of waterways, over 2,000 miles long. These connect the large cities of Duluth, Chicago, and Detroit in the United States and Toronto, Montreal, and Quebec in Canada with the Atlantic Ocean and the route to Europe. Fine bridges, such as the Victoria Jubilee Bridge at Montreal, $1\frac{1}{4}$ miles long, and the QUEBEC BRIDGE (q.v. Vol. IV), make the mighty river no longer a barrier; and hydro-electric installations convert the force of the water into power for Canada's industries. As remarkable has been the work of civil engineers in the COLORADO DESERT (q.v. Vol. III) in the United States, where the building of the great

BOULDER DAM (q.v.) has harnessed the waters of the Colorado River and turned desert into productive land, as well as producing vast quantities of electric power. To achieve these things the civil engineer must make use of many different branches of knowledge, including SOIL MECHANICS, SURVEYING, HYDROGRAPHY (qq.v.), GEOLOGY (q.v. Vol. III), and ECONOMICS (q.v. Vol. VII).

Civil engineering was not distinguished from other branches of engineering until the last 200 years. Most early engineers worked for armies, building FORTIFICATIONS or making SIEGE weapons (qq.v. Vol. X), such as battering rams and catapults. And they were responsible for building the roads and bridges which were essential for the movement of troops and supplies. The Roman armies of occupation in Europe employed brilliant engineers. Remains of the fine, straight ROMAN ROADS (q.v. Vol. IV) which they drove across England still survive in Watling Street, Fosse Way, and others.

After the collapse of the Roman Empire there was little progress in communications in Europe until the beginning of the INDUSTRIAL REVOLUTION (q.v. Vol. VII), the invention of the steam engine, and the development of the use of iron. Then, in the last half of the 18th century, the number of exceptional men who set to work to construct ROADS, CANALS, RAILWAYS, PORTS AND HARBOURS, and BRIDGES (qq.v. Vol. IV) adopted the name of 'civil' engineer to distinguish themselves from the military engineers, and to stress the value of their work to the whole community. Their work provided a system of transport, especially for goods, which made it possible for Britain to take the lead in the industrial revolution and to become 'the workshop of the world'. They also helped to increase production of food for the growing population by schemes of LAND RECLAMATION (q.v.) and DRAINAGE (q.v. Vol. VI).

The most distinguished of the early civil engineers were James Brindley, the pioneer of canals, John Smeaton, who built the Eddystone lighthouse, and Robert Mylne, the engineer of Blackfriars Bridge in London. The next generation produced John McAdam, who developed MACADAM ROADS (q.v. Vol. IV), Thomas TELFORD (q.v. Vol. V), the engineer for the MENAI SUSPENSION BRIDGE (q.v. Vol. IV) and the Caledonian Canal, and John Rennie, who built the great Plymouth breakwater. They were men of

Canadian Ingersoll Rand Co.

BUILDING A HUGE UNDERGROUND POWER HOUSE AT KEMANO, CANADA, FOR THE KITIMAT HYDRO-ELECTRIC SCHEME (q.v.)

resourcefulness and courage, who faced hardship and sometimes risked their lives to master the great forces of nature. They were not so much scientists as appliers of science.

During the 19th and 20th centuries, as sea communications became vastly more efficient, and world markets were opened up for goods and raw materials, many countries of the world made great strides forward. For schemes of industrial and agricultural development civil engineering was essential, and the experience of British engineers was valued all over the world, particularly in the British Empire. In Canada, for example, the enormous RAILWAY SYSTEMS (q.v. Vol. IV), which run over 3,000 miles across the whole width of the North American continent, are among the greatest engineering achievements in the world. In India, the water control, river transport, and irrigation systems, made possible by such engineering feats as the LLOYD BARRAGE (q.v.), have prevented the loss of many millions of lives through famine and flood. In Egypt, the building of the ASWAN DAM (q.v.), $1\frac{1}{4}$ miles long across the river NILE (q.v. Vol. III), has made it possible to control the waters of this great river and bring increased fertility to the country.

In the course of time engineering has become very much more specialized. MECHANICAL ENGINEERING, ELECTRICAL ENGINEERING, MARINE ENGINEERING (qq.v.), and so on are now separate branches, each with specialists with whom the civil engineer must work in close collaboration. For the generation of HYDRO-ELECTRIC POWER (q.v.), for example, the civil engineer works with the electrical engineer in the design of power stations and in working out the sizes of DAMS (q.v.), pipelines, and tunnels. He collaborates with the architect, the mechanical engineer, and sometimes the chemical engineer in building factories, industrial estates, and oil refineries. Civil engineering contractors with the necessary EARTH-MOVING EQUIPMENT (q.v.) have been largely responsible for the production of opencast coal to supplement supplies from the deep mines (see MINING ENGINEERING). With the tremendous development of air and sea transport the special requirements of AIRPORTS (q.v. Vol. IV) and modern DOCKS AND HARBOURS (q.v.) also have to be studied by the civil engineer (see Colour Plate, opp. p. 80).

In preparing modern large-scale development schemes, such as the TENNESSEE VALLEY AUTHORITY Scheme (q.v.) and, more recently, the Colombo Plan for the development of South-East Asia, the civil engineer is faced with tremendous responsibilities. He must consider the resources and economic needs of a large area, and sometimes of a whole country. He must study soil, climate, crop and animal pests, mineral resources, physical geography, and other conditions on which the development of agriculture, industry, power, and transport will depend. He cannot ignore the character and habits of the inhabitants themselves, and must consider how quickly they can be educated and trained to play their part in a changed economy. He must himself balance all these considerations and recommend general lines of development before any question of design or construction arises.

In Britain, the preparation of a large civil engineering scheme is often entrusted to a consulting engineer; he has his own staff of experts, and with their help he first makes a survey, including an investigation of subsoil and foundations, and prepares plans and provisional estimates of cost. When the general scheme is approved, detailed drawings are prepared, together with a specification and a bill of quantities setting out in detail all the separate operations. The contractor who carries out the project generally works under the supervision of the consulting engineer. Civil engineering projects are also carried out by engineers on the staff of government departments, local authorities, public utilities, and large industrial firms.

CLOCKS AND WATCHES. Any clock or watch must be designed so that its hour-hand makes exactly two complete revolutions in the 24-hour period, and the hand must rotate at as uniform a rate as possible so as to show the correct time at the intermediate hours.

Mechanical timekeepers depend for their regularity upon some form of mechanical motion which recurs at regular intervals, and controls the rate of rotation of the hour-hand on the dial. The first mechanical clocks of the 14th century used for this purpose a very crude device in which a suspended beam or 'foliot balance' was pushed first in one direction of rotation and then in the reverse one by means of a toothed 'crown wheel', which engaged in turn with two projections from the axis of rotation of the beam (Fig. 1). The crown wheel was driven, through gearing, by means of a weight suspended from a rope wound on a drum. The regularity of this motion, which depended on the accurate shaping of the crown wheel's teeth, was much affected

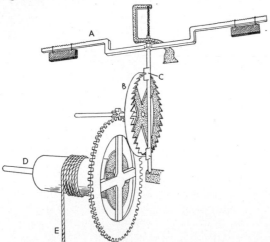

FIG. I. THE FOLIOT BALANCE CONTROLLING THE TIME-KEEPING OF EARLY MECHANICAL CLOCKS, WITH ITS DRIVING MECHANISM

A. Foliot balance. B. Crown wheel. C. Vane. D. Shaft from which dials are geared. E. Rope to which weight is attached

by friction. Consequently, the timekeeping of these early clocks must have been very rough, with errors up to at least 15 minutes per day.

The first known mechanical clock was made in Italy about 1335; the earliest in England which have survived are the Salisbury clock of 1386, still to be seen in Salisbury Cathedral, and the Wells clock of 1392 now in the Science Museum, London—though both were altered in the 17th century to employ a pendulum. Both consist of trains of iron wheels mounted in large iron frames; both have hour-striking mechanisms, and the Wells clock also has quarter-chiming. Large iron clocks of the same type, but gradually growing a little smaller, were installed in churches and clock-towers all over the country in the 15th, 16th, and early 17th centuries.

The first domestic clock, apparently made in Italy in 1364, depended on the same type of mechanism as the tower clocks but was smaller. Fig. 2 shows a 16th-century weight-driven domestic clock which is typical of domestic clocks of the 15th and 16th centuries.

In some of the earliest clocks the hour-numerals were on a disk which rotated past a fixed hand. Some of the public clocks, such as the Wells clock, had elaborate astronomical dials showing the date and also the age and phase of the moon. When a rotating hand was used,

it was an hour-hand only; probably none of these early clocks were accurate enough to make the indications of a minute-hand of any value; many of them, however, were fitted with alarm mechanism.

The first spring-driven or clockwork clocks appeared about the year 1500. Like modern clocks, they were driven by the gradual unwinding of a tightly coiled steel spring, which had to be wound up at regular intervals. Such clocks were usually in the form of a flat drum, to stand on a table, with the dial on the upper surface. The introduction of spring drive raised a new problem for the clockmaker: whereas the pull of a weight remains constant whatever its depth below the drum it drives, the pull of a coiled spring is much greater when fully wound than when almost run down. The foliot balance (replaced by a wheel in portable clocks), which governed the timekeeping of all these early clocks, was sensitive to variations in driving power, so some arrangement to compensate the uneven pull of a spring had to be devised. The first crude attempt to make this adjustment, the 'stackfreed', did so by giving considerable friction

Crown Copyright, Science Museum

FIG. 2. 16TH-CENTURY GERMAN DOMESTIC CLOCK OF IRON
The bell-hammer operates under its own weight

during the spring's fully-wound stages and less friction, with even slight assistance, in its

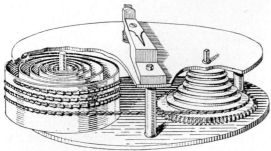

FIG. 3. DIAGRAM OF A FUSEE

The spring is nearly run down and the chain is therefore pulling at the wide end of the fusee

uncoiled position. This was soon superseded by a much better device, called the 'fusee', conceived and sketched by LEONARDO DA VINCI (q.v. Vol. V) in 1490, and first known to have been used in a clock by Jacob Zech (a Czech) in 1525. The fusee consists of a conical drum with a continuous groove cut in it (Fig. 3); the

FIG. 4. BALANCE WHEEL BRASS LANTERN CLOCK BY THOMAS KNIFTON, *c.* 1650

A clock of this type was mounted on a wall bracket with the driving weights hanging freely below

pull of the mainspring inside its drum, or 'barrel', is exerted through a gut cord or chain wound round the grooves of the fusee. When the mainspring is fully wound, the cord or chain is pulling at the narrow end of the fusee, where its leverage is less, while when the mainspring is almost fully run down, the cord or chain pulls at the wide end of the fusee, where it has a much greater leverage. By shaping the fusee to suit the mainspring it can be arranged that the clock works at an almost constant speed for all stages of the spring's winding.

The first true watch—that is, spring clock small enough to be carried about—was made by Peter Hele or Henlein in Nuremberg about 1500. The earliest watches still in existence date from about 1540, and are almost spherical in shape. In the later 16th century, however, watches were usually shaped as flat circular or oval drums.

During the period 1550 to 1650, refinements were made in the construction and cases of clocks and watches. In England the brass-framed 'lantern' clock (Fig. 4) began to replace iron-framed clocks, and brass became common for the plates and cases of spring-driven clocks, and later for wheels. Smaller and less clumsy watches were made. In south Germany there appeared handsome spring-driven clocks of upright form, some with elaborate astronomical dials showing the moon's age and phase, the position of the sun in the zodiac, and the times of sunrise and sunset.

The Italian scientist GALILEO (q.v. Vol. V) had noticed in 1582 that the time of swing of a pendulum was almost independent of its arc of swing, and this observation led him, about 1641, to design an apparatus linking a pendulum with clockwork, but it is uncertain whether he actually constructed it. In 1658 Christiaan Huygens, the Dutch mathematician and scientist, worked out in detail the mathematics of the pendulum and designed a clock controlled by a pendulum: Salomon Coster of The Hague made clocks to this design, examples of which still exist. Huygens showed that a pendulum took exactly the same time to swing all small arcs which vary by only a degree or two, but slightly longer to swing larger arcs. A pendulum swinging freely in a vacuum would be an almost ideal timekeeper, but in practice, owing mainly to air friction, the arc of swing slowly decreases, and some means has to be found of keeping it swinging continuously. There also has to be some kind of link between the swinging pendulum and a clock

BUILDING A RUNWAY ON AN AIRFIELD IN BEDFORDSHIRE

Concrete is being laid on the prepared foundation. It is mixed and deposited by 'pavers', which are followed by a 'spreader' and two 'finishers'

dial. The 'escapement mechanism' both supplies this link and also gives impulses to the pendulum to keep it swinging. A typical escapement consists of a toothed wheel, driven through gearing by a weight or spring, which in its turn drives alternately two 'pallets', connected by a lever mechanism with the pendulum (Fig. 5). The pendulum then receives impulses every swing by way of this lever system, and at the same time allows the toothed wheel to 'escape' through the space of one tooth for each double swing. The rate of rotation of the escape wheel is thus controlled by the pendulum, as also are the hands of the clock which are geared to the escape wheel. A pendulum 39 inches long makes one half-swing in exactly one second, and if its escape wheel has thirty teeth, this wheel will thus make one revolution per minute. It can thus carry a second-hand, and the minute-hand and hour-hand must be geared down still further by 60 to 1 and a further 12 to 1.

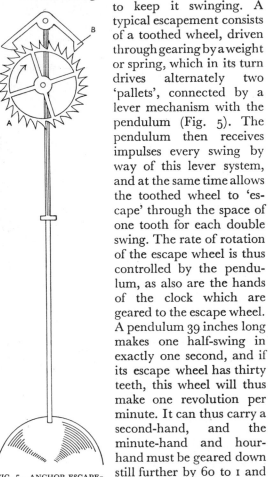

FIG. 5. ANCHOR ESCAPE-MENT FOR PENDULUM CLOCKS

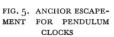

A. Escape wheel. B. Pallet

Huygens used the type of escapement known in his time, but improved escapements followed soon afterwards. A good escapement should give the pendulum an impulse near the centre of its swing, and as little interference as possible elsewhere.

The invention of the pendulum greatly improved the timekeeping of clocks, and pendulum clocks, with both hour- and minute-hands, were soon made in considerable numbers. 'Grandfather' clocks and the so-called 'bracket' clocks for standing on a table or wall-bracket were very popular. In the hands of the great English clock-makers of 1670 to 1750, such as Thomas Tompion, they reached a high pitch of excellence in both mechanical design and artistic appearance.

Meanwhile, another important invention had been made. Hooke, the inventor of the 'anchor' escapement, had attempted to control the time of swing of a watch's balance-wheel by means of a spring. In 1675 Huygens described a watch in which the balance was controlled by a spiral spring of a now familiar type. The English makers, led by Tompion, immediately took up the invention. The time of oscillation of a pivoted balance-wheel controlled in this way by a spring is, like that of a swinging pendulum, almost independent of the arc of swing so that by linking it with a watch mechanism a good timekeeper is obtained. Again the link is an escapement, though of a different type from that used in clocks.

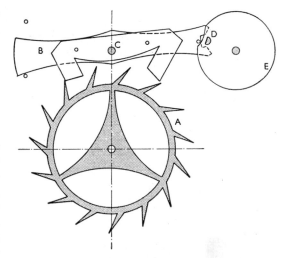

FIG. 6. ENGLISH LEVER ESCAPEMENT FOR BALANCE-WHEEL TIMEKEEPERS

The escape wheel A drives the lever B, pivoted at C, which in turn imparts impulses to the jewelled pin D mounted on the wheel E which is on the same axle as with the balance-wheel

About 1725 Graham perfected a cylinder escapement for watches; but Mudge's lever escapement (Fig. 6), invented about 1755, though not widely adopted until the 19th century, is now almost universally used in pocket watches.

Watches made before the invention of the balance-spring usually had hour-hands only, but afterwards they were usually fitted with minute-hands as well.

Changes of temperature considerably affect the rate of clocks and watches. A pendulum clock with a steel rod loses $2\frac{1}{2}$ seconds per day for a rise of temperature of 10° F., owing to the expansion of the rod, while a watch with a brass balance-wheel and steel balance-spring loses as much as 60 seconds per day, most of this effect being due to the change in stiffness of the balance-spring. As the effect is relatively small for pendulum clocks, domestic pendulum clocks are not usually provided with any kind of temperature compensation, but good-quality portable clocks and watches require compensation. The methods used were originally devised for marine CHRONO-METERS (q.v. Vol. IV), and later applied to watches.

John Harrison, a pioneer in inventing compensating devices for both pendulum clocks and chronometers, invented, about 1726, a 'gridiron' pendulum of alternating brass and steel rods which kept the effective length of the pendulum unchanged with changes in temperature. Later makers have used a combination of zinc and steel in place of Harrison's brass-and-steel gridiron. Another compensating device, which has been much used, is to make the effective size of the balance-wheel vary with temperature. A balance-wheel is made with a rim consisting of two semicircular bimetallic strips of brass and steel, the brass on the outside, one end of each strip being fixed, while the other, carrying a small weight, is free to move. As temperature rises, the brass expands more than the steel, and so the free end of the strip curves inwards, making the balance effectively smaller. The smaller balance would vibrate more quickly if the balance-spring retained its stiffness, but, as we said before, the stiffness of the spring decreases as the temperature rises, and the two effects can be arranged almost to cancel out, leaving only a small residual effect. In 1920 Guillaume in Paris succeeded in making an alloy, called 'invar', whose stiffness was almost unchanged with change of temperature; and now the balance-springs of many chronometers and also pocket watches are made of this or of a similar alloy.

All early clocks and watches had separate keys for winding. The first keyless mechanism was invented just before 1800, and a type devised in Switzerland just before 1850 was found so convenient that by 1900 it was almost universally used. Today, watches are sometimes fitted with a self-winding device, in which a small pendulum, which swings with every movement of the wrist, is used to wind the driving spring.

A clock can also be fitted with an alarm mechanism. A simple form of this employs a bell-hammer driven by a separate spring, which is set off by an adjustable cam, or projection, attached to the hour-hand shaft.

See also TIMEKEEPERS, ANCIENT; TIMEKEEPERS, MODERN.

CLUTCHES. A clutch is a mechanism for engaging and disengaging the drive from one part of a machine to another. The best-known example is probably the clutch in a MOTOR-CAR (q.v. Vol. IV) which engages and disengages the engine from the drive so that either can continue to rotate independently of the other. If it were not for the clutch, every time the car had to stop in traffic the engine would stall because it would have to stop too. Many types of moving machinery as well as cars need some kind of clutch to disengage the drive, or one moving part from another.

The simplest type of clutch is the 'dog clutch', in which a sliding part attached to one shaft and carrying two or more projecting lugs or 'dogs' may be made to engage with corresponding slots in a second part attached to the end of the other shaft. This gives a positive, or solid, drive with no possibility of slipping, so the driven shaft starts with a jerk, which is a disadvantage, for example, for a motor-car.

The 'friction clutch' overcomes this by allowing a certain amount of slipping to take place, so that the drive may be taken up smoothly. Friction clutches may be of cone or plate type; Fig. 1 shows a simple cone clutch. The part B slides on its shaft and, by means of a forked lever engaging with the groove C, may be pressed into contact with the corresponding part A on the driving shaft. The friction between the two at the conical surface transmits the drive from one shaft to the other.

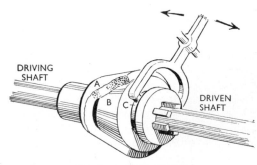

DRIVING SHAFT

DRIVEN SHAFT

FIG. I. FRICTION CLUTCH

A. Cone on driving shaft cut away to show how cone B presses against it. C. Groove in which operating lever engages

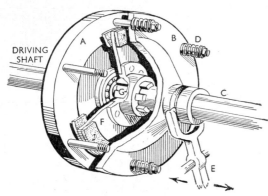

FIG. 2. SINGLE-PLATE CLUTCH
A. Disk on driving shaft. B. Plate. C. Driven shaft. D. Studs.
E. Operating lever. F. Clutch plate. G. Hub

Most road vehicles use a plate clutch, which may be of either the single- or multi-plate type. In Fig. 2, a simplified diagram of a single-plate clutch, the driving shaft carries a disk fitted with a number of studs, each carrying a spring which compresses the plate B on to the clutch plate F. This drives the shaft C through a hub G sliding on splines (grooves cut in the shaft). The clutch plate is faced with brake-lining material to withstand the rubbing, and is free to slide along its shaft. By operating a system of links connected to the clutch pedal the driver can remove the pressure from plate B, and thus cause the clutch to slip. By letting in the pedal gradually, he makes use of this to avoid taking up the drive jerkily. Multi-plate clutches are similar except that there are a number of flat metal plates alternating with plates carrying cork or brake-lining material. Since there are more surfaces in contact, the diameter of the clutch may be made smaller.

The magnetic clutch is another type of friction clutch in which the necessary pressure between the plates is obtained not by springs, but by means of an electromagnetic coil carried in one plate and supplied with current through two slip-rings (see MAGNETS). This attracts the other plate, which consists of a steel ring carried on a flexible steel disk on the other shaft.

Centrifugal clutches are used to allow an engine or motor to run up to speed before taking full load. One form is somewhat like the drum brake used on motor-cars (see BRAKES); the driving shaft carries a disk—with two brake shoes pivoted to it and held clear of the inside surface of the brake drum by springs. When the speed

rises sufficiently the stiffness of the springs is not strong enough to keep the shoes clear of the drum; so they bear against the drum, transmitting the drive to the load.

Another type of clutch sometimes used in vehicles is the hydraulic coupling (Fig. 3). It consists of a rotating part called an 'impeller', consisting of curved passages, somewhat similar to the impeller of a centrifugal pump (see PUMPS), which is driven by the engine. It is enclosed in a circular casing attached to the driven shaft, also consisting of curved passages, and is filled with oil. The impeller acts as a pump, driving the oil round inside the casing, which then acts as a turbine delivering power to the output shaft. Slipping takes place during starting, as for a friction clutch, but the hydraulic coupling is smoother and there are no rubbing surfaces to wear. However, as the driven shaft never reaches the same speed as the driving shaft, there is always some loss of power.

See also Vol. IV: MOTOR-CAR.

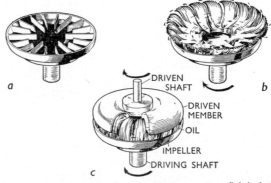

Daimler Ltd.

FIG. 3. PRINCIPLE OF HYDRAULIC COUPLING
a. Impeller with radial vanes. This is filled with oil. b. When the impeller is rotated the oil is driven to the outer side of the vanes. c. The oil is forced against the vanes of the driven member and so rotates it

COAL-CUTTER, *see* MINING MACHINERY.

COFFERDAM. This is a temporary DAM (q.v.) enclosing an area, such as a river bed, which is normally covered by water. The area is sealed off by the cofferdam, as by a wall, and the water is drained away from inside it so that building work can be carried on 'in the dry'. Cofferdams are mainly used in building bridge-piers, dams, barrages and weirs, wet and dry docks and locks, and water channels for power stations and industrial plants.

The cofferdam itself and the underlying soil

strata must be stable enough to prevent the pressure of water from bursting through or heaving up the exposed ground. It is usually not possible to make cofferdams completely watertight at a reasonable cost, and the aim is simply to cut down the inflow of water to the working area to manageable proportions; the water which does get in is led to sumps, clear of the permanent work, and pumped out continuously.

The most common type of cofferdam used in building bridge-piers consists of a rectangular box of sheet-piles. These are vertical steel plates sunk into the earth, the opposite walls of which are held apart, against the pressure of the water from without, by timber or steel struts (Fig. 1).

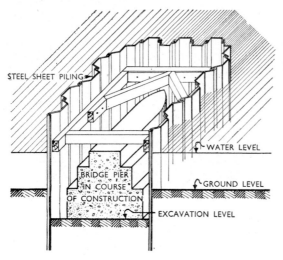

STEEL SHEET PILING
WATER LEVEL
BRIDGE PIER IN COURSE OF CONSTRUCTION
GROUND LEVEL
EXCAVATION LEVEL

FIG. 1. SECTIONAL VIEW OF A BRIDGE PIER COFFERDAM

Sheet-piles are usually made of rolled steel, in sections about 16 inches wide, which interlock with each other; but they may be of timber or reinforced concrete. These piles or sheets are driven into the ground through the water to form a continuous wall surrounding the working area, and rising above the water-level. In a river where the water, on occasions, rises to a considerable height, it may be too expensive to build the wall high enough for security, and it may be decided to risk the cofferdam being overtopped and the works temporarily flooded. In designing temporary structures of this kind, where economy is of first importance, a smaller margin of safety than that applied to permanent works may be accepted. As soon as the cofferdam is in place, the water inside is pumped out, and the building **work can begin.**

Where the area to be enclosed is very large, an embankment of earth or rock, tipped into the water from barges, may be built round the area; the embankment is made watertight by driving sheet-piles along its centre line. This method was used in the construction of the Captain Cook Graving Dock at Sydney during the Second World War.

See also BRIDGE BUILDING; DAMS; DOCKS AND HARBOUR CONSTRUCTION.

COKE OVEN. This is used for making coke as fuel for BLAST FURNACES (q.v.). Such 'metallurgical coke' has to be very hard and porous, unlike the soft, gassy coke which is a by-product of GAS MANUFACTURE (q.v.). Coke from coke ovens is a main product and is made from carefully selected coal.

All coke making consists of baking fine coal in airtight ovens, so that the volatile substances in the coal—that is, the parts that are not carbon or ash—turn to gas and are driven off, much as sap and water are driven out of green sticks if they are left in an ordinary oven. The difference between the coal and the green sticks is that the coal is coked at such a high temperature that it would burn away altogether if any air were allowed into the oven, since air contributes to COMBUSTION (q.v.).

Coke ovens are made of silica bricks (see FIRE-CLAYS AND REFRACTORIES). They are built in groups or 'batteries', the ovens being ranged like a row of tall, thin books on a shelf (Fig. 1), and each separated from its neighbours by flues in which gas is burnt to heat the walls of the ovens. Each end of the oven is made to open, like a door, and in the roof are a number of round holes covered with airtight lids.

An oven usually holds about 15 tons of coal, which is fed in through the holes in the roof by a charging machine. All doors and lids are closed, and the coal remains in the oven for about 18 hours, while gas is burned in the flues on either side. During this time the volatile substances in the coal are turned into gas by the great heat and pumped through pipes, some to be used to heat the coke ovens themselves and the rest to be turned into some useful form in a By-PRODUCTS plant (q.v. Vol. VII). In the end there remains in the oven a mass of white-hot coke, weighing about two-thirds as much as the original quantity of coal.

The doors at both ends of the oven are then

B.I.S.R.A.

FIG. I. CLEANING OUT ONE OF A BATTERY OF COKE OVENS

opened by machines, one of which carries a ram, which is driven forward into the oven to push all the coke out through the far door. Here the coke falls into a steel wagon on rails—the steel is specially made to stand great heat—which takes the coke to a cooling plant. This is a brick or concrete archway in which hundreds of sprays of water are directed on to the coke, using about a ton of water for every ton of coke. The coke is then either stored directly or is spread out on a sloping brick bank to finish cooling before being loaded into wagons for transport to store.

The process is continuous. Each oven is filled immediately after it is emptied, and the charging and ramming machines work round the 24 hours of each day on a fixed schedule. Batteries are often built as units of fifty-four ovens, which gives the operators one oven to deal with every 20 minutes through the 24 hours, and provides an output of about 800 tons of coke a day—the amount which a modern blast furnace might well consume.

Coke for blast furnaces must be strong enough to hold up against the weight of materials in the furnace and porous enough to allow the air and gas in the furnace an easy passage. The quality of the coke can be tested in several ways. In the 'shatter' test, 50 lb. of coke (in lumps of not less than 2 inches) is dropped 6 feet four times on to a steel plate, and the extent to which the coke has broken up is recorded. In the 'abrasion' test, coke is tumbled in a revolving drum.

See also BLAST FURNACE; GAS MANUFACTURE.

COLOUR PHOTOGRAPHY, *see* CINE-CAMERAS AND PROJECTORS. *See also* Vol. VII: PHOTOGRAPHY, HISTORY OF.

COMBUSTION. It was generally believed up to the middle of the 17th century that there were four elements, earth, air, fire, and water (*see* CHEMISTRY, HISTORY OF, Vol. VII). The fact that certain things would burn and other things would not made it appear that only the combustibles contained the element of fire. Fire itself was a mystery.

In the 17th century the scientists BOYLE (q.v. Vol. V) and Hooke showed that combustibles, such as sulphur or charcoal, would not burn except in the presence of air, and a little later it was shown that if a combustible substance was burnt in a vessel containing air, only part of the air was consumed. It was another century before Scheele and PRIESTLEY (q.v. Vol. V) independently discovered that air was composed mainly of two gases (now called oxygen and nitrogen) and that the oxygen was consumed when things were burnt in air. During the 18th century, the idea that fire was a mysterious element lingered on. It was thought that combustible substances contained something (called 'phlogiston') which the combustible lost when burnt. In 1785, however, the French chemist LAVOISIER (q.v. Vol. V) showed that when ordinary things burn, they merely combine with the oxygen in the air, giving out heat as they do so, which raises the temperature of the products of the combustion so high that they may become red or white hot. This to a great extent removed the mystery of fire.

To start a substance burning, two things are needed: a supply of oxygen (usually in the air) and sufficient heat to set the chemical reaction off. All ordinary FUELS (q.v.) begin to vaporize, or give off gases, some time before they become hot enough to burn, and so in practice it is usually the gases given off by substances that burn. If a lighted match is held an inch or so below a spill of paper, the gases can be seen coming off before the paper lights. And jets of burning gas can be often seen spurting from a lump of coal. Flame is simply a region of hot gas in which some of the particles, usually white-hot carbon particles, emit light.

Most fuels—such as coal, petrol, paraffin, or coal gas—are composed principally of carbon (C) and hydrogen (H). In combustion, the carbon combines with the oxygen (O) of the air to give carbon dioxide (CO_2), and the hydrogen to give water (H_2O). If we hold a cold kettle over a gas flame we may see droplets of water condensing on it; this is the 'ash' of the gas flame which normally goes into the air as steam.

When all the constituents of a fuel have completely combined with oxygen, so that everything that can burn has burnt, combustion is said to be 'complete'. If there is a shortage of air (that is, of oxygen), and the chemical reactions are not completed, the combustion is incomplete, and the unburnt gases are lost up the chimney or in the exhaust. There is always some carbon monoxide (CO) (which could be burnt to carbon dioxide (CO_2)) in the exhaust gases from a petrol engine.

An efficient BOILER (q.v.) must be designed to burn the fuel completely. In some designs, air is blown in above the fire as well as under it to ensure sufficient oxygen. The chimney gases from boiler furnaces are often analysed with an instrument called a CO_2 recorder to check on the efficiency of the combustion.

Unlike solids, gases and vapours can be mixed with air, and if the mixture is more or less correct they will burn without any outside oxygen to keep them going. The explosive burning of the mixture of petrol vapour and air in a petrol-engine cylinder is an example. The acetylene torch used by a welder burns a mixture of oxygen and acetylene, and the flame is so hot that it can be used for cutting steel plates even under water.

The ordinary burner of a gas stove uses a mixture of gas and air, the air being drawn in by the jet of gas, and the mixture is released at the end of a tube or through small holes too fast for the flame to spread back to the inside of the burner. This principle was first used by the German chemist Bunsen, who has given his name to the Bunsen burner. If the flame of many gas burners is gently turned down, there comes a point when the flame may spread to the inside of the burner —in fact the burner 'lights back'. Unlike an aerated Bunsen flame, a candle flame is maintained by the air around diffusing into the vapour which distils from the wick.

A gas-air mixture will burn in a closed space only if the proportions of the mixture are right—neither too much air for the gas nor too much gas for the air. That is why a motor-car engine will not 'fire' if the mixture is either too rich or too weak. An ordinary flame burns only in that region where the mixture of fuel vapour and air is within the limits of combustion. This means that a jet of oxygen will burn in a hydrogen atmosphere in just the same way that a jet of hydrogen will burn in an oxygen atmosphere. Davy was the first to appreciate the importance of the limits of combustion when he invented the SAFETY LAMP (q.v.) to avoid explosions of 'firedamp' in coal-mines.

Oxygen is not essential to all forms of combustion, although in practice it is always used. Hydrogen, for instance, will burn in chlorine or chlorine in hydrogen. Some substances can even burn in themselves, the heat set free in their decomposition maintaining the burning. A flame of acetylene, for example, burning in itself (and liberating much soot) can be so maintained.

The oxygen can be within the combustible itself, either mixed in it or as part of its actual structure. Gunpowder and matches are examples of the mixed type: with gunpowder the combustibles, sulphur and charcoal, are mixed with nitre which provides the oxygen. When a match is struck, the friction generates enough heat to ignite the mixture which, when once ignited, continues to burn. With guncotton the oxygen comes from within the nitro-cellulose molecules of which the guncotton is made (*see* EXPLOSIVES).

See also FUELS; HEAT ENGINES.

COMPRESSOR. The most important way in which gases differ from liquids and solids is that they can easily be compressed, or squeezed to occupy a smaller volume (*see* GASES, PROPERTIES OF). A machine for doing this is known as a compressor, of which the ordinary bicycle pump is the simplest example. There are two main classes of compressor—reciprocating and rotary.

Reciprocating compressors are the type used in the LIQUEFACTION OF GASES (q.v.), and also to provide a source of power for the familiar pneumatic road drill. They can compress a gas up to 30,000 lb. per square inch and more (*see* PRESSURE,

Vol. III), but they are not suitable for handling large volumes of air at pressures below 50 lb. per square inch.

The reciprocating compressor (**Fig. 1**) consists essentially of a cylinder (c), piston (P), connecting rod (R), and crankshaft (cs) arranged much the same as in an INTERNAL COMBUSTION ENGINE (q.v.). Except at very high pressures, the valves in compressors are not worked mechanically, but are simply thin metal flaps opened and closed by the air itself. As the piston travels downward, it sucks open the inlet valve (v_1), and gas is drawn into the cylinder. On the return stroke the gas in the cylinder is forced out through the delivery valve (v_2), while the pressure in the cylinder holds the inlet valve closed.

The delivery pipe is smaller than the inlet pipe because the gas, being at a higher pressure, occupies a smaller volume. As gas gets hot when compressed, high-pressure compressors must be cooled, either by blowing air or by circulating cooling water in a jacket round the cylinder. A common arrangement is a two-cylinder compressor in which the gas delivered by the first cylinder is cooled before being passed to the second cylinder and further compressed. The

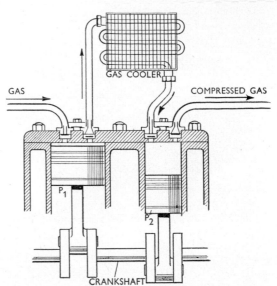

FIG. 2. DIAGRAM OF A TWO-CYLINDER COMPRESSOR
P_1. Piston of first cylinder. P_2. Piston of second cylinder

gas takes up less room after it has been compressed by the first cylinder and so the second cylinder need not be so large (**Fig. 2**).

The two most important types of rotary compressor are the blade type, and the 'positive displacement' type. Until recently, blade-type compressors—of which the ordinary ventilating fan is a simple example—were used only for very low pressures, but now the compressors incorporated into the modern GAS TURBINE (q.v.) can compress air up to 50 lb. per square inch and more. Blade compressors—both ventilating fans (**Fig. 3a**) and compressors for gas turbines (**Fig. 4**)—work on either the radial or axial flow principle; in each case the blades are surrounded by a casing in which the compressed air is collected.

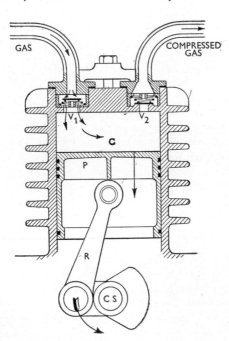

FIG. 1. DIAGRAM OF A RECIPROCATING COMPRESSOR

The piston P is shown on the downward stroke with the inlet valve v_1 open. c. Cylinder. R. Connecting rod. cs. Crankshaft driving piston

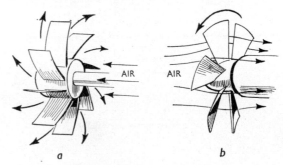

FIG. 3. BLADE COMPRESSORS
a. Radial-flow fan. *b*. Axial-flow fan

De Havilland

National Coal Board

FIG. 4. LEFT: RADIAL-FLOW AIR COMPRESSOR OF THE 'GHOST' TURBOJET
The compressor is joined by the main shaft to the turbine wheel which drives it, seen in the background
RIGHT: 90-INCH DIAMETER TWO-STAGE AXIAL-FLOW FAN FOR MINE VENTILATION

With radial-flow compressors the air enters at the centre of the whirling blades and is flung outwards. For higher efficiencies and pressures, however, axial-flow compressors are used (Fig. 3*b*). These work on the same principle as propellers —the blading 'screws' the air up to the required pressure, and the air travels through the blades from end to end. They can handle much larger quantities of air for a given overall size of machine, but they must run at high speed and must, therefore, be very carefully manufactured and balanced. The ordinary household electric fan is a simple form of axial-flow compressor.

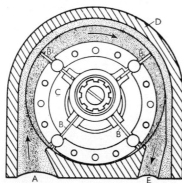

Shorrocks Superchargers Ltd.

FIG. 5. DIAGRAM OF POSITIVE DISPLACEMENT ROTARY COMPRESSOR USED FOR SUPERCHARGING MOTOR-CAR ENGINES
A. Inlet port. B. Vanes. C. Rotor. D. Casing. E. Outlet port

Positive displacement rotary compressors are so called because, as in a reciprocating compressor, the air is pushed through the machine mechanically. A type which is designed for supercharging internal combustion engines consists of a barrel-shaped casing, inside which a rotor with four vanes is mounted out of the centre with the barrel (Fig. 5). Air enters at A, is trapped by the vanes B as the rotor (C) rotates, and is compressed as the space between the rotor and casing (D) diminishes. The compressed air is delivered at the outlet port (E).

See also GASES, PROPERTIES OF; GAS TURBINE.
See also Vol. III: PRESSURE.

CONCRETE CONSTRUCTION. 1.
Concrete is a rock-like material produced by adding water to a mixture of powdered CEMENT (q.v. Vol. VII), sand, and stones. Water causes chemical reactions to take place in the cement, and as a result the paste of cement and water sets hard and grips firmly the sand and stones embedded in it, forming a strong, dense mass. Concrete has been used as a building material for centuries: the Romans, for example, used 'natural cement' for building domes and other works, some of which still exist. In the 18th century the English engineer, John Smeaton, used 'natural cement' for building the Eddystone lighthouse. In the early 19th century artificial Portland cement was invented, and this is now the material most commonly used in making concrete for buildings.

The cheapness, durability, and great strength of concrete, especially when reinforced, and its high resistance to weather, fire, water, and corrosion, make it a particularly suitable material for ROAD BUILDING, BRIDGE BUILDING, and DAMS (qq.v.), for the foundations, framework, floors, and roofs of large buildings of all kinds (*see* BUILDING, PRINCIPLES OF), and for structures in collieries and industrial plants where a steel structure would be corroded by the atmosphere. Unlike steelwork, concrete does not need to be painted to preserve it.

2. STRENGTH OF CONCRETE. This depends on the quality of the stones and sand (called the 'aggregates') in the mixture, the amount of cement used, the ratio of water to cement, and on the age of the concrete.

The aggregates are carefully selected and should contain no impurities which might interfere with the setting of the cement. The stones, or 'coarse aggregate', must be clean so that there is nothing to prevent the cement paste sticking to their surface. Only the strongest stones are used, such as gravels, crushed granite, basalt, and the harder types of limestone and sandstone. The stones must be well graded, usually varying in size from $\frac{3}{4}$ inch to $\frac{3}{16}$ inch (in some dams stones up to 6 inches have been used); the particles of sand vary from $\frac{3}{16}$ inch to dust. To make the concrete compact, the spaces between the stones must be filled with sand: as the volume of the air spaces between the pieces of stone in a heap is a little less than half the volume of the stones, the ratio of sand to stone should be about 1 to 2. The spaces within this mixture of stone and sand must be filled by the paste of water and cement (Fig. 1).

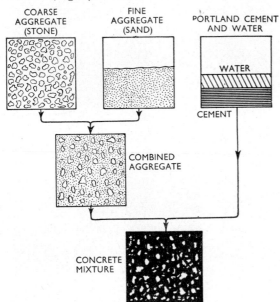

COARSE AGGREGATE (STONE)

FINE AGGREGATE (SAND)

PORTLAND CEMENT AND WATER

WATER

CEMENT

COMBINED AGGREGATE

CONCRETE MIXTURE

FIG. 1. DIAGRAM OF THE COMPOSITION OF CONCRETE

The amount of cement used in the mixture depends on the use to which the concrete is to be put—in general, the greater the strength and durability needed, the greater the proportion of cement. The mixture used for most buildings is 1 part by volume of cement, 2 of sand, and 4 of stones (expressed by the ratio 1:2:4). For large mass concrete foundations the mixture is generally 1:3:6; for structures containing liquids it is 1:1$\frac{2}{3}$:3$\frac{1}{3}$; and for very strong columns and large span bridges it may be as rich as 1:1:2.

In general, the smaller the quantity of water used in a particular mixture, the stronger is the concrete. Too little water, however, prevents the cement from setting or makes it difficult to mix the ingredients properly or to work the concrete into position; too much water allows the larger stones to sink to the bottom of the mixture. An average proportion is a little under 6 Imperial gallons of water to 1 cwt. of cement.

Four weeks after being mixed, ordinary 1:2:4 concrete, with a water to cement ratio of 7 to 10, would need a pressure of about 3,000 lb. per square inch to break it; this is called its 'crushing strength'. During the first year its crushing strength gradually increases until it may reach about 4,000 lb. per square inch. If the aggregate is carefully selected and mixed, and the concrete specially treated, it can reach a crushing strength of more than 10,000 lb. per square inch after 4 weeks. The 'tensile strength' of concrete, that is, its ability to withstand forces pulling it apart, is only about $\frac{1}{10}$th of its crushing strength.

3. REINFORCED CONCRETE. This is a concrete beam or other member, the tensile strength of which has been increased by embedding steel bars in it. A beam supporting a load bends slightly (Fig. 2), the upper edge being compressed and the lower edge stretched (*see* STRESS AND STRAIN). A beam of concrete only, carrying a sufficiently great load, would crack on the bottom edge because it lacks tensile strength; the cracks would spread upwards until the beam broke. Steel bars, however, embedded in the beam near its bottom edge would resist the tensile forces. Reinforced concrete, therefore, has the crushing strength of concrete together with the tensile strength of steel.

Reinforced concrete, first used in France about 100 years ago, is now one of the commonest building materials. As the steel bars enable beams to span large distances and to carry great loads, it is much used for the framework and

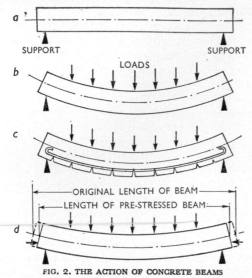

FIG. 2. THE ACTION OF CONCRETE BEAMS

a. Beam before being loaded. *b*. Loaded beam. The upper edge is compressed (contracted) and the lower edge tensile (stretched). *c*. Reinforced concrete beam. The lower edge cracks owing to excessive tensile stress in concrete; steel bars resist tension. *d*. Pre-stressed concrete beam. The pre-stress forces on the beam make all stresses compressive

roofs of large buildings, for bridges, and for large storage bunkers and silos. Huge bunkers, holding 2,000 tons or more of coal, have been built with reinforced concrete, and many power-houses and factories have reinforced concrete chimneys over 300 feet high. A reinforced concrete structure, however, is much heavier than one of steel, and consequently it cannot be used for such very large spans—as, for example, in bridge building. A reinforced concrete bridge in Sweden has a span as great as 866 feet, however, and the bridge at Berwick-on-Tweed and the roof of the Empire Swimming Pool at Wembley have spans of 361 feet and 236 feet respectively. The highest reinforced concrete building in the world, in Brazil, is 500 feet.

Very thin slabs or shells of reinforced concrete, only about 3 inches thick, are used for building domes and vaults—a process known as 'shell construction'. This provides a much lighter roof than one of ordinary reinforced concrete, and the slabs are curved in special shapes to give the greatest strength.

4. PRE-STRESSED CONCRETE. Within the last 20 years new methods of concrete construction, called 'pre-stressed concrete', have been introduced. In one method, a concrete beam is cast with one or more small holes running throughout its length near the bottom edge. When the

concrete has hardened, a cable of high tensile steel wires is threaded through each hole and secured to the concrete at one end. A strong hydraulic jack is attached to the other end of the cable which is then tightly stretched, the jack at the same time compressing the concrete beam by pushing hard against it. When fully stretched the wires are wedged in position, and the jack removed. The tightly stretched steel wires maintain the compression in the concrete which counteracts the tensile forces which tend to pull apart the lower side of the beam when a load is applied (Fig. 2). Sometimes a bar of special steel is used instead of the wires.

Another method of pre-stressing concrete is to pass the tightly stretched wires through the mould before the beam is cast. When the concrete has hardened, the stretching devices are released, and the wires, which are embedded in the concrete, compress the concrete by trying to contract to their original length.

The wires or bars in pre-stressed concrete have a much higher tensile strength than ordinary steel reinforcing bars; consequently less steel is

REINFORCED CONCRETE WATER-TOWER
The tank on the top of the tower contains 300,000 gallons of water

REINFORCED CONCRETE ROOF OF SHELL CONSTRUCTION
The curved vaults between the ribs are only about 3 inches thick

needed, and a beam of high strength concrete can be much smaller, and therefore lighter, than a reinforced concrete beam, and still carry the same load. The compression in the concrete prevents small cracks occurring in the lower surface of a beam, which in an ordinary heavily loaded reinforced concrete beam sometimes occur, letting in water which may rust the steel and seriously damage the structure. There are pre-stressed concrete bridges with spans of 300 feet in France, and a bridge at Shrewsbury as well as roofs of hangars at London Airport have spans of 150 feet. Many other things such as railway sleepers and slabs for floors and roofs can be made cheaply with pre-stressed concrete.

5. CONCRETE CONSTRUCTION. Concrete is usually mixed in machines in a rotating drum. Small mixing machines, turned by hand or driven by a motor, can produce up to $\frac{1}{2}$ cubic yard of concrete at a time, while the largest power-driven machines can produce as much as 250 cubic yards in a working day. Sometimes the mixing machine is installed in a 'batching plant' —a steel tower consisting of large metal bins

filled with aggregates and cement and devices for automatically measuring and feeding into the mixer the exact quantities of each material.

When building a concrete structure, temporary timber or steel moulds, called the 'shuttering' or 'formwork', are first erected on the site in the position the concrete will occupy (*see* BUILDING CONSTRUCTION). If the concrete is to be reinforced, the steel bars are then placed in the shuttering. The freshly mixed concrete is placed into the shuttering round the bars, and consolidated either by hand rammers, by inserting a mechanical vibrating tool in the wet concrete, or by vibrating the mould itself. When the concrete has hardened, the shuttering is removed. During the period of hardening the concrete must be kept damp to prevent its drying out too quickly and cracking. The setting of the cement is a chemical process which gives off heat; if the heat cannot escape it may cause uneven expansion in the concrete leading to cracking. In large concrete structures overheating of this kind is prevented either by embedding pipes in the concrete and circulating cold water through them

REINFORCED CONCRETE CONSTRUCTION

Steel reinforcement bars are fixed in position in the wooden shuttering which is partly filled with newly mixed concrete. The man on the left is immersing the mechanical vibrator into the concrete to compact it

(*see* BOULDER DAM), or by laying the concrete in sections with spaces between to be filled in later. Sometimes special cements that do not generate too much heat are used.

The reinforced concrete frames of small buildings, the walls of houses, small bridges, and such things as lamp-posts and fence-posts are generally 'precast' (*see* PREFABRICATION). Moulds of the right size and shape are prepared on the floor of a factory or some other suitable place; the steel bars are placed in the mould, and the freshly mixed concrete is rammed round them. When the concrete has hardened, it is removed from the mould ready to be fixed in position wherever it is needed. Concrete building blocks, paving stones, and some other products which do not need steel reinforcement are generally mass-produced by machines which can turn out many hundreds an hour. Concrete pipes, sometimes as much as 6 feet or more in diameter, are often made in a cylindrical mould mounted in a machine which rotates so rapidly that the con-

crete is flung violently against the sides of the mould to form the dense hard wall of the pipe; this is called 'spun-concrete'.

See also BUILDING, PRINCIPLES OF; BUILDING CONSTRUCTION; STRUCTURAL STEELWORK.

See also Vol. VII: CEMENT.

CONDENSER, ELECTRIC. This is a device for storing small quantities of electricity. The simplest and oldest kind of electric condenser, the Leyden jar (Fig. 1), invented by van Muschenbroek in 1746, consists of a glass jar of about 1 pint size, with coatings of tin-foil glued to its outer and inner surfaces. The inner coating, which must not touch the outer one, is joined through a short piece of chain to a central metal rod fixed in a cork in the neck of the jar.

Fig. 2 shows how the Leyden jar, or any other kind of condenser, is used to store electricity. The outer tin-foil coating is joined to one end of a high-voltage battery by a wire or some other electrical conductor; the inner coating is joined to the other end by a wire which passes through an ammeter, an instrument to measure electric current. When the battery is first connected, the

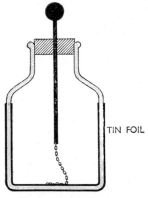

FIG. I. LEYDEN JAR

ammeter shows a momentary current that quickly dies away to nothing. This current is the electricity flowing into the condenser, and it stops when the condenser is fully charged. If the ammeter connexion is then removed from the battery and touched on to the outer coating of the Leyden jar, as shown by the dotted line in Fig. 2, the ammeter will show a momentary current in the opposite direction to the first, as the stored electricity in the condenser is being discharged. Thus a condenser is no more than a pair of electrical conductors separated by a thin insulator.

The quantity of electricity that can be stored in a condenser depends on what is called its 'capacitance', and the unit of measurement is the 'microfarad'. Even condensers of very large capacitance store only small amounts of electricity: a large condenser, for example, used in radio work and charged by a 200-volt battery,

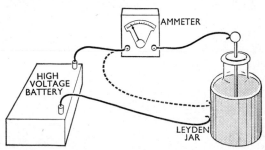

FIG. 2. LEYDEN JAR USED TO STORE ELECTRICITY

stores only enough electricity to light a 1-watt torch bulb for $\frac{1}{5}$th second. Such a condenser, however, by being made to give up its store of

electricity much more quickly, could light a 1,000-watt bulb for $\frac{1}{5000}$th second with hardly any loss—and this is often very useful.

In modern condensers each conductor usually consists of a set of thin, flat, metal leaves called 'plates'. The two sets are interleaved (see Fig. 3), so that each side of each plate faces a plate attached to the opposite conductor. The greater the area of metal sheets facing each other, or the thinner the insulation which separates them, the greater the 'capacitance' of a condenser. A small condenser of fixed capacitance in a wireless receiver may contain six sheets of metal foil, separated by sheets of waxed paper or thin slices of the mineral mica.

The capacitance of some condensers, such as those which tune a set to a wireless wavelength (see RADIO ENGINEERING), can be varied by turning a knob, causing the two sets of leaves to slide

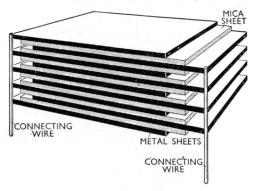

FIG. 3. MODERN CONDENSER

in and out of one another so that the area of overlap ('plates' face to face) is altered. For this purpose the plates, which must be stiff, are made of aluminium roughly of the thickness of a postcard, and are insulated by an air-space of about $\frac{1}{16}$th inch.

It was once thought that the stored electricity was somehow condensed on the plates—hence the name condenser, but it is now known that it is actually stored by straining the insulator between the plates, rather as ENERGY (q.v.) is stored in a wound-up spring. Since condensers can hold small quantities of electricity at high voltages, they are used wherever this characteristic is desirable—for example, in smoothing out the ripple in a RECTIFIER, in providing the store of very high-voltage electricity needed for flash tubes (see HIGH-SPEED PHOTOGRAPHY), and in many applications in RADIO and ELECTRONICS (qq.v.). Condensers are also used to reduce the arcing (sparking) that occurs when the opening of a small switch (*see* SWITCHGEAR, ELECTRICAL) interrupts an electric current: the condenser, which is connected across the switch, stores the electrical energy that would otherwise be dissipated in the arc, thus preventing the switch contacts from being burned by the arc, and reducing the interference caused to radio receivers.

See also RADIO ENGINEERING; HIGH-FREQUENCY CURRENTS; ELECTRONICS.

CONDENSER, STEAM, *see* STEAM ENGINE.

CONVEYORS.
The principle of conveying loads is very ancient. Primitive drawings show long lines of slaves laboriously passing full baskets of material from hand to hand and then passing back the emptied baskets. These long chains of men endlessly circulating baskets were a form of human conveyor. Nowadays mechanical power has replaced manpower and although there are many different types of conveyors, these can with certain reservations be said to consist of a moving endless belt or steel cable passing around pulleys at the ends, and supported by an intervening structure.

The material to be conveyed may rest directly on the carrying surface of an endless belt or chain, or it may be carried in a bucket suspended from a moving endless steel cable.

Probably the most widely used conveyor is the rubber-belt type (Fig. 1). The rubber belting on which the material is carried is constructed of a number of layers or plies of stout, cotton-duck fabric, cemented together and covered by rubber. The fabric withstands the pull in the loaded belt caused by the friction of the rollers over which the belt moves; the rubber cover protects the fabric from wear. The greater the length of the conveyor and the heavier the load to be carried, the greater is the number of plies in the belt,

John Laing & Son Ltd.

FIG. I. A RUBBER CONVEYOR BELT ON A BUILDING SITE CARRYING ROCKS AND EARTH TO A TIP WHERE THEY ARE DISCHARGED

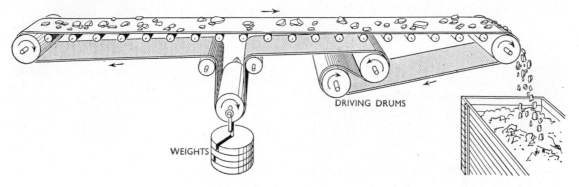

WEIGHTS

DRIVING DRUMS

FIG. 2. DIAGRAM OF A CONVEYOR BELT

The weights pull down the central pulley giving added tension and taking up any slack in the belt

which may range from three to fifteen, though belts with four to eight plies are the most common.

The speed and the width of the belt depend on the job it has to do. Some belts travel at only a few feet per minute, whilst others move at as much as 10 miles per hour; while the width varies from a few inches to several feet. The advantages of belt conveying are the continuous flow of material and the very high capacities which are possible with this form of haulage, together with the fact that they can be used on gradients which would be too steep for lorries or trains. An idea of the amount of carrying that a conveyor belt can do may be gathered from the fact that a belt 3 feet wide moving at 500 feet per minute will shift no less than 1,500 tons of coal per hour.

Belt-conveyor haulage is most suitable for operations involving the movement of large quantities of material, and belt conveyors are used extensively in MINING and CIVIL ENGINEERING (qq.v.). Some 90% of the total output from British collieries is carried at some stage or other along part of the 1,800 miles or so of belt conveyors in use underground. A series of belt conveyors was used to transport over 10 million tons of building material for the construction of the Shasta Dam on the Sacramento River near Coram, California (see CENTRAL VALLEY PROJECT). This system made use of twenty-six 36-inch-wide conveyor belts laid in line and feeding on to each other. The belts had six plies and travelled at 555 feet per minute. With one exception the conveyors were powered by 200 h.p. motors.

The belt must, of course, grip the driving drum tightly. This grip is maintained by applying ten-

sion to the belt as it leaves the driving drum, this being known as the 'slack side tension' or 'added tension'. On large conveyors a heavy pulley is introduced behind the driving drum to give the required added tension and also to take up any slack in the belt (Fig. 2). Heavy-duty conveyors often have more than one driving drum as this lessens the possibility of belt slip, and decreases the amount of slack side tension needed.

A recent British invention is the cable belt conveyor; in this the rubber carrying-belt is supported between two cables which take the stress caused by the load and the friction in the conveyor run. The use of these cables allows a much greater operating length of conveyor than is possible with the conventional rubber belt type—it is now possible to have single conveyors up to 6 miles in length.

The other principal types of conveyors in which the material to be transported rests directly on the carrying surface include the scraper chain conveyor and the shaking conveyor. In the former, an endless chain is driven between sprockets at each end and slides along the bottom of a steel trough (Fig. 3). This type of conveyor is very robust and is well-suited for working on steep gradients, since the arms on the chain prevent material from slipping backwards; but they work at a comparatively slow speed. Sometimes instead of arms the chain is fitted with buckets. An example of this type of chain conveyor is the DREDGER (q.v. Vol. IV) used to clean up harbours and river beds.

Shaker conveyors consist of lengths of steel troughs joined together and caused to jerk backwards and forwards by gearing or rotating unbalanced weights. The entire structure is moved forwards 6 inches or so and is then jerked back.

Hugh Wood & Co.

FIG. 3. COAL BEING LOADED ON TO A 'PYTHON' SCRAPER CHAIN

Because the backward jerk is so rapid, the material resting in the troughs is caused to slide forward, and so it proceeds with each successive jerk along the line of troughs to the discharge point. Shaker conveyors are much used in factories for the movement of parcels and packages.

In the aerial ropeway conveyor, the material is fed into large buckets suspended from a moving endless steel cable supported some 30 feet or so above the ground by pylons. The buckets, clamped to this cable, are carried along to the discharge point, where they are automatically tipped and then returned to the filling point. These aerial ropeways, which are often several miles long, are widely used in the disposal of debris and refuse. Many industrial undertakings near the coast carry their discarded material from the works to the sea by means of such conveyors, as in this way they need not interfere with normal road or rail traffic. Another application of the aerial ropeway conveyor is the *téléphérique*, often seen on the Continent and used frequently to transport skiers to the top of snow-covered slopes (*see* MOUNTAIN RAILWAYS, Section 3, Vol. IV).

There are many other different types of con-

veyor, some of them designed for one particular duty only. These range from small rotating conveyors carrying bottles to be filled and corked automatically (*see* DAIRY INDUSTRY, Vol. VII) to the huge mobile CRANES (q.v.) slowly moving backwards and forwards above loading bays in docks and factories.

Except in those instances where the conveyor is installed on a downhill gradient—in which case gravity does the work—the driving drum, pulley, or sprocket is driven by means of a motor and gearing. Electric motors are by far the most common, although compressed-air motors are sometimes used, especially if the conveyor is installed in a place where the use of electricity may be considered dangerous, such as a coal mine or a factory manufacturing explosives.

See also CRANES; EARTH-MOVING EQUIPMENT.

CORROSION. This is the slow, gradual attack made on the surfaces of METALS and ALLOYS (qq.v.) by the atmosphere or by water. The best-known example is the rusting of ordinary iron and steel, but most metals corrode, though some more slowly than others. Tens of thousands of tons of iron and steel are washed into the sea every year as rust from the United Kingdom alone, and at least £50 million is spent annually in Great Britain in preventing corrosion.

The processes that attack exposed metals, both pure metals and alloys, are essentially chemical (*see* CHEMISTRY, Vol. III). The simplest of them is tarnishing, which is usually the result of a gentle reaction between the metal and a gas— that is, the atmosphere around us. Sometimes oxygen combines with the metal to form an oxide; more frequently the air, containing traces of sulphur compounds, reacts with the metal to produce a thin layer of metallic sulphide. The blackening of silver and the darkening of copper and brass are well-known examples of tarnishing.

When a metal tarnishes something is added to its surface and adheres to it; but in corrosion the metal is usually slowly eaten away. One cannot say that one metal always resists corrosion better than another. The order of resistance depends on circumstances. The 'noble' metals, platinum, gold, and silver, resist corrosive attack from either the atmosphere or sea water; but these are far too expensive to be used by engineers except in very special cases. Stainless steel also resists corrosion in many circumstances, though not in all, but it, too, is expensive. All the common metals and alloys—iron, steel, aluminium, copper, brass, zinc, and tin—corrode, but at different rates according to the characteristics of the metal, the nature of the medium that is attacking, and also the circumstances: for example, mild steel corrodes in the open air more than a hundred times as rapidly at Sheffield or Glasgow, where the air is heavily laden with the chemical by-products of industrial processes, as at Khartoum in the Sudan, where the atmosphere is dry and not contaminated. In industrial towns, nickel, tin, or zinc resist attack far better than iron or mild steel.

In perfectly dry air, which is rarely found outside a laboratory, ordinary metals do not corrode at all. In the dry, frozen air of Antarctica, common steel has remained for years without rusting. There must be moisture in the air for corrosion to occur, though perfectly pure water—which is as rare as dry air—hardly causes any corrosion at all. Most corrosion, therefore, comes from the chemical action that ensues when a metallic material is in contact with both the oxygen of the air and some substance dissolved in water. Both rainwater and the moisture that condenses on exposed objects always contain some dissolved substances; these may be atmospheric gases such as carbon dioxide or sulphur dioxide, or they may be salts. Near the sea, there is always some common salt in rain or moist air, while in industrial towns the moist air always contains some sulphates. Up to a point the more of these dissolved substances there are the worse the corrosion. High concentrations are, however, usually less active than moderate ones. Metals vary in their reaction to these substances. Iron and ordinary steels are attacked by ACID solutions but resist solutions of ALKALI (qq.v. Vol. VII); aluminium and its alloys behave in the opposite way.

Corrosive attacks take several forms. Corrosion may occur more or less uniformly over the whole of an exposed surface, producing a fairly even layer (as of rust on iron). If the metal is left undisturbed, the layer may itself protect the metal against further attack, and eventually all corrosive action ceases. In India a famous iron column has been standing, without undergoing any change, for many centuries, having covered itself with a protecting layer of hardened rust. The beautiful green skin or 'patina' that develops on copper roofs consists of a corrosive layer under which corrosive activity has come to an end. When, however, the corroding metal surfaces are subject to wear and tear by handling or rough weather, as occurs on ships, on the pillars of harbour works, or on moving vehicles, the corrosion products are rubbed away almost as quickly as they form, fresh surfaces are exposed to attack, and the corrosion continues. When a piece of metal is partly immersed, the attack is most severe at the water-line.

In some cases the corrosive attack takes place quite differently. A slight, general attack over the whole surface is accompanied by an intense action at a few isolated places, where the metal is penetrated deeply and fairly rapidly. The intense attack usually takes a path around the microscopic grains or crystals composing the metal, and since its progress cannot be detected from any marks on the surface, this inter-crystalline form of corrosion may have dangerous consequences.

The progress of the more uniform type of corrosion may be measured by noting the weight of metal lost in, say, successive months or years. If the metal surface is undisturbed, so that the corrosion products remain where they are formed, the metal may actually gain weight; but if the

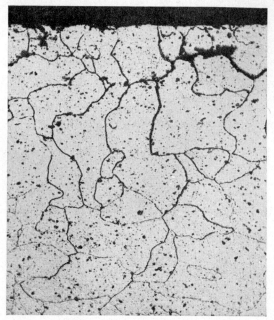

SECTION OF METAL SHOWING INTER-CRYSTALLINE CORRO-
SION
Highly magnified

corrosive layer is being continuously removed by wear or the weather, the weight of the metal progressively becomes less. Such a method, however, is useless for measuring inter-crystalline corrosion, so it is better to measure the loss of strength (see STRESS AND STRAIN) than the loss of weight. The strength of a piece of metal can be halved in a few weeks by inter-crystalline corrosion quietly extending the very fine cracks which are formed between the crystals on the surface when corrosion begins.

If one metal is placed in contact with a different metal the speed of corrosion of one of them is frequently increased. Iron corrodes more rapidly when in contact with brass or bronze, for example; but if iron or steel is in contact with zinc, it is the zinc which corrodes the more quickly. The iron or steel is protected for a long time: hence the use of zinc-plated steel in the form of 'galvanized iron'. If there is danger of corrosion, aluminium should never be placed in contact with copper or its alloys, for the metals act like the two 'poles' of an electric battery, which become active if linked together by moisture of an acid or salty character (see BATTERY, ELECTRIC). Different phases of an alloy act as poles of tiny electrical cells, as do parts of pure metals that, during manufacture, have been mechanically deformed by differing amounts (see HEAT TREATMENT, Section 6). A noticeable amount of electrical activity takes place if the metal contains impurities or suffers mechanical strain, or if the surface bears any dirt, scale, rust, scratches, and other blemishes—for all those things act as electrical 'poles'.

Corrosion is prevented by covering the metal or alloy with a protective layer to keep out the moisture—either a resistant metal like chromium, a chemical, or a coating of paint or grease (see SURFACE TREATMENT).

See also TINPLATE.

CRANES. These are the tools used by industry to lift and transport loads from one position to another. In the past very primitive appliances were used for this task and, as they generally depended on manpower for energy, the loads lifted were very much restricted. Today, loads of 300 tons and upwards are handled by power-driven cranes under the control of an operator who sits comfortably in the crane cab manipulating the various handles which control the motions of the crane.

As well as lifting capacity, the size of the crane structure, the speed of operation, and the area within which the crane operates may also affect its design. Cranes of large lifting capacity may actually weigh less than cranes of smaller load capacity.

Apart from small hoists used in engineering shops, all modern cranes are power operated. Where the crane is stationary—in an engine room, for example, or alongside a harbour—it is almost always electrically driven, since electric motors are smaller and more convenient than other forms of motive power. Mobile cranes, on the other hand, like those used on the railways and for civil engineering and building, are usually diesel-driven. Some steam cranes are still made, and small mobile cranes are sometimes driven by petrol engines.

The main types of cranes are hoists and pulleys, overhead travelling and Goliath cranes (span type), and jib or cantilever cranes (radius type).

1. HOISTS AND PULLEYS. These machines are simple units, generally fixed in one position and provided with a grooved barrel or plain drum which is driven through gearing by the power unit. The hoisting (or hauling) rope is coiled on to the barrel, and sometimes a system of pulley

blocks is used (as on ships' derricks) in order to obtain greater lifting capacity at a slower speed. In order to vary the speed, the mechanism of the winches (or hoisting machinery) may also be fitted with a change-gear device, and a CLUTCH (q.v.) may be used to free the barrel from the gearing in order to lower the load quickly under the control of a brake.

In the simplest hoist the rope from the hook is led over a pulley (A) and then to the drum. The load rises at the same speed as the rope is hauled in. If, however, the rope is hitched to some fixed point (c), led round a pulley (B) to which the hook is attached, and then over the pulley (A), the hook will rise only half as fast as the rope is hauled in. This mechanical advantage enables twice the load to be raised for the same power. The hoists shown in Fig. 1c and d can raise three and four times the original weight at a third and a quarter the speed.

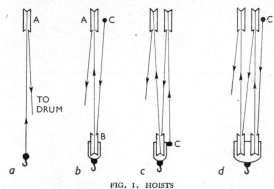

FIG. 1. HOISTS

a. Simple hoist with one pulley, A. b. Hoist with two pulleys, A, B, and rope fixed at c. c. Hoist with three pulleys and rope fixed at c. d. Hoist with four pulleys and rope fixed at c

In a Weston's block, a type much used for hoisting loads, the upper pulley is really two pulley wheels, or 'sheaves' as they are called, of slightly different diameters, fastened together so that when one turns the other turns. The lower pulley is a single wheel, and to this the hook and load is attached. An endless chain passes round the three wheels. To prevent slip, the upper double pulley has recesses cut in its grooves into which the links of the chain fit. As the continuous chain is pulled, it is hauled in over the larger diameter pulley slightly faster than it is paid out over the other, and there is, therefore, less chain in the loop supporting the hook. The rate the hook rises depends on the difference in the diameters of the two pulleys. If the pulleys have

widely different diameters, the loop supporting the hook is shortened quickly, pulling the load up quickly; but only light loads can be raised. If the diameters are more nearly equal, the load is raised more slowly, and so a greater load can be raised for the same pull on the chain.

2. OVERHEAD TRAVELLING CRANES AND GOLIATH CRANES. The overhead travelling crane, one of the most useful machines in modern engineering, is installed in practically every building where heavy loads have to be moved about. In its simplest form it is merely a strong girder—or steel beam of I section—placed across the building under the roof, with wheels at each end running on similar girders along each side of the building. A trolley carrying a winch driven by an electric motor runs along the girder from side to side of the building so that, by moving the girder and trolley, the winch can be placed over almost any part of the floor (Fig. 2). Such an arrangement serves practically the whole floor area without wasting valuable floor space or interfering with work in progress on the floor. The crane is usually controlled from a cabin mounted at one end of the crane girders.

In steelworks, overhead travelling cranes are used for handling hot and molten metal, careful precautions for safety having to be taken. Modern cranes can transport a ladle containing 300 tons of molten steel. Some special cranes are fitted with tongs to grip the hot slabs or ingots of metal when they are being handled for HEAT TREATMENT (q.v.).

Goliath cranes, though overhead cranes, have girders carried on leg structures which allow them to travel on the ground (Fig. 3). There are other forms, such as semi-Goliath, which run on one elevated track and one ground track, and cantilever, with girders extended beyond the leg structures; but in all types there is a trolley for hoisting and lowering, which travels along the horizontal girder, and the whole structure also travels.

3. JIB OR CANTILEVER CRANES. In this type of crane the load is suspended from a jib, boom, or cantilever at some distance from the centre-line of the crane. The jib and its load must therefore be counterbalanced to prevent the crane toppling over. The load can be hoisted or lowered, luffed or derricked in or out (that is, the horizontal distance from the centre-line can be altered as required), slewed in either direction, and

FIG. 2. 100-TON ELECTRIC OVERHEAD TRAVELLING CRANE WITH 10-TON AUXILIARY HOIST, INSTALLED IN A POWER STATION

Sir W. Arrol & Co.

FIG. 3. 20-TON ELECTRIC TRAVELLING 'GOLIATH' CRANE
In the centre background derrick cranes can be seen

travelled. Cranes of this kind are usually to be found at docks or shipyards and construction yards, and there are the following types:

(*a*) *Derrick cranes*. The Scotch derrick, as it is called, is one of the earliest forms of crane known, and many old examples with the jib and back stays constructed of wood are still in use. The slewing motion, however, is restricted to approximately three-quarters of a revolution, as the back supporting stays occupy almost a quarter of the full circle (*see* Fig. 3).

(*b*) *Wharf cranes*. These are heavy cranes, often with a lifting capacity of up to 50 tons for servicing and fitting out ships (in dry docks and wet basins). They operate at relatively slow speeds on the pulley block carrying the main lifting hook; but a secondary hook is often supplied so that light loads can be handled much faster. Travelling cranes of this type have an elaborate system of rail wheels arranged on bogies at each corner of the carriage so that heavy loads are distributed evenly over as great a length of track as possible. The jib can be luffed by hauling in or paying out multiple ropes, but the better cranes now usually have long, twin, steel screws attached to the superstructure which engage large bronze nuts mounted on the jib structure, so that when the screws are rotated they vary the inclination of the jib (*see* Fig. 5).

(*c*) *Level luffing cranes*. In jib cranes, when the distance from the centre-line is reduced by luffing or derricking in, the jib point is lifted up, and the load suspended from the point of the jib is also raised, using up an unnecessary amount of energy in the operation. In order to overcome this difficulty, arrangements are made so that the main lifting cable is automatically paid out when the jib is raised, and the load remains at the same height. In this way and by balancing the jib weight about its pivoting point, or fulcrum, low power consumption and higher speeds of operation are attained. For loading and unloading ships' cargoes speedily and efficiently, cranes of this type are unsurpassed, and several may be used at the same time on different holds of the same vessel. Capacities vary, but loads of 3 to 5 tons are commonplace. Sometimes, instead of the usual cargo hook for slinging loads, a grab is fitted which handles bulk material such as coal and sand. The grab is opened and closed by the crane driver from his cabin.

(*d*) *Tower or cantilever cranes*. These serve building berths in shipyards and are used for fitting

Sir W. Arrol & Co

FIG. 4. 30-TON ELECTRIC TRAVELLING TOWER CRANE

out ships (Fig. 4). The structure of the tower crane is relatively simple. A tower (which can be of the fixed or travelling type) supports a mast which rotates inside it. The top of the mast is connected to booms, which extend horizontally at the forward end to form a track for a movable load trolley, and at the rear end to support the counterbalance and operating machinery. The driver's cabin is usually mounted at the top of the mast, and as these cranes are generally very high above ground level, there is usually a telephone for communication with the driver.

Formerly, fixed cranes of 5 tons capacity at 100-foot radius (that is, horizontal distance from the centre-line) were adequate for most shipyards, but today travelling cranes of 30–35 tons capacity at 150-foot radius are often needed.

(*e*) *Giant cranes* (or *hammerheads*). These are somewhat similar to tower cranes but very much larger and are used for installing heavy machinery into place in ships. They can lift loads up to 300 tons, and can work up to 180 feet from the centre-line. In the common British design a large ring of rollers with a centre-pin is mounted on top of a square tower for supporting and rotating

FIG. 5. 250-TON GIANT CRANE WITH 20-TON JIB CRANE
On the left is another jib crane

the boom, along which the load trolley runs (Fig. 5). Various supplementary lifting units are usually fitted, such as auxiliary trolleys or jigger hoists for light loads, and sometimes, also, a separate jib crane which runs the full length of both booms. This can be used to service the main machinery of the parent crane. Telephone communication and lifts for access to the operator's cabin are necessary, together with an elaborate system of control gear. Cranes of this type weigh many times their own maximum lifting capacity.

(*f*) *Floating cranes*. These are useful for loading and unloading ships in ports or harbours where there is no permanent heavy crane equipment. There are various designs such as 'rotating or non-rotating', 'derricking (luffing) or fixed jib', 'propelled or non-propelled pontoons', and each has its own advantages. The supporting barge or pontoon must be stable, and the loads must be carefully handled as the barge heels over as the load is lifted, though it rights itself as soon as the load is released. Since they are extremely mobile and no expensive concrete or masonry foundations are needed, floating cranes are useful in any port.

4. GENERAL. Elaborate safety precautions, which are essential in modern crane design, have greatly reduced crane accidents which were too common in the past owing to primitive devices and ignorance of the limitations of machinery. Modern cranes are fitted with automatic safe-loading indicators which give visual and audible warning of dangerous conditions, limit switches which restrict motion within the range required, and powerful brakes which automatically control the loads when power is cut off. All gearing, where possible, is enclosed in oiltight gear cases, running on ball or roller bearings.

See also LEVERS; MECHANICAL HANDLING.
See also Vol. IV: PORTS AND HARBOURS.

D

DAMS. 1. These are obstacles built across rivers or lakes to hold back the water. The reservoirs which they form are used to store water for many purposes: to ensure a regular WATER SUPPLY (q.v.) for towns and cities; for IRRIGATION (q.v. Vol. VI); for FLOOD CONTROL; or for HYDRO-ELECTRIC POWER (qq.v.). Often one dam is used for several purposes. In the mountains of Scotland, for example, many great dams span the glens, holding huge volumes of water with pipe-lines running down hundreds of feet to feed the turbines of a hydro-electric power station; at the same time the dams store water against dry periods. In the TENNESSEE VALLEY AUTHORITY Scheme (q.v.) many of the dams are used for four purposes—hydro-electricity, irrigation, flood control, and improvement of navigation.

Central Press

FIG. I. CLAERWEN DAM, WALES. A GRAVITY DAM

The highest dam in the world is at present the BOULDER DAM (q.v.) in the United States, but this will be exceeded by the La Grande Dixence and Mauvoisin dams, now under construction in Switzerland. La Grande Dixence, situated in the High Alps south of the Rhône Valley, will take 10 years to build. With a height above its foundations of 915 feet, it will contain over 8 million cubic yards of concrete.

2. MATERIALS AND TYPES OF DAM. There are a number of types of modern dam, constructed on quite different principles according to the nature of the country and the foundations. It may, for example, be best to adopt a design for which local materials can be used—earth, stone, or sand for concrete—and so save transport costs. There is the danger that, though the dam itself may be solid and watertight, water may seep through the earth underneath it and in course of time eat away its foundations, or, cascading over the top, it may carry away the supporting ground on the downstream side, or it may carve a channel round the flank. All such considerations influence the design of the dam.

(a) Earth and stone dams. The oldest dams were made of earth and stones, probably carried in baskets on the labourers' heads, and perhaps strengthened with brushwood or timber cribs. Others consisted of stones and lumps of rock tumbled into place and filled in with earth. The Romans, and the Egyptians before them, made dams of masonry in North Africa, and there are some masonry dams in Spain, built in the 16th century; one of them, at Alicante, is over 134 feet high. Their design shows little knowledge of the mathematics of dam construction, so that usually there must have been a great waste of labour and materials.

A dam of earth or rock, or both combined, is still often used. It has a fairly gentle slope, and this directs most of the weight of the water downwards upon the solid earth. If the material is not itself impervious to water, a layer of concrete or puddled clay (clay, sand, and water mixed) is put down, either in the centre of the bank or on its upstream face. This layer must continue down below the surface until it reaches a water-resisting stratum of soil, and far enough outwards on either side to prevent any serious leakage.

(b) Gravity dam. A dam which holds its place against the horizontal push of the water by its own weight is called a gravity dam (Fig. 1). It must have foundations firm enough not only to

Ferruzzi, Venice

FIG. 2. LUMIEI DAM, ITALY. AN ARCH DAM

Daily Record-and-Mail, Glasgow

FIG. 3. LOCH SLOY DAM. A BUTTRESS DAM

support its weight but also to prevent any tendency for the dam to slide downstream. A solid gravity dam may be made of rubble or squared stone with cement mortar, or of mass concrete, generally without steel reinforcement. The BOULDER DAM (q.v.) in the United States is of this type; its foundations go down as far as 137 feet, and its height above the river bed is 589 feet.

(*c*) *Arch dam.* An arch of brick or stone, as for a bridge or a doorway, can carry the weight of masonry above it by transmitting the thrust through the abutments to the ground (*see* BUILDING, PRINCIPLES OF). In an arch dam (Fig. 2) the arch is laid flat on the ground across the reservoir outlet, like a big **U** with its curve upstream. Instead of the weight of masonry, there is the horizontal push of the water against the curve of the **U**, and this is transmitted to the ground at the two ends. This type of dam is suitable only where the gap to be spanned is not very wide, and where there is perfectly solid rock to take the two ends of the **U**—the abutments. An arch dam does not need to be as heavy as a gravity dam. A famous example, the Lumiei dam in Italy, 449 feet high and made of concrete, is only 51 feet thick at its base.

(*d*) *Buttress dam.* This type combines the principles of both the gravity and arch dams (Fig. 3). It consists of a series of buttresses placed at intervals across the outlet and connected by horizontal arches. The buttresses, which hold their place by gravity, form the abutments of the arches, and there must, therefore, be good rock foundations for each buttress.

Buttresses are also used in the **T** or bull-head dam, which on the drawing-board looks like a series of capital **T**s, with their cross-strokes joined together: the down-strokes of the **T**s, pointing downstream, are the buttresses. This type is now becoming popular; a recent example is the Errochty dam, part of one of the Scottish hydro-electric schemes.

The Ambursen type of dam looks rather like the bull-head—a series of joined **T**s; but the face presented to the water is sloped so that the thrust is neither horizontal nor vertical. One of the biggest dams of this type is the Rodriguez dam in Mexico, which is 240 feet high; its upstream face has a slope of 1 to 1.

3. SPILLWAYS. Water not wanted for the reservoir must be passed downstream so that the river below it does not run dry and so that in

Agent General for Tasmania

A MULTIPLE-ARCH DAM ON GREAT LAKE, TASMANIA

times of flood the water-level in the reservoir can be controlled. This is usually done by a 'spillway' over the top of the dam. But, especially if the dam is high, the cascading water may wash away the ground below and weaken the foundations unless they are specially protected. One method of preventing this is by a 'ski-jump' spillway. If, for example, the power house of a hydro-electric scheme is built into the dam across its full width, a chute is made down the back of the dam and over the top of the power house, thus causing the surplus water to fall well downstream of the building (Fig. 4). Other methods of discharging surplus water are by culverts, or channels, built into the dam, by a spillway round the side, or by a tunnel cut through the flanking rock.

If the water carries much silt this must be passed down with the water; for silt tends to sink to the bottom in still water, and so in time might choke the reservoir. In the Nile barrages in Egypt this is done by sluices placed at bed level in the dam, through which the silt-laden water passes.

4. DAM CONSTRUCTION. When selecting a site for the dam, the engineer must take into consideration the purpose of the dam, and therefore how much water the reservoir should hold. He must discover how much water comes down the river in rainy periods and in drought, and whether more water can conveniently be brought from streams in neighbouring valleys by tunnels

through intervening hills. He must then look for a natural basin which will contain the required amount of water without too much adaptation, and which has a narrow enough neck across to be spanned by a dam. Then he must decide what type of dam can be most economically built across this outlet, how high it must be to provide the water he wants, how strong to hold the weight of water, and whether the foundations are good. When the water-level is raised it may engulf farms, villages, a road, or a railway, and the engineer must decide whether and where these can be moved or new ones built. He must

A. Coyne & J. Bellier

FIG. 4. SKI-JUMP SPILLWAY AT AIGLE DAM, FRANCE

also take into consideration the natural beauty of the countryside—indeed, often the new reservoir enhances it. All this demands skilful SURVEYING and a detailed knowledge of SOIL MECHANICS (qq.v.) and GEOLOGY (q.v. Vol. III), besides engineering skill.

As the dam has to be built across a river bed, the water must first be drained away. It may be possible to divert the river into a temporary channel, but, if that is impossible, a U-shaped COFFERDAM (q.v.) is built out from one bank to the middle of the river. The water is pumped out from inside the cofferdam, and half the dam is constructed 'in the dry'. When that is finished, the cofferdam is flooded and removed, and a new one built out from the other bank, inside which the rest of the dam is constructed. Meanwhile the river passes through temporary openings or through the sluices of the completed part.

As most dams are built in isolated places, a special camp often has to be built for the workmen, with canteens and other provisions. Complicated transport arrangements must be made for the delivery of materials to the site, and for a light railway, cableway, or cranes both to bring the materials to the point where they are to be used and to carry away the excavated earth and rock. The materials—earth, masonry, or concrete—have to be thoroughly tested for strength and resistance to penetration by water.

See also ASWAN DAM; BOULDER DAM; LLOYD BARRAGE; WATER SUPPLY; NEW YORK WATER SUPPLY; HYDROELECTRIC POWER.

DENSITY, *see* Vol. III: DENSITY.

DIESEL ENGINE, *see* INTERNAL COMBUSTION ENGINE, Section 4.

DIRECT CURRENT, *see* ELECTRIC CURRENT, Section 9.

DISTILLATION, *see* Vol. VII: DISTILLATION.

DISTRICT HEATING, *see* HEATING.

DOCKS AND HARBOUR CONSTRUCTION. Docks and harbours consist, basically, of a number of quays, to which the ships are made fast, and which must have sufficient depth of water for the ships to remain afloat at all tidal levels. The quays must be accessible by road and usually by railway, and must be provided with

CRANES (q.v.), warehouses, and other necessary dock equipment.

Whether PORTS AND HARBOURS or closed DOCKS (qq.v. Vol. IV) are built in a particular place depends on many factors, but especially on the difference between high and low tide. When this is small, a harbour can be built with quays open to the sea—as at Southampton which has a tidal range of only 13 feet, or in Mediterranean ports where the tidal range never exceeds 6 feet. At Avonmouth, however, which has a range of as much as 41 feet, or at Liverpool where it is 27 feet, enclosed docks have to be built so that the water can be kept at high-tide level by means of lock gates. Otherwise, at low tide, there would not be sufficient water to keep the ships afloat; or, if the harbour were made deep enough to keep them afloat at any state of tide, very high and expensive quay walls would have to be built.

In designing a harbour the engineer has to consider the strength and direction of the prevailing winds and the height of the waves. He must know whether to expect large deposits of sand or mud, which often appear where a river meets the sea, forming 'bars' which may block the harbour entrance unless constantly dredged. Such problems are now often investigated by means of model experiments. If a harbour or dock is to be built on a river estuary a small-scale model is made of the estuary channels and ship berths. The model bed of the river and sea is covered with fine sand, water is added to the correct level, and the rise and fall of the tides is reproduced by a machine. A series of tests covering thousands of tides is made in a few weeks,

Rendel, Palmer, and Tritton

LARGE STONES ARE USED IN THE CONSTRUCTION OF A RUBBLE MOUND BREAKWATER AT HAIFA HARBOUR

Leith Dock Commission

CAISSONS FOR A DEEP-WATER QUAY AT LEITH: TWO ARE COMPLETED AND THE CENTRE ONE IS UNDER CONSTRUCTION

and shows, by the movement of the sand, where dangerous shoals or sandbanks will form. Adjustments can then be made by altering the position and design of the quays, and by building banks and walls to control the direction of currents.

Models are also used to test the design of breakwaters, which protect harbours against heavy seas so that ships can lie safely at anchor. The earliest kind of breakwater consisted of a huge mound of stone laid on the bottom and rising well above high-water level, the front and back faces being sloped. One of the finest of these is the Plymouth breakwater, designed by John Rennie, and constructed, between 1811 and 1848, by depositing nearly 4 million tons of broken stone, covered with a layer of ashlar or dressed stone. The seaward slope has an inclination of 1 in 5, and the landward slope 1 in 3.

Later, breakwaters were made of concrete blocks dumped into the sea to form a mound. These sometimes weighed 40 tons or more and were lowered into the water by large cranes and set in regular courses by divers. Sometimes the foundations were prepared by using large diving bells or caissons, which enabled men to work on the sea bottom, materials being passed down to

them through air-locks (*see* DIVERS AND DIVING EQUIPMENT, Vol. IV).

In the Mediterranean the pontoon or 'caisson' type of breakwater has been much used. This consists of a series of concrete boxes, open at the top, which are constructed ashore and then launched into the sea, in which they float. They are towed out to the site of the wall and are sunk by being filled first with water and then with sand, stone, or concrete. They rest on foundations previously levelled by divers. It was this form of construction which was used for the temporary harbour at Arromanches (known as Mulberry Harbour) during the invasion of Normandy in the Second World War. The pontoons in this case were towed across the Channel and sunk in position by being filled with water. When most of them were later raised, the water was pumped out again so that they floated and could be towed away.

Either concrete blocks or pontoons may be used for building the quays and jetties inside a harbour. Where the ground is soft, however, piles, generally of reinforced concrete, are driven into the sea bottom by pile drivers (*see* BUILDING CONSTRUCTION), and are then braced together

CONSTRUCTION OF A DEEP-WATER QUAY AT DAR ES SALAAM

The quay is made in sloping blockwork, the blocks being of precast concrete weighing from 12 to 16½ tons each

MONOLITH CONSTRUCTION AT THE PORT OF LONDON

and decked over with concrete beams and slabs in order to form a quay. In some cases cast-iron piles are used, and in others steel cylinders, both types having screws at their lower ends. These screws may be as much as 8 feet in diameter, and the work of the 'screwdriver' is often done by a steam-driven winch. Most of the well-known pleasure piers at sea-side towns are constructed in this way.

Another form of construction is the pile and cylinder system. The site of the quay is first excavated and dredged back to form a sloped bank. Lines of vertical concrete cylinders, made up in suitable lengths, are then sunk through the bank. Sometimes reinforced concrete piles are driven down within the cylinders, which are then filled with concrete.

In 'wet' docks (docks which are always filled with water) the water is kept at high-tide level. The entrance is controlled either by gates, which can be opened only when the water-level on both sides is the same, or by locks, which enable ships to pass in and out at any state of tide. These are the same in principle as canal locks (*see* Locks and Weirs, Vol. IV) but very much larger. They have steel gates, which are opened and closed by hydraulic or electric machinery, with openings controlled by valves to raise or lower the water-level. A usual size of a lock for ocean steamers is 1,000 feet long by 100 feet wide, with a depth of 40 to 50 feet at low water.

Until about 50 years ago the walls of wet docks were made of solid masonry or concrete, built up from trenches excavated in the bottom and lined with timber. Other methods are now more generally used: one of these is to build a number of hollow concrete blocks, called 'monoliths', on the surface and to sink them into the ground by excavating the soil from under them. This is done by mechanical grabs working inside the monoliths.

This method is also used for constructing lock entrances, and 'dry' docks where the hulls of ships can be cleaned, painted, and repaired. A large modern dry dock is about 1,200 feet long and 160 feet wide, while the depth of water at the entrance is generally not less than 45 feet. Such a dock contains about 50 million gallons of water, which can be pumped out in about 4 hours. The massive walls are made nearly vertical, without steps or 'altars', which were formerly used for propping up the vessels with timber shores. Most merchant ships are now more

flat-bottomed and can rest on timber blocks on the bottom of the dock without support for their sides. Subways, built inside the dock walls, carry the network of water mains, electric cables, and so on needed for repairs, as well as large culverts (pipes in the dock walls) for filling and emptying the dock. Sometimes lifts for the repair gangs are also constructed inside the dock walls, and a sewer connexion may be provided in the dock floor as the ships' crews very often continue to live on board.

See also Vol. IV: Docks; Ports and Harbours.

DRAINAGE, *see* Land Reclamation. *See also* Vol. VI: Drainage, Land. *See also* Vol. X: Drainage.

DRAWING INSTRUMENTS. Straight lines, accurate curves and angles, and accurate measurements are all essential in Engineering Drawing (q.v.). Because of this, special precision instruments are needed (Fig. 1).

Special smooth, flat drawing boards with at least one edge straight are used, and the drawing paper is pinned on to these with drawing pins. All horizontal lines in the drawing are made with a T-square (so called because of its shape). All vertical lines are made with a set square in conjunction with a T-square, for two sides of the set square form a right angle (Fig. 1*f*). By turning the set square on its side, its other angles can be used. There are various shapes of set square, the most common being a 45° one, in which two of its angles are 45°; and a 60° type in which the set square has its right angle, one angle of 60°, and one of 30°.

If it is necessary to draw a line at an angle which is not within the various combinations of set squares, either an adjustable square is used, or the angle is marked off on the drawing using a protractor.

Measurement for length is done by means of a scaled rule. This is like a ruler but, in addition to being marked in inches, it is also marked in the scales commonly used. Thus in Fig. 1*g*, for example, the scale (a) shows actual inches. In the bottom scale (b), the divisions are only half the size, thus representing inches when drawn to half-scale—that is, each division is actually only half an inch. A draughtsman drawing to half-scale would use this bottom scale and consider these divisions as if they were actually inches. His finished drawing would be half the actual size, and he would mark it accordingly; scale: ½ in. = 1 in. Other sides of the scaled rules shown carry other commonly used scales—the triangular type carrying twelve different ones. Lines are not drawn directly from the scaled rule, which is used only for measurement. The required measurement is taken from it and transferred to the drawing either directly or by using dividers, the line being drawn by the T-square or set square.

Drawings are made in pencil of a grade suitable to the surface of the material and with a sharp chisel point. The drawings are subsequently copied, or traced, in ink to facilitate reproduction (see DRAWING, REPRODUCTION OF). Special pens are used, as shown in Fig. 1e. They are charged with drawing ink, which is an intense black, and are so shaped that a space is maintained between the pen and the straight edge so that the ink does not run under the edge. The thickness of the line is controlled by the adjusting screw.

Circles are drawn by means of special compasses, as shown in Fig. 1b, c. They can be fitted either with pencil lead or drawing pen. The screws are used to adjust the compasses to the required diameter. The instrument Fig. 1a is a divider for measuring off distances. For other curves, a French curve (Fig. 1d) is used, a portion of this being selected to fit the curve to be drawn.

Apart from drawing instruments, special

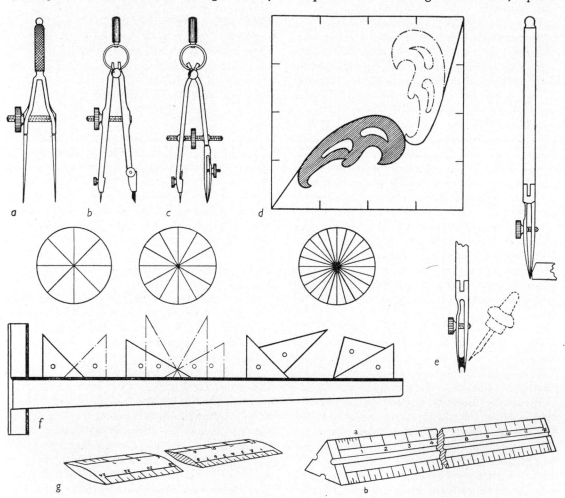

FIG. 1. DRAWING INSTRUMENTS

a. Dividers. *b.* Compass with pencil. *c.* Compass with pen. *d.* French curve. *e.* Pens showing method of filling and drawing. *f.* T-square and set squares. The circles show the angles that can be drawn by 45° and 60° set squares arranged as on the T-squares. *g.* Scales marked in inches and half inches

draughting machines are also used. Some of these are very ingeniously designed to allow perspective or other forms of three-dimensional views to be made from normal orthographic projections (*see* ENGINEERING DRAWING).

DRAWING, REPRODUCTION OF. Whenever an ENGINEERING DRAWING (q.v.) is made, it is important to be able to copy it cheaply and quickly. A number of copies may be needed for various departments, such as the PRODUCTION ENGINEERING Department (q.v.) or Progress Department, in addition to the copies needed in the workshop where the part is being produced. There must also be copies available for replacement.

A tracing of the original drawing is usually taken in ink, and this acts as the 'master' from which all copies are reproduced.

Methods of copying go back as far as the Industrial Revolution—James Watt (the inventor of the steam engine) actually took out a patent for 'A New Method of Copying Letters and Other Writings Expeditiously', as long ago as 1780. His methods would astonish the modern print-room. Here is his own description, for instance, of the ink he used for preparing drawings for copying:

'Take four quarts, ale measure, of spring water, one pound and a half avoirdupois weight of Aleppo galls, half a pound of green copperas or green vitriol, half a pound of gum arabic, four ounces of roach allum; pound the solid ingredients, and infuse them in the water six weeks or two months, during which time the liquor should be frequently shaken; strain the liquor through a linen cloth, and keep it in bottles closely corkt for use.'

Modern and much more simple methods use specially prepared papers and chemicals. The best-known process, introduced in 1842 by Sir John Herschel, is the 'blueprint'. The tracing is placed over a chemically prepared paper and exposed to light, which reacts on the part of the paper not protected by the lines of the drawing. The print is 'developed' by being placed in water, when the whole surface of the paper, except for the lines in the drawing, turns blue, the lines remaining white. This produces the familiar 'blueprint' in which the 'drawing' appears white on a blue background. In modern blue-printing machines a very bright light is produced from mercury-discharge lamps.

Crown Copyright

FIG. I. A CONTINUOUS PHOTO-PRINTING MACHINE
The speed of the canvas feed belt is varied to ensure correct exposure of the negatives

A number of other copying processes have been developed, including some in which the drawing appears dark on a light background; and methods have been devised that eliminate the lengthy process of washing and drying, inevitable with blueprints. One modern photo-printing machine uses the dry process of development. The print is made on sensitized paper which is exposed to ammonia vapour. The drawing and sensitized paper are fed into the machine, and within a minute the finished print is delivered into one tray and the drawing into another. This process, with no fixing or washing, eliminates the danger of shrinkage or expansion of the print.

The 'dye-line' process, named from the chemical employed, produces black lines on white paper. The print is exposed in a machine of the type shown in Fig. 1. It then passes over a roller which damps its surface with the developing fluid. Pencil and ink, through which different amounts of light penetrate, produce different colours on the print if special paper is used.

There are also other photographic methods of reproduction, of which the Photostat machine is a well-known example. This is a self-contained apparatus comprising a camera, a copying board of sufficient size to accommodate drawings up to 40 inches by 50 inches, and developing and

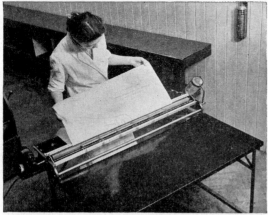

FIG. 2. A DEVELOPING MACHINE USED FOR THE SEMI-DRY DYE-LINE PROCESS

printing baths. It is capable of producing negatives up to a maximum size of 18 inches by 24 inches and can carry a roll of sensitized paper up to 350 feet in length. It produces a reproduction of the drawing in negative form, from which any number of positive prints can be made by recopying it in the camera.

Drawings may be reproduced by an electrical process called xerography. In this a thin sheet of metal is coated with a material which is given a positive electric charge. When it is covered with the drawing and a light shone on to it, the part not covered with the lines of the drawing loses its charge while the parts beneath the lines retain it. The surface is dusted with a negatively charged powder which sticks to the charged portion only. To make a print a positively charged paper is put over the plate. The particles cling to the paper which is then removed and, when heated, the particles fuse to give a black line.

See also Vol. VII: PROCESS REPRODUCTION.

DREDGING, *see* FLOOD CONTROL. *See also* Vol. IV: DREDGER.

DRILLING AND BORING MACHINES. **1.** In every branch of engineering holes have to be made to accommodate the bolts and screws that are used to hold parts together. The main function of the drilling machine is to produce circular holes, and it is found in every factory and workshop. As hand tools, drilling machines are older even than LATHES (q.v.).

The modern machine consists in essence of a vertical revolving spindle carrying at its lower end the cutting tool, known as the drill. The work which is to be drilled is held, or clamped, to the machine table immediately below the spindle, or sometimes it is locked in a drilling jig (*see* JIGS AND FIXTURES) and the revolving drill is fed downwards into the work (Fig. 1).

The wide variety of drilling machines needed to meet modern requirements can be divided broadly into four groups: the single-spindle drill press; radial drills; multi-spindle drills; and multi-head drills.

The simplest types, the single-spindle drills, are designed for drilling only one hole at a time; one of the commonest of these is the floor, pillar, or pedestal type. Some smaller types are built to stand on a work-bench instead of on their own pedestal. These drills, used for drilling smaller holes, are known as sensitive drills, because the drill is fed by hand and its sensitive movement enables the operator to feel the cutting action and to control the rate of feed. The heavier floor-type machine uses larger sized drills and often works at a high rate of production. The machine is operated by its own electric motor,

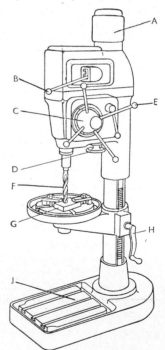

FIG. 1. FLOOR-TYPE DRILLING MACHINE

A. Driving motor. B. Change speed lever. C. Coarse feed hand wheel. D. Fine feed hand wheel. E. Power feed change lever. F. Drill. G. Work clamped to work-table. H. Handle for raising table. J. Work-table for large work-pieces

but the feed of the drilling spindle to and from the work can be disengaged at will and the feed applied by hand, using a handwheel operating through gears.

The radial drilling machine (Fig. 2) is used primarily for heavy work, where it is more convenient to keep the job stationary and to move the drilling spindle over the work. The spindle (A) is carried in a drilling head (B), which can be moved along a radial arm (C) mounted on a heavy vertical column (D). The arm can be rotated on the column and also moved up and down it to suit work of different thicknesses. All the movements are usually power driven and are controlled from the drilling head itself.

Modern drilling machines usually have geared drives, so that the drilling speed can be varied according to the requirements of the job.

When a number of holes have to be drilled in one workpiece, it is convenient to use a multi-spindle drill, a machine with a dozen or more drilling spindles, all mounted in one head and driven from a central shaft through gearing. They are all rotated and fed downwards together, so that a pattern of holes can be drilled simultaneously into the work, which is held in a drilling jig.

The most modern development is the multi-head machine which must be specially built for a special purpose. It may have horizontal as well as vertical multi-spindle heads, so that holes can be drilled into the top and the sides of the work at the same time. In one such example, ninety-eight holes are drilled in a component in a single operation.

Twist drills (*see* p. 163) are so widely used that they have been standardized in a British Standard Specification. A twist drill is made of high-speed steel (*see* IRON AND STEEL) and may be tipped with tungsten carbide for drilling very hard or abrasive materials. It has a cylindrical body in which are cut two spiral grooves or 'flutes' that provide the cutting edges and allow the waste material, or swarf, to escape from the hole. The edges at the point of the drill are ground to an angle which, on standard drills, is 118°.

Holes which have to be very accurate are often first drilled slightly undersize and then 'reamed'. The reamer (*see* p. 163), which has straight flutes, removes only a little more metal to bring the hole accurately to the exact final size.

Sometimes a hole has to be recessed to take the

FIG. 2. RADIAL DRILLING MACHINES DRILLING HOLES IN A HEAVY CASTING

A. Spindle. B. Drilling head. C. Radial arm. D. Vertical column. E. Other workpieces mounted ready for drilling

head of a screw. For conical screw heads this process, which is known as 'countersinking', is done by a countersink drill. For cylindrical or 'cheese headed' screws, the end of the hole has to be enlarged either by a counterbore or sometimes by a larger-size twist drill. The piece projecting from the end of the counterbore engages with the original hole and acts as a guide or pilot.

2. FINE BORING. Two modern machines have been developed to produce holes of extreme accuracy, beyond the capability of the drilling machine. For the first of these, the precision-boring machine, the workpiece is fixed, and a stiff revolving spindle, carrying a single-point cutting tool, is directed into a pilot hole which is previously made by drilling. The diameter of the hole is progressively enlarged by increasing the distance that the cutting tool projects from the spindle.

The second precision machine is the jig-boring machine, which can place holes in a workpiece to an accuracy within one ten-thousandth of an inch. The table on which the work is mounted rides on a slide which can move it in two directions at right angles to each other, so that the work can be brought into any working position under the tool spindle. The work is positioned under the tool with great precision by using

FIG. 3. 42-FT. VERTICAL
BORING MILL

A. Revolving work-table.
B. Tool spindles. C. Cross-beam with operator's
platform
Craven Bros., Manchester

measuring devices, now usually built into the machine, which are a special feature of jig borers. Another feature is the accuracy and robustness of the boring spindle, which rotates in special bearings contained in a sheath, and which can be raised or lowered to provide the feed for the drill or cutting tool. The hole is first drilled and then enlarged in the same way as with a precision-boring machine.

Wickman Ltd.

FIG. 4. HORIZONTAL BORER BORING A LARGE HOLE IN A
CASTING

The planer type of jig borer has the boring spindle housed in a saddle, which travels along a cross-beam to make a transverse movement, while a longitudinal movement is obtained by moving the table. These machines, primarily developed for making jigs and fixtures, are now also used for production operations where components have to be made to a high degree of accuracy and yet not in sufficient quantities to justify making expensive jigs.

Because of the high accuracy to which jig borers have to work, they are usually housed in temperature-controlled enclosures in the works.

3. BORING MILLS. These are more like lathes than drills, and are used for boring large diameters. The work rotates on a table, and the cutting tool can be fed sideways so that, as each cut is finished, it can be moved farther across into the work to take another cut, until the final diameter has been reached. These machines are often very large—one recently completed can take work 42 feet in diameter weighing over 100 tons, and it weighs over 600 tons itself (Fig. 3).

4. GUN-BORING MACHINES. These are used for the difficult boring of long gun barrels. The whole gun barrel is held and rotated in a large, hollow, horizontal, driving spindle, fixed to a long machine bed (Fig. 4). The cutting tool, projecting from the end of a massive boring bar carried on a saddle, is slowly fed into a roughly formed hole in the barrel as the gun rotates. On some machines the boring is carried out from both ends simultaneously. The boring bar, which is necessarily long, has to be supported in a bearing near the mouth of the bore in order to give it additional rigidity. A machine of this type with a bed 88 feet long will accommodate gun barrels up to 24 feet in diameter and over 30 feet in length. Guns are also bored on gun-boring LATHES (q.v.), in which case the barrel, clamped to a faceplate, rotates on large supporting rollers. The boring bar is mounted in the lathe saddle and is fed into the gun from one end in the same manner as on gun-boring machines.

See also MACHINE TOOLS; SCREW-THREADS.

DYNAMICS, *see* MECHANICS.

DYNAMO, *see* ELECTRIC GENERATORS.

DYNAMOMETER. This word, derived from Greek words for 'power' and 'measure', means a machine which measures ENERGY (q.v.). Most dynamometers 'absorb' the energy that they are measuring, that is, they convert it into heat or electric current. Nearly all engines are tested on 'absorption dynamometers' before delivery to the user.

To test an engine in this way, it must be resisted. Thus an absorption dynamometer must have some means for applying a resistance to the rotation of the engine shaft to which it is coupled. At first, this resistance was created by a friction brake, and then by a rope-brake, in which a rope is coiled once or more round the flywheel on the engine shaft, sometimes with wooden blocks between. The pull on the rope indicated the power of the engine. These types, however, are not very suitable for modern engines.

The type in most general use is a hydraulic dynamometer. It consists of an inner wheel fitted

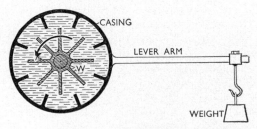

FIG. I. PRINCIPLE OF THE HYDRAULIC DYNAMOMETER
w. Wheel driven by engine

with blades revolving in a watertight casing (Fig. 1). The engine turns the wheel, which stirs the water, causing drag which tries to turn the casing round. This casing is connected by a lever arm to a weighing machine. The more powerful the engine driving the inner wheel, the heavier the weight needed to hold the casing still.

The work done by the engine in exerting a force against the lever arm during each revolution is equal to the weight multiplied by the distance through which the arm would travel if it were rotating. The work done per minute, that is, the 'power' absorbed by the dynamometer, is the work done per revolution of the engine multiplied by the number of times the engine revolves per minute. So if we determine the weight that just holds the lever arm steady when the engine is running at a certain power output, and if we measure the speed of the engine, we can calculate the horse-power. Hydraulic dynamometers have been made up to 60,000 b.h.p. (brake horse-power).

As well as hydraulic dynamometers there are also electric dynamometers (usually direct current) in which the engine power is converted into useful current by means of an ELECTRIC GENERATOR (q.v.). Another type, of partly electrical nature, is the eddy-current dynamometer; this absorbs power by creating electrical eddy currents which are dissipated as heat and cannot be put to useful work. It is nevertheless a popular machine because it can be controlled electronically and can thus have numerous automatic features imparted to it.

All these dynamometers make it possible to measure the 'overall efficiency' of the engine, that is, the ratio between the energy in the fuel consumed and the energy produced by the engine. The electric dynamometer can also act as a motor to drive the engine. Thus it is possible to find the power needed to overcome the wasted energy (friction of pistons, bearings, and so on) in reciprocating engines (*see* INTERNAL COMBUSTION ENGINES).

STEAM ENGINES, STEAM TURBINES, and GAS TURBINES (qq.v.) can be tested in the same way. The purpose of a turbine, however, being often to drive electric generators, the generators themselves are sometimes used as dynamometers, by measuring the volts and amperes produced and from them calculating the power of the turbine. Such methods involve a knowledge of the efficiency of the generator—that is, the amount of

Heenan and Froude

TESTING THE BRAKE HORSE-POWER OF AN EXPRESS LOCOMOTIVE ON HYDRAULIC DYNAMOMETERS AT THE BRITISH RAILWAYS
LOCOMOTIVE WORKS AT RUGBY

electrical energy which it produces for a given input of power to its shaft.

Reaction gas turbines for aeroplanes ('jet engines') develop no external power at all, and therefore no dynamometer can be used. Such engines are tested by mounting them on a 'thrust cradle', which is connected to some form of weighing machine to measure the direct push exerted by the engine.

Gas turbines are, however, often made in a form in which they can drive aeroplane propellers (propeller turbines), ships' screws, electrical generators, and so on. Such engines usually have speed-reduction gearing between the turbine itself and the final output shaft, and they can then be tested by dynamometers of conventional types. But for research purposes, when the turbine must be tested without any reduction gearing, special dynamometers able to run at very high speeds are designed. Dynamometers have been made for running at 24,000 r.p.m. (revolutions per minute) and it seems probable that small units may reach 100,000 r.p.m. in the future.

Sometimes, as when testing the power of railway locomotives, it is not convenient to couple dynamometers directly to the axle shaft. The driving wheels in such cases rest on rollers, and the dynamometers are coupled to the roller shafts; at Rugby, British Railways have installed the finest test plant of this kind in the world.

See also ENERGY.

E

EARTH-MOVING EQUIPMENT. Nearly all CIVIL ENGINEERING schemes (q.v.) of any size involve the movement of large quantities of earth and in some, such as road, railway, and airfield construction, earth dams, and irrigation schemes, the movement of earth is the most important part. The speed and cost of this kind of work, therefore, depend very largely on the methods which are available for earth moving. In Britain until the latter end of the 19th century, and in some parts of the world even today, an abundance of very cheap labour made it possible to move large quantities of earth by hand with the assistance of horse or donkey transport: indeed, many of our early RAILWAYS and CANALS (qq.v. Vol. IV) were built in this way.

Towards the end of the 19th century, when steam power began to be used, earth was dug and loaded by means of steam shovels, and carted away and tipped into position by wagons hauled by steam locomotives. This method remained the most important one until the early 1930's, when the rapidly developing diesel engine, with its much greater compactness, began to replace the steam engine. The diesel engine made it possible to use a wide range of specialized types of earth-moving equipment, and so considerably to reduce the time needed to carry out civil engineering jobs involving a lot of earthworks. The improvement in methods has very nearly kept pace with the general rise in prices so that, in fact, it costs little more today to remove large quantities of earth than it did 50 years ago. This is most important in industries such as cement and brick manufacturing and coal and iron ore 'opencast' MINING (q.v. Vol. VII): indeed it is only the development of very large mechanical excavators which has made 'opencast' mining for coal an economic possibility in Great Britain. Most of the development of earth-moving plant has

taken place in the United States, where there has been the greatest demand for it and where its manufacture is now a very important industry.

In earth moving, and by earth is meant every kind of mineral formation from mud to the hardest rocks, there are three processes to be considered: these are (*a*) digging and loading, (*b*) transporting, (*c*) placing into position. Some types of equipment are intended to carry out all three operations and others only do one or two. Which type or combination of types is most suitable for a particular job depends on such considerations as the hardness of the material, the thickness and shape of the layer which has to be dug, the distance it has to be removed, and so on. Basically there are two main types of equipment, the scraper and the mechanical excavator: the scraper is intended to do all three operations; while the mechanical excavator only digs and loads, and so, if the material has to be placed and levelled into position, it must work in conjunction with some form of vehicle for transporting and with a bulldozer.

The scraper is in essence an open steel box on wheels. The plate which forms the bottom of the box projects in front and has a sharp knife-like blade attached along its length: the side of the box over this blade can be raised and lowered (*see* Fig. 1). When the scraper is in operation, the forward end of the box is lowered so that the blade rests on the earth, the side is raised, and the whole box drawn forward. The action is like a carpenter's plane, the blade cuts into the earth and scoops it up into the box behind; when it is full the blade is raised, the side lowered, and the whole box pulled to wherever the earth has to be tipped.

The considerable power needed to pull the scraper is provided by a powerful tractor attached by a draw bar to the front. Tipping is carried out by raising the front side and pulling forward the rear side to eject the earth. Scrapers are made in all sizes to hold from 4 to 25 cubic yards, but they will, of course, dig only comparatively soft material. The tractor most often used for pulling is a tracked vehicle—that is, it runs on tracks like a tank (*see* TRACK MECHANISM)— because this type grips the ground better and can therefore exert a greater pull. Such tractors, however, have only a comparatively slow maximum speed, so it is not economical to use them when the earth has to be hauled a long way to be

John Laing & Son Ltd.

FIG. 1. 'CATERPILLAR' TRACTOR PULLING SCRAPER WITH ELEVATOR ATTACHMENT FOR LOADING THE TRUCK WHICH FOLLOWS IT UP

John Laing & Son Ltd.

FIG. 2. WALKING DRAGLINE WITH ANOTHER TYPE OF DRAGLINE IN THE BACKGROUND

tipped. There is a tendency now, therefore, to develop scrapers designed to be hauled at high speeds by wheeled tractors which have very large rubber tyres with specially designed treads. In favourable conditions these tractors will pull the scraper while loading, but if the ground is slippery or hard they have to be assisted by bulldozers pushing from the rear.

The bulldozer is simply a track-laying type of tractor with a wide, shallow plate in front, which is used for pushing. The tractor can, of course, at the same time be used for pulling.

The mechanical excavator is stationary while actually digging but will propel itself on tracks or, in the case of the largest types, on pads worked by cams. Basically it is an undercarriage carrying an engine which operates a number of drums round which wire ropes are wound: when the drums are revolved, the rope is let out or pulled in to operate a bucket carried on an equipment attached to the front of the machine. There are a number of different types of equipment and buckets which permit the excavator to carry out different types of digging.

The 'dragline' is a long lattice-work jib or arm through which runs a wire rope, carrying a scoop-shaped bucket at its end. When digging, the bucket is thrown out and pulled along the ground towards the machine, scooping up material on its way (Fig. 2). For depositing, the machine is rotated into the correct direction, the bucket is let out, and the back pulled up so that the material drops out. The dragline has a comparatively large radius of action and is used mainly for digging deep holes or for any operation entailing what is known as 'digging and throwing', where the material dug has not got to be carted away. The same type of jib is used for the 'grab', but the bucket is rather like a hinged shell and is lowered and raised straight down and up. It is used in confined spaces where a large radius of operation is required. The 'crowd shovel' uses a short, heavy jib and a bucket which is scooped upward when digging. It is the equipment generally used for loading earth into vehicles to be carted away (Fig. 3). The 'backacter' or 'trench hoe' is a rather similar equipment, but the digging motion is toward the machine, and it is used for excavating trenches. The 'skimmer' is used for removing and loading thin layers of earth: the short heavy jib is held parallel to the ground, and the bucket travels along it away from the machine.

John Laing & Son Ltd.

FIG. 3. A CROWD SHOVEL

The dragline and the crowd shovel are very much the most important of these equipments, and they are the ones which are used in opencast mining. Very large machines indeed have been developed for carrying these equipments: there are draglines in existence with jibs 300 feet long and buckets of 45 cubic yards capacity, and there are crowd shovels of the same capacity. These very large machines are usually electrically operated, a small power station being built near where the machine is to operate, and electricity fed into it by cable.

For working with crowd shovels of over $1\frac{1}{2}$ cubic yards capacity the ordinary lorry is not large or robust enough, and special dump trucks are used.

See also ROAD BUILDING; CRANES; CONVEYORS.

ECHO-SOUNDING APPARATUS, *see* HYDROGRAPHY; ULTRASONICS.

ELECTRICAL ENGINEERING. This concerns everything that has to do with the generation and use of electric currents. It is a fairly new branch of engineering, and as we know it today it has very largely grown from Michael Faraday's famous discovery of a method for producing an electric current by moving a copper wire near a magnet (*see* ELECTRICAL ENGINEERING, HISTORY OF).

The methods and machines used by electrical engineers cannot be understood without knowing something of the nature of ELECTRICITY (q.v. Vol. III), and how the ELECTRIC CURRENT (q.v.) behaves when it flows through a metal wire. The method of producing an electric current discovered by FARADAY (q.v. Vol. V) is described in the article on INDUCTION, ELECTRIC, and one of its many uses is considered under TRANSFORMER, ELECTRIC. The two most important groups of electrical machines are ELECTRIC GENERATORS and ELECTRIC MOTORS. Electric power is produced in POWER STATIONS and is distributed all over Britain by the overhead electric CABLES of the GRID SYSTEM. The distribution is controlled by SWITCHGEAR (qq.v.). The installation and maintenance of electrical supplies in the home are described in Vol. XI in the article ELECTRICITY, DOMESTIC.

The grid system deals with the distribution of electric power over long distances and at very high voltages, but the distribution over the public supply mains under streets and inside houses takes place at lower voltages.

Small electric currents are often used in portable electrical equipment such as torches, portable radio sets, and so on. These equipments cannot be joined to the public mains, and their electric current is usually supplied by a BATTERY (q.v.), in which a chemical action is used to produce current. An electric current can also be used to produce a chemical action by being passed through a suitable liquid solution. This chemical action is made use of in accumulators and for depositing thin coats of metals, such as chromium or silver, by the process called ELECTROPLATING (q.v.).

Electric currents are necessary to the workings of telephones, telephone exchanges, and trunk cables (*see* TELEPHONE ENGINEERING).

See also ELECTRONICS.

ELECTRICAL ENGINEERING, HISTORY OF.
The history of electrical power may be said to have begun in 1831 with the discovery by Michael FARADAY (q.v. Vol. V) that an electric current could be induced in a wire by moving it through a region influenced by a magnet (*see* INDUCTION, ELECTRIC). Before then, the only convenient source of electricity was the primary BATTERY (q.v.), in which small quantities of

Crown Copyright, Science Museum
FARADAY'S MAGNET AND DISK, 1831
This was the first magneto-electric machine to generate a continuous electric current. By spinning the copper disk rapidly between the poles of the large magnet, a weak electric current was generated which deflected the pointer of the sensitive galvanometer on the stool

electricity are generated by chemical means. Faraday's discovery opened up the possibility of generating large electric currents by using mechanical force. His original magneto-electric machine, or 'dynamo', could generate only enough electricity to light a small torch bulb—if such a thing had existed in those days—but it was the beginning from which all future current-producing machines or ELECTRIC GENERATORS (q.v.) have developed.

Faraday's discovery caused great interest throughout the scientific world, and within a few months H. Pixii of Paris had produced a further machine. In this machine, when a permanent horseshoe magnet was rotated in front of two bobbins with iron-cores and coils of wire wound round them, an ELECTRIC CURRENT (q.v.) was generated in the coils of wire.

Not only had these machines a very small output but there seemed to be no good use to which this form of power could be put, for there were no electric lamps or motors to make a demand for large electric currents. In 1838, however, Jacobi introduced ELECTROPLATING (q.v.); but even then the demand was limited until the use of electric current to operate carbon-arc lamps for LIGHTHOUSES (q.v. Vol. IV) was evolved. This led to rapid development. Sir Humphry DAVY (q.v. Vol. V) had discovered in 1809 that an electric flame, or arc, giving off a brilliant light, is produced when two carbon rods joined to a source of electricity (a battery in his case) are touched together and then slightly separated. In 1858 two generators of 3 horse-power—a great power for that day—were installed at the South Foreland lighthouse.

Early machines were all fitted with inefficient permanent magnets, but scientists early realized that greater output would be possible with electromagnets (see MAGNETS, Section 2). One had, indeed, been used in a primitive machine by Sturgeon as early as 1832, but it was not until 1863 that Wilde patented his first machine with powerful electromagnets, energized by the current from a second small dynamo or generator perched on top of the main machine.

The use of a separate small dynamo to provide the magnetizing current was inconvenient, and within the next few years a 'self-exciting' dynamo was developed simultaneously by the inventors, Varley, Wheatstone, and Siemens. They made use of the fact that the field magnets of any

Crown Copyright, Science Museum

WILDE'S DYNAMO, 1863–5

Powerful electromagnets increased the current generated

dynamo retain a small amount of magnetism almost indefinitely. This residual magnetism can be built up progressively by current from the dynamos, and a large output achieved. The important principle of self-excitation was universally adopted.

Until about 1880 the chief use for generators was to supply current for arc lights, but these were not widely used because the carbons needed frequent attention. In 1877, however, this difficulty was largely eliminated by the invention of the 'Jablochkoff candle'—a simple kind of self-regulating arc lamp that could burn for $1\frac{1}{2}$ to 3 hours without attention, the carbons being controlled by springs. As these new lights were installed in public places and shops, crowds flocked to see the brilliant illuminations. A demand was thus created for more and larger generators, which were for the most part installed singly as private undertakings; there were as yet no central power stations or public supplies.

The invention of the incandescent filament lamp by Swan in 1878 and EDISON (q.v. Vol. V) in 1879 started a widespread demand for electricity, and this led to the building of central

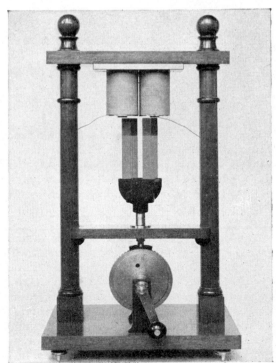

Crown Copyright, Science Museum

REPLICA OF PIXII'S GENERATOR, 1831

MODEL OF THE FIRST POWER STATION IN THE WORLD

Crown Copyright, Science Museum

The boilers on the ground floor supplied steam to drive the generators and the engines on the first floor. The second floor contained carbon regulators to control the generated current and on the third floor there was a bank of lamps for testing the generators

power stations, and to the beginning of the use of electricity as a source of power in industry.

The electric lamps of the 1880's were dull and inefficient by modern standards—they were only of 12 to 16 candlepower. But in spite of this their simplicity and convenience made them more attractive than gas for ILLUMINATION (q.v.). In the early years, however, while there were neither electric mains nor general wiring, the installing of electric light was very expensive.

The first POWER STATION (q.v.) to be erected in a central position to serve many customers was built by Edison in Pearl Street, New York, in 1882. It was to supply electricity to consumers who used Edison's own carbon filament lamps—the station being designed to provide current for 10,000 lamps—the first supply of electricity for the ordinary private citizen. Edison's power

station—of which a model exists in the Science Museum at South Kensington—was equipped with six dynamos giving 110 volts and driven by six 175-h.p. steam engines. It carried on its pioneer task for 8 years until destroyed by fire. Other power stations were soon set up, both in America and Britain.

The development of central power stations gave rise to many new problems concerned with distributing the current, and, indeed, apart from the development of high-speed ALTERNATING CURRENT generators (q.v.) of ever-increasing capacity, this has been the main concern of electrical engineering since 1880. A given amount of electric power can be transmitted in two ways—either as a small current (amperes) at very high pressure (volts), or a large current at fairly low pressure. The second way is the more wasteful, for the powerful current loses much of its energy in heat by the effort of forcing its way through the wires. Therefore the electric power from the power station is generally put through a TRANS-FORMER (q.v.) to reduce the current and increase the voltage. Voltages as high as 132,000 are now in common use for long-distance transmission, and in a few cases voltages more than three times as high are used.

High voltages require alternating current generators as well as transformers to change the voltage. The early dynamos nearly all produced direct current; and it was not until about 1880, with the invention of electric lighting which worked equally well on alternating current, that it was worth while to build alternating current (A.C.) generators. Development was then rapid, and by 1889 Ferranti had designed a 1,000-kilo-watt machine (about 1,300 h.p.) for the new Deptford power station near London. This generated at 10,000 volts, and the supply was carried into London by an underground CABLE (q.v.), which had paper insulation inside it and which had to be manufactured and laid in 20-foot lengths. Many technical problems had to be overcome, and many lessons learned, before the installation was successful.

Early generators were slow machines driven by ordinary STEAM ENGINES (q.v.), but in 1884 Sir Charles Parsons invented the STEAM TUR-BINE (q.v.) and used it to drive a small A.C. generator at a speed of 18,000 revolutions a minute. By 1900 turbo-alternators (turbine-driven A.C. generators) of 1,000 kilowatts were working, and by 1912 a 25,000-kilowatt set was built for Chicago.

All this was made possible by the transformer. Faraday, as early as 1831, had discovered that if two separate coils were wound on an iron ring, the making or stopping of a current in one coil would result in a brief flow of current in the other. But the principle was not used in the trans-forming of electric power until 1882, and then, in less than 10 years, transformers of 200 kilowatts, working at 10,000 volts, were being designed for the London Electric Supply Corporation. The early transformers lost much power because the poor quality of the iron cores resulted in wasteful heating. But in 1903 the use of silicon steel cores overcame most of this waste, and a large modern transformer may waste no more than 1% of the power that it handles.

High-voltage transmission and transformers have made it practicable and economic to trans-mit electrical power over long distances—from the generating stations built where plenty of coal can be cheaply delivered to industrial or resi-dential areas where electricity is wanted. This has greatly affected the LOCALIZATION OF INDUS-TRY (q.v. Vol. VII), for it is no longer necessary to concentrate factories round coal-fields. Also generating stations can now be connected, as in the British GRID SYSTEM (q.v.), so that they can pass on current from one area to another with ease.

Although people are inclined to regard elec-tric light and heating—and perhaps radio—as the most important of the uses to which elec-tricity is put, it is probable that the ELECTRIC MOTOR (q.v.) has had a wider influence than any other upon our way of life during the present century. Perhaps its most important use has been in transport. The first ELECTRIC RAILWAY in Britain was the City and South London Railway, opened in 1890, and the first electric TRAMWAY system in a British town started in Leeds in 1891 (qq.v. Vol. IV). It is difficult to imagine what life in London, Paris, or New York would be like today without electric railways.

The electric motor is becoming more and more essential for countless industrial purposes, for drills, lathes, and other MACHINE TOOLS (q.v.), for electric lifts, escalators, and ventilating fans, and for many domestic purposes such as vacuum cleaners, refrigerators, washing machines, and food mixers.

See also Vol. III: ELECTRICITY IN NATURE.

ELECTRICAL INSTRUMENTS

ELECTRICAL INSTRUMENTS are used to measure various quantities connected with the flow of ELECTRIC CURRENT (q.v.).

1. GALVANOMETERS. In 1819 the Danish scientist Oersted demonstrated the magnetic effect of an electric current (*see* MAGNETS) with an instrument consisting of a magnetic compass placed near a straight copper wire. When no current flows through the wire, the compass needle points to the North; but when an electric current is passed through the wire the needle moves away from the North, the amount by which it moves being a measure of the strength of the current. This simple device responds only to quite powerful currents, but it can be made responsive to much weaker currents if the copper wire is wound into a coil with several turns over and under the compass (Fig. 1), for this greatly increases the magnetic effect of the current. Galvanometers owe their name to galvanic electricity, the name once given to battery currents

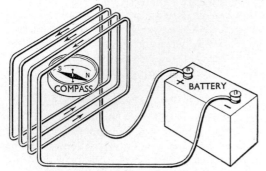

FIG. 1. PRINCIPLE OF THE GALVANOMETER

When an electric current flows through the wire, the compass needle is deflected by the amount corresponding to the strength of the current

(the only currents then known) in honour of the 18th-century Italian scientist, L. Galvani. They are delicate instruments and not suitable for everyday use in electrical engineering.

2. MOVING-IRON AMMETERS. A widely used device to measure current depends on the fact that a coil of wire carrying a current acts like a magnet and attracts pieces of iron. In Fig. 2 the magnetism produced by the current in the coil of wire attracts a pear-shaped piece of soft iron, A. The iron is free to turn on a spindle, s, and when it is attracted it moves towards the coil to the position shown by dotted lines. The extent to which it moves is indicated by the pointer P on a graduated scale. When no electric current is flowing, the pointer points to the zero mark, and the stronger the current the stronger is the attraction, and the farther the pointer moves over the scale. The scale of a 'moving iron' instrument can be marked to indicate directly the

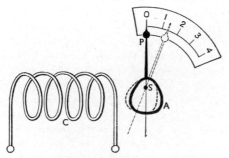

FIG. 2. MOVING-IRON AMMETER

A. Soft iron. s. Spindle. P. Pointer. c. Coil through which current flows

strength of the current in amperes (the units of current), in which case the instrument is called an ampere-meter, or ammeter. The magnetic attraction remains the same in whichever direction current is flowing through the coil, so the instrument can be used to measure either A.C. (alternating current) or D.C. (direct current). Moving-iron instruments are both cheap and reliable, but they do give incorrect indications when strong magnetic influences are near them, and they are not suitable for measuring weak currents.

3. MOVING-COIL AMMETERS. These are the most commonly used instruments for measuring the strength of currents. A moving-coil ammeter works in a very similar way to an ELECTRIC MOTOR (q.v.), both depending upon the magnetic effect of an electric current, which causes a natural force to act on a wire carrying a current when a magnet is near by. In Fig. 3 the current

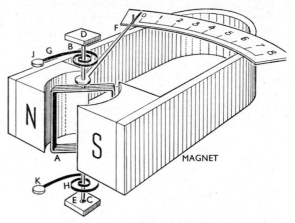

FIG. 3. MOVING-COIL AMMETER

A. Copper coil. B, C. Spindles. D, E. Pivots. F. Pointer G, H. Springs. J, K. Terminals

is carried by an oblong coil, A, which has several strands of copper wire to increase the magnetic effect. This coil is fixed to two steel spindles, B and C, which have needle-pointed ends working in pivots, D and E. A light pointer, F, fixed to one of the spindles, moves over a scale as the coil turns on its spindles. Two spiral hairsprings, G and H, fixed to the two spindles, are used to connect the moving coil to the electric circuit at J and K, and also to twist the spindles so that the pointer is normally held at zero mark on the scale. The coil is surrounded by the pole pieces, N and S, of a powerful horseshoe magnet. When an electric current comes from a battery or generator and passes via the hairsprings through the coil, magnetic forces make the coil turn on its spindle, and the pointer moves along the scale. The stronger the current the stronger the magnetic force, and so the farther the pointer moves. The scale can be marked to read the strength of the current in amperes. When the current is switched off, the hairsprings return the pointer to the zero mark.

The direction of the magnetic forces depends on the direction in which the electric current is flowing through the coil, so that moving-coil instruments are suitable only for measuring D.C., and can be used to measure A.C. only by first converting it to direct current with a RECTIFIER (q.v.) and then measuring the direct current. Moving-coil instruments are rather more expensive than moving-iron instruments, but as they are more accurate and can measure much weaker currents, they are widely used. In practice a stationary iron cylinder is usually placed inside the moving coil because this increases the magnetic effect of the current.

4. USE OF AMMETERS. These are connected to electric circuits to measure the strength of the currents that are flowing. It is important that the ammeter should offer as little resistance as possible to the flow of the current, which is needed to light lamps, drive an electric motor, or perform some other task. A low resistance could be obtained by winding the ammeter coil with thick wire, but it is usually more convenient to use thin wire for the coil and to pass only a small part of the main current through the coil. Most of the current is diverted through a separate low-resistance conductor called a 'shunt', which is joined in parallel with the ammeter (Fig. 4a). If, for example, the resistance of the coil is nine times greater than that of the shunt, then the main current divides so that nine-tenths of it passes through the shunt (to light the lamps or drive the motor) and only one-tenth through the coil (to work the ammeter).

5. USE OF VOLTMETER. Galvanometers and ammeters can be used not only to measure the strength or quantity of an electric current (amperes) but also to serve as voltmeters—that is, to measure the current's pressure (volts). When the instrument is used to join together two points in an electric circuit, the strength of the current that flows through it depends both on the instrument's resistance and on the pressure of current between the two points. Since the resis-

tance of the instrument is fixed, the moving pointer must indicate changes in pressure or voltage. If too much current is allowed to pass

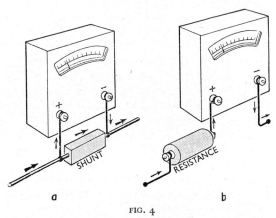

FIG. 4

a. Shunt used to divert current so that only part flows through ammeter. *b.* Instrument used as voltmeter connected in series with resistance

through the voltmeter, the voltage of the entire circuit would fall below its true value, and so give an incorrect result. The electrical instruments used as voltmeters are, therefore, connected in series with a coil of high-resistance wire (Fig. 4b) to reduce the flow of current to a negligible amount.

6. ELECTROSTATIC VOLTMETER. The ideal voltmeter is one that does not pass any electric current at all. This type, which is called an electrostatic voltmeter, does not work well at voltages lower than about 50 volts, but it is very useful for measuring high voltages. The instrument (Fig. 5) consists of a moving vane, A, which

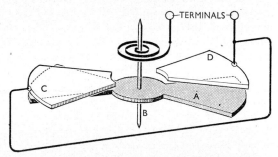

FIG. 5. ELECTROSTATIC VOLTMETER
A. Moving vane. B. Spindle. C, D. Fixed plates

is a butterfly-shaped piece of thin aluminium mounted on a spindle, B. The spindle has pivots, a pointer, and a hairspring, just like the moving-coil instrument shown in Fig. 3. One terminal of the voltmeter is joined to the moving vane, and the other terminal is joined to two wedge-shaped aluminium plates, c and d, which are fixed near the moving vane, but not touching it. When the voltmeter is not connected to an electric circuit, the moving vane does not over-lap the fixed plates. When the voltmeter is con-nected to a circuit, and there is a voltage between its terminals, small amounts of electricity are stored on the fixed plates and on the moving vane on the principle of a CONDENSER (q.v.). The result is that the plates attract the vane, which turns on its spindle against the force of the hair-spring. The greater the voltage, the more elec-tricity is stored and the greater is the attractive force. Electrostatic voltmeters, like moving-iron instruments, can be used directly in A.C. cir-cuits.

7. WATT-HOUR METER. An important kind of electrical instrument is the electricity meter, used both in factories and in ordinary homes to measure the number of units of electricity con-sumed. In houses connected to A.C. mains, as most are nowadays, these meters consist of a small electric motor, a brake, and a set of dials that counts the number of turns made by the motor. The moving part of the motor is simply a very light horizontal disk of aluminium which can usually be seen moving behind a small glass window at the front of the meter. This disk is fitted to a vertical spindle that drives a chain of gear wheels, each wheel carrying a small pointer. The gearing is such that each pointer turns round ten times for one turn of the pointer to the left of it. Two electromagnets are placed near the disk, their fluctuating magnetic fields causing alternating currents to flow in the disk by elec-tromagnetic induction (see INDUCTION, ELEC-TRIC), and setting up forces that drive the disk round. It is braked by the similar but opposing forces produced by two permanent magnets also fixed near it. One electromagnet produces a driving force that depends on the pressure (volts) of the mains supply, and the other produces a force dependent upon the strength (amperes) of any current which is being drawn upon by elec-trical appliances in use. The speed that the motor disk reaches against the braking action of the permanent magnets depends upon the effect of both electromagnets—that is, upon the voltage multiplied by the current, giving the electrical power in watts. The greater the power the greater is the speed of the disk, and the longer the time for which the power is used the more turns the disk will be able to make. The total number of turns of the disk registered by the counter dials, therefore, depends upon the power (watts) and the time (hours)—that is, the dials show how much electrical energy (watt-hours) has been consumed. The commercial measurement of electrical energy is in Board of Trade Units, each of which is equal to 1,000 watt-hours (1 kilowatt-hour); and house meters are arranged to read directly in Board of Trade Units.

8. MEGGERS. Before a newly wired electric circuit, such as the electric lighting and power system of a new factory or house, is connected to the mains for the first time, it is prudent to check the connexions. Accidental contacts leading to short-circuits can cause very powerful currents to flow which may damage the wiring by over-heating it. The electrical instrument used for wiring tests consists of a small portable ELECTRIC GENERATOR (q.v.) which is turned by hand, and a sensitive ammeter to measure any current that flows. This instrument is connected to the wiring with all switches 'off', so that no current should be flowing from the mains, and the handle of the generator is turned. The ammeter will then show a current if any short-circuits are present, and these can be found and removed. These instruments can be made so sensitive that they can measure the minute electric currents that will leak through ordinary insulating materials. They are called 'meggers', which is short for megohm-meters, because they can measure electrical resistances of several millions of ohms—one million ohms being called a 'megohm'.

See also ELECTRICAL ENGINEERING; ELECTRIC CURRENT; MEASUREMENT, UNITS OF.

ELECTRIC BATTERY, see BATTERY, ELEC-TRIC.

ELECTRIC CABLE, see CABLES, ELECTRICAL.

ELECTRIC CLOCKS, see TIMEKEEPERS, MODERN.

ELECTRIC CURRENT. This is a stream of electricity which flows through a conductor, such as a wire, which is connected to a source of electricity—a BATTERY or an ELECTRIC GENERA-TOR (qq.v.). Very little is known of the nature of ELECTRICITY (q.v. Vol. III), but electrical engineers know a great deal about how electric currents behave, and can put them to many uses.

1. CONDUCTORS AND INSULATORS. ATOMS (q.v. Vol. III), of which all matter in the universe consists, are made up mainly of elementary particles of which, from the point of view of the electrical engineer, the most important are those called electrons. Each electron carries a small amount of negative electricity. In substances that can conduct electric currents, such as metals and carbons, some of the electrons can move freely, and when a battery is connected to both ends of a metal wire, the free electrons in the wire flow steadily and quite slowly along it at the speed of about one inch a minute. This stream is the electric current. The electric disturbance, however, which causes the electric current to start flowing, moves at 186,000 miles a second, the speed of light, and electric signals can therefore cross the Atlantic by submarine cable almost instantaneously.

Some substances are conductors of electric current; but there are many substances the electrons of which are not free to move, and no electric current can be made to flow through them. These materials, which include rubber, glass, dry air, paper, and many plastics, are called non-conductors or insulators, since they can insulate (that is, keep separate) the path of a particular current.

Although an insulator cannot carry a current, it can, in certain circumstances, play a limited part in storing a small electrical charge (*see* CONDENSER, ELECTRIC).

2. THE CIRCUIT. A simple example of an electric current at work is an electric torch; Fig. 1 gives a simplified diagram of a torch, with arrows showing how the current flows. The battery supplies the current when the spring switch has been pushed forward to touch the brass neck of the bulb at A. The current starts from the brass cap at the top of the battery, which is called its 'positive terminal'. Then it flows through the metal point at the base of the bulb, through the glowing filament in the bulb, out through the screw-neck of the bulb, through the spring switch and contact switch, and back to the battery's zinc base, which is its 'negative terminal'. The current flows all the way through wires, springs, and other parts made of metal. It has been the custom for many years to show the electric current as flowing from the positive to the negative terminal, although it is now known that in metal wires the free electrons actually move in the opposite direction.

When the spring switch is pushed back it makes a break in the conducting path, and the light goes out. An electric current will not flow unless conductors form a complete 'circuit'—that is, a path the two ends of which are joined together so that the current can flow round and round. The moment the circuit is cut or broken in any way, all electrical activity stops.

A current can leak, either to other conductors, or to the earth, which is itself a conductor; by this way electric power may be lost, and people and machinery injured. Conductors, therefore, are generally insulated by some non-conductor, such as rubber tubing, to prevent their touching other conductors. If the non-conductor is too weak, or becomes damaged by wear, current may be forced through it and cause damage. (A flash of lightning is an example of terrific voltage forcing current through the air to the earth.)

If a leaking current takes a short cut from its proper path and rejoins its own circuit at some point which was not intended, the accident is known as a 'short-circuit'. The result often is that far more current than was allowed for will rush through some electrical instrument, such as a lamp or a coil, and the great heat produced will melt its wires. To prevent this, fuses are inserted in most circuits; these are pieces of thin wire which melt very easily if the temperature begins to rise, and their melting instantly cuts the circuit, stopping the current (*see* ELECTRICITY, DOMESTIC, Vol. XI).

3. RESISTANCE. When the electric current flows through a torch bulb the filament is heated, becomes white-hot, and gives out a bright light. The other conductors in the torch also are heated by the flow of current, but not nearly so much

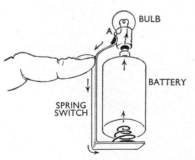

FIG. 1. DIAGRAM OF A TORCH

because, being thicker, they do not offer so much resistance to the flow of current as the very thin wire of the filament. A thin wire has a greater resistance to the flow of electric current than a thick wire of the same material. A long wire has a higher resistance than a short wire of the same thickness and material; and wires of some materials, such as the alloys eureka and nichrome, have higher resistances than similar wires of pure metals, such as copper and silver. If the same current is passed through wires of different resistances, the one with the highest resistance is heated the most.

The heat produced when an electric current flows through a conductor with a high resistance is used for many purposes besides lighting: it is used, for example, in electric fires, irons, kettles, and cookers in the home, and in electric furnaces in factories. The strength of an electric current is measured in amperes, named after a French scientist, and is usually abbreviated to amps. Resistance is measured in units named after the 19th-century German scientist G. S. Ohm (*see* Section 7).

4. SERIES AND PARALLEL CONNEXIONS. Electrical conductors can be joined together in two

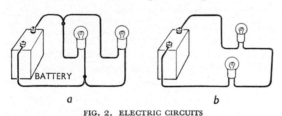

FIG. 2. ELECTRIC CIRCUITS
a. Lamps joined in parallel. *b.* Lamps joined in series

ways, as illustrated in Figs. 2*a* and *b* which show two electric lamps joined to a battery. In Fig. 2*a* the lamps are joined side-by-side, or 'in parallel', and each takes a separate current from the battery. In Fig. 2*b* the lamps are joined end-to-end or 'in series', and the same electric current has to pass through both of them. When two similar lamps are joined in parallel their combined resistance to the flow of current is one-half that of one lamp alone, for there are two paths for the current to take: when three lamps are so joined their combined resistance is one-third that of one, and so on. But when the two lamps are joined in series their combined resistance is double that of one alone, for the current has to overcome the resistance of each lamp in turn. Similarly, for any number of lamps (or other

conductors) joined in series the combined resistance is equal to their separate resistances added together. Lamps are usually connected in parallel, for when they are connected in series the failure of one lamp breaks the circuit, thus stopping the current, and putting out all the rest. This may happen, for example, with the series-connected sets of lamps used to decorate Christmas trees.

5. MAGNETIC EFFECTS. A current produces not only heat but magnetic effects. For that

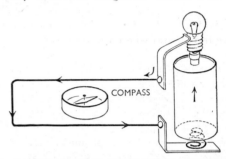

FIG. 3. MAGNETISM INDUCED BY ELECTRIC CURRENT FLOWING IN WIRE CONNECTED TO TORCH BATTERY

reason the needle of a small compass will move if placed near a long wire loop connected to the ends of a torch battery (Fig. 3). Magnetism spreads out from a wire, following the direction of certain 'lines of force' (*see* INDUCTION, ELECTRIC, Section 1). Magnetic principles account for all modern electric power, thanks to the use of electromagnets (*see* MAGNETS, Section 2).

6. ELECTROLYSIS. Fig. 4 shows an electric torch with an extended wire that has been broken. The ends of the wire are dipped in water in which common salt has been dissolved. When the spring switch of the torch is pushed forwards,

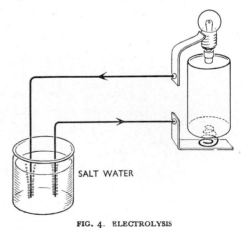

FIG. 4. ELECTROLYSIS

DIESEL GENERATOR IN A FACTORY POWER STATION

the electric current flows through the salt water, the bulb lights, and tiny bubbles of gas appear at the wire ends. These are produced when the salt is split up by the current into its chemical parts, an effect that is called electrolysis. One important use of electrolysis is for depositing thin coatings of chromium, silver, or other metals on cutlery, jewellery, and so on (*see* ELECTROPLATING).

7. POTENTIAL DIFFERENCE AND ELECTROMOTIVE FORCE. When an electric current flows around a circuit, electricity is neither made nor destroyed but is simply caused to move. For instance, if the strength of the current that flows through a lamp is measured with two ammeters (*see* ELECTRICAL INSTRUMENTS), as in Fig. 5, it will be found that the current that flows into the lamp is equal to the current that flows out of the lamp. The lamp clearly is not using up electricity; but it must use up something to produce heat and light, and that something is ENERGY (q.v.). The amount of energy used up, and so the amount of heat and light produced, depends on what is called the 'potential difference', or electric

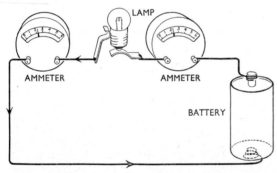

FIG. 5. MEASURING CURRENT FLOWING THROUGH A LAMP

pressure, required to drive the electric current through the lamp. If we compare the electric torch and its battery with a steam engine and its boiler, we might say that the electric potential is similar to the pressure of the steam, and the strength of the electric current is similar to the amount of steam that flows through the steam pipe per second. Potential difference is the difference between two electric potentials: for instance, the potential difference across the lamp is the difference between the electric potentials of the wires on each side of the lamp. Electric potentials and potential differences are usually expressed in volts, named after an Italian scientist, Volta (1745–1827), and are often referred to as voltages.

Potential differences can be measured directly with a voltmeter. The potential difference needed to make enough current flow to light up a typical torch bulb is 1·5 volts, but the potential difference needed by the more powerful bulbs used for lighting houses is usually between 200 and 250 volts. The battery or generator has to overcome this potential difference to make the electric current move around the circuit, and this it does by exerting an 'electromotive force' (E.M.F.) which, like the potential difference, is measured in volts.

The potential difference needed to drive a given current through a conductor depends on the strength of the current and on the resistance of the conductor. The stronger the current and the higher the resistance, the higher must be the potential difference. This potential difference (volts) can be easily calculated by multiplying the current (amps.) by the resistance (ohms). For example, a conductor with a resistance of 2 ohms carrying a current of 3 amps. must have a potential difference of $2 \times 3 = 6$ volts. This law, discovered in Cologne in 1827 by the scientist Ohm, is called Ohm's Law.

8. POWER CONSUMPTION. The rate of using electric energy is called the power consumption, and is expressed in watts; single-element electric fires, for example, usually have power consumptions of about 1,000 watts. The power consumption of an electrical device is obtained by multiplying together the strength of the current through it (amps) by the potential difference across it (volts). Thus, a motor-car headlamp bulb that takes a current of 3 amps when the potential difference across it is 12 volts, has a power consumption of 36 watts. Again, if an electric fire consumes 1,000 watts when connected to 250-volt mains, then the strength of the current flowing through it is 1,000 divided by 250, that is, 4 amps. Electrical power can be changed into mechanical power by an electric motor, and 746 watts of electrical power are needed to equal one horse-power.

9. DIRECT AND ALTERNATING CURRENT. The electric currents that have been described so far have all been of the kind that flow steadily in one direction—from the positive to the negative terminal of the battery. Such currents are called direct currents or D.C. Electrical engineers also find it convenient to use electric currents that surge backwards and forwards around the circuit, changing their direction of flow at regular intervals. Such currents are called ALTERNATING CURRENTS or A.C. (q.v.).

See also ELECTRICAL ENGINEERING; ELECTRIC INSTRUMENTS; HIGH-FREQUENCY CURRENTS.

ELECTRIC GENERATORS.

These are machines that produce very powerful ELECTRIC CURRENTS (q.v.) when they are driven by some sort of engine. The generators in electric power stations are usually driven by STEAM TURBINES (q.v.), although in countries with suitable rivers great dams are built, and the generators are driven by water power (*see* HYDRO-ELECTRIC POWER).

All electric generators produce their electricity by moving a copper wire near a powerful MAGNET (q.v.), an action which causes an 'induced' current to flow. Lines of magnetic force exist in space round all magnets (*see* MAGNETISM, Vol. III), and the direction in which the 'induced' current flows through the wire depends on the direction in which the wire moves and also on the direction of the magnetic force (*see* INDUCTION, ELECTRIC).

The simple electric generator shown in Fig. I is the type often driven by model steam engines. The generator consists of a coil of copper wire, ABCD, fixed to a spindle turning freely in bearings and driven through a pulley at the end. The coil rotates between the poles of a horseshoe magnet, and it is joined to two brass rings, called 'slip rings', which are fixed to the spindle on disks of hard rubber that insulate them. The purpose of the slip rings is to enable an electrical connexion to be made to the coil as it is turned continuously round, the connexions being made by carbon blocks or 'brushes', which are pressed against the slip-rings by springs. A lamp connected to the brushes gives an easy way of showing when current is flowing. When the coil, which is set turning by means of the pulley, is in the position shown in Fig. I, its two sides, AB and CD, are moving in opposite directions across the lines of magnetic force which run from North to South of the magnet; the A–B part of the wire is moving away from the onlooker, and the C–D part is moving towards him. The currents induced in the wire by the presence of the magnet-poles are also moving in opposite directions, one to the left and the other to the right of the picture. But since the wire is a loop the result is that both currents run together and form one current going round the whole loop. This current is led

by way of the brass slip-rings to the lamp, and lights it. (The wire passing to the farther slip-ring must pass well inside the nearer slip-ring, as

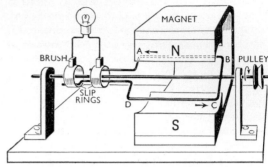

FIG. I. DIAGRAM OF A SIMPLE A.C. ELECTRIC GENERATOR
The coil ABCD is driven from the pulley

it is important that there should be no electrical contact between the two rings.)

The direction of the generated current is shown for four successive positions of the coil in Fig. 2. At *a* the current flows around the coil in the direction DCBA, when the coil is turning in the way shown by the circular arrow. At *b* the coil has made another quarter of a turn; the sides AB and CD are now moving along the lines of

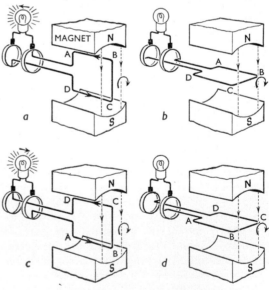

FIG. 2. GENERATING A.C. CURRENT
a. Coil is across the poles of the magnet so current flows
     and lights lamp.
b. No current flows.
c. Current flows in opposite direction from *a* and lights
     lamp.
d. No current flows.

magnetic force (and not across them as in *a*) so that no current is now generated. At *c* the coil has made a second quarter turn; the side AB is now where CD was in *a*, and is once more cutting across the lines of magnetic force, but in a direction opposite to that of *a*. Therefore the current induced in AB also flows in the opposite direction, and similarly for side CD. The general direction of the current, in fact (as shown by arrows), never changes in relation to the magnet poles, or to an onlooker; but since the two halves of the wire loop are constantly changing places with one another as the loop itself spins round, the current in each half-loop is continually reversing its direction. At the position shown at *c* the electric current through the lamp is flowing in the opposite way to that of *a*. At *d*, after a third quarter-turn, the sides of the coil are again moving along the lines of magnetic force, as they did in *b*, and no current is induced. After a fourth quarter-turn the coil is back in the position shown in *a*, so that the whole process can start again and be repeated for each turn of the coil.

Fig. 3 shows in diagrammatic form the strength and direction of the current throughout two complete turns of the coil. The current flows backwards and forwards through the lamp, and

PART OF THE COILS IN THE LARGEST OUTPUT WATER-TURBINE-DRIVEN ALTERNATOR EVER BUILT IN GREAT BRITAIN

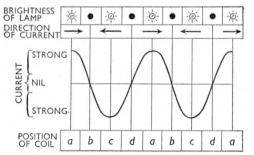

FIG. 3. STRENGTH AND DIRECTION OF CURRENT IN GENERATOR IN FIG. 2

completes one to-and-fro movement, or cycle, for each revolution of the coil. This kind of electric current is called ALTERNATING CURRENT (q.v.) or A.C., and an A.C. generator is called an alternator.

Most of the electric current generated in POWER STATIONS (q.v.) is A.C., and their powerful alternators work on exactly the same principle as the simple generator of Fig. 1. They are, however, much more compactly and robustly made, for large alternators are sometimes driven by steam turbines of many thousands of horse-

power, and generate enough current to supply a town. Alternators also have rotating coils with many turns, wound round iron cores, in order to strengthen the induced current. The magnets used in large alternators, which must be very strong, are always electromagnets, and are made active with current provided by small direct current generators. In large alternators, the electromagnets usually rotate inside a stationary coil from which the A.C. is collected.

It is sometimes necessary to generate an electric current that flows continuously in one direction: that is, direct current or D.C. The continually reversing behaviour of the current produced by the generator of Fig. 1 could be avoided by changing over the connexions between the lamp and the slip-rings each time the generated current falls to zero, as at *b* and *d* in Figs. 2 and 3. This can be done automatically by joining each end of the rotating coil to one-half of a split brass ring. The two half-rings, carefully insulated from one another (Fig. 4), take the place of two complete slip-rings, and the carbon brushes are arranged to rub on this split ring, which is called a commutator. Each time the coil reaches the positions shown in Fig. 2*b* and *d*, the split-ring device reverses the lamp connexions, and so the

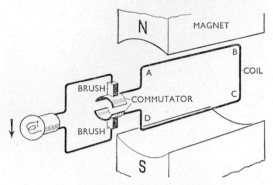

FIG. 4. DIAGRAM OF A D.C. GENERATOR

current flows always in the same direction through the lamp—although it still continually reverses its direction in the rotating coil. Such D.C. generators are often called dynamos, and are widely used to generate currents for charging accumulators, for electroplating, and for exciting the electromagnets used in large alternators.

The D.C. generated by the simple dynamo of Fig. 4, with its single rotating coil and two-section commutator, is represented in Fig. 6*a*. It flows always in the same direction, but its strength varies widely as the coil turns, and indeed falls to zero twice during each revolution. A smoother and more constant D.C. can be generated by using several coils spaced around the spindle of the dynamo, each joined to a separate pair of sections on the commutator. Fig. 5 shows a dynamo with two rotating coils, A and B, and a four-section commutator. The D.C. generated

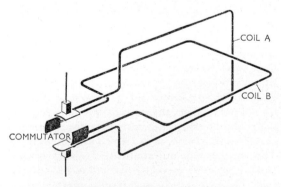

FIG. 5. TWO-COIL DYNAMO WITH FOUR-SECTION COMMUTATOR

by coil A alone is shown in Fig. 6*a*, while Fig. 6*b* shows the current from coil B alone. Because coils A and B were at right angles to each other,

the strength of the current is at its maximum in one coil when it is zero in the other. The commutator connects each coil to the lamp when the current in that coil is near its maximum strength, and disconnects the coil before its current has fallen too much. The resulting current from the two coils (Fig. 6*c*) is much smoother than the current from either coil alone. A powerful dynamo may have twenty or more coils equally spaced around the spindle, connected to a commutator with forty or more sections.

The commutators of large dynamos are built up from strips of copper and mica (a strong, thin, mineral insulator) placed side by side. It is necessary to ensure that the carbon brushes make good electrical contacts with the commutator, or the current will 'spark' across any small gaps, and the heat will burn out 'pits' or hollows in the

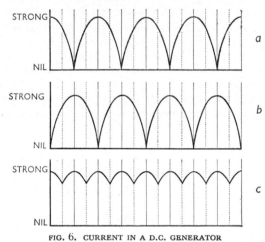

FIG. 6. CURRENT IN A D.C. GENERATOR

a, b. Current generated by coils A and B respectively in Fig. 5*c*. Resultant current

commutator, making an uneven surface which will impede the current and cause loss of power. A piece of glass-paper is, therefore, usually rubbed to-and-fro under each brush to 'bed-down' the brush in position, its face curving to fit the commutator. Moisture, oil, and dirt must all be kept away from the commutator and brushes.

Alternators and dynamos are no longer of the simple, open type (Fig. 2), but are built in an enclosed form.

See also ELECTRIC CURRENT; POWER STATION.

ELECTRICITY, *see* ELECTRICAL ENGINEERING. *See also* Vol. III: ELECTRICITY IN NATURE.

ELECTRICITY METER, *see* ELECTRICAL INSTRUMENTS, Section 7.

ELECTRIC MOTORS. 1. These are machines which change electric power into a mechanical driving force. They range from small motors in electric fans and vacuum cleaners to very large ones that drive electric trains and heavy machinery. The main advantages of electric motors over other kinds of motor are quiet, smooth running, cleanliness, ease of control, and relatively small size.

All electric motors depend on the magnetism produced by an ELECTRIC CURRENT (q.v.), and on the fact that MAGNETISM (q.v. Vol. III) is a strong natural force which has certain powers of attracting and repelling. Magnetic force (apart from natural magnetism in the earth) not only exists near a MAGNET (q.v.) but also arises near any wire through which an electric current is flowing. The region in which this force is felt is called a magnetic field, and each magnet or wire has its own field, in which the forces follow definite directions (*see* Fig. 1). An engineer uses these forces by bringing together a magnet and an electrified wire in such a way that the magnet repels the wire. To build an electric motor he places near a stationary magnet a kind of wheel with a number of wires arranged around its rim; when the current is switched on in those wires, some of them are thrust from the nearest part of the magnet; since the magnet is fixed, the wires must move, and in doing so they pull the rim of the wheel round with them. That is the basis of nearly all electric motors.

The straight lines of force of the magnet (Fig. 1a) and the circular ones of the wire (Fig. 1b) affect one another when the wire is placed near the magnet. Fig. 2a shows a wire placed between

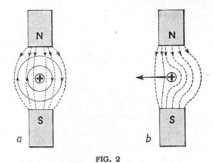

FIG. 2

a. Magnetic fields of magnet and electric wire
b. Resulting field forcing wire to left

current are shown by full lines, those of the magnet by dotted lines. Fig. 2b shows the result—a combined magnetic field. Where the lines of force are in opposite directions they cancel each

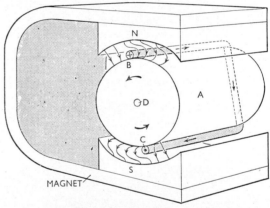

FIG. 3. PRINCIPLE OF AN ELECTRIC MOTOR
A. Armature. B, C. Armature coil. D. Spindle

other, and where they are in the same direction they crowd together. In some ways lines of force act like stretched elastic bands which try to shorten themselves. Their pressure causes the wire to shoot to the left as if under the action of a catapult.

Fig. 3 shows how magnetic force is applied to a current in a very simple kind of electric motor. A horseshoe magnet has curved pole-pieces, N and S. The rotating part (armature, A) of the motor is mounted on a spindle between the pole-pieces. The armature is an iron cylinder with a coil of insulated copper wire wound on it lengthwise. The driving current flows through the armature coil, round the cylinder lengthways

the poles of a horseshoe magnet and at right-angles to its field; the lines of force due to the

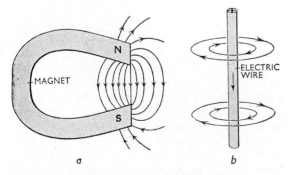

FIG. 1. MAGNETIC FIELDS
a. Field of magnet. b. Field of electric wire

from B to C. The combined lines of force of magnet and current together produce a catapult action forcing the upper part of the copper wire to move to the left of the diagram and the lower part to the right; the result is that the whole cylinder turns as shown by the curved arrows. When it has made half a turn, portion B of the armature coil has come to the bottom, and portion C to the top. The currents are then flowing in directions opposite to those in Fig. 3, and would reverse the forces on the cylinder and stop it. But to avoid this the currents are reversed in both parts of the armature coil, by an automatic rotating switch (the commutator) fixed to the armature spindle (*see* ELECTRIC GENERATORS).

A diagram of a complete electric motor is shown in Fig. 4. The armature A, made of soft iron, a metal which does not retain magnetism, is wound with coils of insulated copper wire. Several turns of wire are used to increase the force exerted. The armature spins round on a spindle between the two poles of a horseshoe magnet. Farther along the spindle of the armature is a commutator C, consisting of two half-rings of copper mounted on some insulating material. The armature wire has two ends, one joined to each segment of the commutator. Electric current from a battery comes through wires to a couple of metal knobs or clips (the terminals, T), and is led to the rotating commu-

electric motors are more or less complicated versions of the extremely simple one described here.

In the simple model shown in Fig. 4 the armature has to be carried on by its own momentum past the point where the commutator interrupts the armature current before reversing it. On

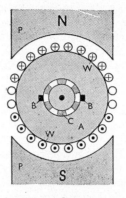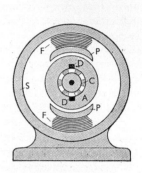

a   *b*

FIG. 5. DIAGRAM OF A LARGE ELECTRIC MOTOR

a. Armature winding all round core. *b*. Armature with field magnet. A. Armature. W. Wires with current flowing in opposite directions. C. Commutator. D. Brushes. P. Pole-pieces. F. Field coils of electromagnet. S. Iron shell

larger motors a continuous drive is obtained by distributing the armature windings all round the iron core (Fig. 5), so that there are always some wires close to the poles of the magnet. The windings are connected in a complicated way so that all the wires near the same pole carry currents flowing in the same direction. For this purpose the commutator is divided into many copper strips, insulated from each other by mica, a mineral which can be split into thin wafers and which has strong insulating properties. In big motors, carbon brushes are used to make a good contact with the commutator. Electromagnets are used in all but the smallest motors to develop a strong magnetic field and so a powerful driving force. These 'field magnets', as they are called, are arranged as an iron shell with two or more pole-pieces. The magnet shell protects the armature and supports the bearings and brushes.

The electrical resistance (*see* ELECTRIC CURRENT, Section 3) of the armature winding of a motor is very small, and when it is first connected to a battery a very powerful electric current flows. The current causes a strong force to act on the armature, which begins to turn and speeds up rapidly. The effect of the movement of a wire near a magnet is to induce a new electric current in the wire (*see* INDUCTION, ELECTRIC). Therefore,

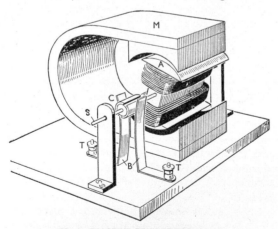

FIG. 4. DIAGRAM OF ELECTRIC MOTOR

A. Armature. S. Spindle. C. Commutator. T. Terminals
B. Brushes. M. Magnet

tator through springy metal strips B, called 'brushes'. From the commutator the current flows to the wire windings, starting off the magnetic action between magnet and armature. All in a motor, as the armature wires move past the field magnets, an induced electromotive force appears in them which opposes the force of the battery supplying the driving current. The result is that the armature current is reduced and, as the induced electromotive force increases with the speeding up of the motor, less and less current is drawn from the battery. The motor settles down to a steady speed when the battery current produces just enough driving force to work against the motor's 'load'—that is, the burden of its work, such as driving a water pump. If the load is increased (as, for example, by making the motor drive two water pumps instead of one) the motor slows down and takes just enough more current from the battery to suit the new load. The adjustment of an electric motor to its load is therefore completely automatic.

Large electric motors would take such enormous currents from their electric supply when they were first switched on that they would damage themselves. A variable electrical resistance, or 'starter', is therefore connected between the motor and the supply to absorb part of the supply voltage. As the motor speeds up, the starter resistance is gradually cut out. Passengers in certain parts of a London 'tube' train may hear loud 'clicks' as the driver cuts out each resistance as the train gains speed.

The windings of the electromagnets of a motor are called the 'field coils'. Fig. 6a shows the field coils joined directly across the supply; such a motor is said to be 'shunt-wound', because the field coils are in shunt, or parallel, with the armature. In Fig. 6b the field coils are connected between the armature and the supply; motors of

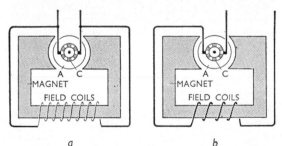

a   *b*

FIG. 6. *a.* SHUNT-WOUND. *b.* SERIES-WOUND MOTORS
A. Armature. c. Commutator

this sort are called 'series-wound'. These two kinds of electric motor are used for different purposes. Shunt-wound motors run at an almost constant speed, and only slow down very slightly

English Electric Co. Ltd.

THE ARMATURE OF A MOTOR WITH A PEAK RATING OF 17,500 HORSE-POWER

when the load increases. They cannot, however, be safely started with a load connected, and are most suitable for driving light machine-tools such as electric drills. Series-wound motors slow down much more than shunt-wound motors as their load increases, but they exert a very strong starting force. They are used where heavy loads have to be started quickly, as in electric trains or lifts.

An electric motor can be reversed by reversing the direction of the current in either the armature or the field coils, but not in both. It follows that when a motor is connected to an alternating current (A.C.) supply, even though the current is continually reversing, the motor will continue turning in one direction, because the current is reversed in both armature and field coils together.

Motors of the kind described so far are called commutator motors, and are widely used in domestic appliances.

2. SYNCHRONOUS MOTOR. Another type of A.C. motor is called the synchronous motor, because it synchronizes, or keeps in step, with the reversals or alternations of the current from the A.C. supply. A very simplified synchronous motor is shown in Fig. 7; the moving part or

English Electric Co. Ltd,

ELECTRIC MOTORS IN A STEEL WORKS

rotor consists of a straight magnet, shaped like a bar, mounted on a spindle between the poles of an electromagnet. When the electromagnet is connected to an A.C. supply, its magnetism reverses regularly as the current changes its direction, and its poles become alternately North or South, as in Fig. 7a and b. The synchronous motor is not self-starting, the rotor needing a light tap or shake to make it spin. Once it is spinning at the correct speed, its South pole is always approaching the upper pole of the electromagnet when the latter is a North pole (Fig. 7a). And, by the time the electromagnet current has changed the upper pole to a South pole, the rotor's North pole is approaching it (Fig. 7b). The attraction between the North pole of the rotor and the South pole of the electromagnet and vice versa pulls the rotor around. The correct speed is reached when the rotor turns once for each complete alternation of the A.C. supply, equalling 50 revolutions a second. This is the kind of motor which drives electric clocks.

3. INDUCTION MOTOR. This type has three electromagnets, each connected to a separate A.C. supply of 50 cycles per second in such a way that the electromagnets combine to produce a magnetic field which rotates so that the direction of the magnetic lines of force turns completely round once during each alternation of the current. The rotating part of the motor is a cylinder or rotor of soft iron, wound with coils of

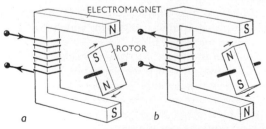

FIG. 7. DIAGRAM OF SYNCHRONOUS MOTOR

copper wire joined to form complete loops. The rotating magnetic field causes alternating currents to flow in the rotor's coils by electromagnetic induction. These alternating currents are then acted upon by the magnetic field, and a force is exerted to turn the rotor. Most large A.C. motors are induction motors.

See also ELECTRIC CURRENT; INDUCTION, ELECTRIC; ENGINES, HISTORY OF.

ELECTRIC RAILWAYS, *see* RAILWAY CONSTRUCTION, Section 4; RAILWAY ROLLING STOCK, Section 5. *See also* Vol. IV: ELECTRIC RAILWAYS.

ELECTROLYSIS, *see* ELECTRIC CURRENT, Section 6.

ELECTROMAGNETIC INDUCTION, *see* INDUCTION, ELECTRIC.

ELECTROMAGNETS, *see* MAGNETS.

ELECTRON GUN, *see* CATHODE RAY TUBE.

ELECTRONICS. This is the name given to the various uses, outside the main field of radio, of electron 'tubes', and particularly of those tubes known as THERMIONIC VALVES (q.v.). More and more electronic devices are being used by scientists and engineers as measuring instruments, for automatic controls, and in electronic computers, that is, machines for making difficult calculations with great speed and accuracy (*see* CALCULATING MACHINES).

Thermionic valves are important in electronics for two main reasons. First, the electric

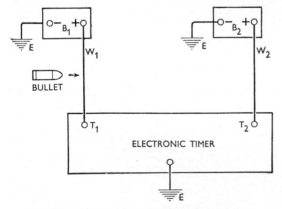

FIG. 1. HOW AN ELECTRONIC TIMER WORKS

B_1, B_2. Batteries. E. Earths. W_1, W_2. Wires connecting batteries to electronic timer. T_1, T_2. Start and stop terminals

currents that flow to their anodes (positive plates) can be switched on and off by quite small controlling voltages in much less than one ten-millionth of a second. Secondly, a thermionic valve can convert a small alternating current or voltage 'signal' into one of similar nature but of much increased strength—a single valve can, in fact, 'amplify' a signal by as much as 200 times.

A good example of the use of thermionic valves as high-speed switches is the electronic timer which is used in order to measure the speed of a rifle bullet. The bullet, travelling from left to right in Fig. 1, breaks a very thin wire w_1, thus stopping the flow of current from the battery B_1 through a circuit in the timer. The electronic timer is arranged so that this action switches on the timer itself. Similarly, when the bullet breaks the second wire w_2, the timer is switched off. The speed of the bullet can then be worked out from the time shown by the timer and the measured distance between the two wires.

The electronic timer works by counting the vibrations (about a million per second) of a piece of quartz crystal about the size and shape of a halfpenny. The principle is much the same as that of an ordinary stop-watch which works by counting the swings of a balance wheel (about 5 per second). The crystal vibrates when it is connected to a thermionic valve oscillator and generates a HIGH-FREQUENCY CURRENT (q.v.) that surges to and fro exactly 1,000,000 times in each second. The timer counts the surges completed by the current during the interval to be measured, and when it stops, the answer is shown on a set of dials. Thus, if 119,732 surges were shown, the length of the interval must have been 119,732 divided by 1,000,000, or 0·119732 of a second.

The arrangement of the electronic timer is shown in Fig. 2. The high-frequency current from the valve oscillator and its quartz crystal vibrator is taken through an electronic switch to a chain of six identical counter units. The electronic switch is an arrangement of thermionic valves that connects the high-frequency current to the counter chain when the electrical current flowing in the 'start' circuit is interrupted (as it was by the bullet in Fig. 1), and similarly disconnects it when the 'stop' circuit current is interrupted. The counter units count in tens, and when ten current surges have been received, the counter dial returns to 0, and one surge of

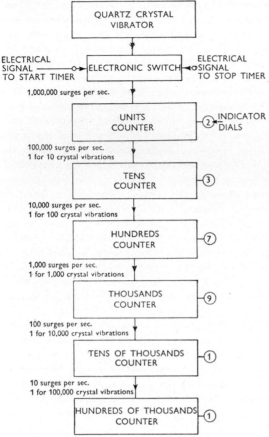

FIG. 2. ARRANGEMENT OF AN ELECTRONIC TIMER

current is passed on to the next counter. When ten groups of ten have been marked on this counter, it also returns to 0, and a surge of current is passed on to the hundreds counter. When ten hundreds have been built up in the same way, a surge of current is passed to the thousands counter—and so on.

Each counter unit is identical, and the operation of the first one is illustrated in Fig. 3. The high-frequency current flows in an electric circuit that is connected to a pair of thermionic valves, v_1 and v_2. These valves are joined together in such a way that when one of them takes anode (or positive plate) current it prevents the other from doing so; so there is always one valve 'on' (that is, taking anode current), and one valve 'off'. The circuit is arranged so that each surge of high-frequency current turns off the valve that is on and turns on the valve which is off. Hence when the timer is started, the first surge turns v_1 off and v_2 on, the second surge

turns v_2 off and v_1 on, and so on. The counter unit also contains a ring of five valves, v_3, v_4, v_5, v_6, and v_7, joined together in such a way that when any one takes anode current it prevents the other four from doing so. It is arranged that whenever v_2 goes off it passes on a current surge to the ring of five, and the first such surge turns v_3 off and v_4 on, the next turns v_4 off and v_5 on, and so on round the ring. When the last valve in the ring, v_7, is turned off it sends on a surge of current to the next counter unit, and v_3 is turned on again. Now, v_2 sends on one surge of current for each two such surges from the quartz crystal vibrator, and v_7 sends on to the next counter unit one surge for each five from v_2, or one for each ten from the crystal.

Electronic timers similar to those just described are used at Greenwich Observatory and are the most accurate clocks in the world, keeping time to $\frac{1}{1000}$th of a second per day. Electronic counters are also used with devices called Geiger-Müller tubes to measure the RADIOACTIVITY (q.v.) of materials in atomic energy research. Many counters are used in factories to count manufactured objects passing rapidly along a moving belt. The objects pass through a beam of light focused on a PHOTOCELL (q.v.), and as they do so, the current produced by the cell first falls and then rises again as the objects pass out of the beam. Thus one surge of current is produced for each object and the electronic counter counts the surges.

Thermionic valves are used in all kinds of automatic controls. In scientific work, for instance, they are used to control temperature, the pressure and moistness of the air, or the voltage of an electric power supply. In factories they are used in devices that measure and control the

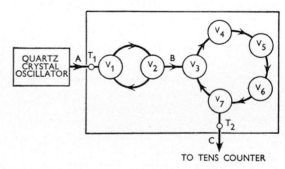

TO TENS COUNTER

FIG. 3. UNITS COUNTER OF AN ELECTRONIC TIMER
At A 1,000,000 surges per second, at B 500,000 surges per second and at C 100,000 surges per second are passed. T_1, T_2. Input and output terminals. v_1–v_7. Thermionic valves

thickness of paper in a paper mill (*see* PAPER MAKING, Vol. VII), the position of paper sheets in a colour-printing press (*see* PROCESS REPRODUCTION, Section 6, Vol. VII), or the timing of an automatic electric welder (*see* WELDING), just to mention a few of their uses. Thermionic valves containing a small amount of hydrogen gas or mercury vapour are often used, as these valves, size for size, can handle much larger currents than can an ordinary vacuum valve without special gas. The electronic automatic control shown in Fig. 4 is to prevent a boiler chimney sending out black smoke. The chimney has two small holes or 'windows' in its sides, through which an electric lamp sends a beam of light to a photocell. When the chimney is clear of smoke, the light falling on the photocell causes it to

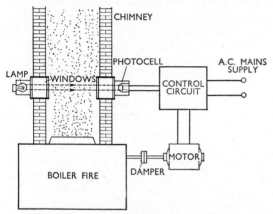

FIG. 4. DIAGRAM OF AN ELECTRONIC AUTOMATIC CONTROL FOR PREVENTING A BOILER CHIMNEY FROM SENDING OUT BLACK SMOKE

generate a small electric current that controls a thermionic valve in the control circuit. If the boiler fire makes black smoke, the light beam is obscured, the photocell current disappears, the control valve operates an alarm bell to warn the stoker, and also switches on an electric motor that moves dampers to increase the supply of air to the fire and so to stop it smoking.

Thermionic valve amplifiers are used in radio, and to amplify the speech and music signals in electric gramophones, cinema projectors, and public address systems at railway stations and other places (*see* SOUND RECORDING). Valve amplifiers are used to make measuring instruments more sensitive: for example, brain surgeons use valves to amplify the minute electric currents flowing in the head in order to help them to diagnose illnesses of the brain. An arrangement con-

sisting of a microphone, amplifier, and an electronic instrument called a wave analyser, which separates and measures each of the different parts of a mixed wave, is used by engineers to detect the vibrations of machinery in order to remove them and so avoid noise and wear.

Thermionic valve oscillators generating powerful high-frequency currents, which alternate 20 million times or more per second, are used to heat objects that do not conduct electricity. The oscillations cause electric forces to act on the atomic particles of the non-conducting object, making them vibrate. In vibrating they generate heat, which is actually produced inside the object by the vibration of its particles. Doctors connect these oscillators to metal plates placed near a patient's body to produce a gentle healing warmth, and in this 'short-wave diathermy', as it is called, the heat is produced inside the patient's body where it can do most good (*see* RADIOTHERAPY, Vol. XI). Furniture, and some parts of aeroplanes and boats, can be made from strips of wood that are bent to the right shape in a press and then fastened together by a plastic compound that sets when heated. The plastic is set by this electronic method of heating from the inside.

See also THERMIONIC VALVES; HIGH-FREQUENCY, CURRENTS.

ELECTRON MICROSCOPE. This is an electrical instrument that produces greatly enlarged pictures of small objects. Its design resembles in many ways the design of an ordinary optical MICROSCOPE (q.v.). Both instruments use a LENS (q.v.) to illuminate the object, and two more lenses to form magnified images of it; but whereas the optical microscope uses ordinary light rays and its lenses are curved pieces of glass, the electron microscope uses rays that consist of high-speed streams of the minute particles of negative electricity called electrons (*see* ATOM, Vol. III), and these are focused by lenses that consist of powerful electromagnets (*see* MAGNETS).

Fig. 1 is a diagram of an electromagnetic lens. An electric current is passed through a winding of many turns of insulated copper wire, and the magnetism produced by the current is concentrated by a cylindrical iron shell into the small gap between two conical iron pole-pieces. Each pole-piece has a small central hole, about $\frac{1}{10}$ inch in diameter, for the electrons to pass through. When a stream of electrons rushes through the holes, the magnetism, acting on the moving electrons, brings them together at a focal point, the electromagnet acting as an electron lens.

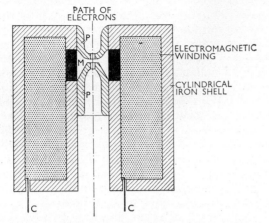

FIG. I. DIAGRAM OF AN ELECTROMAGNETIC LENS

P. Conical iron pole-pieces. M. Magnetic field of lens
C. Electrical connexions

The general arrangement of an electron microscope is shown in Fig. 2. Its various parts are mounted inside a metal container from which all the air has been removed. The electrons are emitted by a V-shaped piece of tungsten wire, made white-hot by an electric current. The

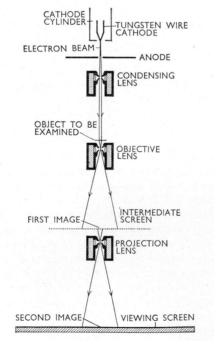

FIG. 2. DIAGRAM OF AN ELECTRON MICROSCOPE

electrons emerge as a spreading cone-shaped beam from a hole in the metal cathode (negative) cylinder that surrounds the tungsten wire. They are accelerated to a high speed by the attraction of the metal anode (positive) disk, which is connected to a RECTIFIER (q.v.) producing a high voltage of about 60,000 volts. The electron beam then passes through the first magnetic lens which, acting like an optical condenser, concentrates the beam on the object to be examined in the microscope. The object is mounted on a very thin film of cellulose, supported by a piece of fine wire gauze. Some of the high-speed electrons pass through the object, and some are stopped by it. Different parts of the object stop more or fewer electrons, so producing an electron image of the object, much in the same way as a partly transparent object with a light held behind it produces an optical image by different parts of the object stopping more or less of the light.

After passing through the object the electrons go through the second magnetic lens, which is called the 'objective'. This lens produces the first enlarged electron image, about 100 times enlarged. This electron image can be seen by focusing it on to an intermediate screen of fluorescent material, which glows brightly when electrons strike it (see CATHODE RAY TUBE). When the image has been sharply focused by adjusting the current in the magnetic objective lens, the intermediate screen is removed, and the third magnetic lens then magnifies a small part of the first image and projects it on to the final fluorescent viewing screen. This magnification is again about 100 times, so that the total magnification of the original object is 10,000 times. The final viewing screen can be replaced by a photographic plate when photomicrographs are required.

An electron microscope may be about 6 feet long; it is much larger and more complicated than an ordinary optical microscope and can use much higher magnifications without the image becoming fuzzy—magnifications as much as 100,000 times are used. The smallest details that an optical microscope can possibly reveal are those separated by about one wavelength of ordinary light, that is by about 20 millionths of an inch. The high-speed electron rays in an electron microscope behave rather like waves with a wavelength about 100,000 times smaller than ordinary light. Electron microscopes cannot, however, yet take full advantage of this very small wavelength, because of the imperfection of their magnetic lenses, and the smallest object yet distinguishable by an electron microscope is about one 10 millionth of an inch across.

No living specimens can be examined with an electron microscope, because an object to be examined has to be cut into a slice no more than 2 or 3 millionths of an inch thick so that the electrons can pass through it, and has to be placed inside the microscope in its vacuum. The surfaces of thick, solid, objects can be examined by making replicas of them in a very thin film of a plastic substance called polystyrene and placing these replicas in the microscope. Electron microscopes are proving of most value for research on smoke and dust particles, powdered pigments for paints, disease-producing bacteria and viruses, and the minute crystals of which metals and alloys are made. They can even be used to see some of the largest molecules (*see* CHEMISTRY, Vol. III).

See also MICROSCOPE.

ELECTROPLATING. This is a way of using electricity to cover articles with a thin coating of metal: silver-plated spoons and chromium-plated motor-car bumpers are familiar examples. The process is based on electrolysis (*see* ELECTRIC CURRENT, Section 6)—the power of a current, when flowing through a liquid, to cause chemical change in certain substances.

A brass spoon to be silver-plated is joined to one end (the negative) of an electric circuit and dipped into a bath filled with a solution of silver and potassium cyanides in water. The other (positive) end of the circuit is joined to a silver bar which is also dipped into the plating bath. When a strong current is switched on and flows through the bath, it causes the silver particles in the dissolved silver cyanide to be deposited as a layer on the spoon, and at the same time it continually replaces this silver by silver dissolved from the bar. Thus as long as the electric current flows, silver is removed from the bar and deposited on the spoon. When a sufficiently thick plating has been deposited, the current is switched off.

The thickness of the silver-plating on good quality electroplated spoons is about one-thousandth of an inch. Very much thinner coatings are generally used in gold-plating (*see* GOLD AND SILVER WORK, Vol. VII); articles made of low-carat gold are sometimes plated with about 10 millionths of an inch of pure gold to improve their colour—a coating so thin that 400 such coatings would be needed to equal the thickness of a single page of this book.

Articles are chromium-plated not only because of the lustre it gives them but also to prevent CORROSION (q.v.). It is difficult to produce thick coatings of chromium, and so when steel objects are to be chromium-plated they are first electroplated with nickel to a thickness of about one-thousandth of an inch and then finished with a chromium 'flash' about 20 millionths of an inch thick. Steel and iron articles are sometimes protected from rusting by being electroplated with zinc or cadmium.

It is possible to electroplate not only with pure metals such as silver and chromium but also with certain alloys, such as brass or stainless steel. Aluminium and certain other metals are sometimes protected from corrosion by a process called 'anodizing'. The aluminium article is dipped into a bath of a suitable solution and joined to the positive, instead of the negative, end of an electric circuit, and this produces on the articles a thin but very strong coating of oxide from the oxygen generated by electrolysis; this oxide coating protects the article against further attack (*see* SURFACE TREATMENT).

Electroplating is carried out in baths which may be as large as 6 feet long by 3 feet wide by 3 feet deep. These baths are often wooden with a lead lining to protect the wood from the acid, or of concrete protected by asphalt. Large articles to be plated are hung from wooden beams, and small ones are placed inside a slowly rotating perforated 'barrel'. Before plating they are thoroughly cleaned from dirt, rust, and grease. The special generators used for electroplating provide electric currents of up to 2,000 amperes at a voltage of 6 volts. In some large electroplating plants the articles are suspended from a moving conveyor belt which carries them automatically through cleaning baths, plating bath, rinsing bath, and drying chamber. Each generator supplies several plating baths. The composition of the solution, the temperature, and the strength of the electric current must all be carefully controlled; and the solutions used are often extremely poisonous or corrosive, and must be treated with great respect.

One important use of electroplating is for making copper plates for printing books by the process known as electrotyping (*see* PRINTING, Vol. VII). These printing plates may be plated with chromium, which lasts without wearing twice as long as case-hardened steel. Electroplating is also used in the manufacture of gramophone records to produce several copper copies of the wax disk cut in the original sound-recording process.

Copper and other metals are refined or purified by electroplating. The wires and cables used in electrical engineering must be made of pure copper because very small amounts of certain impurities such as phosphorus greatly increase the electrical resistance of copper. The ingots of crude copper, which are about 97 % pure, are refined by making them the positive connexion in an electroplating bath of copper sulphate and sulphuric acid solution. The crude copper is dissolved, the impurities collect as a sludge on the bottom of the bath, and pure copper is deposited on thin sheets of refined copper connected to the negative terminal. Electrolytically refined copper is about 99·98 % pure. Gold, silver, tin, and zinc are also refined in this way.

Coatings of some non-metallic substances can be deposited by the use of an electric current, although the process is not an example of electrolysis but of a phenomenon called 'cataphoresis'. For example, if an electric current is passed through a suspension of rubber latex in water, rubber can be deposited on a zinc mould connected to the positive terminal of the generator. This process of 'rubber-plating' can be used to make rubber articles up to about $\frac{1}{4}$ inch to $\frac{1}{2}$ inch thick.

See also SURFACE TREATMENT.
See also Vol. VII: GOLD AND SILVER WORK; SHEFFIELD PLATE.

ENAMELLING, see SURFACE TREATMENT. See also Vol. VII: ENAMEL.

ENERGY. 1. This word means the capacity for doing work. When we say that a ton of coal, a lake of water high above a generating station, an electric battery, or a red-hot iron 'contains' a certain amount of energy, we are not referring to anything that we can take out of the water, or coal, or whatever it is; we are saying something about the state that it is in. The coal possesses potential energy because the chemicals in it are in a condition to combine with oxygen, releasing heat energy. The water possesses potential energy because it is in a condition to fall. The amount of potential energy it possesses depends on how far it can fall. It could fall to the centre of the earth, in theory; but in practice we always measure potential energy relative to a given fall. When it does fall, its energy is changed into kinetic energy, or energy due to its movement. It can then be made to do work. In other words energy is a state of affairs, and not a 'thing' at all.

Energy in the form in which it is directly available for doing work is known as mechanical energy. Only two sources of mechanical energy are naturally available—WIND POWER and WATER POWER (qq.v.)—and, since the energy requirements of the world today are very much greater than can be conveniently and economically supplied by winds, waterfalls, and tides, the engineer is very much concerned with the conversion of other forms of energy into the mechanical form.

At present, by far the greatest and most important source of natural energy available is in the form of chemical energy from natural FUELS (q.v.). Another natural source of energy is radiation from the sun (see SOLAR ENERGY). There is also electrical energy from lightning, though this is in far too unmanageable a form to be put to practical use. In recent years, a new source of energy has been successfully exploited—a source which in future times promises to be of far the greatest importance—and that is matter itself. Energy derived from the actual destruction of matter (as opposed to chemical energy, which springs merely from the rearrangement of matter) is popularly termed 'atomic', though the correct term is NUCLEAR ENERGY (q.v.). Finally, there is a rather special form of energy—HEAT (q.v. Vol. III). Heat is not a source but a form of energy—and the distinction is an important one. Just as several thousand tons of water in a lake are a source of energy only if the lake is high up a mountain, so several thousand therms of heat are a source of energy only if the heat is available at a high temperature. Moreover, heat is the lowest form of energy. The other forms—chemical, electrical, mechanical, nuclear—are, in the natural course of events, constantly being converted to heat, but the heat can be converted into one of the other forms of energy only with considerable waste (see HEAT ENGINES). Heat at a high temperature is in its nature constantly being converted to heat at a low temperature, but the reverse is not possible without the expenditure of mechanical energy (see HEAT PUMP).

2. *Conversion of energy into work.* The conversion of mechanical energy into work is dealt with in MECHANICS (q.v.). The conversion of chemical energy into work is almost invariably achieved in practice by first converting the chemical energy into heat. The fuel, in fact, is burned, either under a boiler or in the engine cylinders, and the heat is then converted to work in a heat engine. Nuclear energy is converted into heat in a more direct way (*see* NUCLEAR POWER). Electrical energy can be converted into work direct, by means of an ELECTRIC MOTOR (q.v.), but in practice electricity is not a primary source of energy. It can be obtained direct from chemical energy by means of the electric BATTERY (q.v.), but it is usually derived from a source of mechanical energy (such as a steam engine or water turbine) by means of an ELECTRIC GENERATOR (q.v.). As a form of energy, electricity is important simply because it is so convenient and can so easily be transported to where it is needed.

3. *Conservation of Energy.* When one form of energy is converted into another, no energy is destroyed in the process. This fact, known as the Law of Conservation of Energy, may not at first sight appear to be true. We know, for example, that it is not possible for a dynamo, driven by an electric motor, to generate enough electricity to keep the motor going. But this is because some of the energy of the motor is wasted as heat in the windings and bearings of the dynamo, and the motor itself wastes some of the current provided by the dynamo in the same way. This wasted energy, however, has not been destroyed; it has been converted into heat. Again, if a tightly coiled and secured spring is put into a bath of acid and dissolved, the mechanical energy in the spring would appear to have been lost. The acid, however, gets hotter when a coiled spring is dissolved than when an uncoiled spring is dissolved; the mechanical energy in the coiled spring has been converted into heat.

See also MECHANICS; HEAT ENGINES.
See also Vol. III: HEAT.

ENGINEERING. Before the INDUSTRIAL REVOLUTION (q.v. Vol. VII) the only engines were engines of war, and the engineer as we know him today did not exist. The special talent of the first great engineers, such as Trevithick, Watt, and Brunel, who ushered in the age of steam, was a blend of practical craftsmanship and mechanical insight. Today, very few engines can be built by that mixture of experience and 'a good eye' which served the first engineers so well. Machines have to withstand such tremendous stresses and to be capable of such complex motions that abstruse and specialized calculations taking hundreds of factors into account are needed in the design of even quite a simple machine like a motor-car engine. So, as engineering progresses, engineers must become ever more 'scientific' and more specialized. Today, the ramifications of engineering are so wide that it is impossible to attempt a satisfactory classification, but it may help to clear our ideas if we regard the subject as divided first of all into uses. The main divisions of engineering may be quite arbitrarily listed as follows:

1. *Mechanical engineering.* Steam engines; internal combustion engines; turbines (steam, gas, water); pumps; compressors; machine tools; mechanisms.

2. *Electrical engineering.* (*a*) Power: generators; motors; transformers; transmission (power lines and so on). (*b*) Electronics: radio; radar; television.

3. *Civil engineering.* Dams; tunnels; roads; and so on; land reclamation and development.

4. *Structural engineering.* The structural details of all large buildings and bridges.

5. *Chemical engineering.*

The following special branches include some or all of the above, but are worth noting specially: aircraft engineering; marine engineering; automobile engineering; railway engineering; armament engineering.

Any one of these branches of engineering will at some time or another demand the special services of the following: the metallurgist; the strength of materials expert or 'stress man'; the thermodynamics or heat expert; the mechanics of machines expert; the various production engineering experts such as the engineering designer or the jig and tool designer; the mathematician specializing in engineering problems; and many more.

The engineer also depends on the 'pure' scientists—the chemists, physicists, and even biologists—to give him the basic information about the behaviour of MATTER (q.v. Vol. III) which he needs. He must also pay attention to the economists, and those who sell and use the products of his work, to assure himself that he is in fact producing what is wanted, and economically (*see* ECONOMICS, Vol. VII). A car must not only go—it must be saleable, and a railway locomotive which is too expensive to operate and maintain is useless, however excellent it may be as a piece of fine engineering.

Whatever branch the engineer decides to follow, he needs a good general education, a fair knowledge of mathematics and physics, and then, above all, practical experience. British engineers on the whole have led the world in the creation of entirely new developments such as the steam engine and various kinds of turbine engines. They have, however, until recently, shown less appreciation than American engineers of the economic problems that engineers must face in designing products for world markets (*see* MARKET, Vol. VII).

All these different aspects of engineering are dealt with in this volume in separate articles such as MECHANICAL ENGINEERING, ELECTRICAL ENGINEERING, CHEMICAL ENGINEERING, CIVIL ENGINEERING.

ENGINEERING DESIGN. An inventor may have a brilliant idea for something new but be quite unable to put that idea into effect so that, when it is built, it will work as he had planned. He may, for instance, have an idea for a better kind of aircraft but, though the idea itself may be perfectly sound, when he makes a model based on it, it may not fly because, perhaps, he has not used strong enough materials, or one of the methods of holding the parts together has failed, or for one of many other possible reasons. To work out all these details—in fact, to turn the dream of the inventor into practical reality—is the job of the engineering designer.

The designer must understand materials so that he can choose those that will stand up to whatever the invention demands of them; he must consider each component part separately and also as part of the whole; and he must lay down each in an ENGINEERING DRAWING (q.v.) so that production engineers, who will eventually be responsible for making the product, can understand immediately what is needed (*see* PRODUCTION ENGINEERING) (Fig. 1). The engineering designer is, in fact, the vital link between theory and practice, sharing both the artistic, or visionary, sense of the inventor and the practical mind of the engineer.

Choice of materials will depend on many factors, but there are two primary considerations, strength and weight; and the relation between these two depends on what the invention is re-

quired to do. For example, if the product being designed needs above all mass and high rigidity —such as a new heavy grinding machine—heavy materials must be used for its base to give the machine its rigidity and thus prevent vibration. If, however, the product is an aircraft or a component part of an aircraft, where lightness is an essential characteristic, a material combining to the highest degree strength with lightness must be chosen—in other words, it must have a high strength/weight ratio.

In many instances of engineering design, there may be various materials which would satisfy one particular requirement, none of them absolutely perfect but all adequate. The engineering designer has then to take into consideration other qualities of the materials—their availability, for example, and their cheapness.

For determining what strength a material has, he relies largely on formulae as well as on his knowledge of the characteristics of different materials. Formulae and stress analysis will also tell him how to allow in his design for many of the stresses under which the material will operate (*see* STRESS AND STRAIN). Such calculations are based on the theory of elasticity. If you try to pull apart a coiled spring with your hands, the spring will resist the force applied to it, and try to bring your hands back together again. The spring, in fact, is under a condition of strain; it resists the force being applied and returns to its original shape once the force is removed. However, if the spring is pulled too hard—if too much force is applied—it will lose its 'springiness' and, when released, will not return to its original shape, but will be permanently deformed.

All materials have this property of elasticity to a greater or lesser degree; and this provides one of the major problems for the engineering designer. If the 'elastic limit' of the material is exceeded by placing it under too great conditions of strain, the material will become permanently deformed, or will even break.

For simple applications these formulae and the theory behind them will give the engineering designer the information he requires. But many applications are often complicated by other variable factors. For example, if a material is subjected to an alternating stress (such as a spring which is repeatedly and rapidly being compressed and released, and then compressed again), slip occurs in the actual particles of the material itself, which results in its having a very

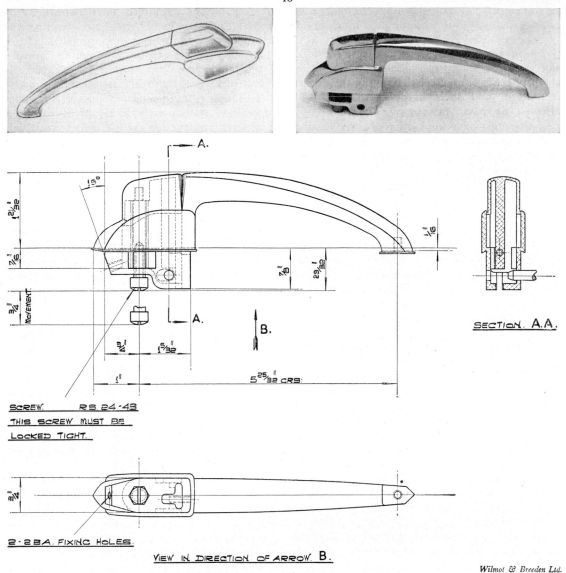

Wilmot & Breeden Ltd.

FIG. I. THE DESIGN OF A MOTOR-CAR DOOR HANDLE

Above left, the designer's drawing; right, the finished handle. Below, the engineering drawing

much lower elastic limit. The material can then fail at much lower applied stresses than those which would normally be indicated by the usual elementary formulae.

This condition is known as 'fatigue failure' (*see* METALS), and is of particular importance in designing high-speed machinery or in applications where VIBRATION (q.v.) is experienced, such as a bolt or rivet holding parts together in an aircraft. Fatigue failure is very complicated to determine, since so many factors are involved,

including how much the stress varies, what the average stress is, and how rapid is the vibration.

In other high-speed applications too, particularly at high temperatures, another problem arises. The metal, although still perfectly solid, can actually 'flow' and thus change its shape (that is, suffer plastic deformation) and its properties. This factor is of primary importance in the design of the turbine blades of jet engines (*see* GAS TURBINE), and one which necessitated special alloys being developed that would stand up to operation at tremendous speeds under high temperature without exhibiting too much of this undesirable property.

There are also many other factors to consider. For example, many machining processes alter the properties of metals by changing their grain formation, and their hardness may also be affected (*see* HEAT TREATMENT). The engineering designer must have knowledge of these matters and allow for alterations in properties of the materials he has specified during the actual production processes.

Even in a comparatively simple component, the stresses are not evenly distributed throughout, but will be at a maximum where there is any abrupt change of cross-section, even if this is very small, such as a hole, or a narrow raised portion, or even a small notch—a condition known as 'stress concentration'. These and other variable factors often face engineering designers with much more complex problems than can be solved by the basic formulae and theory of the strength of materials.

Modern electronic calculating machines and 'computing engines' (*see* ELECTRONICS) help to solve the vastly complicated mathematical equations that these many variables produce, since they can solve such problems much more quickly than even the fastest mathematicians (*see* p. 54). But, even with this brilliant development, the designer is often forced to use other methods.

One of the methods used by the designer is to make carefully designed models (*see* MODEL ENGINEERING) with which he can test his new product. Designing of models has become a very specialized part of engineering design, for to be of any value they must be designed as carefully as the finished product; every part to be tested must simulate in the model as exactly as possible the conditions that will exist in the finished product, reduced to the scale on which the model is built. Some devices, especially those concerned with high-speed flight of aircraft, are tested in WIND TUNNELS (q.v.).

The strength of materials can also sometimes be analysed in the laboratory by using tensile testing machines and other devices. By another method, involving a phenomenon known as photo-elasticity, POLARIZED LIGHT (q.v.) is passed through a model made of a special transparent material which is then submitted to the type of stresses which the actual object will experience. The effect of the light on this material is to produce a pattern in the transparent material showing just how the stress will be distributed (*see* Colour Plate, opp. p. 368).

Another device available to the engineering designer for measuring strains and stresses is the electric strain gauge. This depends on the fact that when an electric conductor is stressed or strained mechanically, its electrical resistance is altered. In practice these conductors, which can be very small and light, are insulated and firmly attached to the object about which information is needed. For instance, a number of these can be attached to various parts of an aircraft which is about to be taken on a test flight, or to a piece of machinery on a test bed. Each strain gauge, being firmly attached to its particular component, will move as the area to which it is attached moves. Each gauge is connected by wires to a measuring instrument which records the change in electrical resistance, thus indicating the movement, or deformation, of that particular area under it.

A resistance bridge circuit is used for static testing, and further devices are used for testing dynamic strain, especially with aircraft. In fact, it is possible to place a number of gauges on a single spar of an aircraft, for example, and so to obtain information at various positions along it. A record is made of them all during an actual test flight, and this can be analysed to provide the engineering designer with the practical information he needs.

Although problems concerned with the strength of materials are the most numerous and usually the most important which the designer has to deal with, there are also others. The engineering designer must consider the requirements of standardization, and he must aim at simplicity of design as far as possible. If, for example, he designs a number of different components which are very nearly but not quite identical, production will be correspondingly more difficult and more expensive. Indeed, were he to do this, the PRODUCTION ENGINEERING department (q.v.), on seeing such designs, would almost certainly ask whether they could not be modified or adapted so as to produce one general design which, by compromising a little here and there, could serve for them all. Such a simplification whereby the same blank could be used for each component would save work all along the line—work in the drawing office, in ordering the raw material, and in the actual tooling and machining. Consequently productivity could be increased and the cost of production reduced.

Various national and international standards of design have been laid down, and the designer must for practical reasons comply with these where they apply. For example, in a design where an assembly is involved, he would not plan for the use of special components where suitable standardized ones were available—he would not, for instance, specify a special screw thread in a hole unless it was absolutely necessary, since this would involve making special screws or bolts as well as threading tools.

Engineering designers must also appreciate the actual degree of accuracy required in practice, and design the product accordingly. To design to an unnecessarily high degree of accuracy would be uneconomical. Where high accuracy is required, it is indicated by limits on the drawing: for example, the statement '±0·001 inch' against a dimension of, say, 2·5 inches would indicate that it must not be more than one-thousandth of an inch larger or smaller than 2·5 inches. Where a high-surface finish is required, another symbol is used on the drawing to show the area which needs this finish, for all surfaces of the product would not need a highly finished machined surface.

The designer must also consider the appearance of his finished article, and must produce a design which will give a finished product not only functionally sound, but also aesthetically pleasing to the eye.

See also PRODUCTION ENGINEERING; STRESS AND STRAIN; MODEL ENGINEERING.

ENGINEERING DRAWING.

An engineering drawing expresses on paper a true-to-scale picture of an object, which conveys to a skilled engineer an exact picture, not only of the size and shape of all the parts, but how they fit together to form a working mechanism. The drawing may be the actual size of the object, or drawn 'to scale' larger or smaller than the object. The relation of the size of the drawing to the size of the object is called the scale and is generally expressed by a fraction, thus: scale $\frac{1}{32}$. Drawings are usually made on transparent material such as tracing paper so that they can be copied by one of the photo-printing processes (see DRAWING, REPRODUCTION OF).

A PERSPECTIVE drawing (q.v. Vol. XII) shows an object as an observer sees it; but, because lines appear to get closer together as they recede from

a

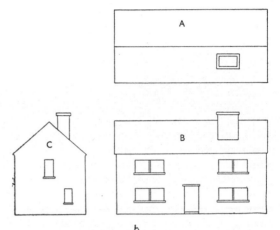

b

FIG. I. *a.* PERSPECTIVE DRAWING. *b.* ORTHOGRAPHIC PROJECTION

A. Plan. B. Side elevation. C. End elevation

the spectator, it does not show the exact dimensions of the object (Fig. 1*a*). To show three dimensions to a single true scale on a sheet of paper, which has only two dimensions, it is necessary to make several drawings, showing all the aspects in turn (Fig. 1*b*). Seen from above, the house appears as A; this is called the plan. The view from the side, or side elevation, is B, and the end elevation is C. If the dimensions of A, B, and C are drawn to scale, these drawings give all the external dimensions of the house. A 'section' (Latin *sectio*, a 'cutting-off') shows the inside of an object as if part of it were cut off. A section can be a plan, or elevation, or indeed a view from any intermediate angle.

1. ORTHOGRAPHIC PROJECTION. Fig. 1*b* is called an orthographic projection. There are two ways of making this so that it is quite clear which part is represented in each drawing. In 'First Angle Projection' (Fig. 2) the object is first drawn as though it were lying flat on a table and viewed from above. This gives the plan A. If the object is turned upwards through a right angle

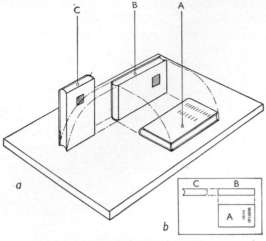

FIG. 2. FIRST-ANGLE PROJECTION
a. Perspective view. *b*. Drawing
A. Plan. B. Side elevation. C. End elevation

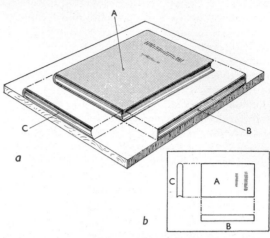

FIG. 3. THIRD-ANGLE PROJECTION
a. Perspective view. *b*. Drawing
A. Plan. B. Side elevation. C. End elevation

and again viewed from above the side elevation B is seen; this is drawn above or beneath the plan. If it is then turned through another right angle to the left, the end elevation C is seen from above; and this is drawn to the left of the side elevation. Thus Fig. 2*b* shows the plan and elevations of the object (drawn in perspective in Fig. 2*a*) in their relative positions.

In 'Third Angle Projection', instead of imagining that the object itself is moved so that the different sides can be seen from the same position, it is the spectator's position which is changed (Fig. 3). The three drawings are made as though seen from a point at right angles to each side, the plan A from above, the side elevation B from the side, and the end elevation C from the end. The

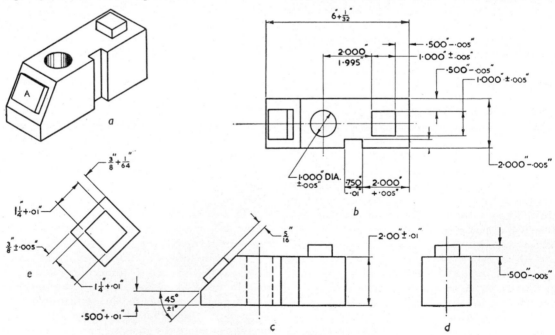

FIG. 4. PERSPECTIVE AND THIRD-ANGLE PROJECTION OF AN ENGINEERING COMPONENT
a. Perspective. *b*. Plan. *c*. Side elevation. *d*. End elevation. *e*. Plan of sloping end

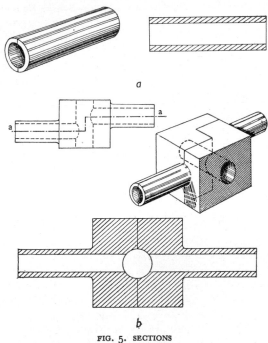

FIG. 5. SECTIONS

a. Cylinder and section. *b.* Plan, perspective, and section through a–a of component

drawings are placed in their relative positions so that it is clear which is which.

The method of drawing actually used is that which describes the particular object in the best way. A simple object, such as a cylinder, may need to be drawn only from two views, the plan and one elevation; but a complex shape may need auxiliary views to show details which are not at right angles to the plan or elevations. Thus, the sloping end A in Fig. 4 is drawn in plan *e*, in addition to the plan *b* and elevations *c* and *d*.

Dimension lines are fine parallel lines projecting from the part but not joined to it. Between these lines is another with an arrow at each end; on this line the dimension figures are shown. It is not usually possible or, indeed, necessary, to make objects exactly the sizes given, therefore the designer indicates by how much the dimensions can be allowed to vary. The allowances, or 'tolerances' (*see* PRODUCTION ENGINEERING), are indicated after the dimension. In Fig. 4*c* the height of the object is given as 2·00 inches ±0·01 inch; in other words, the height can be 0·01 inch greater or smaller than the actual nominal dimension of 2 inches. This is called bilateral tolerance; unilateral tolerance allows

a variation only in one direction: the width in *b*, for instance, can be 0·005 inch less than 2 inches but must not be greater.

The inside shape of an object can be shown, if it is simple, by dotted lines on the plan or elevation, as the hole is shown in Fig. 4*c*. For more complicated objects a section is required. Fig. 5*a* is the section of a cylinder, showing it as it would appear if it were cut along its axis and one-half were removed. Fig. 5*b* is a more complicated object in which the internal features are not all in the same plane. The planes of the section are shown on the plan by the line a–a.

2. PICTORIAL REPRESENTATION. It is often necessary to show what an object looks like in three dimensions. The simplest way of doing this is by isometric projection (Fig. 6). *a* is the plan and *b* the elevation of a cube, drawn from the angle at which the projection is to be viewed. In the isometric projection *c*, the diagonal CD is the same width as on the plan, and the horizontal lines AC and AD are drawn at an angle 120°. The vertical line AB is made the same length as AC and AD, and the cube is completed by drawing horizontal lines parallel to AC and AD and vertical lines parallel to AB. The vertical lines may be drawn the same length as in the elevation.

To make a perspective drawing it is necessary not only to know the plan and elevation of the object but also to decide the position from which it is most useful to view it; that is, the distance and height of the spectator's eye in relation to

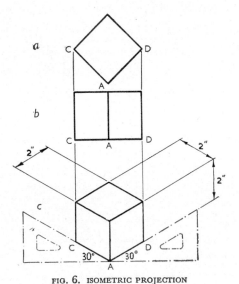

FIG. 6. ISOMETRIC PROJECTION

a. Plan. *b.* Elevation. *c.* Isometric projection

the object. If the eye is above the object, the top will be seen and receding lines will appear to run upwards; if the eye is low, the receding lines above the eye-level will appear to run downwards. If the spectator is near, receding lines will appear to run at a sharper angle than if the eye is far away (Fig. 7).

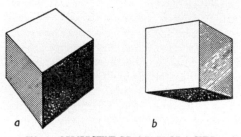

FIG. 7. PERSPECTIVE DRAWINGS OF A CUBE

a. Seen from above and near to spectator. *b.* Seen from below and farther from spectator

If the spectator looked at an object through an upright sheet of glass, and traced the shapes of the object on the glass exactly where his eyes saw them, a perspective drawing would be produced. In practice the draughtsman draws on a sheet of paper exactly what he might have traced on the upright sheet of glass. The imaginary glass with its flat surface represents what is called the 'picture plane'. At the height of the spectator's eye he imagines a horizontal line known as the 'horizon line'. At a point on that line exactly in front of his eye he imagines a point which he calls the

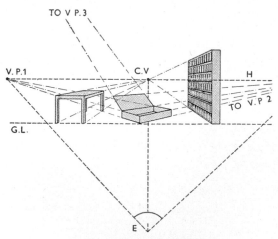

FIG. 8. PERSPECTIVE DRAWING

H. Horizon. cv. Centre of vision. GL. Ground line. E. Position of spectator's eye (its distance from the picture plane). VP1, VP2, VP3. Vanishing point of sides and lid of box

'centre of vision'. Any straight line which he sees in the picture plane, and which is parallel to the line running from his eye to the centre of vision, will itself appear to run from the object towards the centre of vision. This is because parallel lines appear to recede until, if extended, they would meet in the distance at a point called the 'vanishing-point'.

In Fig. 8 there is a table standing on the ground to the left of and below the spectator's line of vision; there is also a bookcase standing to the right of the line of vision, its top being above it. Since the receding lines of all these objects are parallel to the spectator's line of vision, they appear to run directly towards the centre of vision. There is also a box in the diagram which is standing so that its lines are not parallel to the spectator's line of vision. Therefore the vanishing-points of the sides of this box are at different points on the horizon line—VP 1 and VP 2. The position of these points depends on the distance of the spectator's eye (E in Fig. 8) from the picture plane. Lines drawn from E to the horizon line at the same angles as the sides of the box give their vanishing-points. The vanishing-points of the open lid of the box which is tilted are not on the horizon line but above it.

To find the lengths of lines in a perspective drawing it is necessary to know the height of the spectator's eye above the ground. This is shown by a line parallel to the horizon and below it, called the 'ground line'. The lengths of horizontal lines can be found by relating them to actual measurements on the ground line. The lengths of vertical lines are found by relating them to actual measurements at right angles to the ground line.

ENGINES, HISTORY OF. About 2,000 years ago, a Greek called Hero invented a steam turbine like that in Fig. 1. But this toy turbine spun round for amusement only, and did not turn machinery. For centuries men still had to rely for power on the muscles of themselves and their animals, supplemented by WATER POWER and WIND POWER (qq.v.). By the 17th century the need for power began to outrun these primitive resources, the main demand coming from MINING (q.v. Vol. VII). The demand for metals and coal was increasing, and as mines were dug deeper, the existing machines were not capable of pumping out the water. Men therefore began to consider how they might apply the power of STEAM (q.v.) to the task of draining the mines.

Many years of difficult experimenting led at last to the creation of the first successful steam engine, shortly after 1700, by the Dartmoor ironmonger and blacksmith, Thomas Newcomen (Fig. 2). The success of this engine lay behind the great expansion of English mining during the 18th century. After 1720 the engine was widely used in Cornish tin-mines, and by 1769 fifty-seven Newcomen engines were pumping water from coal-mines in the Newcastle area.

Nevertheless, the Newcomen engine was what we should call inefficient, that is to say, it was very wasteful in fuel and therefore costly to run. It was James WATT (q.v. Vol. V) who traced one main cause of this inefficiency.

In the Newcomen engine the heat of the fire is transferred to the steam, and, of the heat in the steam, some is expended heating up the cylinder, some does useful work, and some is carried away by the cold water that condenses the steam. This cold water also cools the cylinder, and thus carries away the heat that the steam originally gave to heating the cylinder. Thus, only a small proportion of the energy in the steam is

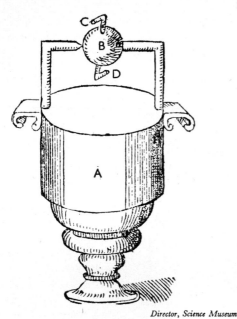

Director, Science Museum

FIG. 1. HERO'S TOY STEAM TURBINE

Steam produced in the boiler A passes up the pipes into the pivoted sphere B. As the steam issues from the jets c and D this reaction makes the sphere rotate

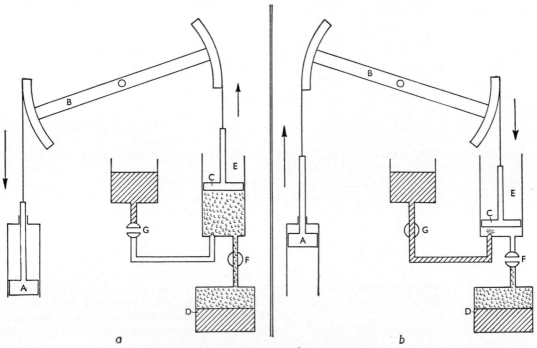

FIG. 2. DIAGRAM OF NEWCOMEN'S PUMPING ENGINE

a. The weight of the pump piston A, pulling the beam B down, raises the piston c. This draws the steam from boiler D into the cylinder E when the valve F is open. *b.* When the valve F is closed and G open, a jet of water is injected into the cylinder, condensing the steam and producing a vacuum. Atmospheric pressure pushes the piston c down and the pump piston is raised

Crown Copyright, Science Museum

FIG. 3. BOULTON AND WATT'S ROTATIVE BEAM ENGINE, 1788

flooding and finding the Newcomen engine too costly, was saved by Watt's engines, and forty had been installed in Cornwall by 1800. They were also used for working the bellows of BLAST FURNACES (q.v.). They were, however, suitable only for pumping or other purposes involving nothing but reciprocating or to-and-fro motion; but in 1781 Watt adapted his engine for driving rotary machinery (Fig. 3), so making it available for almost every job where power was needed.

During the 19th century steam was used in almost every industry that needed power on a large scale. The Lancashire cotton industry, which had been built on power from water-wheels on the numerous streams of the area, was by 1800 using steam in eighty-four of its mills, and by 1850 the cotton industry was using 71,000 horse-power of steam, against a mere 11,000 h.p. of water power. Meanwhile Trevithick and many others were developing Watt's cumbersome if effective monster into the neat high-speed, high-pressure engine of today (*see* STEAM ENGINE). These improved engines became suitable for use in transport. Steam-driven ships were well established on American rivers by 1815, while ocean steam navigation developed in the 1840's (*see* STEAMSHIPS, Vol. IV). Serious experiments with steam LOCOMOTIVES (q.v. Vol. IV) on land began at the end of the 18th century, and after 1830 the steam-driven railway became the backbone of inland transport.

Even in Watt's time, it was realized that the roundabout process of using steam to move a piston rod backwards and forwards and then converting this to-and-fro motion into rotation by means of a crank or similar mechanism had its disadvantages, and that it should be possible to use the steam to produce rotation directly. The better engineers, however, knew that a STEAM TURBINE (q.v.) could not be a practical proposition until both materials and engineering methods were greatly improved; and, in fact, it was not till 1884 that Charles Parsons produced

actually turned into useful work. Watt realized that if the steam could only be condensed in a vessel separate from the cylinder, this could be kept permanently cold while the cylinder and piston could be kept permanently hot. This arrangement would save, on every cycle, the heat formerly wasted in reheating the cylinder after it had been cooled by the condensing water.

In 1769 Watt brought out his improved engine with separate condenser. Let us look again at Fig. 2. The water tank above valve G is replaced in Watt's engine by a closed vessel, the condenser, kept permanently cold by being immersed in water; and the cylinder is kept permanently hot by the steam jacket which surrounds it. In the first stroke the valve G is closed, and the action is exactly as in Fig. 2, except that a small pump has created a vacuum in the condenser. On the working stroke, valve G is opened and valve F closed, and the steam rushes into the condenser where it is condensed to water, and a vacuum is created in the cylinder; the rest follows as in Fig. 2. The important difference is that there is now no waste of heat in alternately heating and cooling the cylinder.

Watt's much more economical engines were soon installed everywhere in England where heavy pumping had to be done (except at coal-mines, where cheap waste coal made the Newcomen engine still worth while). The Cornish tin mining industry, threatened with extinction by

Director, Science Museum

FIG. 4. PARSONS' ORIGINAL STEAM TURBINE AND DYNAMO

the first successful turbine (Fig. 4). (This was first used to generate electricity, and by 1912 turbo-generators of 25,000 kilowatts (about 33,000 h.p.) had been built.) Then Parsons turned to ship propulsion, the only other major industry that could use turbines of the large sizes that gave greatest efficiency. Parsons' turbine-driven launch, the *Turbinia*, created a sensation at the naval review of 1897 by greatly exceeding the speed of the fastest destroyers then in existence (Fig. 5).

Both the reciprocating steam engine and the steam turbine use the heat in one place, the boiler, to raise steam, and then use the steam in another place, the cylinder or turbine, to produce useful work. It was realized that it might be more efficient to burn the fuel directly in the cylinder. In this way arose the idea of the INTERNAL COMBUSTION ENGINE (q.v.). The Dutch scientist Huygens tried as early as 1680 to make an engine deriving its power from the explosion of gunpowder in the cylinder; but the practical problems of making an internal combustion engine are far more difficult than for steam, and attention for some time was diverted to the evolution of a successful steam engine.

Towards the end of the 18th century the idea of the internal combustion engine was revived. Coal-gas, which was widely used after 1812, provided an ideal fuel, and rapid progress was made. But it was not till 1860 that the Frenchman Lenoir produced the first commercially successful gas engine, some 400 of which were in use in his own country within 5 years. Two years later, another Frenchman, Beau de Rochas, invented the four-stroke engine, which was used by the German Dr. Otto to create the Otto 'Silent' engine in 1876.

The advantage of the gas engine was that it could be made in small units, and could therefore serve many industries which could not use steam. But after electric power came into use about 1900, providing much more convenient small-scale power engines, the gas engine slowly went out of use. Its importance is that it led the

Photograph, Science Museum

FIG. 5. THE TURBINE-DRIVEN LAUNCH *TURBINIA* AT SPEED IN 1894

(By courtesy of Parsons' Marine Steam Turbine Co. Ltd.)

FIG. 6. DAIMLER'S FIRST CAR, 1886
(*By courtesy of Deutsches Museum, Munich*)

Photograph, Science Museum

way to the much more effective petrol engine, which is merely a gas engine with slight changes to enable it to vaporize and use a liquid fuel.

Petroleum (*see* OIL, NATURAL, Vol. III) was discovered in Pennsylvania in 1858, and this led to attempts to make petrol engines, culminating in Daimler's engine in 1884. The result revolutionized transport (Fig. 6). It made possible the MOTOR-CAR and—even more important—the AEROPLANE (qq.v. Vol. IV).

In 1892 the first diesel engine, using heavier oil, was patented, but was not made fully practical for several years. It was evolved by a gradual development from the petrol engine through engines using heavier and heavier oil. This engine will not only use the crudest oil but can be adapted to use even such odd fuels as sawdust or even powdered kitchen refuse. This development of the internal combustion engine —more efficient and therefore cheaper than steam—has proved most successful in ship propulsion, and by 1930 a greater tonnage was being powered with diesel than with steam.

The most recent development of the internal combustion engine is the GAS TURBINE (q.v.)—a turbine which is turned directly by the hot gases produced by burning the fuel. The gas turbine to work efficiently must run at very high temperatures, and the chief difficulty has been to find materials for the turbine blades which will remain undistorted even when very hot and

rapidly rotating. The gas turbine is still, in general, less efficient than steam and therefore more costly to run, but it is light and costs little to build. It can also be started and stopped at a moment's notice, whereas a steam turbine is uneconomical unless it runs continuously for long periods. Because of these special features, therefore, it has been used for certain purposes— for example, as the power unit of the railway locomotive, and also as an essential part of the engine of jet-propelled aeroplanes (*see* AIRCRAFT ENGINES, Section 2, Vol. IV). ROCKET PROPULSION (q.v.) may become very important in the future of flying, though at present practical difficulties confine it to very special uses, such as helping the take-off or providing extra power for short bursts at high speed.

The next useful addition to our power resources is likely to be atomic energy (*see* NUCLEAR ENERGY), but this will not involve a new type of engine, at any rate in the foreseeable future; the actual engine will probably be a steam turbine, the steam being raised by a nuclear pile instead of by burning coal or oil.

See also STEAM ENGINE; STEAM TURBINE; INTERNAL COMBUSTION ENGINE; GAS TURBINE.

EXPANSION AND CONTRACTION. Most substances, whether solid, liquid, or gaseous, expand when heated. An engineer generally has to make some allowance for this expansion when he is building a structure or piece of machinery. For example, railway lines are normally laid in lengths with a small gap between each length, so that the line can safely stretch a fraction of an inch longer in very hot weather; without that safety gap, the rails might buckle dangerously on an ordinary 'sleeper-and-ballast' railway track. Some railways, such as the London Underground, prefer to weld their lengths of rail together, but guard against buckling by special methods of anchoring the track.

Another example is the 'seizing' of a motor-car

engine when the piston jams against the cylinder walls. The reason for this may be the lack of lubricating oil, which causes FRICTION (q.v.) to develop and, consequently, the piston to get hotter. The heating then causes an extra expansion of the piston which has not been allowed for in the design, and the piston wedges itself in the cylinder.

1. SOLIDS. If the length of a rod is measured at different temperatures it will be found that it expands or contracts according to the rise or fall in temperature—in fact, that its changes of length are directly proportional to the changes of temperature. The change of length which occurs for each unit length of a solid, for a temperature rise of one degree, is called the 'coefficient of linear expansion' of the solid, and is generally denoted by the symbol α. If, for example, we have a bar of iron 50 feet long at a temperature of 0° C., and we heat it to 100° C., the change of temperature would cause the bar to expand; and if we then measured it we would find its new length to be about 50·06 feet. The change of length per unit length (that is, for 1 foot) for a temperature rise of 100° would therefore be 0·06 ÷ 50, which is 0·0012; and the change for 1° C. would be 0·0012 ÷ 100, which is 0·000012 —a very small amount. For iron, therefore, 0·000012 = α (the coefficient of linear expansion); for other metals the coefficient α has different values. If we know the value of α for any solid we can calculate what the changes of length would be for particular changes of temperature.

In actual practice the coefficient α varies slightly with the particular part of the temperature scale over which the measurements are taken, and generally a mean value between certain temperature limits is specified. It will be seen that α is independent of the unit of length used in the measurement. If, however, the temperature rise is measured in Fahrenheit instead of Centigrade units, α will have a different value.

One of the most accurate methods of determining α is by the 'comparator method' (Fig. 1). The specimen in the form of a bar is mounted in a temperature-controlled bath so that it is free to expand. Fine scratches are made near the ends of the bar, and these are brought under a pair of travelling microscopes fitted with micrometer screws (see LENGTH-MEASURING, INSTRUMENTS), adjusted until they are vertically over the scratches. Then the temperature of the bath

is raised, and the microscopes are adjusted until they are once again over the scratches. The change in length can be determined by the readings of the micrometers, and hence the coefficient α can be found from the original length, change of length, and temperature rise.

Although the power of expansion in materials is undesirable in many ways, it can be put to some very good uses. Steel tires, for example, are shrunk on to the wheels of a railway carriage. The tire is made of slightly less internal diameter than the diameter of the wheel. When it is heated, it expands sufficiently to be slipped over the wheel; and then as it cools it grips on to the wheel so tightly that no other means of securing it is necessary. The barrel of a large gun consists of several cylinders mounted one inside the other, the outer ones of which are shrunk in turn on to the inner; this gives the barrel greater resistance to the shock of firing.

Expansion of metals and alloys, in particular steel, plays an important part in engineering.

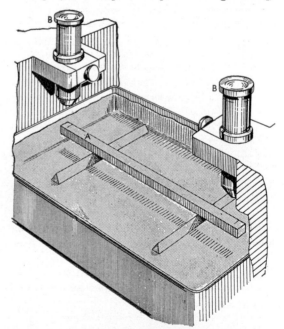

FIG. 1. COMPARATOR METHOD OF DETERMINING THE COEFFICIENT OF LINEAR EXPANSION
A. Bar to be tested. B. Microscopes

Expansions as the result of heating involve only small strains, but the stresses (see STRESS AND STRAIN) required to stop these strains from taking place are often large, so that the designer has to allow for these temperature effects either by leaving expansion joints, as in railways, or else by making due allowance in the design for the increase of stress in the structure caused by the expansion. Certain ALLOYS (q.v.), such as invar (an alloy of nickel and steel), have been specially developed to have the minimum amount of expansion and contraction—a very low α coefficient. These are used for such purposes as the manufacture of precision-measuring instruments. On some instruments, such as the hot-wire ammeter (see ELECTRICAL INSTRUMENTS), expansion is used to enable measurements to be made. The fact that some metals expand more than others has been put to use, for example, in the bimetallic strip (see THERMOSTAT).

2. LIQUIDS. It is possible to have only a volume expansion in the case of a liquid, as it assumes the shape of the vessel into which it is poured. A difficulty at once arises in determining the coefficient of expansion as the vessel that contains the liquid will also expand, and only an 'apparent' expansion will be obtained. To find the 'absolute' expansion, allowance must be made for the expansion of the vessel.

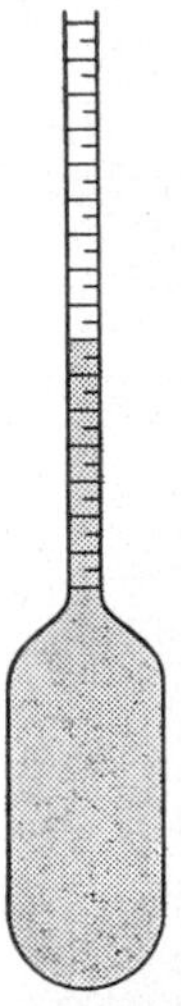

One method of determining the coefficient of expansion of a liquid is by means of a 'volume dilatometer' (Fig. 2). The apparatus consists of a bulb with a very narrow graduated tube. The liquid is poured in, the dilatometer is immersed in a bath at a temperature of, say, 10° C., and the reading of the tube gives the volume. The bath is then heated to, say, 100° C. temperature, and when a new reading is taken, the difference between the readings will give the increase in volume. To find the mean coefficient of volumetric expansion over the range 10° to 100° C. we employ a similar method of calculation to that used for the linear coefficient.

FIG. 2.
DIAGRAM OF
A VOLUME
DILATO-
METER

Probably the most common use to which the expansion of a liquid is put is the ordinary THERMOMETER (q.v.), where the liquids used are either mercury or alcohol. The principle is exactly the same as with the volume dilatometer.

3. GASES. The volume that a particular mass of gas occupies depends upon two things, the temperature and the pressure. If the pressure is kept constant and the volume of the gas is measured at different temperatures, the coefficient of increase in volume at constant pressure is obtained and is defined as

$$\frac{\text{Increase in volume at constant pressure}}{\text{Volume at 0° C.} \times \text{change in temperature}}.$$

It has been found by experiment that the value of this coefficient is very nearly the same for all gases and has, in fact, a value of $\frac{1}{273}$ per degree Centigrade. So that a gas at constant pressure expands by $\frac{1}{273}$ of its volume at 0° C. for every degree rise in temperature.

If a given mass of gas is at a certain temperature, it may have any volume, for it will always completely fill the container that it is in. But if the volume of a given amount of gas is increased by using a larger container, the pressure the gas exerts on the walls is reduced; similarly if the volume is reduced the pressure is increased in proportion. This is stated in Boyle's Law (see PRESSURE, Vol. III).

EXPLOSIVES. An explosive is either a single chemical substance or a mixture, in which a chemical reaction can be set off so as to produce large amounts of gas at high temperature and pressure in a very short time. When the gas moves outwards at great speed (the explosion), the air surrounding the explosive is compressed suddenly, and this causes the bang. The energy in the expanding gas can be used to break up masses of rock, coal, or other substances (see BLASTING), as a weapon of war in exploding BOMBS AND MINES (q.v. Vol. X) or propelling projectiles from guns (see ARTILLERY, Vol. X), or in geophysical PROSPECTING (q.v.).

There are two kinds of explosives—high explosives and propellants. When a high-explosive charge is set off, it detonates—that is, a shock wave, a wave of pressure, passes through the explosive from one end to the other, causing a violent chemical reaction at each point that it passes. The chemical reaction helps to keep the wave moving on at very high speed and also converts the material behind it into a hot gas that expands very quickly. The shock wave moves through the explosive at 2,000 to 8,000 yards per second.

T.N.T. (trinitrotoluene), a single chemical substance, is probably the best known high explosive. It is made from toluene, one of the liquid products from the coal tar produced in the distillation of coal to form coke (see GAS MANUFAC-

TURE). The toluene is 'nitrated' in successive stages by treatment with nitric and sulphuric acids.

Propellants are used to make a short, powerful non-destructive push, as, for instance, in a gun. A propellant explosive charge is made up of a large number of small pieces or grains, which do not detonate, but burn: that is, when the explosive is set off by a hot flame, the surface of each piece gives off hot gas. It burns inwards at a few inches a second until the grain is consumed.

Gunpowder, the earliest known propellant explosive, is a mixture of charcoal, saltpetre, and sulphur. It was made by Roger BACON (q.v. Vol. V) in about 1250, though it was probably discovered much earlier. By the middle of the 14th century, the military uses of gunpowder were well established, but it was not until 1660 that methods were devised for using gunpowder to blast rock. Gunpowder remained the only effective explosive until the 19th century when in 1846 two new explosives were discovered: nitroglycerine, made by nitrating glycerine, and nitrocellulose, made by nitrating woody substances. These could be made to detonate or burn. Some 25 years later, Alfred NOBEL (q.v. Vol. V) invented safe methods of making and setting off nitroglycerine explosives.

Most commercial high explosives now are mixtures of nitroglycerine, ammonium nitrate, and cellulose (usually in the form of sawdust). The nitroglycerine is the sensitive part of the mixture, the other two ingredients providing the energy and gas in the explosion. These explosives are made by absorbing purified nitroglycerine in sawdust to make a nitroglycerine 'dope'. The dope is taken to a mixing house where it is mixed with fine ammonium nitrate and other ingredients. The mixing machines are designed so that there is as little friction as possible for fear of generating enough heat to set off the mixture and cause an explosion. Some explosives can be set off by shock, so the processes and machines used to make them have to work very smoothly.

High explosives are set off by being given a strong mechanical shock. This is obtained from the explosion of an even more sensitive substance (usually lead azide or fulminate of mercury) in a detonator, a small metal capsule containing the substance (see FUZE) placed in contact with the high-explosive charge.

I.C.I.

INSERTING EXPLOSIVE CARTRIDGE IN A BOREHOLE DURING TUNNELLING

High explosives are mostly used in peace time for blasting. They are set off in holes drilled in the rocks or coal, and reduce the amount of work in quarrying and mining by breaking up the material. With coal, however, there is great danger that the flame from the explosion will ignite firedamp—an explosive gas found in coal mines (see COAL-MINING, Vol. VII). Gunpowder, widely used at one time, has caused many explosions in 'fiery' mines. During the early part of the 20th century, safety explosives—so-called 'permitted explosives'—were developed for use in coal-mines. These contain mixtures of nitroglycerine (or T.N.T.) and ammonium nitrate together with flame-quenching and cooling materials such as common salt. When the charge is set off it detonates in the normal way, but the heat is absorbed by the salt before the gas has expanded far enough to reach and ignite a pocket of firedamp. The use of such explosives has made coal-mining much safer—indeed, now, firedamp is ignited only about once in ten million shots fired.

Firearms need a much less violent action than blasting to shoot out the projectile at good speed without damaging the gun. Propellant explosives, with their slow rate of burning, produce

DRILLING HOLES FOR EXPLOSIVE CHARGES AT THE I.C.I. ANHYDRITE MINE AT BILLINGHAM-ON-TEES
The air-driven percussive drills are mounted on a hydraulically operated carriage

gas slowly enough to do this satisfactorily. Gunpowder, the first propellant, was followed at the end of the 19th century by cordite. This is a horny plastic made from a mixture of nitroglycerine and guncotton—itself a powerful explosive formed by treating cotton with a mixture of nitric and sulphuric acids and then purifying and drying it. Propellants are all set off by flame—as, for example, by the cap of a shotgun cartridge.

Propellants are now used not only for the cartridges of military and SPORTING GUNS (q.v. Vol. IX) but also for the so-called 'power cartridge' applications, such as the submarine gun, a device used for driving steel bolts into steel plates in sunken ships for SALVAGE purposes (q.v. Vol. IV). Power cartridges are also sometimes used for starting aeroplane or tractor engines, and for ROCKET PROPULSION (q.v.). Special new propulsive compositions have now been produced for such purposes as the jet propulsion of toy motor-cars, boats, and aeroplanes and even for dispersing the new insect-killing compounds such as BHC (benzene hexachloride) (see INSECTICIDES, Vol. VI).

Explosives are safe to the experts who have learned how to handle them, but very dangerous to others. Far too many terrible accidents have happened because people who are not properly instructed and authorized have attempted to experiment or interfere with them. Only specialists should handle them.

EXTRUSION, see FORGING AND PRESSING, Section 4.

F

FATIGUE FAILURE, *see* Engineering Design; Metals, Section 7.

FENS, RECLAMATION OF. This immense scheme of Land Reclamation (q.v.), the biggest and most successful scheme ever attempted in Britain, has been gradually carried out, with continual extensions and improvements, for over 300 years. It has transformed an area of once useless marshes, covering about 1 million acres in Bedfordshire, Cambridgeshire, and Norfolk, into some of the richest farmlands in Britain. Altogether about 2 million acres benefit from the Drainage (q.v. Vol. VI) and Flood Control schemes (q.v.) that have been or are being organized.

The fenland swamps were caused by the waters of the Great Ouse and its tributaries which used to spill into the area and then escape past King's Lynn to the Wash. In addition, as large areas are below high-tide level, and as the land was open to the sea, the country was flooded by salt water with each high tide. A scheme for draining the Great Fen, **as it was then called,** was first prepared at the beginning of the 17th century by a Royal Commission appointed by James I. Nothing was done, however, until 1631, when a Dutch engineer, Sir Cornelius Vermuyden, began work on a drainage scheme promoted by the Earl of Bedford. Twenty years later Vermuyden had excavated two large, parallel channels, known as the Old Bedford and the Hundred Foot Channels, each about 21 miles long and 70 and 100 feet wide respectively, which carried away the swamp water from high-lying marshes in Bedfordshire. These channels, however, caused worse flooding at their lower end, in the area known as the 'South Level' of Cambridgeshire, which was also the area most affected by flooding from the sea.

To rescue this area, high banks were built along the course of the tidal Ouse to keep the river to its proper channel, and a floodgate or sluice (*see* Locks and Weirs, Vol. IV) was constructed at Denver. The sluice prevented the sea

Reece Winstone

THE RIVER DELPH BETWEEN MEPAL, CAMBRIDGESHIRE AND WELNEY, NORFOLK

On the right is the Old Bedford River running parallel with the Delph, contained within two banks, its level several feet above the surrounding country

coming up the river at high tide and released the river water into the sea at low tide. Once the flow of the Ouse was under control, work began on draining the area. Primitive pumps, imported from Holland and driven by windmills, were used to lift the water. Each consisted simply of a paddle wheel, similar to a steamship's, fitted with hollow scoops which lifted the water into specially constructed drains. These 'scoop-wheels', though later driven by steam instead of wind power, remained in use for over 200 years. They have now been replaced by modern electrically driven pumping machinery (*see* PUMPS).

The draining of the Fens has always been difficult, for the soil consists largely of peat, a fibrous substance which is easily compressed and holds a lot of water. When drained the peat shrinks very considerably, so that the water has to be pumped higher and higher to reach the river. In 1848, in order to calculate the amount of shrinkage, an iron column called 'Holme Post' was sunk into the soil until its top was level with the surface. In 1932, after 84 years, the top of the column was nearly 11 feet above ground. The ground still continues to shrink, though not so rapidly.

Another complication has always been the Denver sluice, which shuts off the sea at high tide. With the sluice closed, all the water flowing into the tidal Ouse from the Ten Mile and Ely-Ouse rivers, and from the tributaries, has to be impounded above Denver until the tide turns and the sluice can be opened. In times of flood these rivers are so full, largely owing to improved drainage of the land, that when impounded they break their banks, often causing severe damage to the South Level. In 1947 nearly 40,000 acres were flooded. To prevent this, work has now begun on a large channel, up to 200 feet wide and over 20 feet deep, running close to the Ouse from Denver to King's Lynn. This relief channel will carry away much of the water that would otherwise be impounded and, as it has a sluice at its lower end which will close during high tide, it can itself store much extra water in times of flood. In times of extreme flood an area of 400 acres, normally under cultivation, will be used as an extra storage reservoir.

See also LAND RECLAMATION; FLOOD CONTROL; ZUIDER ZEE PROJECT.

FILM PROJECTORS, *see* CINE-CAMERAS AND PROJECTORS, Section 2.

FIREARMS, *see* BALLISTICS. *See also* Vol. X: WEAPONS, HAND. *See also* Vol. IX: SPORTING GUNS AND RIFLES.

FIRECLAYS AND REFRACTORIES. These are substances which are especially resistant to heat and melt only at very high temperatures. For example, the bricks at the back and sides of a domestic fireplace are refractory firebricks, for the heat of a coal fire would damage ordinary building bricks. Refractory clays are found in nature, and are either made up into bricks or are crushed and used loose—rammed dry, or wetted and used like cement. Many industries use refractories, but chiefly the IRON AND STEEL INDUSTRY (q.v.) and the glass industry (*see* GLASS MAKING, Vol. VII). We will describe the use of refractories, therefore, in a steel-works.

Molten steel is of a terrific heat. The refractory lining of a steel-making furnace must be relied on not to melt at a temperature of very nearly 1,700° C., when lumps of iron and steel scrap are melting like fat in a frying-pan. In addition, the whole process of steel making is a chemical one, and the lining must also be able to resist attack by various chemical compounds at very high temperatures.

There are two main groups of refractory materials, one or other of which the steel maker chooses when he is building his furnace, according to the nature of the impurities he is going to

INTERIOR OF A BASIC OPEN HEARTH FURNACE FOR MAKING STEEL

The gas and air 'ports' are seen at the end of the furnace and the 'taphole' at the bottom right-hand corner (*see* p. 412)

remove in the SteeL-making process (q.v.). If the raw materials are comparatively pure, and only the excess carbon has to be removed, he will build his furnace of acid refractories. If, as is far more usual, his raw materials are comparatively impure, and silicon and, above all, phosphorus have to be removed, he must build his furnace of basic refractories. This is because the lime used in removing phosphorus creates a 'slag' (a kind of scum), and this attacks an acid lining and causes it to crumble away.

A third group of refractory materials, known as neutral, is neither acid nor basic, but although it resists the attacks of slag it is not so good as the others at resisting heat. The commonest neutral refractory is fireclay, from which ordinary fire-bricks are made. Others are chromite and graphite. All these, particularly fireclay, are used in BLast Furnaces (q.v.) to make iron, but will not stand the fiercer conditions in a steel furnace. Glass furnaces, too, are often built of firebricks.

Acid refractories consist mainly of silica (a material of which sand is an impure form). They, as well as fireclay, are found in various parts of the world, often in the same ground as coal (this is the reason for the location of Sheffield). Over nine-tenths of the minerals ganister and quartzite is silica, and bricks made from them are used for steel furnace roofs and linings, while silica sand is used in furnace bottoms. The melting-point of this material is high (1,710° C.), but the bricks need careful handling as they tend to crumble and flake in sudden changes of temperature. Silica bricks, as well as firebricks, are used in building glass furnaces, but in the steel industry furnaces built with basic refractories are nearly always used.

Basic refractories are made from minerals rich in magnesium, lime, and chrome. Dolomite, a Limestone (q.v. Vol. III) containing magnesium, occurs in many places in Britain, and is the most widely used basic refractory. The other minerals in use are magnesite and chromite.

Basic bricks, though some will stand temperatures up to 1,880° C., are not as strong as silica bricks at high temperatures; and in most basic furnaces only the parts in actual contact with the steel—the bottom and lower sides—are of basic refractory materials. There are various ways of overcoming the weakness of basic bricks: for example, some furnaces have basic roofs in which each brick is individually hung

B.I.S.R.A.

SUSPENDED ROOF OF ALL-BASIC OPEN HEARTH FURNACE

on wire from a framework. Such furnaces can be worked at a very high temperature and rate of production, but they are naturally expensive to build, for a medium-sized steel furnace may contain a million bricks.

See also BLast Furnace; SteeL-making.

FITTING. In spite of all the ingenuity and accuracy of modern Machine Tools (q.v.), there are still many parts in manufactured goods which have to be made or finally adjusted by hand to fit other parts. Work of this kind is known as 'fitting' and is carried out by fitters, who are highly trained craftsmen with a good working knowledge of the whole process from the original engineer's drawing to the finished article. The work of the fitter is particularly important in the building of prototypes, machines for experimental work, research apparatus, and in the erection of machines and factory plant.

In a sense, the fitter's craft is one of the most satisfying in engineering because he has to depend on his own skill, rather than on machinery, to produce work of high accuracy. The tools he uses are, in fact, unspectacular, but the skilled fitter uses them to produce work of the highest quality.

1. *Fitter's tools.* The fitter usually works at a strongly made bench, provided with a number

FIG. 1. A FITTING SHOP

On the left a fitter is filing a part held in a vice. On the right a surface plate and surface gauge are being used

Ph. Associated British Machine Tools Makers Ltd.

Wadkin Ltd.

of drawers in which to keep tools, and carrying a vice in which work can be held while he is operating on it (Fig. 1). Most fitters possess their own set of tools in which they usually take great pride. A typical set includes a 6-inch and a 12-inch engineer's rule, marked in fractions of an inch and in millimetres, a pair of 'odd-leg' dividers for scribing lines from the edge of work, inside and outside calipers with screw adjustment for fine setting, a pair of dividers for scribing holes, a centre punch, hammers, a universal square, a scriber for scoring lines on the surface of metal, a VERNIER calliper (q.v.), and a 1-inch micrometer for taking fine measurements, a set of scrapers, a small spirit level, pliers and side cutters, a set of screwdrivers, a pair of V-blocks, a set of feeler gauges for testing clearance, a set of screw-pitch gauges (*see* SCREW-THREADS), and a pair of snips or hand shears.

Other tools he needs, which are usually provided by his employers, include drills, reamers, hacksaws, files, and soldering irons.

Before modern machinery was available, fitting could be very heavy work indeed, but now much of the labour has been removed by the use of powered hand tools such as the electric hand drill or pneumatic chisel. Many of these small powered tools can be used for a variety of different purposes.

2. *Marking-out*. The fitter must start by marking out his work, so that he knows exactly where to remove metal in order to make the finished job. This he does by scoring, or scribing, lines on the metal itself. To make it easier to see the lines, he sometimes coats the surface with chalk, whitewash, or a solution of copper sulphate and dilute nitric acid before scribing the lines.

To mark where holes are to be drilled, he makes a small indentation with the centre punch at the place where the hole is to come, and then scribes a circle of the exact size of the hole with the dividers. The kind of tools used generally depends on the degree of accuracy needed. For unimportant work, an ordinary rule can be used; but the spacing of lines and holes sometimes has to be very accurate—perhaps within $\frac{1}{1000}$ inch either way: in this case vernier height gauges and other fine measuring instruments must be used. The work has to be placed on a surface plate which has an absolutely flat surface or, in the case of larger work, on a marking-out table, and these very accurate instruments are used to scribe lines at the exact height required (Fig. 2).

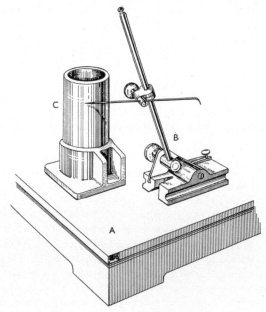

FIG. 2. A. Surface plate. B. Surface gauge. C. Casting

3. *Filing*. This is one of the most important and skilled hand operations, and one of the first

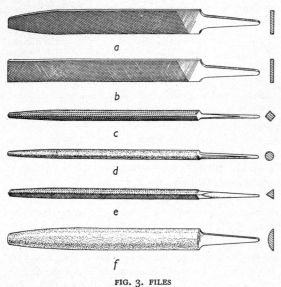

FIG. 3. FILES
a. Flat. *b.* Hand. *c.* Square. *d.* Round. *e.* Triangular.
f. Half round

things that an apprentice fitter is taught to do accurately. A skilled fitter must be able to file a piece of metal to given dimensions within less than $\frac{1}{100}$ inch and make sure, at the same time, that the surface is really flat.

There are many kinds of file, in various shapes and lengths and with different sizes or pitches of teeth (Fig. 3). Files with one set of teeth cut across the other are known as double-cut files. In carrying out a filing job, the fitter probably starts with a coarse file to remove most of the metal as quickly as possible, and then he uses

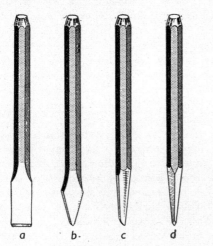

FIG. 4. COLD CHISELS
a. Flat. *b.* Cross-cut. *c.* Round nose. *d.* Diamond

progressively smoother, or finer, files as he approaches the finished measurement. By this, and by different ways of manipulating the file, he can finish with a very smooth surface without unnecessarily wasting time in 'roughing' off the comparatively large amount of material while he is getting down to size. The work is held in the vice on the bench.

4. *Cutting.* Thin metal sheet can be cut to shape with hand shears or 'snips'. Thicker metal and rods, tubes, and bars are cut with an ordinary hacksaw. Where a very heavy cut has to be taken, the work is probably done on a power-operated hacksaw in order to save energy and time.

Another method of cutting metal is with an engineer's chisel, of which there are various types. Sheet metal can be cut roughly to shape with a flat chisel, and the same tool can be used for cutting slots in thin sheet material. Cross-cut chisels are used for cutting grooves, round-nose chisels for cutting channels, as in bearings, and diamond chisels for V-grooves (Fig. 4).

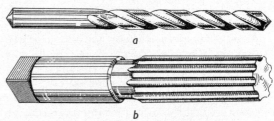

FIG. 5. *a.* TWIST DRILL. *b.* REAMER

5. *Drilling and reaming.* In most factories, drilling is a separate operation undertaken by semi-skilled workers, but the fitter must often drill holes himself. He usually has only to make holes that can be drilled with a hand drill or a power-operated portable drill. If a more accurate hole is needed, he may use a 'reamer', which brings to exact dimensions a hole made slightly smaller than is needed (Fig. 5).

6. *Screw threading.* A fitter's need for screw-threads is normally limited to those he can produce by hand. Internal threads are cut with a set of taps and wrench, and external threads with a stock and die (Fig. 6).

7. *Scraping.* This is a very skilled operation, chiefly used in fitting BEARINGS (q.v.) to their shafts, and for the production of dead flat surfaces for the sliding ways of machine tools. There are various types of scrapers. When a flat surface

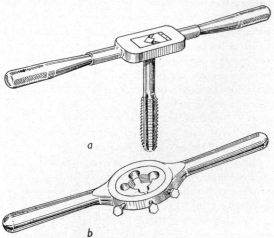

FIG. 6. *a.* TAP WRENCH WITH TAP FIXED IN WRENCH JAWS
b. STOCK AND ADJUSTABLE DIE

is to be scraped, an absolutely flat surface plate coated with a marking substance is rubbed over the work to mark the high spots, which must then be scraped away. This marking and scraping is continued until the marking shows evenly over the whole surface, with no high spots.

8. *Assembly and erection.* An important part of fitting lies in the final assembly of a machine or in the erection of machinery. Thus, the assembly of a locomotive from its machined component parts requires accurate fitting in order that the moving parts shall have sufficient, but not excessive, clearances. In a similar way, the erection of, say, an electric crane must be carefully carried out to ensure that it will safely raise and lower its load.

Most fitters have a specialized knowledge of particular types of machinery; those dealing with electrical apparatus thoroughly understand contacts and insulation, while those working on steam engines or hydraulic machines are concerned with 'glands and packing', which are so adjusted that, while leakage of steam or water is prevented between the moving part and the gland, no undue friction is set up.

Thus, fitters are not only very skilled craftsmen, but also have specialized knowledge according to the class of work which they do.

FLOOD CONTROL. Floods, caused by rivers or the sea, have always been one of the most destructive forces of nature, but until recently the main factors which caused them and the best methods of controlling them were not well understood. Most rivers in times of flood overflow their natural channels and spread into an area which, if the flood is severe, may consist of the whole width of the river valley; engineers call this area a flood plain. Many towns have been built in the past in such areas, and when a serious flood occurs it may cause great damage and loss of life. For example, a disastrous flood of the Ohio River, U.S.A., took place in 1937, overwhelming the town of Huntingdon; and 9 million dollars have since been spent in building $12\frac{1}{2}$ miles of embankments to protect the town.

Floods of short duration, caused by intense local storms, occur in the upper parts of a river basin or in short, steeply sloping rivers. In the lower reaches of large rivers serious floods, which may last for many days, are caused by continuous heavy rain over large areas. Denudation of the land by SOIL EROSION (q.v. Vol. III) also causes floods because the soil cannot absorb the rain which runs off quickly into the river. Another frequent cause is a rapid thaw of ice and snow accompanied by rain. In southern England and the Midlands in 1947 the ground was frozen hard after a very cold February and was covered in snow to a depth equivalent to 4 to 6 inches of rain. The thaw came with the heaviest rainfall ever recorded for March, and the resulting floods were the most widespread in living memory.

RIVERS (q.v. Vol. III) often carry down large quantities of silt, which is deposited where their flow is checked near the mouth. If the river mouth is not dredged, the bed of the river gradually rises until the water overflows, flooding the land. The INDUS in India, the YELLOW RIVER in China, the NILE in Egypt, and the MISSISSIPPI in the U.S.A. (qq.v. Vol. III) are examples of rivers where this type of flooding occurs. Flooding is also caused near the mouth of a river by flood waters meeting exceptionally high tides. In 1928, when the Thames, swollen by inland rains, met high tides and strong winds blowing at the same time from the North Sea, the result was a sudden flood which drowned people in London basements. High tides themselves can cause serious flooding, too, when the sea-level is further raised by winds blowing towards the coast. In February 1953 the general level of the North Sea was raised by exceptionally high winds from the north piling up the waters against the coast of Holland. The high tides which occurred while the sea-level was raised caused disastrous floods not only in Holland but also along the east and south-east coasts of England from Lincolnshire to Kent.

Before methods of flood control can be worked out, it is necessary to have records, covering as long a period as possible, of the rainfall over the river basin, of the flow in the river and its tributaries (*see* HYDROGRAPHY), of the amount and nature of the silt, and of tidal levels both in the river and at its mouth.

The most effective method of controlling river floods is to build large reservoirs which can store the peak flood waters of the river and then release them slowly after the flood period. But these are only possible in river valleys in which a DAM (q.v.) can be built; and they are usually uneconomical unless they can be used for other purposes, for example, IRRIGATION (q.v. Vol. VI), HYDRO-ELECTRIC POWER, or WATER SUPPLY (qq.v.), as well. On the River Tennessee in the United States, twenty multi-purpose reservoirs of this kind are controlled by the TENNESSEE VALLEY AUTHORITY (q.v.). In primitive flood control schemes natural depressions in the ground took the place of reservoirs. These were often highly effective, and can still sometimes be used: in 1952 a flood control scheme for the river Euphrates was completed, using the Habbaniya depression, which the Babylonians had used thousands of years before.

Another method of flood control is to increase the height of river banks by constructing massive embankments or levees. These are built in much the same way as earth dams (the object in each case being to hold back water), though they do not compare with a large dam in height or breadth. The inside faces, wherever they are likely to be attacked by powerful currents, are given extra protection below flood-water level, for example, by brushwood, stone, concrete, or piling. For thousands of years land used for cultivation on the lower reaches of great rivers, such as the Nile or Indus, has been protected in this way.

These high embankments, though they restrict the river to its natural channel, may, however, have dangerous consequences. If the banking merely passes the excess water down the river worse flooding may be caused downstream: in the Mississippi, for example, which has 2,620 miles of such embankments, the flood-level has been raised 15 feet in this way since 1882, and

Lewis and Duvivier

CONSTRUCTION OF CONCRETE SEA-WALL AT PALLING, NORFOLK, FOLLOWING DISASTROUS FLOODS IN FEBRUARY 1953, WHICH INUNDATED A LARGE STRETCH OF THE COUNTRY
Old groins to prevent lateral drift of beach material can be seen at right angles to the new wall

the banks have been raised 22 feet. The bed of a river, too, may be raised by deposited silt, as in the Yellow River in China, until the water overtops the embankments, which may have to be raised again and again.

Sometimes, if a river follows a snakelike course, wandering from side to side through a flat plain, floods can be controlled by digging new channels and building banks which straighten the course of the river and so increase its slope and, therefore, the speed of the current, so that less silt is deposited. Dredging (*see* DREDGER, Vol. IV) is another method of keeping the channel free for the passage of floods; but this has to be repeated at frequent intervals, and is often expensive.

If coastal areas are not protected from flooding by the sea by such natural defences as rocks or sloping beaches of sand or pebbles, breakwaters and sea-walls have to be built. Coastlines in all parts of the world are continually changing with the action of frost, variations in temperature, waves, gales, and tidal currents. Even rock cliffs can be worn away in time, the smaller pieces which are broken off being rolled about on the sea-bed until they form rounded pebbles or sand. Sloping banks of pebbles (or 'shingle') destroy the energy of the waves before they reach the solid coastline. But sometimes storms or changes of tidal current can cause more shingle to be washed away than is deposited, and then the sea may break through the unprotected coastline and flood the land.

Shingle and sand are moved along the coast by a sideways drift of the sea. To trap some of the moving shingle, and so increase the size of the beach, structures called groynes are built. These are generally of timber, with heavy planks between, the top plank being placed just above the surface of the beach. When the shingle has built up to this level, a further plank is added, and so on. The movement of sand can also be controlled by building low, rounded, concrete groynes, or by laying large blocks of stone on brushwood.

Wherever the shingle does not give enough protection, a sea-wall of stone, heavy mass concrete, or heavy timber is constructed. Sometimes, if sufficient stone is not available, large brushwood mats are anchored down on the face of the wall by a shallow layer of stone. The seaward face of the wall may be sloping or vertical; and sometimes it is broken up into steps so that waves rushing up the slope lose some of their force. A sea-wall needs deep foundations, and is most effective when placed at or above the high-water level of ordinary spring tides, leaving a strip of beach as a protection against storms or exceptionally high tides due to winds. If a strip of beach is not left open, the bottom of the wall may be worn away, or the wall itself weakened

by the pressure of water. A sea-wall is often strongly protected at its toe by steel piles driven into the sand to a depth of 10 feet and more

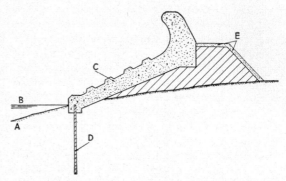

FIG. 1. SECTION OF A HEAVY SEA-WALL

A. Beach. B. Normal high flood level. C. Concrete wall. D. Steel piles. E. Concrete protection to back of wall

(Fig. 1). These prevent the undertow of the waves drawing away the sand on which the wall is built. To prevent waves overtopping the wall, a curved deflector or wave-wall is sometimes built on top of the seaward face to throw back the waves. The back of the wall must also be protected with stone or concrete because in a gale large volumes of spray may be carried by the wind over the top of the wave-wall. A dyke that is withstanding a frontal attack may be destroyed from the rear, if it is not sufficiently strengthened, by water pouring down its back and washing away the earth.

Sometimes 'wave-breakers' are used so that the waves lose some of their energy before they reach the sea-wall or beach. These may consist of closely spaced, heavy timbers driven into the sea-bottom 50 feet or more from the sea-wall, with their tops at high-tide level.

See also DAMS; LAND RECLAMATION.
See also Vol. III: RIVERS.

FLYING INSTRUMENTS, see AUTOMATIC CONTROLS, Section 2; GYROSCOPE, Section 2. *See also* Vol. IV: FLYING INSTRUMENTS.

FORGING AND PRESSING. 1. Forging is the shaping of metal by hammering or squeezing, the metal being heated—sometimes to a high temperature. Large-scale forging in modern industry is often called 'pressing', but this term is also used of the stamping out of thin pieces of cold metal, or, indeed, of the pressing of any

Laing

BUILDING A CONCRETE SEA-WALL ON THE EAST COAST

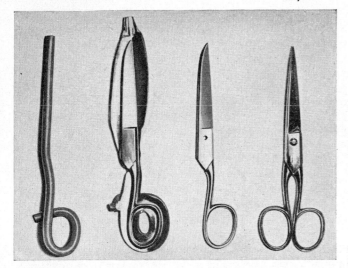

British Ropes Ltd.

FORGING SCISSORS FROM WIRE

Four stages in the process are shown on the left: 1. Wire is cut into lengths and bent and the loops are spot welded to the shaft. 2. The wire is pressed over a die in a 280-ton press, making one blade complete with cutting edge; this process is being done in the right-hand picture. 3. Surplus metal is removed and the blade sharpened. 4. The blades are nickel-plated and riveted together

material. This article, however, deals only with metals.

Although all forging is based on the blacksmith's ancient method of hammering his horseshoes into shape, a very wide variety of presses has been developed to carry out this work, some being used to make very small parts, such as a thimble, and others very large ones such as the huge propellor shafts of great ocean liners. Presses for such purposes are enormous and exert a great deal of power. The largest can exert forces of over 18,000 tons.

There are two main points to realize about forging and pressing. First, METALS (q.v.), although they are solid, can actually flow, in not so different a way from the flow of a very sticky liquid. If it were not for this property, metals could not be pressed, but would break as soon as the press started to form them into the shape required. Secondly, unlike machining (see MACHINE TOOLS) where the metal is cut into shape, pressing and forging, by using the plastic property of metals, produce shapes without cutting the metal at all but by squeezing it.

2. FORGING. The first presses were for forging and were a direct development of the blacksmith's forge and anvil. Probably the origin of all these was James Nasmyth's steam hammer. This machine was designed in 1839 for forging an enormous wrought-iron paddle-shaft for a steamer. It used a heavy hammer, which was lifted by means of steam power, and then allowed to drop on to the metal being forged. The steam hammer performed exactly the same kind of work as the blacksmith's hammer but, by making use of steam power to lift the hammer, provided an enormously greater forging capacity.

Modern forging presses can make forgings up to 200 tons in weight; but such large presses usually employ HYDRAULIC POWER TRANSMISSION (q.v.), using oil pressure to force down the hammer. When shaped pieces of metal are wanted in large numbers, a process known as 'drop forging' may be used. Both the hammer and the anvil carry a die, or hollowed-out shape. The metal, after being heated to make it more plastic and so more easily formed, is placed in the die of the anvil. The hammer then descends on it, forcing the metal between the two dies and thus squeezing it into the required shape. The dies themselves are very expensive, but once installed they are most efficient for mass production. Typical drop forgings are motor-car crankshafts and connecting rods, gear blanks (the rough gearwheel before the teeth have been cut), and steam-turbine blades. The degree to which the metal is heated before being forged varies according to the metal used and the type of work being produced.

A piece of metal can be not only hammered

into a given shape, but also squeezed along its length between dies which cause bulges to occur. This process was first developed for producing the heads on bolts, but it is now used for a number of other purposes where bulges in a length of metal are needed.

About 300,000 tons of forgings are made in Britain in a year.

3. STAMPING. Presses can also be used for punching holes in sheet metal and for a number of similar purposes. The machines, which are known as stamping presses, range in size from very large machines to small ones mounted on a workbench.

The general principle of punching is to place the metal on the table of the machine over a die, and then to bring down under power the ram (or hammer) of the press, which carries a punch. This pierces the metal, and moves through the die underneath, thus punching the hole by shearing the metal between the edge of the punch and the die. When the sheet metal on the table is the workpiece, and the piece punched out to form the hole is scrap, this is called punching. The procedure may, however, be reversed, the punch cutting out pieces from the sheet metal of a shape required for some part. When this is

done, the piece punched out is the workpiece, and the metal from which it was punched is scrap. In this case, the press is punching out 'blanks' which are the general shape of a part subsequently to be finished by other machining processes, and the procedure is known as 'blanking'. Presses can also be used for bending and forming sheet metal into parts of complex shapes, or embossing the metal with a pattern.

4. EXTRUDING. In this method, the metal in the form of a solid cylinder or 'slug' is placed in a special extrusion press and then squeezed out, like toothpaste out of a tube, under very high pressure exerted by a hydraulic ram, through a die with an opening of the chosen shape. Some softer metals such as lead can be extruded cold, but many have to be heated. The process is used for producing TUBES (q.v.), rods, and various solid and hollow parts. It can also be used to put a coating of metal on some other part—such as lead cover on an electric cable.

5. DRAWING. As well as by forging, punching, or extruding, metal may be formed by being stretched—a process for which drawing presses are used. The metal sheet is stretched over (or drawn into) a die on one side of the sheet by a mating die on the other side, thus producing the desired shape. Bowls, cups, and similar objects can be formed in one piece by this process. The design of dies for deep drawing—that is, drawing parts which are deep as compared with their diameter—is very complicated, and often such drawing has to be carried out in a number of progressive steps. For this work, multiple action presses are used, for these provide the various steps needed to produce the finished drawn part.

6. RUBBER PRESSES. These are so called because one of the two dies placed one above and the other below the sheet of metal is replaced by a flat, thick pad of rubber. This, being plastic, automatically takes up the form of the other die when the press brings them together with the metal sheet between. The sheet, therefore, also takes up the shape of the single die. This is useful for very large sheet pressings, and is used particularly in the motor-car and aircraft industries. Presses are now in use which are large enough to produce the roof of a car complete. The bed area of the press may be as large as a small room.

7. OTHER METHODS. Many different methods are used to feed sheet metal to presses for punching or forming; a common method is to feed in

Vickers Ltd.

FORGING A LARGE HOLLOW SHAFT

the metal continuously from a roll. Also, in order to keep up with the high-production speeds needed in modern industry, many different types of automatic and high-speed presses, including dieing machines, have been developed. Some of these have speeds capable of turning out small pressed parts of a highly accurate shape at a rate of 1,000 per minute.

The press is the most important machine in the PLASTICS industry (q.v Vol. VII), where it is used to squeeze the plastic (often in the form of a powder) into specially shaped moulds to produce the varied types of plastic articles now on the market. Metal powders also are pressed into 'compacts' of various shapes, and are then heated in a furnace—a process known as 'sintering'—till they become a unified piece of metal of the desired shape. This 'powder metallurgy' has a great future, since complicated parts can be pressed in one operation instead of having to be made by a number of lengthy or difficult machining processes.

Vickers Ltd.

A BATTERY OF LARGE PRESSES FOR PRODUCING METAL MOTOR-CAR BODIES

FOUNDATIONS, see BUILDING, PRINCIPLES OF, Section 2.

FREQUENCY MODULATION, see RADIO ENGINEERING.

FRICTION AND LUBRICATION. 1. When we slide one solid body over another—for example, a brick over a table—there is always a certain amount of resistance to the motion. This resistance is called 'friction', and it can vary very greatly. Everyone knows how smooth and easy it is to slide on ice, for in this case the friction is very low. But the friction on the soles of one's shoes when walking along a road is quite high, and it is difficult to slide. Friction, in fact, depends on the types of surfaces in contact. It also depends on the weight, or load, pressing the sur-

faces together. An understanding of the laws of friction and of how to control friction is essential if modern machinery is to be made to work.

An easy way to illustrate the laws of friction is to take an ordinary brick, tie a piece of string round it, and put it on a flat surface, such as a table (Fig. 1). The brick can be dragged along the table by the string, and the force needed to do this can be measured. First, it will be found that this force is the same whether the brick is standing on its end, or on its side, or lying flat on the table. The area of the brick touching the table makes no difference. This might be called the first law of friction—that the friction is independent of the area of the sliding surfaces.

If another brick is put on top of the first one, thus doubling the weight, it will be found that the force needed to drag them along the table is now twice as great. For a pile of four bricks it would be four times as great, and so on (Fig. 1b). This means that the friction is proportional to the applied load—and this might be called the second law. It means that for any particular pair of surfaces the ratio of friction to load is always

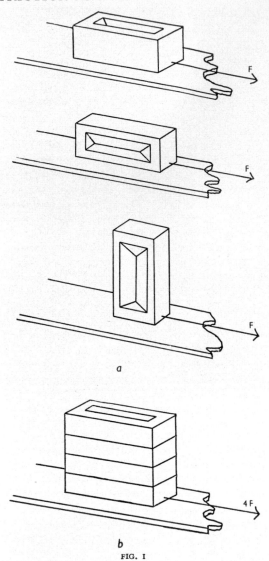

FIG. I

a. Friction (F) is independent of the area. *b.* Friction (4F) is proportional to the load

about 20% of the power is wasted in overcoming the friction. In an aeroplane piston engine the waste is about 9%, and in a turbojet engine it is 1 to 2%. Even more important than the power loss is the damage done by friction, since it can wear away important parts of the engine. Bearings, if not protected from friction, can become so hot that they will seize up. There are instances, however, where friction is useful: a high coefficient of friction is required in the brake linings of a motor-car, and such linings are designed from materials which will provide this property.

2. AREA OF CONTACT BETWEEN SOLIDS. There is no such thing, except in theory, as an absolutely smooth surface. Even the most highly polished surface is actually made up of microscopic hills and valleys, and the form these take, together with their size, determines what is known as 'surface finish' (Fig. 2). These 'hills' and 'valleys' may be only a few millionths of an inch deep, but they are, for all that, very large compared with the size of the molecules of which the substance is composed. When two solids are placed in contact, only the 'hills' come in contact with each other, and most of the surface is not in contact at all. The real area of contact between surfaces is therefore very small, and varies with the load; for flat steel surfaces it may be less than one ten-thousandth of the apparent area.

Since all the load is taken only on the high points, it is obvious that the pressure in these regions must be very great. If, for example, two steel surfaces are put together, even with a load of a few ounces, the pressure over the small regions of contact can exceed 100 tons per square inch. As these naturally cannot stand up to such high pressures, they will, in effect, be squashed down until their cross-section is sufficiently great to support the load.

the same. This ratio is called the 'coefficient of friction'.

The coefficient of friction differs for different solids. For ice sliding on ice, for example, it is very low—about 0·02—so that a pull equal to about $\frac{1}{50}$th of the weight of the block of ice will cause sliding. For clean metals sliding on one another, it is much higher—about 1—so that a pull equal to the weight of the metal to be moved has to be applied to make it slide.

Friction in machinery causes a great deal of waste of energy. In a motor-car, for example,

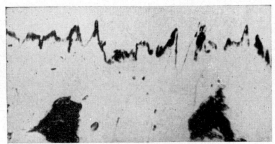

FIG. 2. HIGHLY MAGNIFIED SECTION SHOWING THE HILLS AND VALLEYS ON A STEEL SURFACE WHICH HAS BEEN GROUND WITH CARBORUNDUM

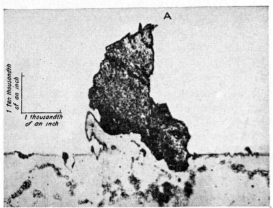

1 ten thousandth of an inch

1 thousandth of an inch

FIG. 3. FRAGMENT OF COPPER (A) WELDED ON TO A STEEL SURFACE AFTER A COPPER SLIDER HAS PASSED OVER IT ONCE

The welded junction is very strong and the break has occurred in the copper (highly magnified)

Figs. 2 and 3 from F. P. Bowden and D. Tabor ,'Friction and Lubrication of Solids'

The intense pressure on these microscopic peaks will cause an actual sticking together, or 'pressure welding', at the tiny points of contact between the two sliding surfaces. If one surface is then made to slide along the other, force will have to be applied to break these little welded junctions before sliding can begin. It is the continual forming and breaking of these welded junctions which is largely responsible for the friction of metals and of many other solids. If metal surfaces are examined under the microscope after sliding has occurred, it is sometimes possible to see the marks left by these welded junctions (Fig. 3).

3. TEMPERATURE OF SLIDING SURFACES. If the surfaces are sliding at an appreciable speed, another important factor comes in. The work done to overcome the effect of friction is dissipated mainly in the form of heat. When this happens with metals, the tiny points of contact may be red hot, or even white hot, although they are so small that to ordinary observation there is no sign of this, and the metal appears to be quite cool. These high temperatures can cause the metal surfaces to soften in the spots of contact.

The 'hot spots' play an important part in a number of physical processes. There is strong evidence, for example, that in the polishing of metals and other solids, the local heating at the points of rubbing causes them to soften or melt. The melted metal is then smeared over the surface, filling up or bridging over the scratches so as to form the polished layer. It is this which is largely responsible for the low friction of highly polished surfaces. This surface heating can also be important in lubrication.

4. LUBRICATION. One of the most effective ways of reducing the friction of solids—say, of two pieces of metal—is to put a layer of oil or grease between them. If the layer of oil is a comparatively thick one, so that the surfaces are separated by an appreciable distance, the method is called 'fluid lubrication'. The molecules of which the oil is composed will attach themselves to each surface of the metals and, when the surfaces move, the successive layers of molecules in the oil will have to slide over one another. The frictional resistance will, therefore, depend on the ease with which the oil molecules can slide on themselves; that is, on the 'viscosity' of the oil. It is obvious that under these conditions the surfaces of the metals will not be damaged at all. Engineers, therefore, design their machines, if they can, so that they can use fluid lubrication. This is particularly important in the design of BEARINGS (q.v.).

It is not always possible, however, to maintain this condition, particularly if the load is heavy and the sliding speed is low. The metal surfaces may become separated by a layer of oil only one or two molecules thick. This condition is called 'boundary lubrication', and however good the boundary film is, it cannot protect the surfaces completely. Irregularities in the surface will penetrate the film of oil, and some metallic contact will take place in small regions. The heat which such contacts will produce will drive off and decompose the lubricant, and consequently the hot spots may grow in size. In course of time seizure of the metal can occur.

If the sliding conditions are severe, 'extreme pressure' lubricants are often used as well as the ordinary lubricant. These have a special chemical composition so that, if frictional heating is taking place, they combine with the hot metal to form a thin solid film of metal sulphide or chloride on the surface, which protects the metal from seizure.

Much experimental work is being done to find lubricants with better molecular construction than the mineral oils which are now generally used as lubricants.

FUELS. 1. These are substances which, when burnt, give heat which may be used directly, for example, to warm a house or to smelt iron, or indirectly, to be converted into light or mechanical energy for driving an engine.

The most important property of a fuel is its 'calorific value', that is, the quantity of heat which can be obtained from a given quantity of it. For practical purposes in Britain this is usually expressed as British Thermal Units (B.Th.U.) per pound, a B.Th.U. being the amount of heat required to raise the temperature of 1 lb. of water by 1° Fahrenheit. The calorific values of different commercial fuels depend very largely on the amounts of carbon and hydrogen in them (the heat evolved being derived from the COMBUSTION (q.v.) of these elements to carbon dioxide and water), and varies from about 8,000 B.Th.U. per lb. for wood to about 19,000 B.Th.U. per lb. for fuel oil.

Calorific value is not the only property of fuel to be considered. Ease of handling and control may be of decisive importance, especially, for example, in fuel for ships; and in other cases a fuel may be chosen because it is readily available and cheap.

Fuels are of three kinds—solid, liquid, and gaseous.

2. SOLID FUELS. The main kinds of natural solid fuel are wood, peat, lignite (or brown coal), bituminous coal, and anthracite; in addition, coke is an important solid fuel which is derived from bituminous coal.

(a) *Wood.* This, with other plant material, was the only fuel used by man for many centuries, and is still an important fuel in many parts of the world today, particularly in countries which have no other fuel readily available. Wood, in fact, provides the equivalent of about 200 million tons of coal a year, or approximately one-twelfth of the world's total fuel supply.

(b) *Peat.* Though there are large deposits of peat (*see* MOORLAND AND MARSH, Vol. III) in many parts of the world (including Britain), the total resources of this fuel probably amount to no more than 1% of the world's resources of coal. As peat in its natural state contains over 90% of water, the collecting and drying of it make it in most parts of the world too inconvenient and costly to be practical.

(c) *Lignite and brown coal.* These are types of 'immature' COALS (q.v. Vol. III) which are intermediate in character between peat and bituminous coal.

The world reserves of lignite are about 1¼ mil-

lion million tons (nearly 80% of which is in North America). This is about a quarter of the world reserves of bituminous coal and anthracite. The greatest production of lignite is in Europe, particularly in Germany and Czechoslovakia, though much is also produced in Australasia and North America. Great Britain has only one lignite deposit—a small pocket at Bovey Tracey in Devonshire.

(d) *Bituminous coal, anthracite, and coke.* Bituminous coals and anthracites, the world reserves of which are about 5 million million tons, provide over half the world's fuel supply. The world production is about 1,200 million tons a year, so that even allowing for a large increase in production, the coal reserves for the world as a whole should last for perhaps 2,000 years. In the United States the reserves are relatively much greater, and in Great Britain they are much smaller, being probably sufficient to maintain a supply of 250 million tons a year for the next 200 years. Actual production in Great Britain was 223 million tons in 1951 (*see* COAL-MINING, Vol. VII).

When coal is heated at a high temperature in a COKE OVEN (q.v.), that is, out of contact with air, the gas and tar (the 'volatile matter') are driven off, and coke is left. With some coals the coke residue is a powder which cakes easily; with others it is non-caking.

Bituminous coals, which have a carbon content of about 75 to 90%, provide about 90% of Great Britain's output. Anthracites, the coals of greatest 'maturity', have a carbon content of over 93%.

The main uses of coals are as 'steam coals', 'coking coals', and 'gas coals'. 'Steam coals', that is, coals used for raising STEAM (q.v.), once had to be non-caking or only weakly-caking, so that they would burn freely on the grate; and, still where the draught is limited, such coals have to be used. With the development of forced draught, however, modern boiler plant can deal with almost every type of coal. Powdered coal, usually called 'pulverized fuel', is also widely used today.

'Coking coals' are those which when heated in a coke oven give a strong, hard coke suitable for metallurgical purposes. Such coke must be able to withstand, without breaking up too much, the heavy burden of iron ore in a BLAST FURNACE (q.v.), in which the iron oxide in the ore is reduced to metallic iron (pig iron) at a high temperature. The essential properties of a coking coal are a caking power and a relatively low content of volatile matter. The coking coals of finest quality in Great Britain are found in Durham and South Wales.

Gas-making coals, or 'gas coals', in contrast to coking coals, must have a high content of volatile matter to ensure a high yield of gas when the coal is carbonized in a retort. The horizontal retort, which until recently was used in gasworks (see GAS MANUFACTURE), requires a fairly strongly caking coal. Now, however, it has been largely replaced by the vertical retort, which operates continuously (coal being fed in at the top while coke is discharged at the bottom) and a less strongly caking coal is suitable. The carbonization of coal at gasworks produces not only gas, but also coke, and this represents the largest part of the original coal (at least 60% by weight). Coke from gasworks is used for heating furnaces, making producer-gas and water-gas, raising steam, and for space heating (that is, heating factories, offices, and houses).

3. LIQUID FUELS. Those used in Great Britain are obtained from crude mineral oil, or petroleum, oil-shale, and coal, and of these by far the most important are those obtained from petroleum.

(a) *Oil fuels from petroleum.* World reserves of crude petroleum (see OIL, NATURAL, Vol. III), the product of the oil well, are very much smaller than those of coal—probably only enough for 50 to 100 years. Actually, only about 13,000 million tons, or enough for about 20 years at the present rate of consumption (600 million tons a year) are known to exist, but for the last quarter of a century, the discovery of new reserves has more than balanced consumption.

Crude petroleums, which may vary considerably in chemical composition, are never used directly as fuels but have to be distilled (see OIL REFINING, Vol. VII) and, after various refining treatments, yield petrol, paraffin, gas oil, diesel oil, fuel oil, and tar. Only a small part of the world's supply of petrol is obtained by the direct distillation of petroleum. The main part is made from heavier oils by 'cracking', that is, by breaking them down under very high temperatures and thus converting them into the lighter petrol by the action of heat and pressure. Fuel oils are usually blends with various other oils of the residues from the distillation of crude petroleum.

At the moment, petrol is the most important of all petroleum products, and is produced in the greatest quantity. In order to ensure good engine performance, petrol must have good ignition properties, and these are measured by comparison with the liquid octane. The 'octane number' increases as the ignition properties improve. Thus Standard Grade Motor Spirit has an octane number of 70–72 whereas Premium grade petrols may have an octane number as high as 90. In aircraft, especially for military use, the piston engine is now being superseded by the jet engine, the fuel for which is heavier than petrol and nearer to paraffin.

The two chief grades of paraffin are burning oil, used in various kinds of lamps and stoves, and vaporizing oil, used mainly in spark-ignition engines for tractors and small fishing boats.

The product of petroleum called 'gas oil' was so-named because it was originally used for gas making, and it is still used for this purpose in gasworks. Another oil of the same type is diesel oil, used for modern, high-speed, compression-ignition engines, or diesel engines (see INTERNAL COMBUSTION ENGINE, Section 4). Diesel oils may vary considerably in quality, and high-speed engines run efficiently only on high-grade diesel oils.

There are various grades of fuel oil, which, after petrol, is the petroleum product made in the greatest quantity. It is used for raising steam on land and sea, and for heating furnaces, making steel, and other industrial purposes.

(b) *Oil fuels from oil-shale.* Oil-shale contains a substance called kerogen which, on heating, breaks down to give SHALE OIL (q.v. Vol. VII). Crude shale oil is rather similar to crude petroleum and yields similar products, though these are, in general, more difficult to refine. In 1951 26 million gallons of crude shale oil were produced in Scotland. Oil-shale could make a large contribution to world fuel supplies, and we may soon see the commercial development of a shale oil industry in the United States. World reserves of oil-shale are at least 470,000 million tons, from which some 22,000 million tons of oil could be obtained.

(c) *Oil fuels from coal.* When coal is carbonized to yield gas and coke, there are two valuable liquid by-products, namely coal tar and benzole. From the tar may be made a liquid fuel, commonly called 'pitch-creosote', which is rather like petroleum fuel oil and is used for similar purposes. Motor benzole, which is used for the same purpose as petrol, may be made from the benzole.

4. GASEOUS FUELS. These are of two general kinds, 'natural gas' and manufactured gases.

(*a*) *Natural gas*. This is usually found with petroleum, though sometimes each of these substances occurs alone (*see* GAS, NATURAL, Vol. III). It consists mainly of methane, with small amounts of other chemicals, and has a calorific value of about 1,000 B.Th.U. per cubic foot.

The use of natural gas in America has expanded enormously in recent years. There is practically none in Great Britain, though efforts are now being made to collect and use the small amounts of methane often found in association with the coal seams.

(*b*) *Manufactured gases*. Though these are made to some extent from petroleum oils, they are mainly derived from coal and coke. The chief of such gases are coal-gas, producer-gas, and water-gas.

Coal-gas is made by the carbonization of coal (*see* GAS MANUFACTURE); its chief constituents are hydrogen (55%), methane (20–25%), and carbon monoxide (10–15%), and its calorific value is usually about 500 B.Th.U. per cubic foot. It is used industrially for such purposes as heating metallurgical furnaces, as well as in the home for cooking and heating.

Producer-gas is manufactured by passing a mixture of air and steam through a red-hot bed of fuel. It contains mainly carbon monoxide (25–30%), hydrogen (10–15%), and nitrogen (50–55%); its calorific value is about 130 or 160 B.Th.U. per cubic foot according to whether it is made from coke or coal. Amongst its many industrial uses are its use in the steel industry for heating open-hearth furnaces, and in the gas industry for heating retorts.

Water-gas is made by passing steam through red-hot coke, and consists mainly of carbon monoxide (40%) and hydrogen (50%); its calorific value is about twice that of producer gas. Its chief use is in the gas industry, where it is mixed with coal gas before distribution.

(*c*) *Liquefied petroleum gases*. These provide a special case of a gaseous fuel which is distributed in a liquefied form under pressure in steel containers. It is a convenient fuel for use in, for example, country districts, where a piped gas supply is not available. One of its trade names is 'Calor Gas', which consists to a large extent of the easily liquefied gas, butane.

See also COMBUSTION; POWER; ENERGY.
See also Vol. III: HEAT.

FURNACE, *see* BLAST FURNACE; STEEL-MAKING.

FUZES. These are devices containing explosive charges, fired electrically, by flame, or by shock, and used to set off the explosive filling in ARTILLERY shells, grenades, BOMBS AND MINES (qq.v. Vol. X), FIREWORKS (q.v. Vol. IX), and BLASTING charges (q.v.). Their main object is safety.

There are three main types of fuzes for artillery shells and mortar bombs: percussion fuzes, time fuzes, and proximity fuzes. Some fuzes include a combination of more than one type.

There are two kinds of percussion fuzes. With 'direct action' fuzes a metallic needle or 'striker', which must be in the nose of the shell, is driven into the fuze when the shell or bomb hits the target. With 'graze' fuzes an internal mechanism fires the fuze, when the whole shell is slowed down on striking the target. A graze fuze can be anywhere in the shell.

Time fuzes are either of 'mechanical' or 'combustion' type. The former contains a clockwork mechanism which starts as the shell leaves the gun and bursts the shell after a set time. Combustion fuzes achieve the same effect by the burning of a train of slow-burning powder. The combustion fuze is the less accurate, and is thus restricted to those shells in which the exact position of burst is not important.

Proximity fuzes are a modern development whereby the fuze is able to detect by radio waves the target which it is approaching, and to cause the shell to burst at a short distance from it. They are expensive but much more accurate than the older time fuzes, and they are simple to use, needing no setting before being fired.

There is a very wide range of aircraft bomb fuzes, including all the types so far described. Barometric fuzes, which cause bombs to explode at a suitable height above ground-level, and delay fuzes, in which the delay may be from

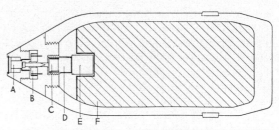

FIG. 1. HIGH EXPLOSIVE SHELL WITH DIRECT ACTION NOSE FUZE

A. Striker. B. Safety device. C. Detonator. D. Fuze magazine. E. Boost pellet. F. High explosive

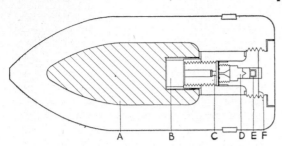

FIG. 2. ARMOUR-PIERCING HIGH EXPLOSIVE SHELL WITH
GRAZE ACTION BASE FUZE

A. High explosive. B. Boost pellet. C. Ignitable high
explosive. D. Striker. E. Detonator in pellet. F. Safety
shear wire

minutes to weeks, were very extensively used during the Second World War.

Fuzes for booby traps and anti-tank mines are of the direct action type, usually set off by pressure or by the release of a spring mechanism by means of trip wire; or they are of the electrically fired type which may be automatically operated or manually controlled from a distance. The simplest form of firework fuze is touchpaper, that is, paper impregnated with nitre, which smoulders briskly. For bigger fireworks a type of 'safety fuze', which is formed from a column of slow-burning powder encased in a flexible covering, is most general. A typical rate of burning of safety fuze is about 20 inches per minute.

Demolition or blasting charges are fired by safety fuzes, electrical fuzes, or detonating fuzes. The safety fuze described above is simple and reliable and needs no apparatus other than flame to ignite it. For large-scale demolition, however, electrical firing is preferred, since it is possible to control it from a point remote from the firing, and so in greater safety. A detonator in the main charge contains a small quantity of heat-sensitive explosive in which a fine resistance wire is embedded. It is fired by passing a small electric current through the wire to heat it.

The detonating fuze consists of a column of high explosive, encased in a flexible fabric or soft metal casing, about $\frac{1}{4}$ inch in diameter. When the high explosive is detonated at one end, the effect passes rapidly to the main charge at the other end. Since fuzes of this kind detonate at the rate of many thousands of feet per second, it is possible to ensure the practically simultaneous firing of a number of charges in a complicated demolition system. The various charges can be connected by detonating fuze to a central point, and an electrical fuze used to fire them, by pressing a switch some distance away.

See also EXPLOSIVES.

G

GALVANOMETER, *see* ELECTRICAL INSTRUMENTS.

GASES, PROPERTIES OF. 1. NATURE OF GASES. All MATTER (q.v. Vol. III)—solids, liquids, and gases—consists of molecules in motion. When these molecules are moving sufficiently slowly and are sufficiently close together for the forces of attraction between them to lock them together into a rigid shape, the matter is 'solid'. When HEAT (q.v. Vol. III) is added, the molecules move faster until at a certain temperature—different for different molecules—they are moving at a speed which to some extent overcomes the effect of the forces between them, and the solid becomes 'liquid'. If still more heat is added, the molecules reach a speed at which they can overcome altogether the forces of attraction between them and can move freely in any direction; at this point (the 'boiling-point') the liquid turns into a form of gas called 'vapour'. At this stage it is possible to reconvert the vapour to a liquid at the same temperature by applying PRESSURE (q.v. Vol. III), which brings the molecules close enough together for the forces of attraction to act. But if more heat is added there comes a stage when the gas reaches the 'critical temperature', above which the molecules are moving so rapidly that no amount of pressure will liquefy the matter without the removal of heat (*see* LIQUEFACTION OF GASES).

Any substance can become a gas if the temperature is high enough; what we commonly call gases are those elements or compounds which are 'in the gaseous state' at everyday temperatures, such as hydrogen or air.

2. BOYLE'S AND CHARLES'S LAWS. A gas has two useful and important properties—it is highly elastic and can be compressed; and it expands enormously (compared with liquids and solids)

for a relatively small change in temperature. Long before the nature of gases was understood, the rules governing these two properties had been laid down for a few simple gases.

In the 17th century, the English chemist Robert BOYLE (q.v. Vol. V) discovered that if a fixed mass of gas was compressed at constant temperature, the increase in pressure was proportional to the decrease in volume.

More than 100 years later, the French scientist Charles discovered that, if the pressure of a fixed mass of gas was kept constant, equal changes in temperature produced equal changes in volume. This is not quite the same thing as saying that the increase in volume is proportional to the increase in temperature, because that would be true only if the volume was 0 when the temperature was 0; this is obviously untrue since a gas can occupy a large volume at 0° C.

By repeating Charles's experiments under the same conditions for several gases, it was calculated that they all would have shrunk to vanishing-point at the same temperature, about −273° C., even though their rates of expansion through the experimental temperature range were different. This temperature was therefore called Absolute Zero (*see* TEMPERATURE, MEASUREMENT OF). In fact, all real gases become solid several degrees above it, but it has been found convenient to imagine theoretical gases called 'perfect gases', which obey Boyle's and Charles's laws exactly. The behaviour of real gases is so nearly the same as that of perfect gases at anything except extreme temperatures that engineering calculations on HEAT ENGINES and COMPRESSORS (qq.v.) can often be made with sufficient accuracy by assuming that real gases are perfect.

3. STORAGE OF ENERGY. Because a gas expands so greatly on heating, it is a specially good medium for turning heat into work—indeed, all heat engines make use of a gas (usually air or steam) as the working substance: the compressed and heated gas expands, driving the engine, all the time either receiving or giving out energy in one form or another. Since ENERGY (q.v.) cannot be created or destroyed, the heat given to the gas must equal the energy stored by the gas plus the work done by the gas over any given period. The operations in a heat engine or compressor usually happen so quickly that there is no time for the gas to receive or give up heat. A gas,

THE CONSTRUCTION OF A CEMENT WORKS NEAR SHOREHAM, SUSSEX

At the left is one of the washmills where the clay, chalk, and water are mixed to make cement slurry.
The steel structure behind the chimney is a kiln shed, and beyond this are the cement silos

therefore, expanding and doing work without receiving any heat, must give up an amount of energy equivalent to the work done. But the energy stored by the gas depends entirely on the motion of its molecules—the faster their motion the more the energy. So if the gas loses energy, the molecules must slow down, and any such slowing down will show itself as a drop in temperature. In practice, therefore, if a gas expands and does work without receiving any heat, its temperature drops, and, conversely, if a gas is compressed (that is, work is done on the gas) without losing any heat, its temperature rises. When we pump a bicycle pump, for example, we compress the gas (air) in it, and the pump gets hot. The air in a diesel engine can be heated sufficiently by compression to ignite the charge of fuel oil injected at the top of the stroke (*see* INTERNAL COMBUSTION ENGINE, Section 4).

The amount of heat that must be added to a given mass of gas to raise its temperature by a given amount is the specific heat of the gas, and this depends on what the gas is doing while the heat is added. The engineer uses two specific heats for gases—the value when heat is added at constant pressure and that when heat is added at constant volume, the first being bigger than the second by an amount equivalent to the work done by the gas as it expands to keep the pressure constant.

All the engineer's calculations on the behaviour of gases under different conditions, for which he uses CALCULUS (q.v.), depend on the three fundamental properties of a gas—its elasticity, its expansion on heating, and its capacity to store energy.

See also ENERGY; HEAT ENGINES; COMPRESSOR.
See also Vol. III: MATTER; PRESSURE.

GAS MANUFACTURE. Gas distributed in Great Britain for heating, cooking, lighting, and power production is usually either coal-gas, or a mixture of coal-gas with water-gas, carburetted water-gas, or producer-gas, all of which may be made at a single gasworks.

Coal-gas is made by heating coal to about 1,000° C. in an airtight container. 'Bituminous' coal (*see* FUELS) is chiefly used. This, when heated to a temperature of about 400° C., decomposes, becomes plastic, swells, and gives off a mixture of gases. As the temperature increases it continues to give off gas, but at about 500° C. the plastic mass solidifies into a porous mass of coke.

Coals which leave only a powdery residue instead of coke are useless for carbonization, as are those which give very poor yields of gas. Coals which give a very hard, strong coke but only moderate yields of gas are generally carbonized in COKE OVENS (q.v.) for the production of coke for blast furnaces and other such uses. Two widely used types of plant for gas manufacture are horizontal retorts and continuous vertical retorts.

Horizontal retorts are tubes of fireclay or silica generally of ⌓-shaped cross-section, about 22 feet long, 16 inches high, and 24 inches wide. From six to ten such retorts are arranged horizontally in one 'setting', a row of settings being placed side by side in a 'retort house'. Each retort is fitted with cast-iron, gas-tight mouthpieces and doors and also pipes connected to the mouthpieces to carry away the gas.

The retorts are heated by producer-gas, generated in producers built of firebricks in the basement of the retort house. In each producer a bed of burning coke about 5 feet deep is supplied with a controlled quantity of air; the oxygen in the air combines with the carbon in the coke to form carbon monoxide, together with a small quantity of carbon dioxide. Some steam is also passed through the fire, and this limits the temperature of the fire, and reacts with the carbon in the coke to form a mixture of hydrogen, carbon monoxide, and carbon dioxide known as water-gas. The result is producer-gas, a mixture containing about 26% of carbon monoxide, 12% of hydrogen, 7% of carbon dioxide, and 55% of nitrogen (from the air supplied to the fire). This passes upwards and is burned with a further supply of air around the retorts. The ashes left in the producer from the burning coke are removed with long pokers, rakes, and shovels at intervals of 8 to 12 hours.

Coal stored in overhead bunkers is charged into the retorts by a charging machine, and then the retort doors are closed. The gas made in the retorts leaves through the offtake pipes and is collected, purified, and stored as described below. The charge usually takes from 10 to 12 hours to carbonize, and then the retorts are discharged by a 'discharging machine', which pushes the coke out at the opposite end of the retorts into a CONVEYOR (q.v.). There the coke, which is at a temperature of about 1,000° C., is 'quenched' with water, and then taken to a coke-grading plant to be sorted by mechanical sieves or 'screens' into different sizes for use as smokeless solid fuel. (Some of the coke made is supplied to the producers without quenching.) The retorts are then recharged with fresh coal, a proportion being discharged and recharged each hour. Each retort holds about 14 cwt. of coal when charged, and therefore carbonizes about $1\frac{1}{2}$ tons of coal per day.

Continuous vertical retorts are of either rectangular or elliptical cross-section, arranged vertically and heated by producer-gas. They are about 26 feet high, and the cross-section varies from 3 feet to 8 feet by 10 inches at the top, expanding so that the dimensions at the bottom are from 7 to 10 inches greater. Coal enters the retort at the top from an auxilliary coal hopper and travels slowly down the retort, which is always full. The coal carbonizes progressively as it descends and reaches the bottom fully converted to coke. It is removed by a mechanical 'coke extractor' at the bottom of the retort and dropped into a coke box, where it is cooled by steam and sometimes also by water-sprays. The steam reacts with the hot coke to form water-gas, and all the gas leaves the retort by an offtake pipe at the top. The largest continuous retorts carbonize over 10 tons of coal per day.

The crude coal-gas leaves the retort at a temperature of 200 to 600° C., and contains among other impurities tar, naphthalene, ammonia, hydrogen sulphide, and water vapour. The gas offtake pipes lead the gas from all the retorts into a big pipe called the 'hydraulic main', where it is partly cooled and washed by being bubbled through or sprayed with water. Much of the tar condenses, some of the ammonia dissolves in the water, and the temperature is reduced to about 60° C. The gas is then further cooled to atmospheric temperature by being passed through condensers, where it is cooled by water or air, and where almost all the tar, much of the naphthalene, and the surplus water vapour condenses and more of the ammonia dissolves in the condensed water.

As the retorts are to some extent porous, in order to prevent loss of gas, the PRESSURE (q.v. Vol. III) in them is kept almost exactly equal to that of the atmosphere by a steam-driven 'exhauster'—a form of pump. This follows the condenser and pumps the gas away from the retorts and through the rest of the purifying plant at a pressure of about 2 lb. per square inch.

In a modern plant the last traces of tar

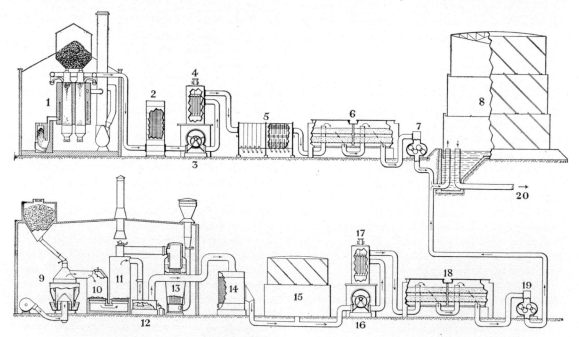

FIG. I. DIAGRAMMATIC ARRANGEMENT OF A GASWORKS

1. Continuous vertical retort house. 2, 14. Water-tube condensers. 3, 16. Exhausters. 4, 17. Electrostatic tar precipitators. 5. Ammonia washer. 6, 18. Oxide purifiers. 7, 19. Station meters. 8. Gasholder. 9–13. Water-gas plant. 9. Generator. 10. Carburettor. 11. Superheater. 12. Wash box. 13. Waste heat boiler. 15. Water-gas relief holder. 19. 20. Main to consumers

FIG. 2. PART OF A HORIZONTAL RETORT HOUSE

Overhead are coal bunkers; to the right charging and discharging machines, and to the left retort mouthpieces and doors, with gas offtakes above

are then removed by subjecting the gas to an electrostatic charge at about 30,000 volts, which makes the tar particles fly out of the gas. The tar-free gas then passes through an 'ammonia washer', a vessel divided into a number of compartments filled with brushes or boards, which are kept wetted by a small quantity of water flowing through the compartments in the opposite direction to the gas. The ammonia in the gas dissolves in the water to form 'ammoniacal liquor', a BY-PRODUCT which goes to make sulphate of AMMONIA. The tar condensates are sent to a DISTILLATION plant (qq.v. Vol. VII) where various pure chemicals and other useful products are recovered.

Hydrogen sulphide is next removed by passing the gas, together with about 3 per cent. of its volume of air, through a series of cast iron or concrete 'purifier boxes', containing a special form of oxide of iron. Four such boxes, each about 35 feet square and 6 feet deep, will purify

$2\frac{1}{2}$ million cubic feet of gas per day. The hydrogen sulphide in the gas reacts with the iron oxide to form iron sulphide, which in turn reacts with the oxygen in the air to re-form iron oxide and sulphur. The sulphur remains mixed with the oxide, and after some months the oxide is removed from the boxes, exposed to the atmosphere, and returned to use. After being used twice or three times in this way the oxide contains about 50 per cent. by weight of sulphur, and is used for the manufacture of sulphuric acid (see ACIDS, Vol. VII).

The gas, now purified of tar, naphthalene, water vapour, ammonia, and hydrogen sulphide, passes through a 'station meter' where its volume is measured, and finally into the gasholders for storage. In some gasworks, the gas is washed with oil to recover benzole, before storing.

Most gasholders consist of a telescopic cylindrical container, the bottom of which is sealed in a large tank of water. There is also a water

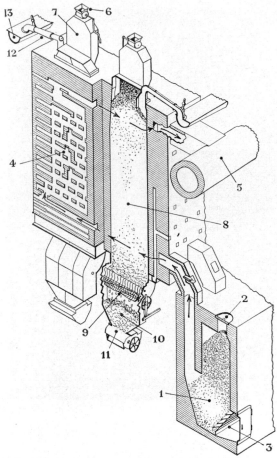

FIG. 3. SECTION OF A CONTINUOUS VERTICAL RETORT

1. Producer for heating retorts. 2. Producer filling hole and lid. 3. Step-grate and cleaning door. 4. Flues for heating retorts. 5. Waste gas collecting main. 6. Coal charging valve. 7. Auxiliary coal hopper. 8. Retort, showing coal change. 9. Coke extractor. 10. Coke box. 11. Coke discharge door. 12. Gas offtake pipe. 13. Hydraulic main

and a 'superheater'. Air is blown through the burning coke to raise the temperature of the fire. The hot gases from the fire pass through the carburettor and the superheater to a stack. After about a minute a valve on the stack is closed, and steam is blown through the fire. The steam reacts with the carbon in the coke to form water-gas, which passes through the carburettor and superheater. At the same time 'gas oil' (a liquid like crude paraffin oil) is sprayed into the carburettor. The oil is vaporized, the vapours are decomposed to hydrocarbon gases in the carburettor and superheater, and the mixed water-gas and 'oil-gas' leave the plant through a wash-box, where they are partly cooled and washed with water.

The action of the steam cools the fire, and after about $1\frac{1}{2}$ minutes the steam and oil are shut off, the stack valve is opened, the air blast is resumed, and the cycle of operations is repeated.

The cooled gas is collected in a small gasholder, pumped through a set of purifiers as in the case of coal-gas, and then mixed with the coal-gas before being passed into the gasholders. The 'calorific value' of the mixed gas (that is, the amount of heat in a cubic foot of gas) can be adjusted by the quantity and calorific value of the water-gas added. Most modern water-gas plants are automatic, all the complicated valve changes being carried out by an automatic controller, while ashes and clinker are removed continuously by a revolving grate.

Producer-gas, which can be made in a generator like that used for water-gas, is also used to adjust the calorific value of coal-gas.

One ton of coal produces about 13,000 cubic feet of coal-gas, 10–14 gallons of tar, 20–30 lb. of sulphate of ammonia, 3–4 gallons of crude benzole, 30 lb. of sulphur, and 13–14 cwt. of coke, of which from 2 to $3\frac{1}{2}$ cwt. are used for heating the retorts.

Purified coal-gas usually has a calorific value of between 560 and 620 B.Th.U. per cubic foot (see FUELS). Gas manufacturers are required by law to state the calorific value of the gas they intend to supply, and to maintain that standard —usually between 400 and 500 B.Th.U. per cubic foot. The calorific value of the coal-gas is adjusted to the 'declared value' by the addition of water-gas (about 300 B.Th.U. per cubic foot). When vertical retorts are used, the calorific value may be controlled by adjusting the amount of water-gas made in the retorts.

seal between each of the telescopic sections or 'lifts', which are kept upright either by a column framework or by spiral guide rails attached to the sides of the lifts. In some gasholders, instead of a water seal, the gas is stored below a piston sliding up and down in a large fixed cylinder.

The gas flows from the gasholder through underground mains to the consumers, and when the mains are long it is often pumped out by 'boosters'.

Carburetted water-gas, or water-gas mixed with 'oil-gas' (see below), is made in a separate plant consisting of a brick-lined 'generator', containing a bed of burning coke, a 'carburettor',

Gas must also, by law, be supplied in Britain at a minimum pressure sufficient to balance a column of water 2 inches high, that is, 2 inches water gauge (*see* PRESSURE GAUGES, Section (*a*)).

The size of the gasworks varies enormously. The largest works, at Beckton (*see* Vol. VII, p. 203), carbonizing over 6,000 tons of coal per day, can produce well over 120 million cubic feet of mixed coal-gas and carburetted water-gas from it. There are some works which produce less than 10 million cubic feet of gas per year, but such very small works are uneconomical and are slowly being closed down, and gas supplied from larger works through high-pressure mains.

Although gas is measured by volume, in cubic feet, it is sold according to its heating power, in therms (1 Therm = 100,000 B.Th.U.). The volume of gas (in cubic feet) multiplied by its calorific value (in B.Th.U. per cubic foot) and divided by 100,000 gives the number of therms.

See also Vol. VII: GAS INDUSTRY.

GAS TURBINE.

This is a form of INTERNAL COMBUSTION ENGINE (q.v.) in which the hot gases, produced by burning fuel in air, are made to turn a specially shaped wheel (the turbine wheel) directly—on the windmill principle—instead of pushing pistons up and down as in the reciprocating engine.

Because of the continuous, smooth nature of its internal processes, the gas turbine, like the STEAM TURBINE (q.v.), is almost completely free from vibration; and this, together with its essential simplicity, makes it more reliable and easier to maintain. It is lighter and less bulky than the piston engine, and it can be built in larger sizes to give higher powers from single power units. For all these reasons, the use of gas turbines is increasing for all forms of transport, on land, sea, and in the air. It may be wondered, in view of all these advantages, why the gas turbine engine was not introduced sooner, especially since the general idea of a gas turbine is not a new one. Indeed, the idea of using the energy in hot gases to turn a wheel directly is perhaps a more obvious one than the more complicated system employed in piston engines. In fact, the turbine principle is more difficult to apply in practice.

The first small and relatively inefficient gas turbines were operated by the exhaust gases from piston engines, and these were used to drive superchargers (air compressors used to feed a greater mass of air at increased pressure into the cylinders of a piston engine). It was not until just before the Second World War that successful self-operating gas turbines were made, and then it was for aircraft propulsion (*see* AIRCRAFT ENGINES, Section 2, Vol. IV). About the same time that aircraft turbines were being achieved both in Britain and in Germany, the Swiss had developed gas turbines for stationary use and were considering them as power units for railway locomotives (*see* GAS TURBINE LOCOMOTIVE, Vol. IV).

Fig. 1 illustrates diagrammatically the basic principles of this type of engine, and makes clear the technical difficulties which delayed the development of successful gas turbines. A is the air intake through which air passes to the compressor (B). On emerging from B into the combustion chamber (C), the air is at a high pressure and hotter than it was, owing to the compression (to at least 50 lb. per square inch). Fuel is injected into the compressed air, and burned with high efficiency in the combustion chambers. The combustion raises the temperature to 850° C. or more, and this expands the air. The resultant gases at high pressure and temperature blow continuously on to the turbine wheel (D). After they

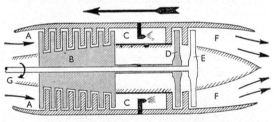

FIG. 1. DIAGRAM OF A GAS TURBINE

A. Air intake. B. Compressor. C. Combustion chambers. D. Turbine wheel driving compressor. E. Turbine wheel driving propeller. F. Tailpipe through which gases escape. G. Propeller shaft. The large arrow shows the direction of flight, the smaller ones the direction of air and burnt gases

leave D, the gases, still at a fairly high pressure and temperature and still expanding, can be used either (as shown in the diagram) to turn another turbine wheel (E) or else to produce a propulsive jet directed through a nozzle or tailpipe (F), as in an aircraft jet propulsion engine. In the type of engine shown in the diagram the turbine wheel (E) can be used to turn the propeller of an aircraft or ship, or the wheels of a locomotive or road vehicle, while the wheel (D) supplies the power to turn the air compressor.

The material of the turbine wheels is continuously exposed to the very hot gases, and the

de Havilland

DE HAVILLAND 'GHOST' TURBOJET ENGINE OF 5,000 LB. SEA-LEVEL STATIC THRUST, USED TO POWER THE 'COMET I' AIR-
LINERS AND 'VENOM' FIGHTERS

On the right is the air intake to the centrifugal compressor. In the centre, between the compressor and turbine, are nine
combustion chambers, and on the left is the tailpipe from which the hot gases of the propelling jet emerge

demands made on the metals used for the blading of a gas turbine are very heavy—even more than for a steam turbine. Another problem concerns the efficiency of the air compressor; if this is inefficient, it will absorb too much power itself, and so much of the available energy of the gases will be used up in the turbine wheel (D) that there will be little left to deliver as thrust, or as useful power from the second wheel (E). Gas turbines, therefore, could not be developed until very efficient air compressors had been evolved, as well as steels or other metals able to resist high temperatures.

For some purposes, the piston type of engine is still preferable to the gas turbine. Its fuel consumption is usually quite appreciably lower for a given power output, but this has to be offset against its greater weight. Also, it has proved difficult to make satisfactory gas turbines of low power output, suitable, for example, for road vehicles, although efforts are being made to solve this problem (*see* ROAD TRANSPORT ENGINES, Vol. IV).

There are many possible variants of the basic gas turbine principle. For example, the air compressor may be of either the centrifugal (radial) or axial type. In the former, the air is compressed by being flung outwards, in a sort of paddle-wheel; while in the latter, the compressor itself looks rather like a turbine wheel with many rows of blading, through which the air is 'screwed up'

to the required pressure as it flows from end to end. Again, the turbine wheels may be on one shaft, as shown in the diagram, or they may be on separate shafts. All these different types may be found in engines used for rail, road, marine, or aircraft propulsion.

The gas turbine has special advantages for aircraft propulsion, owing to its low weight and small size, and it has found in aviation its first important application and the greatest stimulus for its development. As an aero-engine it is used either for pure jet propulsion or to drive a conventional PROPELLER (q.v.).

See also WATER POWER; STEAM TURBINE; INTERNAL COMBUSTION ENGINE.

See also Vol. IV: AIRCRAFT ENGINES.

GEARS. 1. The term 'gearing' is applied to assemblies of toothed wheels which transmit rotary motion from one shaft to another. Two toothed wheels, fixed on two separate shafts, are brought together so that their teeth intermesh, and when one wheel is rotated, its teeth push those of the other, making it turn also. The main advantages of gears are that the speed transmitted from one shaft to another always has the same ratio; that power can be 'taken round corners', as it were, by gearing which operates at right angles or, in fact, at any angle required; and that it is possible to change speed by 'changing gear', as in a motor-car—that is, by altering the ratios of the gears employed. But, though the principle is simple, the designing of gears is not simple at all; it is a very specialized part of engineering calling for considerable technical knowledge.

The gear-teeth themselves do not 'mesh', or contact each other, along the whole of the tooth surface. Instead, they contact each other at a point A, the 'point of contact', and their surfaces 'roll' upon each other almost without slip (Fig. 2). The profiles of the teeth are curved in a special way to prevent the speed of rotation varying as different parts of the curve come into contact. The curve most commonly used is an

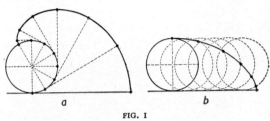

FIG. I

a. Involute curve. *b.* Cycloid

'involute', although a 'cycloid' is also used in special cases (Figs. 1*a* and *b*).

As the gear-wheels revolve, the point of contact, A, follows the so-called 'line of action', along which the force transmitted acts. This is at right angles to the surface of the tooth and, with teeth having the involute shape of profile, is a straight line—as seen in Fig. 2. If a line is drawn between

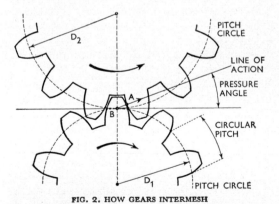

FIG. 2. HOW GEARS INTERMESH

D_1, D_2. Diameter of gears. A. Point of contact. B. Apex of angle of pressure

the centres of the gears and another line at right angles to it through point B, the line of action will form an angle with this line, known as the 'pressure angle'; this is usually designed to be either $14\frac{1}{2}$ or 20°. If gear-wheels are to be inter-

changed one with another, as happens when the ratios between gears is changed, the pressure angle of all the wheels concerned must be the same.

The actual effective diameter of the gear-wheel is clearly somewhat less than its actual diameter, since the wheels are intermeshing rather than simply touching at their circumferences. This effective diameter is represented by an imaginary circle, known as the 'pitch circle', and when two wheels are correctly engaged, their pitch circles touch at the point B, called the 'pitch point'. The effect is, therefore, of two wheels rolling together, their diameters being equal to the respective pitch circle diameters D_1 and D_2. But whereas two ordinary wheels would slip if rolled together, gear-wheels, because their teeth are in mesh, cannot slip, and so provide a 'positive drive'.

The distance between similar faces of any two adjacent teeth of a gear-wheel is called the 'circular pitch'. It is measured along the arc of the pitch circle and obviously must be equal for any two mating wheels. It comprises one tooth thickness and one gap width, each equal to a half of the pitch. In any gear-wheel, therefore, the circular pitch may be found by dividing the number of teeth into the circumference of the pitch circle.

One of the most important things to determine about any two geared wheels working together is their ratio, because on this depends what speed the driven gear will produce for any given speed of the wheel driving it, as well as the relation between the power at the driving shaft and that delivered at the driven shaft. If, for instance, the driving wheel is twice the diameter of the wheel it is driving, since both wheels are locked together in mesh and cannot slip, the smaller must revolve twice each time the driving wheel revolves once. Thus, any shaft on which this smaller gear-wheel was mounted would rotate twice as quickly as the shaft on which the larger one was mounted. Hence, by using wheels of different sizes, the speed has been doubled—that is, increased by a ratio of 2 to 1.

2. *Types of gears.* Gears may be classified into three main groups. Of these, the simplest and most common type is the cylindrical or 'spur' gear, used to drive shafts which are parallel to each other (Fig. 3*a*). These provide a straight drive, the wheel on the final shaft being parallel to that on the driving shaft. Where it is necessary

do not intersect, 'screw' gears, comprising worms and worm wheels, and 'spiral' gears are used (Fig. 3c and d).

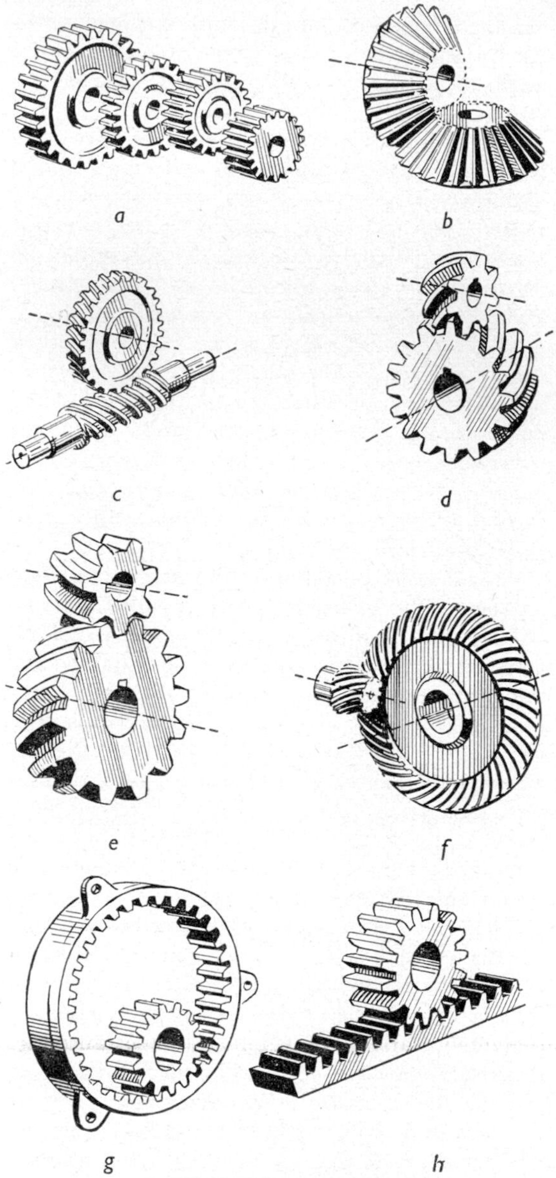

Cylindrical and bevel gears may be designed for internal meshing (Fig. 3g); and all the types of gears mentioned, with the exception of bevels, can be used to drive racks (Fig. 3h), that is, straight flat bars with teeth made to match those of the mating wheels, which are then known as pinions.

The types of gearing mentioned may have several types of teeth, the simplest being the ordinary straight teeth, in which the tooth is parallel to the axis of the wheel (Fig. 3a), helical teeth (Fig. 3e and f), and screw (or spiral) teeth (Fig. 3c and d). Helical teeth, so called because they have the curved form of a helix, are used for cylindrical and bevel gears when smooth and noiseless work is required, as, for instance, in modern motor-cars or for precision drives.

The type of screw gearing mostly used is the worm and worm wheel couple (Fig. 3c), which is particularly suitable for power transmission combined with reducing the speed at a high ratio. Single units can be built for ratios up to 70:1, although 30:1 is seldom exceeded. The worm is basically a screw, set at 90° to the shaft of the worm wheel—a cylindrical form of gear with helical teeth with which the worm engages. As the worm revolves, the sides of its threads slide along the sides of the teeth of the worm wheel, and, pushing them in the direction of the worm axis, make the wheel turn.

When several gear-wheels are arranged to drive one another, the arrangement is known as a 'gear-train'. In a simple train each gear is placed on a separate shaft (Fig. 4a); in a compound train (Fig. 4b), there is more than one wheel on one shaft. Various sets of wheels and shafts can be devised to obtain many speeds.

Gear-trains are usually enclosed in cast iron or aluminium housings, called gear-boxes, partly filled with lubricating oil. For high speeds such

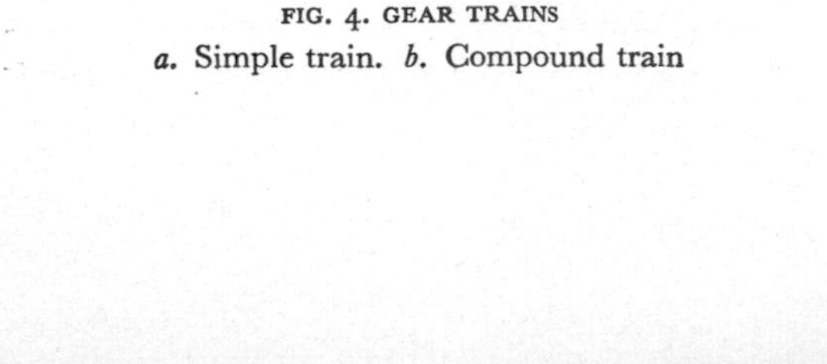

FIG. 3. TYPES OF GEARS

a. Cylindrical or spiral gears with straight teeth. b. Mitre gears with straight teeth. c. Worm and worm gear with screw teeth. d. Spiral gears with screw teeth. e. Spiral gears with helical teeth. f. Bevelled gears with helical teeth. g. Internal gear. h. Rack and pinion

for the drive to be 'taken round corners'—that is, when shafts inclined to each other and with intersecting axes have to be connected—'bevel' gears are used. Where two bevel gear-wheels are identical and the angle between their shafts is 90°, the gear is called a 'mitre' gear (Fig. 3b). When the shafts are at an angle and their axes

FIG. 4. GEAR TRAINS
a. Simple train. b. Compound train

lubrication is not sufficient, and a jet of cooled oil is directed on the working teeth. Shafts run

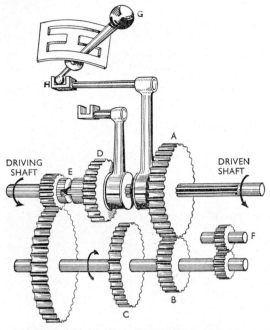

FIG. 5. DIAGRAM OF THREE-SPEED GEAR-BOX

The drawing shows first gear engaged. For the neutral position the lever, G, is moved to the centre of the gate, thus sliding gear A away from B. In second gear the ball of the lever is changed from H to J, and then moves D along to engage with C. For top gear A, B, C, and D are disengaged and the driven shaft is connected directly to the driving shaft by means of a dog clutch E. For reverse, A engages with F, gears B, C, D and dog clutch being disengaged

on ball-bearings at high speeds. A motor-car gearbox is an example of a modern gear-train (Fig. 5).

3. *Gear cutting.* The cutting of gear-teeth from a gear-blank (the uncut piece of metal) is a difficult operation needing special machinery and great precision. One way of doing this is to mill the teeth with a 'profile cutter'—a tool having the same shape as the tooth to be formed and often used on a MILLING MACHINE (q.v.). Another way is to use a templet (a metal pattern of the required shape) and a tracer. The tracer, by following the shape of the templet, produces that shape on the gear-blank ready for the cutting tool to follow. By a third way, the 'generating' method, the cutting tool, working on exact geometrical principles, develops the correct form on the blank by a series of complex movements of both tool and workpiece. This method produces an accurate tooth form, and is often

carried out in a gear-shaper machine. While both the tool and the workpiece revolve, the tool (which is made in the shape of a meshing gear) gradually mills in the workpiece the exact shape of the meshing gear.

Gear-hobbing machines are able to produce various kinds of gears at a high rate of production. These machines use rotating cutters, or hobs, with grooves cut in them to provide a number of cutting faces. As the cutters rotate against the gear-blanks, they cut the tooth shapes required. Hobbing machines have been built with as many as eight spindles, each carrying a hob, and they are completely automatic, except for loading and unloading the work.

Gear-grinders are employed where hardened gears have to be finished to a high degree of accuracy. This method of finishing the gears after they have been hardened avoids the danger of distortion during the hardening process (*see* HEAT TREATMENT). Other methods of producing a very high-precision finish are gear shaving, in which the cutter in contact with the gear-wheel (left purposely slightly oversize) slices off very small particles of metal, and gear burnishing, in which the unfinished gear-wheel is run between hardened burnishing gears to smooth its surface. By a third method, 'lapping', the gear is run in mesh with an appropriately formed lapping wheel carrying a fine abrasive in oil. As they run

FIG. 6. CUTTING A GEAR WITH A MILLING MACHINE

together a rubbing action takes place which produces the high finish.

See also CLUTCHES.

GENERATOR, ELECTRIC, *see* ELECTRIC GENERATORS.

GEOMETRY. This is the branch of the science of MEASUREMENT (q.v. Vol. IV) which studies the properties of flat and solid shapes made up of lines and surfaces. As far as we can tell, geometry arose from the practical needs of surveying and marking boundaries, especially with the ancient EGYPTIANS (q.v. Vol. I), when the river Nile yearly overflowed its banks and swept away landmarks. The methods used were next applied to building, and there is evidence that the Egyptians calculated the volumes of solid shapes by geometry. Later it became the foundation of much astronomical theory, and today the elementary principles of geometry are in constant use in ENGINEERING DESIGN and ENGINEERING DRAWING as well as in SURVEYING (qq.v.).

Familiar objects such as a thread of cotton or the skin of a balloon give a better idea of a line or a surface than definitions in words. If two lines meet, the place where they cross is called a point, and the flat surface in which they both lie is a plane. Points in diagrams are usually indicated by capital letters, and lines by small letters.

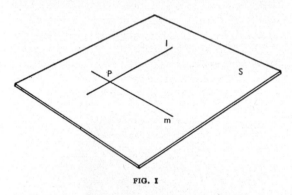

FIG. I

In Fig. 1 the lines *l* and *m* lie in the plane *s* and meet at the point P. If we imagine *l* and *m* to be pivoted at P like the hands of a clock, and one of those lines to swing once all the way round and

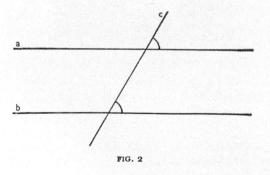

FIG. 2

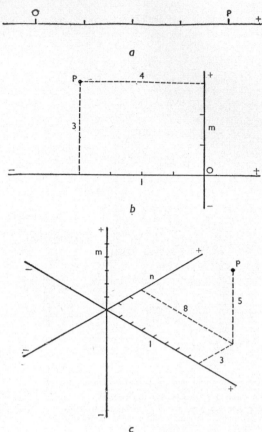

FIG. 3. *a.* A POINT ON A LINE. *b.* A POINT ON A SURFACE
c. A POINT IN SPACE

back to its original position, it will have moved through an angle of 360 degrees, or four right angles. The difference of direction, or 'inclination', of *l* and *m* is the angle between them. When this is one right angle, *l* and *m* are perpendicular to each other.

If two lines *a* and *b* (Fig. 2) make the same corresponding angles with a third line *c* which crosses them (all lying in the same plane), they are said to be parallel, and however much they are extended they will not meet.

Let us take a long straight line *l*, with a fixed point o and a moving point P on it. If we measure the distance of P from o in inches, using the term 'plus' or 'minus' as P is to the right or left of o, we can fix the position of P by one number, or 'coordinate'. In Fig. 3*a* it is 4. Now let us draw a line *m* perpendicular to *l* through o (Fig. 3*b*). P is allowed to move anywhere in the plane of these two lines. We can fix its position by two numbers—its distance from *m* measured parallel to *l*, and its distance from *l* measured parallel to *m*. In Fig. 3*b* its position is given by the figures —4 and 3. Finally, we draw a line *n* perpendicular to *l* and to *m*. P may now move anywhere in space, and we can fix its position by three numbers—its distance parallel to *l* from the plane containing *m* and *n*, and similarly its distance from the plane containing *l* and *n* and that containing *l* and *m*. In Fig. 3*c* its coordinates are 8, 5, and 3. In these examples, o is said to move in one, two, or three dimensions. This is the basis of analytical geometry, where points, lines, and surfaces are represented by arithmetic and algebraic expressions.

A large part of geometry is concerned with flat figures drawn in a plane. The simplest of these is formed by three straight lines, a triangle (Fig. 4*a*). If two of the three sides are equal it is isosceles (Fig. 4*b*); if all three, it is equilateral (Fig. 4*c*). Two triangles of the same shape but of a different size are called similar. Their corresponding angles are equal and each side of the larger angle is the same number of times greater than the smaller—that is, the corresponding sides are proportional. In Fig. 4*d* one is one and a half times as great as the other.

Two triangles which are both the same shape and the same size are called congruent. To draw one triangle congruent to another we must have one of the three following sets of information (Fig. 4*e*):

1. The length of each of the three sides.
2. The size (in degrees) of one angle and the length of the two sides which make it.
3. The size of two angles and the length of a side, with its relative position in the triangle.

The area of a triangle is half the product of the height and base ($\frac{1}{2}h \times b$, Fig. 4*f*).

If squares are drawn on the three sides of a right-angled triangle, the area of the square on the longest side (the hypotenuse) is equal to the sum of the areas of the squares on the other two sides. In Fig. 4*g*, $a^2 = b^2 + c^2$. This property is stated in Pythagoras' Theorem.

A basic principle of MECHANICS (q.v.) is that if three and only three forces are acting on a body which is in equilibrium, then the three forces can be represented in magnitude and direction by the sides of a triangle. Thus knowledge of the properties of a triangle can often be used to solve problems in the branch of mechanics known as statics. By an extension of this principle it is pos-

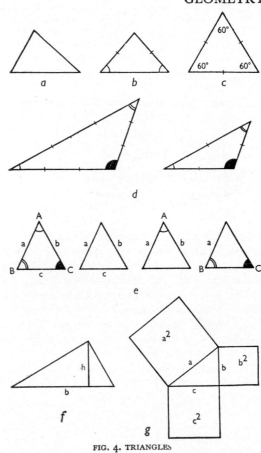

FIG. 4. TRIANGLES

a. Acute angle. *b*. Isosceles. *c*. Equilateral. *d*. Similar (obtuse-angled). *e*. Congruent. *f*. Area of triangle. *g*. Pythagoras' Theorem

sible to calculate the STRESS AND STRAIN (q.v.) in a girder or bridge under any given load.

Many calculations concerning triangles are simplified by TRIGONOMETRY (q.v.).

A four-sided figure, or quadrilateral (Fig. 5), can take the following special forms:

Trapezium	One pair of opposite sides parallel Area: $\frac{1}{2}h \times (a+b)$
Parallelogram	Both pairs of opposite sides parallel Area: $b \times h$
Rhombus	Parallelogram with two adjacent sides equal Area: $a \times h$
Rectangle	Parallelogram with one angle a right angle Area: $a \times b$
Square	Rhombus with one angle a right angle Area: a^2

The most common form of plane curve is the circle (Fig. 6). This is the path of a point which moves at a fixed distance (radius) from a fixed

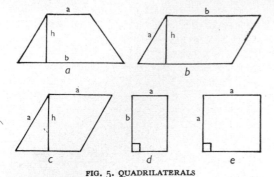

FIG. 5. QUADRILATERALS

a. Trapezium. *b.* Parallelogram. *c.* Rhombus.
d. Rectangle. *e.* Square

circles—that is, rather more than three times as long, or approximately 3·14159, a number represented by the Greek letter π (*pi*). The area of a circle is πr^2—that is, the radius multiplied by itself, then multiplied by π. If r represents units of length (feet or yards, for example), the result will be in square units (square feet or square yards).

If any two-dimensional figure, such as a triangle, circle, or square, is moved out in a direction not parallel to its own plane, it will become

point (centre); the complete path is the circumference of the circle. A line through the centre, cutting the circle into two semicircles, is called a diameter. Within the circle any other line (chord) cuts the circle into major and minor segments. Outside the circle, any line (tangent) which touches the circle makes a right angle with the radius at the point of contact. Two tangents drawn from the same point outside the circle must be equal in length. The part of the area of a circle between two radii is called a sector, and the curved part of its boundary is an arc.

The length of the circumference is the same (constant) in relation to the diameter for all

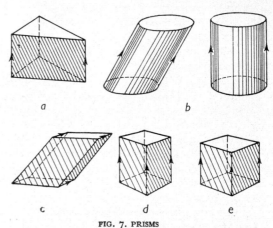

FIG. 7. PRISMS

a. Wedge. *b.* Cylinders; the second is a right prism.
c. Parallelepiped. *d.* Box. *e.* Cube

a solid figure called a prism (Fig. 7). If the direction is perpendicular (at right angles) to its plane it is called a right prism. A circular prism such as a roller is called a cylinder; one formed by a parallelogram is a parallelepiped. If all the faces of the parallelepiped are rectangles, it is a box; if squares, a cube.

A pyramid (Fig. 8) is formed by taking a point v outside the plane of a two-dimensional figure and joining every point of the figure to v. A circular pyramid is called a cone.

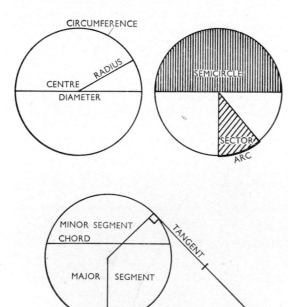

FIG. 6. THE CIRCLE AND ITS PARTS

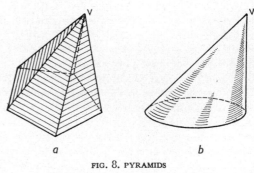

FIG. 8. PYRAMIDS

a. Pentagonal. *b.* Cone. v. Apex

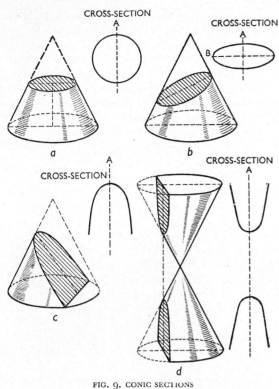

FIG. 9. CONIC SECTIONS

a. Circle. *b.* Ellipse. *c.* Parabola. *d.* Hyperbola

Suppose that a right cone is cut by a plane at right angles to its axis; the cross-section will be a circle (Fig. 9*a*). If the cutting plane is now tilted, the cross-section becomes the shape of an ellipse (Fig. 9*b*); when the plane is parallel to one side of the cone its shape is that of a parabola, the path of a stone flung in the air (Fig. 9*c*); when the plane is vertical the shape is a hyperbola. To get a complete hyperbola another equal cone must

be inverted on top of the first, supplying the other half of the shape (Fig. 9*d*). All these are known as conic sections.

If these shapes are revolved round certain lines or axes, as shown in Fig. 10, they make solid figures; a sphere (like a ball), an ellipsoid (an 'egg'), a paraboloid (like a headlamp or searchlight reflector), and a hyperboloid, which are common forms of curved solids in geometry.

Geometrical drawing is also used in dealing with vectors—that is, quantities involving not only numbers (such as 7 miles) but also their direction (such as 7 miles north-eastward). The difference is important.

Suppose a crew, rowing a boat across a river ½ mile wide in still water with no wind or current, rows straight across (o to A) in 15 minutes, they will move at a steady 2 miles per hour (Fig. 11). But it a current is flowing at 4 miles per hour,

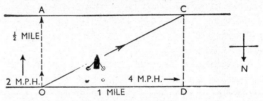

FIG. 11. VECTOR DIAGRAM

they will drift downstream at the same time. In 15 minutes they would have drifted one mile down to D. The combined effect of the oars and the current therefore take the boat along the thick line oc, the actual track of the boat. Since it takes 15 minutes for the boat to get from o to c, we can, by measuring the length of oc (1⅛ miles) work out the actual speed of the boat: it is, in fact, 4½ miles per hour.

The rectangle is a vector diagram adding two

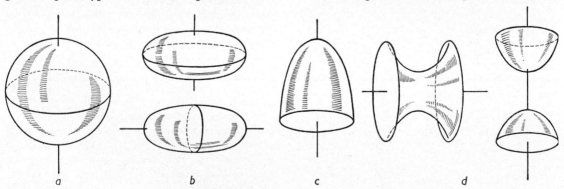

FIG. 10. SOLID FIGURES MADE FROM THE REVOLUTION OF CONIC SECTIONS

a. Sphere. *b.* Ellipsoid; the upper is oblate (revolved about short axis) and the lower prolate (revolved about long axis). *c.* Paraboloid. *d.* Hyperboloid; left, of one sheet (revolved about horizontal axis); right, of two sheets (revolved about vertical axis)

vectors OA and OD (the velocity of the boat and the velocity of the current) to give an answer OC (the velocity of the boat in the current).

See also ARITHMETIC; ALGEBRA; GRAPHS; TRIGONOMETRY; SURVEYING.

GRAPHS. These are mathematical diagrams comparing two or more sets of figures in a pictorial way. Graphs not only often present information in a way more easily understood, but they also sometimes make it possible to carry out calculations by making measurements with a ruler which would otherwise involve long 'paper sums'.

The framework of a graph is a pair of straight lines, like a capital L, of which the horizontal bar acts as a scale for one set of units, often of time, and the vertical bar for some other unit of measurement—tons, miles, or numbers of people, for example. Sometimes the lines are curved for convenience, as on a recording barometer where the sweep of a moving pen must be allowed for (*see* METEOROLOGICAL INSTRUMENTS).

Graphs are generally (but not necessarily) drawn on 'squared paper', as the squares often assist the calculation. Each point on the graph is found by measuring inward from a point on one of the scales (Fig. 1). A vertical line running up from the bottom edge and a horizontal line running in from the side are together called 'coordinates'. The lines need not be drawn in, so long as the point to which they lead is accurately marked; but once all the points required have been marked, it is more convenient to link them by a series of lines or a curve.

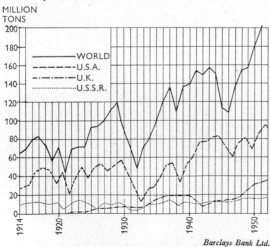

MILLION TONS

———— WORLD
------ U.S.A.
-·-·-· U.K.
············ U.S.S.R.

Barclays Bank Ltd.

FIG. 1. GRAPH OF CRUDE STEEL PRODUCTION 1914–52

The kinds of graphs much used in business to illustrate, say, world steel production, or in showing STATISTICS (q.v. Vol. VII), are usually simple and irregular in shape. More complicated graphs, used perhaps to give information on some fixed law of nature, usually have curves of regular shape. Let us consider a graph designed to show the course of a stone which is thrown up into the air. We will use the symbol h to represent the height of the stone from the ground (expressed in feet) at any particular moment, and the symbol t to represent the duration of time (expressed in seconds). Suppose the stone is thrown straight up from the ground at a speed of 64 feet per second, then its height in feet after a lapse of t seconds is given almost exactly by a well-known formula, $h = 64t - 16t^2$. The term $64t$ represents the distance the stone would have gone vertically upwards were it not slowed down by GRAVITATION (q.v. Vol. III). The term $16t^2$ represents the effect of this slowing down. If we wish to know the height of the stone after 3 seconds, t becomes 3, and the formula reads $h = 64 \times 3 - 16(3 \times 3)$, which is the same as $h = 48$. From this formula we can make a table of the stone's height at various times:

number of seconds elapsed	0	*stone rising*				*stone falling*			
	0	$\frac{1}{2}$	1	$1\frac{1}{2}$	2	$2\frac{1}{2}$	3	$3\frac{1}{2}$	4
height in feet	0	28	48	60	64	60	48	28	0

Points on a graph corresponding to the information in the table will be seen to lie on a smooth curve (Fig. 2). This curve is the graph of the formula, or function, $h = 64t - 16t^2$, and provides an example of the way in which a geometric curve can be reduced to an algebraic expression. From this graph we can read off other information not directly given in the formula or the table, such as the two moments (0·775 and 3·225 seconds) when the stone is exactly 40 feet high.

Frequently the successive points along one or both edges of a graph do not indicate a sequence of natural numbers (1, 2, 3, 4, and so on) but a scale based on the principles of algebra or of LOGARITHMS (q.v.). If, for instance, the vertical scale of a graph is logarithmic, the upper part of any curve will appear to be greatly compressed by comparison with the lower part. Before jumping to conclusions from the appearance of a

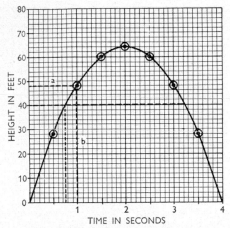

FIG. 2. GRAPH OF THE PATH OF A STONE

a and *b* are coordinates

graph, therefore, it is important to examine the nature of both the vertical and horizontal scales.

See also Vol. VII: STATISTICS.

GRID SYSTEM. This is the British network of high-voltage electric power lines to supply electricity from POWER STATIONS (q.v.) to users in all parts of the country. This system was started in 1926 in order to reduce the average cost of electric power by making it possible to generate most of the power used in Britain in a few large and very efficient power stations, conveniently situated near coal supplies. In this way electric power can be made more cheaply and the nation's limited resources of coal used to the best advantage.

In general the greatest amount of electrical energy per pound of coal consumed is produced by large stations which are kept going continuously at full power. The demand for electricity, however, varies widely during the day and night and from season to season. The demand rises to peaks at about 8 a.m. and 6 p.m., especially in winter, when electric fires and cookers in thousands of homes are switched on. At 8 a.m. the demand for electricity is about four or five times as great as at 4 a.m. Engineers in charge of the grid system meet this problem of changing demand by running the most efficient power stations continuously and by switching in the less efficient smaller stations as the demand increases. These small stations may produce only two-fifths as much electrical energy from a pound of coal as the large stations, but they are shut down as soon as the peak demand has passed.

The grid system and the 300 power stations connected to it are run by the British Electricity Authority, a PUBLIC UTILITY (q.v. Vol.VII) under Parliament's general control, and the switches that connect the power stations to the grid are operated from control centres in London (Thames South and Thames North), Bristol, Birmingham, Manchester, Leeds, Newcastle, and Glasgow. The control engineer in each of these eight centres is surrounded by electrical instruments showing how much electric power is being used by the consumers connected to all the main power lines in his area, and indicator lamps showing which main switches are open and which closed. It is his duty to watch the electric power consumption and to switch the less efficient power stations in and out as needed to meet the peak demands.

The grid system has about 5,000 miles of power lines, most of which is carried overhead by the familiar pylons. These lattice-work towers, usually about 70 feet high and 300 yards apart, are made of galvanized rustproof steel. To save weight the overhead wires are made of strands of aluminium, tightly wrapped around a steel wire core for strength. The wires are hung from long porcelain insulators (*see* ELECTRIC CURRENT), which are corrugated to increase the length of the path over the surface of the insulator along which the electric current might otherwise leak when dirt and rain collect on the porcelain.

A large amount of electric power can be sent over a power line, either by using a low voltage and a large current, or by using a high voltage and a small current. As a large electric current would waste a lot of power in overcoming the electrical resistance of the wires in the power line and consequently heating them, as high a voltage as possible is generally used. The voltage used in the main power lines of the British grid system is 132,000 volts. Even higher voltages are used in some countries, but they lead to difficulties in the design of insulators and switchgear. Work in Britain has already begun on a new system of main power lines working at 275,000 volts. This 'super grid', which will greatly increase the amount of electric power that can be exchanged between different parts of the country, will probably cost about £70,000,000, but it is calculated that it will save about £90,000,000 that would otherwise have had to be spent on additional generators.

Many of the shorter power lines work at lower voltages, such as 66,000 volts or 33,000 volts,

B. I. Catlenders

ELECTRIC POWER LINES CARRYING ELECTRICITY FROM CLIFF QUAY POWER STATION ON THE RIVER ORWELL, SUFFOLK

This power station supplies power to a large part of Suffolk

because on these short lines the amount of power is less, and the lower voltages do not need such expensive towers, insulators, and switchgear. The main power lines are connected to each other and to the shorter lines at sub-stations, which contain SWITCHGEAR and electric TRANS- FORMERS (qq.v.) for changing the line voltage from 132,000 to 66,000 or 33,000 volts. In the country the switchgear and transformers are usually mounted in the open air; in the towns there is no room for these stations with their maze of overhead steelworks and insulators, and the switchgear is enclosed in metal cases and mounted indoors.

Coal could be saved and the cost of electric power reduced if it were possible to do without the smaller power stations. This could be done if there were any way of storing electrical energy without loss, for then the large power stations could work continuously at full load, storing electricity during the night ready for use at the peak demand next day. But no method is yet known for storing large quantities of electrical

energy. However, as it is possible to store mechanical energy by filling the reservoir of water that drives a HYDRO-ELECTRIC POWER station (q.v.), engineers have considered that hydro-electric power stations might be con- structed to meet this problem. During the day they would generate electricity, and during the night their water turbines, supplied with power from the large steam-driven power stations, would work backwards pumping water back into their reservoirs.

Another way for meeting the peak demand without using the smaller steam power stations that has been proposed is to connect the British grid system to hydro-electric power stations in Europe. Tests have been made on a type of 132,000-volt submarine power cable that could be laid across the English Channel. The grid system has already made the generation of elec- tric power cheaper and more efficient, and some scheme such as those described may make further improvements possible.

See also ELECTRIC CURRENT; POWER STATION.

GRINDING MACHINES, *see* MACHINE TOOLS, Section 4.

GUNPOWDER, *see* EXPLOSIVES.

GUNS, *see* BALLISTICS; EXPLOSIVES; DRILLING AND BORING MACHINES, Section 4. *See also* Vol. X: ARTILLERY; NAVAL GUNS.

GYRO-COMPASS, *see* GYROSCOPE, Section 2*b*.

GYROSCOPE. 1. PRINCIPLES OF GYROSCOPE. Originally a scientific toy based on the principle of a spinning top, the gyroscope has now become an important device for giving stability to certain mechanisms such as aircraft navigating apparatus. The revolving flywheel that is the 'heart' of any gyroscopic equipment reacts against any attempt to change its position in space, and this property is put to good use in the gyro-compass, the aircraft automatic pilot, guiding devices for guided missiles, and many other appliances. In its simplest form, the gyroscope consists of a rapidly rotating flywheel, mounted in a series of pivoted frameworks known as 'gimbals' (Fig. 1). Consequently the flywheel rotates on an axis which is itself free to rotate in any direction about the centre of the wheel. Such an arrangement has two remarkable properties.

(*a*). In order to make the axis of the flywheel rotate in any direction, force is needed, apart from any force needed to overcome friction in the gimbal bearings. In other words, the gyroscope tends to remain fixed in space—a property known as 'inertia' (*see* MASS, Vol. III).

(*b*). If an attempt is made to rotate the axis in a given direction (T in Fig. 1), instead of rotating in that direction, it will rotate only in the direction P so as to bring the rotation of the flywheel into line with its own attempted rotation—an effect which has to be prevented, of course, if the gyroscope is to be made to move the way we want it to. This property is known as 'precession'.

These two properties are both shown by the familiar whipping-top. When the top is spinning, owing to its inertia we can whip it as hard as we like without knocking it over. If the top gets a 'list' on it, its property of precession will make it sway round and round its base in the same direction as that in which it is spinning. This is because the tendency of the top to fall over is, in effect, an attempt to move its axis of rotation in the direction A (Fig. 2), and this causes the axis to move in

FIG. 1. SIMPLE GYROSCOPE

Sperry

direction B. This in turn changes the direction of falling, and the result of the continual attempt of these two effects to 'catch up with each other' is the rotary swaying motion C, so familiar in a spinning top.

The gyroscope behaves as it does because any attempt to twist the axis of a rotating body involves accelerating various parts of it; these accelerations need forces (*see* MECHANICS), and the body will always move so that the available

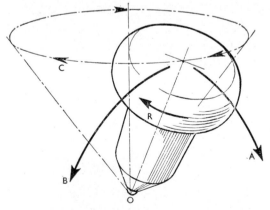

FIG. 2. PRECESSION IN A SPINNING TOP

If the top, while spinning in the direction R, falls in the direction A, precession will make it tend to move in the direction B, and the resultant movement will be in the circular path C

forces—reaction forces at the bearings, and any applied forces—are acting in the directions necessary to produce the required accelerations.

2. Uses of Gyroscope. The gyroscope's properties of inertia and precession are put to good practical use in a variety of ways, some of which are described below.

(*a*) *Aircraft instruments*. When a pilot is flying 'blind', his natural senses—sight, sense of balance, and sense of his own weight (which tell him in which direction gravity is acting)—can be quite misleading. So a series of special aircraft instruments has been developed to tell him what the aircraft is doing—which way up it is, whether it is turning, and, if so, in what direction and how fast, whether it is on a level keel, and so on. The gyroscope is the essential item in many of these instruments, and the two that best illustrate the way in which its properties are used are the rate-of-turn indicator and the direction indicator.

The aircraft rate-of-turn indicator ('rate gyro') consists essentially of a gyroscope mounted not

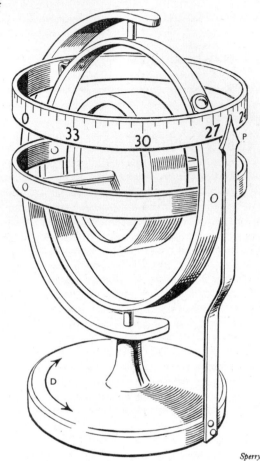

Sperry

FIG. 4. AIRCRAFT DIRECTION INDICATOR
P. Fixed pointer. D. Direction of movement

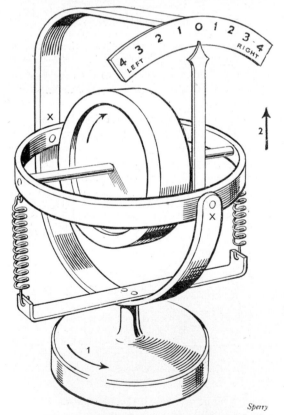

Sperry

FIG. 3. AIRCRAFT RATE-OF-TURN INDICATOR
x. Bearings about which gyroscope axis rotates. 1. Direction of rotation of instrument. 2. Direction of precession

as in Fig. 1 but so that its axis can swing only in one direction (Fig. 3). Here, the axis of rotation can rotate only about the bearings x–x, against the restoring forces of the two springs. If the whole instrument is rotated in direction 1, the gyroscope will start to precess in direction 2, and will tilt in this direction until the restoring forces of the springs are sufficient to balance the tendency to precess. The force needed is proportional to the rate of turn in direction 1, so that the pointer indicates both rate and direction of turn.

The direction indicator consists of a gyroscope mounted as in Fig. 1, with its axis set horizontal as shown in Fig. 4. Since the gimbal mountings are almost frictionless, the gyroscope will remain in its original attitude regardless of movements of its base, and the scale will thus indicate, against a fixed pointer P, any movements of the instrument in direction D. But because the instrument tends to remain fixed in space while the earth itself rotates, the gyroscope does not, in fact, remain motionless relative to the earth, but 'drifts' slightly off its original setting and has to be reset at fairly frequent intervals by reference to a known bearing provided by some sort of compass. The fact that the gimbal bearings cannot be altogether frictionless also calls for resetting.

(*b*) *Gyro-compass*. The gyroscope's rigidity in space causes it to rotate relative to the earth as the earth itself rotates. In the gyro-compass, the gyroscope is linked up with two mercury reservoirs connected by a U-shaped tube. This is done in such a way that the changing angle of the gyroscope due to the earth's rotation tilts the reservoirs; the shifting of the mercury's weight mechanically deflects the gyroscope and makes it precess so that it continues to point to the North. The arrangements needed to do this accurately are very complicated.

(*c*) *General*. Combinations of rate and direction gyros guide the control gear for anti-aircraft gun predictors, GUIDED MISSILE controls (q.v. Vol. X), aircraft automatic pilots, gun turret stabilizers, and many other items of equipment. Large gyroscopes are no longer used for ship stabilization in heavy seas, because with the big ships of today, enormous gyros would be needed

Crown Copyright

FIG. 5. A SHIP'S GYRO-COMPASS REMOVED FROM THE BINNACLE TO SHOW THE GYROSCOPE

to set up precession forces big enough to counteract roll. But in modern ship-stabilizing gear, a small gyroscope is used to detect the rolling motion and to operate servo-motors (*see* MARINE ENGINEERING, Section 7).

H

HARMONICS, *see* Vol. IX: Musical Instruments, Section 3.

HEAT ENGINES. These are any machines that convert Heat (q.v. Vol. III) into work (*see* Mechanics). There are only five types of heat engine of any practical importance—the Steam Engine, with which is included the Steam Turbine (qq.v.); the spark-ignition engine and the compression-ignition engine (*see* Internal Combustion Engine); the Gas Turbine (q.v.); and the jet propulsion and Rocket Propulsion engines (q.v.). In this article we are concerned not with how these various engines work but with certain basic problems that confront the designer of any kind of engine for turning heat into work. The study of these problems is called thermodynamics.

In 1847 the Manchester scientist James Prescott Joule first definitely proved that work could be turned into heat, which was then for the first time clearly recognized as a form of Energy (q.v.). This is formulated in the First Law of Thermodynamics which states that there is an exact equivalence between the mechanical work done and the heat given out as a result. This led scientists to investigate the reverse process, and within a few years many primitive heat engines were developed (*see* Engines, History of). People then began to compare the amount of heat energy in the Fuel (q.v.) being burnt with the amount of work energy that the engine produced. They soon discovered how inefficient the early engines made in the 18th century were—only about 10 per cent. of the heat in the fuel ever appeared as useful work. In spite of many improvements introduced by James Watt (q.v. Vol. V) and others, the efficiency figures had remained obstinately small. Joule had easily converted work into heat at a

much higher rate of exchange. Why, the scientists asked themselves, was this reverse process proving so difficult?

The answer to this question was provided by the brilliant work of two of Joule's contemporaries, the Frenchman Carnot and the German Clausius. They proved that the maximum possible efficiency with which, under normal conditions, heat can be turned into work is about 40%. By 'maximum possible' is meant the highest efficiency that could be reached by a theoretically perfect engine, with frictionless bearings and no heat losses anywhere, not what is, in fact, achieved by an actual engine.

Carnot regarded any heat engine as something that uses a 'working substance'—in a petrol engine, air; in a steam engine, water. This receives heat from a source at a high temperature, converts some of it to work, and rejects the remainder to a 'receiver' at a lower temperature, the whole 'cycle' being repeated over and over again. In a steam engine, for example, the working substance, water, receives heat from the boiler furnace at a high temperature, turning into steam at high pressure in the process; it expands in the cylinder, thus doing work; and it is then condensed in the condenser, giving up the remainder of the heat which it received. The water in the condenser is then pumped back to the boiler to be used again.

Now the heat given up to the receiver during each cycle is wasted, and that is what makes heat engines so inefficient. In a petrol engine, the heat is wasted in the exhaust; in a steam turbine, the heat is given up in the condenser.

The perfect heat engine would be one that could take in heat and turn it all into work, so that no heat was rejected at the lower temperature. Carnot realized that such an engine was impossible, for the simple reason that the working substance must be brought back to its original state before the cycle could begin again. Let us imagine a very simple heat engine in which an iron bar is the working substance. The iron bar is heated over a flame and it expands, doing work, until it is as hot as the flame and can expand no farther. To get any more work out of it it must be allowed to contract by cooling down, and then be returned to the flame for the cycle to begin over again. It makes no difference if we bring in a fresh supply of working substance—a new, cool, iron bar in this case—we have still wasted the heat in the old iron bar.

Carnot then imagined a frictionless engine using a perfect gas (*see* GASES, PROPERTIES OF) as a working substance and working in such a way that there were no incidental heat losses at any stage of its cycle of operations. From the known facts about the way in which a perfect gas expands when heated, the efficiency of this ideal engine can be calculated. Carnot showed that this was $\dfrac{T_S - T_R}{T_S}$ (T_S and T_R are the absolute temperatures of source and receiver respectively). This formula is of great practical importance, because it gives us a standard of reference for assessing the performance of real engines. It also suggests two ways of making real engines more efficient. If a steam turbine plant, for instance, receives steam from the boiler at 900° C. (1173° K.; *see* TEMPERATURE, MEASUREMENT OF) and gives out heat to the condenser at 10° C. (283° K.), its maximum efficiency, if it were ideal, could not be more than $\dfrac{1173 - 283}{1173} = \frac{3}{4}$ which, expressed as a percentage, is 75%. But if we could operate our plant in the Arctic regions, with a condenser temperature of, say, −10° C. (263° K.), the maximum theoretical efficiency would jump to 78%. That is why the engine designer's main task is always to raise the high-temperature end of the engine while reducing the low-temperature end. It explains why steam for the modern turbine is superheated nearly to red heat, while vast concrete cooling towers are built to keep the condenser cool.

Just as water will always try to find its lowest level, so heat will always flow from a body at a high temperature to one at a low temperature, and it is impossible for heat from a cool body to flow of its own accord into a hot body (making it hotter still). This is called the Second Law of Thermodynamics. We now know that this can be explained by regarding heat as the energy of molecular motion and temperature as the tangible effect of molecular velocity (*see* HEAT, Vol. III). Therefore, in any practical engine, not only is some heat from the furnace inevitably reduced to the temperature of the condenser (or exhaust or whatever it may be), but there is a constant tendency for any wastage to appear as low-temperature heat.

It used to be believed that, since the temperature of everything in the world was gradually evening out as heat flowed from bodies of high temperatures to those of low, there would come a time when heat engines would no longer be possible because there would be no temperature difference left to work them between. Our outlook now, however, has been fundamentally altered by the discovery that energy can be obtained from matter itself (*see* NUCLEAR ENERGY), and so the threat of a stagnant universe is removed.

HEATING. In Britain the average air temperature between October and April is about 44° Fahrenheit; to be comfortable indoors we usually need a temperature of from 60 to 67° F., so heating of some sort is needed to make up the difference. Often 'local heating' is used—that is, fuel is burned in open fires, stoves, or gas fires in the room to be heated. In large buildings, however, heat is nearly always generated in boilers at a central point, and distributed to the various rooms.

Methods of heating can be broadly classified as 'convective' or 'radiant'. In convective heating, the air itself is heated; while in radiant heating beams of heat radiate from a hot surface and warm objects placed in their path, but do not heat up the air. For the same degree of comfort the air temperature of the whole room can be somewhat lower than with convective heating. For example, you can be quite comfortable in front of a fire where you are receiving a good deal of radiation, although away from the fire the room would seem too cold.

Most central-heating schemes use so-called 'radiators', though, in fact, about 85% of the heat is given off by such radiators as convection, and only 15% as radiation.

Most central-heating systems use low-pressure hot water. This means that the pipework system is open to the atmosphere at its highest point (the 'vent'), and the water is not heated to a very high temperature. Heating systems with radiators are usually designed on the basis of water leaving the boiler, in the coldest weather, at a temperature of about 180° F., and returning at about 140° or 150° F.

The simplest systems of circulation operate by gravity. Water expands when heated; consequently a column of hot water is lighter than an equivalent column of cooler water. In Fig. 1 a pipe coil containing water has heat applied at one point. The water in the pipe AB being hotter than that in the pipe CD, the pressure, or 'head', of the water at D will be greater than that at A,

FIG. I. THE PRINCIPLE OF GRAVITY CIRCULATION

and the water will tend to move from D to A, thus keeping up a circulation. Gravity circulation, though slow, is satisfactory for small installations such as that shown in Fig. 2. This includes a single radiator for heating, and also a 'calorifier' containing a heating coil to warm domestic hot water. The purpose of the calorifier is to enable the radiator or 'heating' water to be used over and over again. If the kitchen and bath water is constantly being drawn off the radiator supply—as it often is in older installations—fresh water is continually being drawn into the system, and there will be more scale and sediment deposited in the boilers, radiators, and pipes.

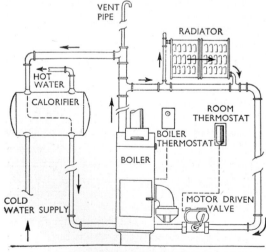

FIG. 2. SMALL GRAVITY INSTALLATION FOR HEATING
WATER AND RADIATORS

If water were circulated at the same temperature throughout the winter, the room would be overheated in mild weather. In Fig. 2, therefore, the temperature of the radiator is regulated by a room THERMOSTAT (q.v.) which, connected to a valve, regulates the flow of water so that the temperature in the room is maintained at the level at which the thermostat is set. The 'boiler thermostat' prevents overheating at the boiler when the room needs only a small amount of heat.

For large buildings, gravity circulation would be too slow, and therefore a pump is fitted to speed up the circulation. Such a system is often designed so that full heating can be maintained by day when the pump is running, and a lower temperature by night when the circulation is by gravity only. In large buildings, the temperature is sometimes controlled automatically by devices fixed outside the building, which take account not only of air temperature, but also of wind, sunshine, and rain, all of which may affect the heat loss from the building. Automatic control ensures steady warmth, and also economy in fuel.

Two methods of installing radiator systems are shown in Fig. 3. In Fig. 3*a* all the radiators on each of the four floors of the building are fed from a horizontal pipe, and in Fig. 3*b* the radiators in a vertical line on all floors have a 'down-feed' pipe. Both diagrams show, in the top left-hand corner, the ball-valve and tank through which the heating system is filled with water: the vent pipe is turned over the tank. In most installations it is necessary to run some pipes in places such as basements or roof spaces, where heat is not required: these pipes must be well insulated in order to avoid considerable wastage of heat and, consequently, of fuel.

The Romans developed a system of central heating in which fires were burned in basement chambers, and the hot smoke from the fires was led through ducts built in the floors and walls. The method of warming the floor by means of hot air in ducts has recently been revived with great success in Liverpool Cathedral. In ordinary buildings, however, the principle is applied by embedding 'panels' of pipes in the ceiling, and circulating hot water through them, so that the ceiling becomes warm and radiates heat to the room. Fig. 4 shows the underside of a ceiling containing a heating panel before the finishing plaster is applied. Ceiling panels operate at

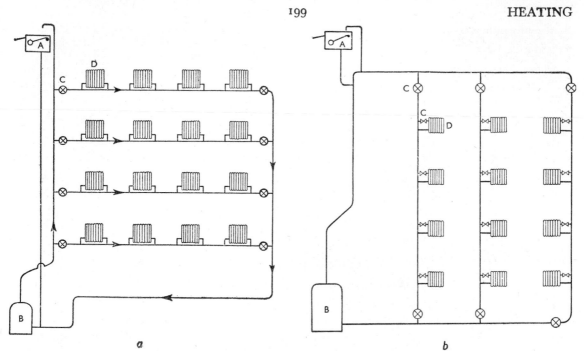

FIG. 3. METHODS OF INSTALLING RADIATOR SYSTEMS
a. Horizontal distribution. *b.* Vertical distribution
A. Supply tank. B. Boiler. C. Valves. D. Radiators

Crittall & Co. Ltd.

FIG. 4. SINUOUS PANEL COIL EMBEDDED IN THE UNDERSIDE OF A CEILING SLAB, BEFORE PLASTERING.
THE COIL IS HEATED BY LOW-PRESSURE HOT WATER

Crittall & Co. Ltd.

FIG. 5. STEEL RADIANT PANELS HEATED BY HIGH-PRESSURE HOT WATER, INSTALLED IN A FACTORY

lower temperatures than radiators, and the maximum water temperature employed is about 120° F. Embedded panels are also used in walls and floors: many modern schools have warmed floors. The advantage of this system is that, the apparatus being entirely hidden, floor space is not taken up by pipes and radiators, and there is no discoloration of decorations due to rising currents of hot air.

In another form of panel warming, flat metal panels with coils of heating pipes welded at the back are fixed to the surfaces of ceilings or walls. These can be run at higher temperatures than embedded panels, without the risk of damage to plaster finishes. Another system is to use specially made wall-paper in which strands of resistance wire are woven. When these wires are connected to the electricity supply, the wall (or ceiling) surface becomes warm.

Very large, lofty buildings such as factories cannot be satisfactorily heated by ordinary convective methods, as the warmed air rises to the roof and is wasted, and the 'working plane' remains cold. A modern method is to use radiant panels heated by means of 'high-pressure hot water': Fig. 5 shows an installation in a large engineering shop. This system, instead of being open to the atmosphere as in the low-pressure system, is closed, and the water is heated under pressure to a temperature of about 350° F. Large amounts of heat can be distributed, but surfaces at such high temperatures must either be out of reach, or guarded by grilles. This system is very suitable for factories, and has also been used in

other buildings: for example, the Ministry of National Insurance offices at Newcastle and extensions to the heating installation at Buckingham Palace.

Another method of warming factories, garages, warehouses, and similar buildings is the 'unit heater'. This consists of an electrically driven fan blowing air over a steam or hot-water radiator rather like that of a car. The unit is suspended overhead, and the warmed air is directed to where it is wanted. A steam-using type is shown in Fig. 6, but unit heaters employing gas and electricity are also made. They are very rapid in action and do not occupy any floor space.

Steam is used much more for heating in the U.S.A. and other countries, where the winters are very severe, than it is in England. Steam has the disadvantage that its temperature cannot readily be altered, as can that of hot water.

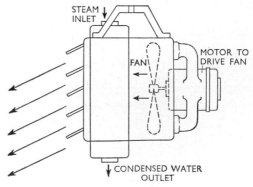

FIG. 6. SUSPENDED TYPE OF UNIT HEATER

When steam condenses to water on cooling, the 'condensate' can cause corrosion of some metals. Steam is often used for transmitting heat in bulk, as, for example, from a central boiler house to the separate blocks of a hospital or institution, where it may be needed for cooking and sterilizing. Heating, however, is nearly always by hot water from steam-heated calorifiers.

'District heating', in which a central boiler house distributes hot water to a number of houses or public buildings, is used more in other countries than in England, though schemes are now in operation in various places in Britain. In Westminster large blocks of flats are served with heat derived as a by-product from the generation of electricity at Battersea Power Station (*see* Vol. X, p. 416). As the demand for heat does not always coincide with the amount available, a large 'accumulator', 126 feet high, stores 500,000 gallons of water at a maximum temperature of 200° F. The accumulator is constructed of steel plate surrounded by glazing; this improves the appearance of the tower and helps to insulate it against heat losses, which are less than 1 per cent. of the heat stored.

The linking of heating with electricity generation is a very promising development. With ordinary methods of generation only about 30 per cent. of the heat contained in the fuel is available as electricity, but if generation is combined with heating, up to 80 per cent. can be used.

See also Vol. III: HEAT.
See also Vol. XI: HEATING, HISTORY OF.

HEAT PUMP. This is a machine that supplies heat for warming buildings by drawing the heat out of river water or the earth or even the air, and delivering it to a hot-water system of the ordinary type. The mechanical arrangements of a heat pump, and the principle upon which it works, are exactly the same as those of a large refrigerator—indeed, the heat pump originally installed at the Royal Festival Hall in London was used to cool the building in summer as well as to heat it in winter.

The article REFRIGERATOR (q.v.) explains how the heat removed in cooling the inside of the refrigerator is delivered to the kitchen. If we imagine a refrigerator on a very large scale with the ice-box in the garden and the high-pressure side indoors, we can see that such a machine could be used to warm the house as it cooled the air outside. The idea of a heat pump of this type was suggested by the famous English scientist, Lord KELVIN (q.v. Vol. V), in 1852. We might well ask what advantage there is in using such a complicated piece of machinery to do a job that can be done by simply burning fuel and, if there is an advantage, why Lord Kelvin's idea was not developed more quickly.

Fig. 1 shows the essential of a heat pump layout. Liquid is evaporated in evaporator coils (A) by absorbing heat from a low-temperature source such as a river. The cold vapour is heated by compression in a compressor (B) and the hot vapour is then led to a condenser (C) where it condenses, and in doing so gives out heat to the water which is led off to radiators (D). Cool water from the radiators returns to the condenser to be reheated. The liquefied vapour is led at high pressure from the condenser to an expansion

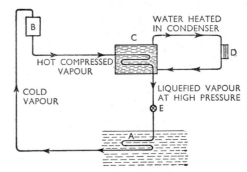

FIG. 1. DIAGRAM OF A HEAT PUMP
A. Evaporator absorbing heat from river. B. Compressor. C. Condenser. D. Useful heat at high temperature. E. Expansion valve

valve (E) where the pressure is reduced and the liquid passes back into the evaporator coils.

As the article REFRIGERATOR explains, the refrigerator, or heat pump, moves a certain number—say h—units of heat from a source at a low temperature to a receiver at a higher temperature for a given consumption of units of heat or fuel or energy (say H), and delivers the $h+H$ units at the higher temperature. Therefore, since the heat in the earth, water, or air is limitless and free, the heat pump delivers over and above the heat (H) derived from its consumption of fuel a quantity of heat (h) which has cost nothing in terms of fuel. On the other hand, the units of extra heat have cost something in terms of wear and tear on the heat pump, which, compared with a stove or boiler, is a complicated and expensive piece of machinery. The economics of a heat pump, therefore, depend on the relative costs of machinery and repairs, and of fuel. In Lord Kelvin's time, coal was very cheap, but since then the price of all fuels has greatly increased, whereas big compressors can now be made more efficient, more reliable, and cheaper; so now the heat pump is becoming a practical proposition. Ordinary direct heating of a large building usually uses a lot of fuel, while under favourable conditions the heat pump needs a much smaller amount of energy to convey the required amount of heat from outside to the interior of the building.

As with the refrigerator, the output of a heat pump installation rises as the temperature difference between the hot and cold sides decreases, and consequently the heat pump is particularly efficient when the required rise of temperature is comparatively small.

A large number of heat pumps is in operation today, particularly in the U.S.A. and Switzerland. The first large installation in England, constructed in 1943, warms the Electricity Board's offices at Norwich from the adjacent River Wensum, and the buildings can be kept comfortably warm even when the river is frozen over. In the heat pump at the Royal Festival Hall in London converted aero-engines were used as compressors, and heat was derived from the River Thames. The compressors were gas-driven, and for a consumption of 60 heat units the plant delivered 85 heat units to the Hall.

See also REFRIGERATOR; HEATING.

HEAT TREATMENT. 1. This term means the heating and cooling, in various special ways, of METALS (q.v.) and their alloys in order, by bringing about changes in their structure, to make them harder or softer, more springlike or more plastic, or to give them other properties which may be desired. Those forms of heat treatment that are intended to harden or strengthen the material can be used successfully only with those alloys which are 'polyphase'—that is, contain two or more phases (see ALLOYS). Since pure metals contain only one phase, they cannot be treated profitably in this way. When a polyphase alloy is heated to an exact high temperature, depending on the composition of the material, one of its constituent phases may blend with another. If the alloy is then cooled very quickly, this blending may persist: alternatively, the phases may separate again, wholly or in part, depending upon the rate of cooling. By varying the temperature of heating, the length of time at that temperature, and the rate of cooling, different types of heat treatment are produced, each being used to develop some particular property that is desired in the metal or alloy. In every form of heat treatment the material is first heated to some temperature which, though high, is below its melting-point.

2. ANNEALING. Both pure metals and alloys tend to become hard and brittle by the forces exerted on them in mechanical shaping (rolling or hammering). This brittleness is often a drawback, and the article in that case can be softened by heating and cooling very slowly. When used for this purpose, heat treatment is called 'annealing'. The material is retained at a high temperature for a long time before being cooled slowly to ordinary room temperature. In some cases the hardness caused by the shaping pressure is an advantage worth retaining, and then only partial heating is needed to make the object slightly less brittle (see Section 6).

3. NORMALIZING. Sometimes a piece of metal or alloy may have internal strains (which might be roughly compared with the muscular tensions in a human arm if it is held stiffly). Strains in metals and alloys are removed by normalizing: the material is heated to a high temperature and, when its temperature is uniform throughout, is allowed to cool in still air—a rate of cooling much quicker than that used for annealing. Both annealing and normalizing are intended to increase either the toughness of the metal or alloy or its ductility (its capacity to be drawn out into a different shape). These processes never strengthen the material.

4. QUENCHING AND TEMPERING. Most alloys, particularly steels, are hardened and strengthened by being heated, then cooled rapidly, most frequently by being plunged into water or cold oil—a process known as 'quenching'. Some materials, such as high-speed steels, are cooled more slowly in a blast of compressed air.

After quenching, many steels are too hard. If they were then either annealed or normalized they would become too soft, so the desired intermediate hardness is achieved by 'tempering' the quenched steel, a process in which the hard material is reheated to temperatures much lower than those used in annealing, normalizing, or quenching. The success of treatments for hardening and tempering depends on a knowledge of the structural changes produced in alloys containing more than one phase. Pure metals cannot be hardened by quenching.

For many centuries the only heat treatment generally practised was that intended to produce the required 'temper' in swords, knives, and other cutting tools. The steel used must have contained about 1 per cent. of carbon, and the sword or knife was heated, after shaping, to a warm-red heat which is about 760° to 780° C. Then it was quenched in cold water, thus becoming very hard. But it also became brittle and, though it would cut excellently after it was ground, it was liable to break because of its brittleness. It was therefore reheated, or tempered at fairly low temperatures, the degree of heating being regulated by the colour that developed on the clean surfaces of the steel. The colour was due to the formation of a thin film of oxide on the steel, and the particular hue was determined by the thickness of this film. The 'temper' colours produced by the various temperatures varied from light straw colour (230° C.) through shades of brown, purple, violet, blue, to grey (330° C.). As its temperature was raised the steel became less brittle and less likely to fracture.

5. CONTROL OF STRENGTH. The combined operation of quenching and tempering is now widely used to produce articles of high strength for modern engineering. Alloy steels, when quenched, may have a strength of 100 tons per square inch or even higher, but they are then rather brittle. By tempering them at temperatures between 300° and 600° C. their strengths may be reduced to 80, 75, 70, 60, or 50 tons per square inch and their brittleness diminished in proportion.

Typical changes in the properties of a strong steel are the following:

	Strength (Tons/sq. in.)	Toughness Ft. lb.
Before heat treatment . . .	60	4
After quenching	110	1
After quenching and then tempering at 200° C.	105	3
After quenching and then tempering at 400° C.	90	5
After quenching and then tempering at 600° C.	65	18

Some high-strength alloys of aluminium have the unusual characteristic that when quenching has been completed, the alloys, though soft, actually harden of their own accord at ordinary

Mond Nickel Co.

QUENCHING IN OIL FOR HARDENING

room temperatures. They do not suddenly become hard, but steadily increase in strength and hardness over a period of 2 or 3 days. Such an alloy which, when quenched, has a strength of 16 tons per square inch may have a strength of 21 tons per square inch at the end of 1 day and of 26 in 3 days. This spontaneous hardening is called 'ageing'. It can be prevented only by keeping the quenched alloy at a temperature of 40° C. below freezing-point for this period. Not all aluminium alloys have this characteristic; some alloys age very well if, after quenching, they are reheated to relatively low temperatures. Treated in this way quenched steels become softer; but quenched aluminium alloys become harder.

Here are test figures for one of these aluminium alloys:

	Strength (Tons/sq. in.)	Ductility Elongation%
Before heat treatment . . .	18	5
After quenching . . .	17	20
After quenching and reheating at 100° C.	20	15
After quenching and reheating at 185° C.	32	8

The properties of copper alloyed with about

Mond Nickel Co.

TEMPERING IN AN ELECTRIC FURNACE

$2\frac{1}{2}\%$ of beryllium are altered in a similar fashion by heat treatment, thus:

	Strength (Tons/sq. in.)	Ductility Elongation %
Before heat treatment . .	40	30
After quenching . . .	33	45
After quenching and reheating at 200° C.	50	30
After quenching and reheating at 350° C.	80	5

The rate of cooling of a heated substance when quenched is extremely important. A cooling treatment will fail unless the whole mass of material cools at more than a certain critical rate. This is difficult with a large mass of metal, for the inside has a natural tendency to remain very hot when the outside has already cooled and hardened. For that reason massive steel parts of engines, ships, and armaments are made in highly alloyed steels which will harden, though cooled at a lower rate than is necessary for unalloyed steels. The inside of a part made in the highly alloyed steel, though it cools during quenching less rapidly than the outside, cools quickly enough to become hard.

6. MECHANICAL HARDENING. Both metals and alloys may be deformed mechanically during the processes of manufacture and so hardened—a quite different process from heat treatment since it involves no changes in the phases of the alloys. Mechanical hardening often causes either pure metals or alloys to become so brittle that articles made of them have to receive heat treatment to avert the danger of fractures. All the mechanical hardening could be removed by fully annealing them, but some articles are more useful, and sufficiently safe, if some proportion of the hardening is left. The articles, therefore, are heated to relatively low temperatures—probably within the range of 150° to 300° C. according to the particular metal or alloy involved. Applied to steels this treatment is generally known as 'blueing', and as 'low-temperature annealing' in connexion with non-ferrous materials.

See also METALS; METALLURGY; ALLOYS.

HIGH-FREQUENCY CURRENTS. 1. These are ELECTRIC CURRENTS (q.v.) that flow in a wire first one way and then the other, reversing their direction as ALTERNATING CURRENT (q.v.) does, but at least 10,000 times a second and even very much faster instead of about 100 times a second. High-frequency currents which flow in aerial wires generate radio waves (see RADIO ENGINEERING), and are much used in radio transmitters and receivers. They are also important in ELECTRONICS and TELEPHONE ENGINEERING (qq.v.).

One complete to-and-fro surge of current is called an 'oscillation' cycle, and the number of cycles completed by the current per second is its frequency. The highest frequency currents used in radio engineering are those of about 10,000 to 100,000 million cycles per second.

High-frequency currents behave like ordinary electric currents in having magnetic effects and in heating the wires they flow through; but the wire carrying the high-frequency current gets hotter because the high-frequency current concentrates in a thin skin near the surface of the wire, whereas the direct current spreads evenly

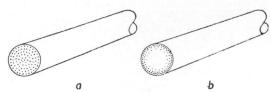

a   b

FIG. I. DISTRIBUTION OF ELECTRIC CURRENT IN WIRES
a. Direct current. b. High-frequency current

throughout the whole substance of the wire (*see* Fig. 1). The concentration of current near the outer surface means that wires offer higher electrical resistances (*see* ELECTRIC CURRENT, Section 3) to high-frequency than to direct currents —the higher the frequency the more the crowding and the higher the resistance. Wires for high-frequency currents—wireless aerials, for example —often consist of several thin strands, for this reduces their high-frequency resistance by increasing their surface area.

Very high-frequency electrical energy can be carried from place to place through hollow copper tubes, about 1 inch by ½ inch in cross-section,

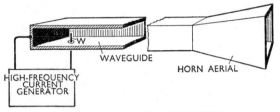

FIG. 2. DIAGRAM OF A WAVEGUIDE

The front wall of the waveguide has been removed and only the beginning and end are shown. w. Wire connected to generator causing electromagnetic wave to pass along waveguide

called waveguides. A high-frequency current passed into a short piece of wire at one end of the tube (*see* Fig. 2) causes an electromagnetic wave to travel along the waveguide. At the other end a high-frequency current can be induced in a similar piece of wire, or the wave can be launched into space to radiate as a free radio wave by opening out the end of the waveguide to make a horn. Waveguides and horns are used as the aerials in RADAR (q.v.), and the spreading waves from the horn are focused into a narrow beam by a reflector made of copper sheet, which acts like the reflector of a motor-car headlamp.

2. *Generation of high-frequency currents.* High-frequency currents are generated by producing

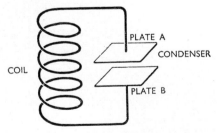

FIG. 3. TUNED ELECTRIC CIRCUIT PRODUCING HIGH-FREQUENCY CURRENT

oscillations in a 'tuned' electric circuit—that is, in its simplest form, a coil of wire joined to two metal plates which do not quite touch each other (Fig. 3). Two plates so arranged form an electric CONDENSER (q.v.) and can store a small quantity of electricity. When the condenser is joined for a short time to a battery, positive electricity collects on one plate and an equal amount of negative electricity collects on the other—thus 'charging' the condenser. If the plates of the charged condenser are now joined to the coil, as shown in Fig. 3, the positive charge flows as a current of electricity from plate A of the condenser to plate B, through the coil, and in passing produces a magnetic effect (*see* INDUCTION, ELECTRIC), which causes the flow to overshoot and so charge the condenser in the opposite direction. The positive charge, now on plate B of the condenser, once more flows back through the coil, and again overshoots, charging the condenser as it was at first. In this way the charge surges backwards and forwards, an oscillating electric current flowing through the coil; but as some of the charge is lost at each passage through the coil because of the resistance of the wire, the oscillations gradually die away (Fig. 4).

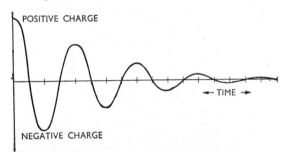

FIG. 4. GRAPH OF THE ELECTRIC CHARGE ON ONE PLATE OF THE CONDENSER IN A TUNED ELECTRIC CIRCUIT

The wavelength of a radio wave depends on the frequency of the oscillations in the transmitting aerial, and the frequency of the tuned circuit depends upon the electrical properties of the coil (its 'inductance') and of the condenser (its 'capacitance'). The inductance of the coil depends on the size of the coil and on the number of turns of wire. Just as the larger pipes of a church organ vibrate more slowly than the rest, the bigger a radio coil and the more numerous its turns, the greater the inductance and the lower is the oscillation frequency. For example, doubling the number of turns on a coil roughly halves the frequency. Again, the bigger the plates of a condenser and the closer they are together, the bigger is the capacitance and the lower the oscillation frequency. For example, doubling the dimensions of the plates roughly halves the frequency. A circuit, therefore, can be tuned to oscillate at a particular frequency by adjusting either the coil or the condenser.

Although in the ordinary way the resistance of the coil wire causes the oscillations to die away, they can be maintained at the same strength (or 'amplitude') by connecting a THERMIONIC VALVE (q.v.) to the tuned circuit; the valve controls the supply of electric power from a battery or dynamo in just the right way to keep the amplitude steady. It gives, as it were, an impulse or push at each oscillation, much as someone might keep a swing going by giving it a slight push once in each oscillation.

A thermionic valve is a device for passing or stopping a flow of electric current. Part of the valve, called the 'grid', has the power (in response to tiny changes in a small regulating current) to make large changes in the amount of main current passed by the valve. The oscillations in the original tuned radio circuit so influence the 'grid' that it makes the valve give the required push, while keeping precisely in step with the tuned circuit's frequency.

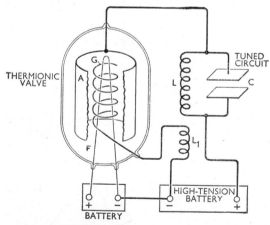

FIG. 5. DIAGRAM OF THE ELECTRIC CIRCUIT OF THE
THERMIONIC VALVE OSCILLATOR

L. Coil. C. Condenser. L_1. Second coil. A. Anode cut away
to show grid G, and cathode filament F

Fig. 5 is a simplified wiring diagram of the electrical circuit of a thermionic valve oscillator. The tuned circuit consists of the coil L and condenser C and is connected between the anode of the valve and the positive terminal of a high-

tension battery. A second coil L_1, with fewer turns, is placed close to L and connected between the grid and filament (or cathode) of the valve. The oscillating current in L creates an oscillating voltage by means of induction in L_1. This voltage in coil L_1, acting on the grid of the valve, controls the flow of current from the battery to the valve's anode. The anode current flows in impulses, one for each oscillation in the tuned circuit, and these impulses passing through the coil keep the oscillations going.

3. *Heterodyne.* It is a general principle of nature that when two waves or vibrations of different frequency are brought together, a third kind of wave is set up, usually much slower, which represents the difference in timing between the first two waves (*see* WAVE MOTION, Vol. III). The drumming sound from aircraft is a familiar instance of this 'beat', or heterodyne, the principle of which is widely used to improve the reception of wireless sets. In order to pick out clearly a wireless station from other stations of almost the same wavelength, a chain of magnifying circuits within the receiver must be tuned with great precision to an exact wavelength. Since it would be difficult to do this for each of the stations which the listener might wish to hear, the heterodyne method provides a solution by converting any signal to a fixed wavelength. The receiver's chain of circuits is permanently tuned to magnify signals of that exact wavelength. The set also contains a circuit which generates oscillations of its own, and this can be combined with the oscillations of the incoming signal to produce a 'beat' note of exactly the wavelength of the fixed magnifying equipment. This generating circuit can be tuned by turning the knob of a condenser so that the difference between the frequency of a selected station and that of the generated oscillations always yields a standard beat. For example:

	Oscillations per second		
	Incoming	Self-generated	Resulting 'beat' note
Light Programme . .	1,214,000	1,664,000	450,000
Northern Region . .	692,000	1,142,000	450,000
Third Programme . .	647,000	1,097,000	450,000

The 'beat' is not a sound wave, hence the term supersonic heterodyne, or 'superhet'. The whistle sometimes heard in a receiver is an unwanted heterodyne 'beat' caused by the receiver's oscillating circuit being out of step with that of a neighbour.

4. *Interference.* Every electric circuit, both for alternating and direct currents, has some inductance and some capacitance as well as resistance, and momentary high-frequency currents are produced in all circuits (even domestic lighting circuits) whenever they are switched on or off. These high-frequency currents usually die away quickly, as in Fig. 4, due to the resistance of the circuit, but when the resistance is low, they may be strong enough to produce radio waves that interfere with radio receivers. This happens particularly in the circuits of sparking plugs in motor-cars, and causes interference to TELEVISION receivers (q.v.).

5. *Piezo-electric vibrators.* There is nowadays such a large number of radio stations that to avoid serious interference each one must keep exactly to its correct wavelength. This is arranged by controlling very carefully the frequency of the high-frequency currents generated in the radio transmitter. For the very precise control of frequency needed for use in a radio transmitter a vibrating slice of quartz crystal is used. Quartz is a transparent, crystalline mineral, thin slices of which, about the size and shape of a halfpenny, are cut in a special direction by means of a revolving metal disk roughened with diamond dust. The thinner the slice the higher the frequency for which it is used.

When one of the quartz slices is squeezed between two metal plates, electricity is produced on its surface, a phenomenon called 'piezo-electricity' from a Greek word for 'pressure'. When the quartz slice with its two metal plates is connected into an electric circuit carrying a high-frequency current, then the slice vibrates in sympathy with the current. A quartz slice can be made to oscillate continuously in the same way as for a tuned circuit by connecting it to a thermionic valve. Quartz, being a very hard substance, changes very little, and so the frequency of the high-frequency current generated by a quartz-crystal-controlled valve oscillator is very constant. This kind of oscillator is used in almost all radio transmitters, and also in electronic timers (*see* ELECTRONICS).

See also ELECTRIC CURRENT; THERMIONIC VALVE; RADIO ENGINEERING; ELECTRONICS.

HIGH-SPEED PHOTOGRAPHY. Some
events which we may wish to study happen so

Prof. H. E. Edgeton

THE SUCCESSIVE BOUNCES OF A GOLF BALL
A series of high-speed flashlight exposures

quickly that they cannot be seen in detail by the human eye—for instance, a rocket projectile in flight, a rotating gear-wheel in a motor-car, the bursting of a tyre, or the explosion of gases in a coal-mine. Some, like a rocket or a bullet, move very quickly out of the field of view; others are completed in a very short time, like a tyre burst or explosion. All of them can be studied by 'slow motion' or 'high-speed' photography, in which pictures taken at a great speed are examined later at a slower speed. Non-luminous objects are in the dark until the moment of exposure, when they are illuminated by a bright light of short duration.

Ordinary CAMERAS (q.v.) never take photographs with exposures less than one-thousandth of a second, but a high-speed camera often makes an exposure of less than one-millionth of a second. In the cinema we see films projected at a speed of twenty-four pictures every second, the same speed at which they were taken in the film studio by the cameras (*see* CINEMATOGRAPHY); but high-speed films can be taken at a rate as high as one

BARN OWL WITH VOLE
Eric Hosking
A single flash photograph triggered by the bird in flight

million pictures per second. Such very short exposures and high picture rates produce both engineering and optical difficulties.

Single short-exposure pictures taken by the light of an electric spark were first made by the English photographic experimenter, Fox Talbot, a century ago, and the principle has been made use of by other photographers. Sometimes the electric spark is made to pass not through air but through special tubes filled with gases called xenon or argon, since these give more light. This is called 'flash' photography. Since the object is in the dark, the shutter can be open, for light reaches the film only for the duration of the flash. Any simple camera is satisfactory for taking such pictures, so long as it has an excellent quality LENS (q.v.)—particularly one of low F-number, to let in plenty of light. The only

essential point is that the image on the film must not be moved during the moment of the exposure.

With a normal cinematograph film, photographed and projected at 24 pictures per second, all movements in the film appear to take exactly the same time as they did in reality. If the film was taken at 100 times as fast a speed (2,400 pictures per second) and still projected at 24 pictures per second, then the apparent motion of the event on the film would be 100 times as slow as it was in reality. We have 'stretched' the time scale of the subject photographed. This is the principle of all high-speed films, however they are taken.

One of the difficulties in taking a series of pictures rapidly one after the other is in moving a new piece of film quickly enough into the focal plane of the camera lens in time for the next picture. For lower picture speeds, this is done discontinuously, that is to say, the film is stationary when the picture is taken. At higher speeds the film is moved at one continuous high rate; at higher speeds still it is wrapped on a rotating drum. At the highest speeds of all the pictures are formed as they are swept rapidly across the film by mirrors rotating at very high speeds.

A wide range of subjects has been photographed at high speed, particularly in engineering processes. The way in which metals, glass, or ceramics break under severe shocks can be filmed. WELDING arcs (q.v.) produce their own light for high-speed films showing their behaviour—so do high-tension sparks and lightning discharges. Diesel engine design has been greatly helped by special forms of high-speed cameras. In the design of jet-propelled aircraft, the new problems of flight at speeds faster than sound (*see* SUPERSONIC FLIGHT, Vol. IV) are studied and photographed first on models in WIND TUNNELS (q.v.). Machinery and machine tools yield up the reasons for their defective operation when filmed by these cameras. Military research owes much to high-speed photography. Projectiles are studied travelling in air, and weapons, such as torpedoes, underwater. Explosions in air and underwater have also been filmed with great success. Recent researches on nuclear explosions have all been helped by high-speed cameras.

Single short-exposure 'flash' pictures have been greatly used in studying bird movements. There is a flashlight photograph on p. 342 of Volume II of this Encyclopaedia, showing a redstart coming to its nest, and here we show a

Crown Copyright
A DIVER SWIMMING IN THE OCEAN WITH A SLOW-MOTION
CINE-CAMERA

barn owl in flight. Slow-motion films taken by high-speed cameras are also invaluable for studying movement. Such films have been taken by frogmen divers swimming under the sea with special cameras. There is much exciting work still to be done in these directions.

See also CAMERA; LENS; CINEMATOGRAPHY.

HIGH-VOLTAGE PARTICLE ACCELERATORS.

These are machines for producing high-speed streams of charged particles of great energy, which are used for studying the nucleus of the ATOM (q.v. Vol. III). The most useful particles are protons (hydrogen nuclei), deuterons (heavy hydrogen nuclei), and alpha-particles (helium nuclei), all of which are positively charged. The nucleus is also positively charged, so it repels the bombarding particles, which cannot enter it unless they are travelling very rapidly.

In 1932 Cockcroft and Walton made the first machine which could produce protons fast enough to disintegrate a nucleus. They used an ALTERNATING CURRENT, the voltage of which was stepped up by a TRANSFORMER to drive an arrangement of CONDENSERS and RECTIFIERS (qq.v.) called a 'cascade generator'. This produced direct current at 600,000 volts. The positive terminal of the generator in the Cockcroft–Walton machine is connected to the top and the negative terminal to the bottom of a long tube from which all the air has been pumped (see Fig. 1a). The voltage is used to drive protons down the tube. These protons are produced at the top of the tube in an ion source, which consists of a glass vessel containing a small amount of hydrogen gas into which fast electrons are injected from an electron gun similar to that used in a CATHODE RAY TUBE (q.v.). Some of the hydrogen atoms in the ion source are struck by fast electrons, losing their own electrons and leaving positively charged hydrogen nuclei or protons. Those protons which escape into the tube are accelerated down it, so that by the time they fall upon a target at the bottom they have a speed of about 10,000 kilometres a second. Some of them strike the nuclei of the atoms in the target, causing them to disintegrate. Similar machines, some of which give voltages up to 2 millions, are still in use in many laboratories.

The energies of the moving particles produced by accelerators are measured in electron-volts. A proton, which carries the same amount of electricity as an electron, having been accelerated

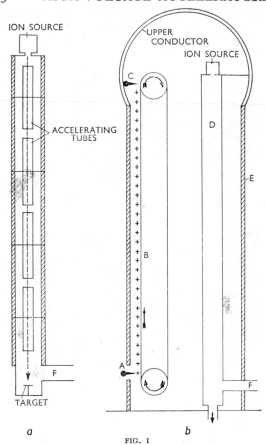

FIG. I

a. DIAGRAM OF ACCELERATING TUBE FOR COCKCROFT–WALTON MACHINE
The dotted line shows the path of the ions

b. DIAGRAM OF THE VAN DE GRAAFF ELECTROSTATIC GENERATOR

A. Comb for spraying charge on to belt. B. Moving belt. c. Comb for removing charge from belt. D. Accelerating tube. E. Insulating column. F. To vacuum pump

by a machine using 1 million volts, has an energy of 1 million electron-volts; but alpha-particles, which carry twice as much electricity as electrons, would have energies of 2 million electron-volts.

In 1936 Van de Graaff invented an accelerator which is often called after him (Fig. 1b). A moving belt of insulating material runs up inside an insulating column into the interior of a hollow conductor. Near the bottom of the belt is a row of metal points, like a comb, which is charged to about 10,000 volts, so that a current flows from the points to the belt. The belt carries the charge up into the hollow conductor, where a second comb removes it. The charge immediately runs to the outside of the hollow conductor, and is not

Professor P. B. Moon

A BEAM OF PARTICLES (DEUTERONS) EMERGING FROM A CYCLOTRON AND IONIZING THE AIR
A. Poles of electromagnet.   B. Vacuum tank.   C. Beam of particles

carried down again on the belt. The hollow conductor cannot be charged up indefinitely, because the charge begins to leak away, down the insulating column and through the gas surrounding the conductor. Nevertheless some Van de Graaff machines will produce more than 5 million volts. In nuclear research the Van de Graaff machine is fitted with an ion source and an evacuated tube for accelerating the particles, like those used in Cockcroft and Walton's machine. Protons, deuterons, and alpha-particles can be accelerated if the upper conductor is positively charged, and electrons if it is negatively charged.

Another important machine is the 'cyclotron', designed in the U.S.A. by E. O. Lawrence, which accelerates electrically charged particles by giving them a large number of small impulses instead of one big one (Fig. 2). Between the poles of a large electromagnet is a tank, from which all the air has been removed, and inside which is a flat hollow cylinder rather like a pill-box divided into two halves, known from their shape as 'dees'. The dees are connected to the terminals of a powerful source of high-frequency alternating current (much like the transmitter of a radio station). There is, therefore, a voltage between the two dees which continually reverses, so that each dee is alternately positive and negative,

FIG. 2. PLAN OF A CYCLOTRON
A. High-frequency alternating voltage. B. Ion source.
C. Deflector plate. D. Opening from which particles
emerge. The dotted line shows the path of the particles

several million times a second. The particles to be accelerated are released from an ion source at the centre, and because they are electrically

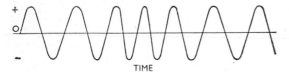

TIME

FIG. 3. DIAGRAM SHOWING THE VARYING FREQUENCY OF THE ALTERNATING VOLTAGE APPLIED TO THE DEES OF A SYNCHRO-CYCLOTRON

charged, when they move between the poles of the magnet, a force acts on them across the direction of motion, and causes them to move in semi-circles inside the dees. The machine is so arranged that every time the particles pass from one dee to the other the voltage between the dees attracts them across the gap, and so increases their speed, making them move in larger and larger semi-circles. They behave rather like a stone tied to a piece of elastic and whirled round: the faster the stone moves, the more the elastic stretches and the bigger the circle. When the particles reach the edge of the dees they can be drawn away from their circular paths by the attraction of a charged plate and made to come out of the cyclotron.

Cyclotrons have been built which give protons with energies of about 10 million electron-volts and alpha-particles of about 40 million electron-volts. But, as it is impossible for anything to move faster than the velocity of LIGHT (q.v. Vol. III), a point is reached at which the particles cannot go round fast enough to be in step with the accelerating voltage between the dees, and the machine ceases to work efficiently. This difficulty can be overcome by varying the rate at which the accelerating voltage reverses (*see* Fig. 3). Those particles which are approaching the outside of the dee during the time when the rate is becoming slower will be caught up and kept in step. When such a cyclotron, called a 'synchrocyclotron', is properly adjusted, the particles emerge bunched together in short bursts or pulses. Fewer particles are produced than from the ordinary cyclotron, but there is, theoretically, no limit to the energy which can be given to them. The size of a synchrocyclotron is limited only by its cost—chiefly the cost of the magnet. The first synchrocyclotron, built by Lawrence in California, had a magnet weighing 4,300 tons with pole faces 15 feet across. It produced sixty

bunches of particles a second and could give energies of about 400 million electron-volts to alpha-particles. A number of large synchro-cyclotrons have since been built, including two in Britain—one at Harwell and one at Liverpool.

The most important recent invention has been the 'synchrotron', a successful attempt to produce a machine using less costly magnets. It might be described as a cyclotron with the middle left out (Fig. 4). The accelerated particles are contained in a ring-shaped evacuated tube called a 'doughnut', and are made to follow a curved track by the forces acting on them from suitably placed magnets. At least once in each lap the particles are accelerated by passing between electrodes which are connected to a source of high-frequency voltage. The particles accelerate until, as they approach the speed of light, their own speed can become no greater, although their energy goes on increasing. Much skill is needed to design a machine in which the accelerating voltage and the particles keep in step, and in which the magnetic field is increased at the correct rate to prevent the particles getting lost by striking the walls of the doughnut. The first synchrotron, a very small one, used for accelerating electrons, began working at Malvern in 1946. Since then a number of synchrotrons for accelerating electrons to several hundred

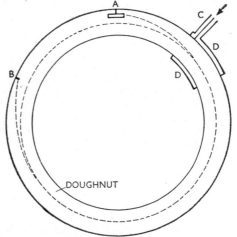

FIG. 4. PLAN OF THE DOUGHNUT OF A SYNCHROTRON

The dotted line shows the path of the particles from the electron source A to the target B. C. Source of power for acceleration. D. Accelerating electrodes

million electron-volts have been built, mostly in America.

Synchrotrons for accelerating protons are very

Nucleonics

THE LARGE PROTON SYNCHROTRON AT BROOKHAVEN, U.S.A., KNOWN AS THE COSMOTRON, WHICH ACCELERATES PROTONS TO ABOUT 3,000,000,000 ELECTRON-VOLTS

A. Magnet.   B. Doughnut.   C. Vacuum pumps

much larger than electron synchrotrons; the first to be operated, in America in 1952, has a diameter of 75 feet. It is called the Cosmotron, because it produces, every few seconds, bursts of protons with energies of 3,000 million electron-volts, about as much as some of the protons found in COSMIC RAYS (q.v. Vol. III). In 1954 work was started on two even larger proton synchrotrons, one in America and one in Geneva, both designed to produce particles with energies greater than 20,000 million electron-volts. The machine in Geneva is so expensive and requires the services of so many highly skilled engineers and scientists that it is only possible to construct and operate it with the international co-operation of most of the European countries.

The Cockcroft–Walton and the Van de Graaff particle accelerator machines were built to break up and study the structure of the lightest nuclei. The first cyclotrons were intended to investigate the heavier nuclei. In the meantime unstable particles called 'mesons', which are much heavier than electrons but lighter than protons, had been discovered in the cosmic radiation. One of these, called the π-meson, was believed to be responsible for holding the protons and neutrons in the nucleus together, and it was found that if the

nucleus was struck by particles of sufficient energy π-mesons could be created in the laboratory. Positively charged, negatively charged, and neutral π-mesons were first produced artificially by the large synchrocyclotron in California in 1948. Other kinds of mesons, heavier than the π-mesons, are being discovered in the cosmic radiation, as well as other unstable particles called 'hyperons', which are heavier than protons. The study of these new particles is revealing new secrets about the structure of matter, and much skill and energy is being devoted to building more and more powerful particle accelerators able to produce these particles in the laboratory.

See also NUCLEAR ENERGY; NUCLEAR POWER.
See also Vol. III: ATOM; COSMIC RAY; MATTER; RELATIVITY.

HOISTS, *see* CRANES.

HORSE-POWER, *see* MEASUREMENT, UNITS OF, Section 2c.

HYDRAULIC POWER TRANSMISSION. The first recorded use of a liquid under pressure for transmitting power between two points is attributed to Joseph Bramah (1748–1814), who employed the principle of hydraulic gearing on a press. Since then, there has been ever-increas-

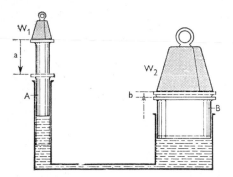

FIG. I. PRINCIPLE OF HYDRAULIC POWER TRANSMISSION
The force exerted by the weight w_1 in pressing down the piston A a distance a is equal to that exerted on the piston B to move the weight w_2 a distance b

ing use of this simple method; one of the most outstanding early examples being the movable roadway of London's Tower Bridge. Today its applications range from the most sensitive devices controlling the flight of aeroplanes to huge presses that can exert a force of 12,000 tons weight or more.

If a leakproof plug or piston is fitted to one end of a pipe, the pressure of the liquid in the pipe will exert a force on the piston proportional to the magnitude of the pressure and the area of the piston (see PRESSURE, Vol. III). If the pipe has a piston at each end and a force is applied to one piston (A), it will generate a pressure in the liquid, which in its turn will exert the same force on the other piston (B) (see Fig. 1). The volume displaced by the movement of one piston must be equal to that taken up by the other; the larger one (B), therefore, will move a shorter distance than the small one (A), but, since (B) has a greater area, it will exert a correspondingly larger force. The work done, which is the combined effect of force and the distance through which it moves, is, of course, the same for both pistons. If, therefore, the piston (A) is 10 square inches and is moved 10 inches by a weight of 10 lb., the piston (B), 100 square inches in area, will move a weight of 100 lb. one inch. This follows the same principle as a simple LEVER (q.v.), in which one point on the lever moves through a large distance under a small force, whilst the other end of the lever moves through a smaller distance but exerts a correspondingly larger force.

The hydraulic press, perhaps the simplest practical application of this principle, has a cylinder fitted with a large piston which moves through a comparatively short stroke and exerts a large force. The supply of liquid for this is provided by a pump, which has one or more small cylinders and pistons operating rapidly through small distances to convert the power of the driving motor or engine into a powerful but slow-moving force at the press. The application of hydraulic power transmission in aeroplanes is much more complicated; it is used for all those services which are too heavy to be operated manually by the crew—for example, lifting the retractable landing gear, lowering the landing flaps, and operating the control surfaces which direct the flight of the machine. Hydraulic power is generated by pumps driven from the engines; control is provided by valves operated by the

High Duty Alloys

A 12,000-TON HYDRAULIC FORGING PRESS

crew; and the power is developed by cylinders and pistons (known as jacks), which are fed by a

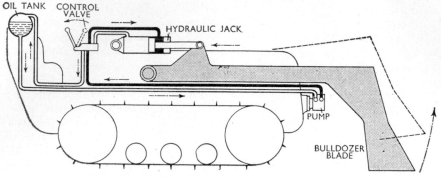

FIG. 2. DIAGRAM OF A HYDRAULIC BULLDOZER

network of pipes winding through the crowded interior of the machine. These pipes conveying the fluid power can run along any convenient path, and bend round corners—a great advantage over a mechanical system where gears or link mechanisms are needed for each change in direction.

The fluid normally used is light oil. A thick, treacle-like fluid would offer too much resistance when flowing through the pipes and valves, but the light oil fluid flows easily and freely. Water itself is used where large quantities of fluid are needed, as for large presses or hydraulic bridges. For smaller systems, such as those on an aeroplane, a very thin oil is better, and also has the advantage that it does not freeze at low temperatures.

Some of the many applications of hydraulics are in everyday use. The bulldozer tractor, for example, is fitted with a hydraulically operated scraper for moving earth (Fig. 2). The externally mounted hydraulic jacks can be seen attached to the arms holding the scraper, which they raise and lower in response to the driver's control valve. This directs the flow of power from a small pump, driven by the tractor engine, which draws oil from a tank mounted behind the driver's seat. A simple example of the use of hydraulics purely as a reduction gear or lever is the self-contained hydraulic car jack (Fig. 3). Fluid pressure is generated by working a small hand pump, which draws oil from a container in the base of the jack and delivers it under pressure to the lifting piston. Hydraulic brakes are used on the majority of modern motor-cars. The foot-brake pedal is connected to a piston which,

when operated, forces fluid through pipes to each wheel brake. Within the brakes are pistons and cylinders which expand the brake shoes when pressure is applied. The equal pressure throughout the hydraulic fluid ensures that the

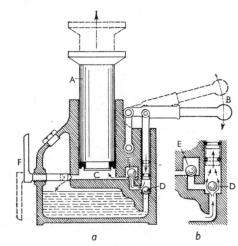

FIG. 3. DIAGRAM OF A CAR JACK

a. Jack in position for lifting. *b.* Valves in position for drawing oil into pump. A. Lifting piston. B. Hand pump. C. Cylinder. D. Pump inlet valve. E. Pump outlet valve. F. Lowering valve (shown closed)

braking force is the same at each wheel (*see* BRAKES AND BRAKING).

See also ENERGY.
See also Vol. III: PRESSURE.

HYDRAULICS. 1. This is the study of how liquids behave when flowing in pipes, channels, and rivers, and when passing through mechanical apparatus such as pumps and turbines. It is based on the theory of HYDRODYNAMICS (q.v.), which is the study of the motion, pressure, and energy of fluids in general.

In order to study more clearly the behaviour of moving liquids, engineers have invented the idea of an 'ideal fluid', one not affected by any disturbances such as FRICTION (q.v.), and they calculate how this would behave in given circumstances. In an ideal fluid, the particles of which it is composed would flow past each other when in motion without friction. Water, however, is not an ideal fluid, but like an extremely thin oil; so unless it is moving very slowly, the particles rub against each other, causing eddies, and this effect is increased by friction against the sides of the pipe or other passage in which the water is flowing. This type of flow, which is what occurs in most circumstances, is said to be 'turbulent' (in contrast to the 'streamline' flow of an ideal fluid). The theory of turbulent flow, which is rather complicated, is based partly on the theoretical behaviour of an ideal fluid and partly on the results of experiments, by which many problems can be solved with sufficient accuracy.

2. *Pipes.* Water, unless it is forced, will flow only downhill. For instance, if a length of hose-pipe is fixed to the bottom of an open water-tank and its outlet is held up to the same level as that of the water-level in the tank, no water will flow out of the pipe. If the outlet is gradually lowered, water will begin to flow, the rate increasing as the lowering is continued. An imaginary sloping straight line over the pipe joining the water-level in the tank and the outlet of the pipe (Fig. 1) is called the 'hydraulic slope or gradient', and is one of the factors that control the rate of flow. The other two factors are the size of the pipe and the roughness of its internal surface. The latter has a very marked effect on the flow; if a smooth pipe becomes badly encrusted inside, the water flow through it may be reduced to only half the original rate

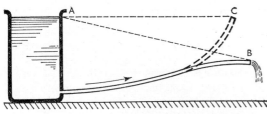

FIG. 1. DIAGRAM OF THE HYDRAULIC SLOPE OR GRADIENT

A. Water-level in tank. B. Outlet of pipe. The line AB is the hydraulic slope. If the pipe rose to the water-level AC there would be no flow

Water flowing in a pipe is usually under some pressure. If an open-ended vertical glass tube were inserted into the pipe, the water would rise in the tube up to a level corresponding to the pressure at that point (*see* PRESSURE GAUGES). If the rise is, say, 5 feet, the pipe is said to be under a 'head' of 5 feet of water. The weight of a water-column with a cross-section of 1 square inch and a height of 1 foot is 0·433 lb. Hence, a head of 5 feet of water is equivalent to a pressure of $0·433 \times 5 = 2·16$ lb. per square inch. Thus head and pressure are the same thing expressed in different ways.

For many purposes it is more convenient to express water pressure in terms of head. For instance, the water mains in a street must be under sufficient head in order to force the water to the top floors of the highest houses. If the houses are, say, 40 feet high, the mains must be under a head of, say, 50 feet at least to enable the water to flow into the houses at a satisfactory rate. Reservoirs are placed on high ground to provide the necessary head for the supply to houses at lower levels (*see* WATER SUPPLY).

3. *Weirs.* A common method of measuring the flow in an existing channel is to construct across it a low wall, or weir, high enough to allow the water a clear fall on the downstream side. The height of the water-level on the upstream side above the weir increases with the volume of flow; this height is known as the 'head' over the weir. There is a definite relation between the head and the rate of flow, so that if the head is measured, the flow can be calculated from a suitable formula.

4. *Orifices.* Another method of measuring water flow is to allow it to flow into an open tank, in the side of which, near the bottom, is a circular orifice or hole. When the flow is steady, the water will stand at a definite height above the orifice. This is also known as the 'head' over the orifice; it will increase or decrease if the flow varies, and can therefore be used to calculate the rate at which the water is flowing into the tank and out of the orifice.

5. *Venturi principle.* A fundamental property of a moving fluid is a definite relation between its pressure and its velocity; if the velocity increases, the pressure decreases, and vice versa.

If a horizontal pipe is gradually tapered down to a smaller size and then tapered out again to the original size, the velocity of the water flowing in it would gradually increase to a maximum rate at the 'throat', or narrowest part, and then decrease to the original velocity on reaching the wider part of the pipe again. Vertical glass tubes are inserted at the beginning of the upstream taper and at the throat; the higher velocity, and therefore the lower pressure, at the throat causes the water-level in the tube at that point to be substantially lower than at the upstream end of the taper. There is, in fact, a definite relation between the difference between these two levels and the rate of flow in the pipe. This is the principle of the 'venturi meter' which is widely used for measuring pipe-flow.

The same principle may also be applied to the flow in an open channel if the sides are gradually narrowed and then expanded to the original width. The higher velocity as the water passes through the gap causes the level to be lowered at that point, the amount of the depression being a measure of rate of flow in the main channel. This local lowering of level may often be seen when a river flows between the abutments of a bridge.

Fox Photos. Ltd.

MODEL OF THE RIVER DEE

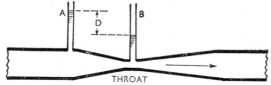

FIG. 2. HOW A VENTURI METER WORKS

The differences of water-level D in tubes A and B is the measure of the rate of flow in the pipe. If the flow increases the difference also increases and vice versa

6. *Water power*. Water possesses ENERGY (q.v.), or the ability to do work, for two reasons, (*a*) owing to its weight when moving under the force of gravity, as when it turns the wheel of a watermill, and (*b*) owing to its velocity, as when it turns the impeller of an impulse turbine.

The rate of water doing work, whether due to pressure or velocity, or a combination of both, constitutes water power; the amount of power, usually expressed as horse-power, depends upon the rate of flow and the pressure or head under which it is used (*see* WATER POWER).

7. *Hydraulic models*. Some hydraulic problems too complicated to be solved by direct calculations can be solved to a high degree of accuracy by experiments with models. Models can be altered and re-altered until the desired result is obtained, and the full-sized works are not constructed until engineers have found out how best

to design them. For instance, a model was made when the channels in the estuary of the River Dee between Chester and the open sea had to be improved in order to maintain a sufficient depth of water for shipping. Trouble was caused by sandbanks changing position owing to the action of the tides combined with the varying flow of the river. This could be put right by constructing long artificial banks called 'training walls', but it was difficult to decide where best to place these walls. So a model of the whole estuary was built, together with hydraulic apparatus for imitating the flow of the river and the rise and fall of the tides on a small scale. Experiments with model training walls in various positions showed exactly where the actual walls should be placed to maintain a permanent deep-water channel in the estuary.

See also HYDRODYNAMICS; WATER POWER; MODEL ENGINEERING.

HYDRODYNAMICS. This is the science which deals with the motion of fluids (liquids and gases) and in particular with the pressures, velocities, and patterns of motion which may occur under various conditions (for example, when an aeroplane moves through air). Modern hydrodynamics is concerned to a very large extent with problems arising in aerodynamics, and the rapid development of the aeroplane has greatly extended its scope.

To solve problems concerned with the flow of a fluid, we can carry out experiments and calculate probable answers by assuming certain properties for the fluid and relying purely on the theories of MECHANICS (q.v.) and allied sciences. The experiments are a check that the theoretical ideas are sound, and the theory can be used to indicate results outside the range of the experiments.

The main difficulty is that if the theory is to take into account the fact that real fluids can be compressed, are viscous ('sticky') to some degree, and conduct heat, the mathematics often becomes much too complicated. Accordingly, the scientist of the 18th century investigated what would be the properties of an 'ideal fluid', which was, for instance, incompressible, inviscid (not sticky), or non-conducting. The simplest 'ideal fluid' which can be imagined would have all these properties. Parts of the theory of its motion agree with the observed behaviour of water or air at low speeds, but others do not. For instance, a body moving steadily through an 'ideal fluid' would not, according to such a theory, suffer any resistance to its motion, whereas any cyclist knows that this result is not correct for air. On the other hand, it was found possible to estimate the lift of an aeroplane wing quite accurately by applying this theory. It was important to discover why the theory was reliable only in some conditions and to improve on it.

In 1904 the German scientist Ludwig Prandtl introduced the idea of the 'boundary layer'. The viscosity of a fluid passing near the surface of a body causes it to 'stick' to the surface, thus slowing it down. If the viscosity of the fluid is small, as in air, this slowing down is noticeable only quite close to the surface of the body, and the layer of fluid affected in this way is called the 'boundary layer'. Prandtl showed that, outside this layer, the fluid behaves almost exactly like an ideal fluid, with no viscosity. The boundary layer is responsible for the resistance of the body, partly because dragging the viscous fluid along the surface produces a frictional force, and partly because it has the effect of altering the shape of the body so far as the flow outside the boundary layer is concerned. Under some conditions the boundary layer may produce a large region of irregular flow, with a very high resistance. This

is what happens when a wing stalls (*see* FLYING, Section 3, Vol. IV). A large amount of the flow about a body may therefore be considered by mathematical methods based on ideal fluids, and it is possible to calculate some of the properties of the boundary layer itself by mathematics, sometimes to the extent of calculating the drag.

Some of the terms used in hydrodynamics have passed into ordinary conversation: 'streamline', for example. A streamline is an imaginary line in the fluid showing the direction of the flow. The particles pass downstream along the streamlines, which therefore cannot cross one another. Since it follows that fluid cannot flow across a streamline, a group of streamlines can be thought of as defining the surface of a 'tube'. All the fluid in this 'tube' will remain in it. Where the streamlines are close together, as at A in Fig. 1, the tubes are thinner, and in order to pass the same quantity of fluid in the same time the fluid must be moving faster than it is at B, where they are wider apart. These properties only apply when the flow is incompressible and steady, that is, when the velocity at any point stays the same at all times. The effect can easily be seen in the con-

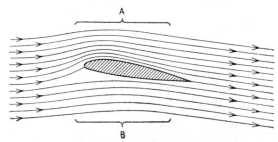

FIG. 1. AIRSTREAM FLOWING PAST AN AIRCRAFT WING
Streamlines are closer together at A than at B

trast between fast, shallow rapids of mountain streams and the slow, deep pools.

In a moving fluid, part of the ENERGY (q.v.) in it is potential energy due to its pressure and part is kinetic energy due to its speed. In a 'tube' the sum of these two parts always remains the same. Therefore, if the velocity is less, as it would be in a wide part of a 'tube', then the kinetic energy is less, and so the pressure increases. Where the velocity is greater (at some narrower part of the tube), then the pressure decreases. So when the airstream is flowing past an aircraft wing, and the shape of the wing causes it to flow more quickly past the upper than past the lower surface of the wing, the pressure on the upper surface is less than that on the lower surface. This, in fact, is what gives lift to the aircraft (*see* FLYING, Section 1, Vol. IV). The relationship between the pressure and velocity of moving fluid is made use of in WIND TUNNELS and in one kind of PUMP (qq.v.).

The English scientist Osborne Reynolds discovered a very useful relationship between the quantities that occur in the theory of the flow of viscous fluids. He found that if the experimenter knew in one particular case the velocity (*v*) of the airstream, the length (*l*) of the body past which the fluid was flowing, and the density (*d*) and viscosity (*μ*) of the fluid, then he could apply this knowledge to different velocities, lengths, densities, or viscosities provided he kept $\dfrac{vld}{\mu}$ constant.

So an experiment on a small model at high speed was equivalent to one on, for instance, a full-size aeroplane at a correspondingly lower speed. This is much used in applying the results of experiments in wind tunnels. The relationship $\dfrac{vld}{\mu}$ is called the Reynolds number.

In Fig. 1 the streamlines are smooth, gentle curves, and the particles of the fluid are moving in a regular, orderly fashion. In many cases, however, the particles may move in a very irregular fashion, which changes from one moment to the next. The flow is then said to be 'turbulent' and it is no longer possible to draw a diagram of the streamlines, such as Fig. 1, which shows the exact flow at all instants. Such a diagram will now show only the average flow over a period of time. In practice, most fluid flows are found to have a certain amount of turbulence, and wind

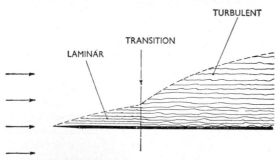

FIG. 2. GROWTH OF A BOUNDARY LAYER AND TRANSITION ON A FLAT PLATE IN A UNIFORM AIRSTREAM
The thickness of the boundary layer is greatly exaggerated

tunnels are carefully designed to reduce the turbulence as much as possible. Turbulence is particularly important in the boundary layer, since the agitated and irregular motion of the particles produces considerable friction as they move past the surface. If the boundary layer can be kept 'laminar'—that is, smooth and free from turbulence, this skin friction, as it is called, is greatly reduced. Modern wing sections, therefore, are often designed to keep as much as possible of the boundary layer laminar. A boundary layer, which is laminar near the front of a wing section, will usually become turbulent quite suddenly, at a point called the 'transition point' (Fig. 2). The position of this point depends among other things on the size and shape of the wing section, the angle of attack, the smoothness of the surface, the turbulence of the mainstream, and the Reynolds number.

In modern aerodynamics where the speeds are very high, a more complicated theory must be used. If a fluid were really incompressible, any pressure change at a particular point would cause a disturbance which would travel at infinite speed through the fluid. In a real compressible fluid such as air, the speed at which a pressure change travels is high, but by no means infinite. Its speed depends on the size of the pressure change, but if this is very small its speed is fixed. The speed at which a very small pressure change travels through a fluid is called 'the speed of sound', since SOUND (q.v. Vol. III) is merely a series of very small pressure changes.

If a body (let us say an aeroplane) is moving very slowly through air, the small changes of pressure which occur near it produce effects which travel in all directions at the speed of sound (about 760 miles per hour). One might say that the air ahead of the aeroplane received warning of its approach, and in Fig. 1 the streamlines ahead of the wing are already spreading out. If the speed of the aeroplane is fairly near the speed of sound, the air ahead of the aeroplane may be imagined to receive less warning of its approach, and the pattern of the flow becomes rather different. When the aeroplane is travelling at more than the speed of sound, the air ahead of it cannot receive any warning and must make way for the aeroplane suddenly and unexpectedly. This produces a distinct discontinuity in the flow, called a 'shock wave' (Fig. 3). This shows that the speed of the aeroplane compared with the speed of sound is most important. Their ratio is called the 'Mach Number'. The speed of sound, though 760 m.p.h. at sea-level,

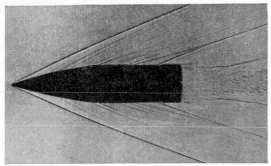

FIG. 3. TWO-POUNDER PROJECTILE TRAVELLING AT 2½ TIMES THE SPEED OF SOUND

depends on the air temperature, and so decreases the higher one goes, to about 660 m.p.h. in the stratosphere.

The shock waves produced when an aeroplane flies at Mach 1 (that is, when its speed is the same as the speed of sound), or faster, may reach an observer on the ground, causing the well-known 'sonic bang'.

HYDRO-ELECTRIC POWER. Water power, unlike coal and oil, is inexhaustible, for it is continually renewed by nature; and hydro-electricity—electricity generated from water power—is becoming increasingly important. Only a small proportion, perhaps no more than $\frac{1}{25}$th, of the possible water power schemes, excluding the power of the tides, has so far been developed in the world. Potential water power is not evenly distributed over the world. In France, for instance, where hydro-electric power is called 'white coal', about half the power comes from water; in Britain only 3 or 4% does; while in countries such as Norway, Sweden, and Canada nearly all the power is developed from water.

Water can be made to turn a water-wheel or turbine (*see* WATER POWER), and this in turn can be made to drive an ELECTRIC GENERATOR (q.v.).

The simplest form of water power scheme is well illustrated at NIAGARA FALLS (q.v. Vol. III). Some of the river water is led into a canal above the Falls, and this flows through tunnels and pipes to a power station below. This 'run-of-the-river' scheme at Niagara develops over 1 million horse-power. But in very few places in the world are the conditions so ideal. Generally it is necessary to build a DAM (q.v.) in order to provide a reservoir to even out the flow of water through the summer and winter and through dry years

and wet years. Sometimes it is necessary to link a number of reservoirs together by means of canals and tunnels and to divert water from one catchment area to another in order to obtain sufficient water. But once sufficient water is available it is often possible to use the same water again and again for power production in a series of POWER STATIONS (q.v.) down the course of a river valley on its way to the sea. The ST. LAWRENCE in Canada, the NILE in Africa (qq.v. Vol. III), the Rhône in France, and many other great rivers are being harnessed in this way. Care has to be taken in such schemes to see that other things such as water supply, irrigation, natural amenities, and fisheries are not adversely affected.

The shorter the distance between the reservoir and the power station in individual schemes the better, so long as this is consistent with obtaining

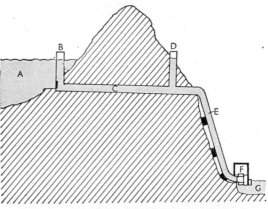

FIG. 1. DIAGRAM OF A TYPICAL HYDRO-ELECTRIC INSTALLATION

A. Storage reservoir. B. Intake shaft. C. Tunnel. D. Surge shaft. E. Pressure pipeline (penstock). F. Power station with turbine and generator. G. Tail race

the greatest possible head of water. Sometimes the power station forms part of the dam, as in the Pitlochry Scheme built for the North of Scotland Hydro-Electric Board (*see* Colour Plate, opp. p. 224). Sometimes, the water is led away from the reservoir through a tunnel to a point on a steep hillside where it drops through steel pipes called 'penstocks' to a power station in the valley below. Such tunnels are usually laid to a slight gradient and are lined with concrete to reduce friction and to avoid blocking by debris.

The pressure pipes forming the penstocks may have to withstand the force of very high heads of water, the highest at present being just over 5,500 feet in Switzerland. In such cases a modern

English Electric Co.

PENSTOCKS DESCENDING TO THE LOCH SLOY POWER STATION BUILT FOR THE NORTH OF SCOTLAND HYDRO-ELECTRIC BOARD

method of strengthening the steel pipes is to bind them with tensioned steel wire, similar to the method used in strengthening a gun barrel. Special precautions have to be taken to prevent the pressure pipes bursting when a machine in the power station is shut down. A relief 'valve', generally in the form of a vertical shaft open to the air, is usually built at the end of the tunnel just before the water enters the penstock, and this allows the water to rise to the top level of the reservoir with sufficient margin to take up the surge when the flow of water is suddenly stopped.

One of the most remarkable developments in recent years in water power schemes has been the lodging of the power houses in chambers excavated out of the rock. Improved rock excavation methods have made this possible, and the lack of space for an outside station in a river gorge, as well as the need for protection from aerial attack, have given great impetus to this development.

Two difficult problems which hydro-electric schemes have to face in comparison with other forms of power are the higher cost of civil engineering work such as dams, tunnels, and penstocks, and the fact that the best sites (hilly or mountainous country with heavy rainfall) are often far from centres of population or industry. In Britain the initial cost of hydro-electric schemes is two to three times that of a power station using coal as fuel; though once the scheme is built, the running costs are very much smaller, since nature, in the form of rain and gravity, does all the work. Increases in fuel prices and reduced rates of interest for financing schemes have, however, improved the comparative position in favour of hydro-electric power. The difficulties of location have been reduced by improvements in transmitting the electric power, the maximum distance at present being about 600 miles in Sweden. Where there is a network of transmission lines connecting a number of power stations, as in Britain, the available water power can be used more economically than in individual schemes.

An important factor of hydro-electric schemes is the preservation of amenities, including salmon fishing. Hydro-electric plant is often installed amidst some of the finest natural scenery, and this need not be scarred, provided care is taken in the design and layout. There is also no need to spoil the salmon fishing. A series of ponds, known as salmon ladders, are built at the side of the

dams; each has a difference in level of about 18 inches, and water flows down the ladder from pool to pool up which the salmon jump. These ladders are costly, however, for a high dam, and so a scheme of water lifts has been developed in Scotland. These are sloping tunnels with trap doors at the top and the bottom. When the bottom door is closed and the top one opened, the water level rises, bringing any salmon trapped in the lift up to the top reservoir level (*see* SALMON, Vol. II).

See also WATER POWER; DAMS; ELECTRIC GENERATORS; BOULDER DAM; KITIMAT HYDRO-ELECTRIC SCHEME; TENNESSEE VALLEY AUTHORITY.

HYDROGRAPHY. Hydrography (from two Greek words meaning 'water-writing') is the science of surveying and mapping seas, lakes, and rivers. These 'sea-maps' are called CHARTS (q.v. Vol. IV). Every sea and coast important to navigation has now been charted, and three nations (Britain, France, and the U.S.A.) publish a set of charts covering the world.

Charts of the sea, particularly near the coast, and of the navigable parts of rivers are of vital importance to shipping. They must show not only the depth of water but also the range of tides, the speed and direction of currents, the shape of the coast-line, important landmarks and hills, and the position of buoys, light vessels, and lighthouses.

Perhaps the most important part of the hydrographer's work is to discover and record the depth of the sea bed so that he can plot the position of shoals (shallow water) and reefs (ridges of rock, shingle, or sand). He does this by 'soundings'. For many generations the traditional method of sounding was for a seaman, standing in the bows of a ship, to drop a lead weight on the end of a thin line until it struck the bottom. Various objects were tied to the line, marking off each fathom (6 feet), so that when the line went slack, showing that the lead had touched bottom, the seaman was able to call out the depth. The practical limit of this kind of work was about 100 fathoms. During the 19th century ships taking soundings in deep water began to use machinery for casting and hauling in the line, and fine wire was used up to 5,000 fathoms (6 miles).

Various other sounding methods have been devised, but they have all now been largely superseded by the 'echo-sounding apparatus'. This emits a sound-signal and 'hears' and registers the echo which is thrown back by the sea bed. As the speed of sound in sea water is known, the time taken by the signal to travel to the bottom and back gives the depth of water. The signal— a short sound, so high-pitched as to be inaudible to the human ear—is given out by an electrically vibrated metal plate, called an oscillator, fitted on the bottom of the ship (*see* ULTRASONICS); the echo is picked up by a receiver working on the same principle, and operates a pen which makes a mark on a roll of paper moved by clockwork. The distance of the mark from a straight line on the paper is in proportion to the depth of the water. This apparatus can take nine soundings every second, and as the ship or boat moves along, the marks on the paper form a continuous record of the depths of water under its keel. The positions of the soundings are then measured and charted.

HEAVING THE LEAD
19th-century engraving, by G. Cruikshank

At sea, when out of sight of land, all positions are found from the sun or stars by means of a SEXTANT (q.v. Vol. IV). The shape of the coast-line and the positions of other features on land or close to the shore are charted by triangulation (*see* SURVEYING).

A simple way of measuring the speed and direction of currents is by observing the movement of a floating object, such as a piece of wood to which a flag is attached. Currents can also be measured beneath the surface, and this is done by suspending a sheet of canvas at the required depth, with a float attached by wires. The position of the float is measured at intervals by a sextant from a boat, or by a theodolite (*see* SURVEYING INSTRUMENTS) from the land.

These methods have now been largely superseded, however, by apparatus known as a current meter. This torpedo-shaped object, which is fitted with a propeller and a compass, is suspended from a moored ship or buoy in such a way that it can swing to face the current. The speed of the current is measured by the revolutions of the propeller, and its direction by the compass. These two measurements are either recorded by an instrument in the meter, or automatically broadcast by a radio transmitter in the meter and picked up by a receiver on land.

Tide gauges, and sometimes tide recorders, are installed in all harbours. Tide recorders consist of a float housed in a well, the bottom of which is open to the sea. As the float rises and falls it operates a pen which records the level on a roll of paper moved by clockwork. Tide gauges consist simply of a vertical wooden board, marked in feet and divisions of feet, fixed to a post or on the dock walls. These, and other records made by various methods all over the world through the years, are compared, the positions of the sun and moon in relation to the earth, which are the causes of TIDES (q.v. Vol. III), being also taken into account. In this way tidal ranges and currents are gradually recorded and charted.

The mapping of rivers is a very important branch of hydrography, though this word is now usually applied only to navigable waters. Hydrology is the term generally used for the study of inland rivers and streams, and how their flow is affected by rainfall and weather conditions generally.

In designing IRRIGATION schemes (q.v. Vol. VI), methods of FLOOD CONTROL, HYDRO-ELECTRIC POWER projects, DAMS (qq.v.), or indeed any

Kelvin & Hughes Ltd.

A SHIP MASTER READING THE DEPTH UNDER HIS KEEL
ON THE CHART OF AN ECHO-SOUNDER

amount and nature of the silt and other matter which the river carries. Investigations of this kind are the special responsibility of hydrological surveyors.

To calculate the flow of a river, the surveyor measures the depths from bank to bank at a certain place, and so works out the cross-section of the water (in square feet). He also measures the speed of the current (in feet per second), by methods similar to those used to measure currents at sea, at various points across the river and at various depths, and works out the average. The cross-section multiplied by the average speed gives the flow (in cubic feet per second). The 'mean flow' is based on many such measurements taken over a period of years. The amount of silt is discovered by analysing examples of the water taken at different points at various depths and times.

See also Vol. III: TIDES; RIVERS; OCEANS.
See also Vol. IV: CHARTS.

HYDROMETER, *see* BUOYANCY.

HYGROMETER, *see* METEOROLOGICAL INSTRUMENTS, Section 4.

structure in or near a river, records are required of the variations in the flow of the water at different seasons and from year to year, and of the

I

ILLUMINATION. This is the art and science of applying light, either natural or artificial, so that we may see and enjoy our surroundings in safety and comfort. In this article we are concerned with the artificial illumination of large buildings and streets; domestic lighting and the history of lighting are dealt with in the article LIGHTING, HISTORY OF, in Volume XI.

Artificial lighting of large areas first became practicable when in 1784 the Argand oil lamp burner was introduced. This used a tubular wick so that air could be drawn into the centre of the flame (see COMBUSTION), giving a much stronger light. Further progress was made when towards the end of the 18th century gas lighting was introduced; but the main developments in illumination have followed the introduction, in the late 19th century, of electric power for lighting.

Arc lamps, in which light is given out by an electric current passing between two carbon rods, were demonstrated by Sir Humphry DAVY (q.v. Vol. V) in 1810; these were the first successful electric lamps. They were too large and inconvenient for use in the home, but many were installed in streets, theatres, factories, and some lighthouses. They are still used to some extent in theatres and in cine-projectors.

The invention by Swan and EDISON (q.v. Vol. V) of practicable carbon filament electric light bulbs in 1878–9 started the modern electric lamp industry. In spite of their low efficiency—most of the electrical energy was converted into heat instead of light—these lamps were widely used because of their convenience. As the result of intensive research, fine wires made of metals of high melting-point—osmium, tantalum, and, later, tungsten—made it possible to increase the efficiency of filament lamps some three and a half times. Further improvements have produced

our modern incandescent tungsten filament lamps, with a further increase of efficiency. Glare from the bright filaments has been reduced by using diffusing bulbs—that is, by 'pearling' the glass by etching it with acid, and recently by coating the inside of the bulb with microscopic spheres of silica to give the 'silver light' lamp.

The efficiency of filament lamps is limited by the maximum temperature that can be used without causing them to burn out quickly. A study was made, therefore, of the light radiated from gases or vapours when electric currents were passed through them, and it was found that the amount (and colour) of the light thus obtained is characteristic of the gas or vapour rather than of its temperature.

In 1932 two practical electric discharge lamps were introduced. In one of these, the light source is glowing sodium vapour (see ALKALIS, Vol. VII) which emits light of a single colour—yellow. In the other the light source is glowing mercury vapour (see METAL ORES, Vol. III) at high pressure, which emits a mixture of violet, green, and yellow light. These lamps were introduced primarily for street lighting. Since they radiate three to four times as much light as can be obtained from an incandescent filament lamp consuming the same amount of electricity, their introduction made possible tremendous advances in street lighting. They are now used throughout the world for this purpose. Their application indoors, however, is limited by their colour, but mercury lamps are used extensively for factory lighting, usually mingled with incandescent lamps which add red light to improve the colour of the light from the high-pressure mercury lamp. Fluorescent materials were also developed which, when coated on to the inside of the lamp, could change unwanted ultra-violet radiation from the electric discharge into useful red light.

Impressed by the good colour of the light obtained from fluorescent materials, research workers set out to design an electric discharge lamp which would give as its main radiation invisible ultra-violet rays, which could then be changed by the fluorescent materials into light. In the modern tubular fluorescent lamp, the electric current passes through low-pressure mercury vapour in a glass tube to generate ultra-violet rays; these are converted into light by a fluorescent powder coating on the inside of the tube. White light can be obtained at between three

Above: Clunie Dam which has enlarged Loch Tummel. Water is led to Clunie generating station through a tunnel two miles long

Below: Pitlochry Dam and Power Station. The fish-pass in the foreground enables fish to ascend the river for breeding

and four times the efficiency of incandescent filament lamps.

Both the electric discharge and fluorescent lamps need special circuits to prevent their being damaged and sometimes to help them start up when the ELECTRIC CURRENT is switched on (q.v.).

The amount of light from a lamp is measured by comparison with that from a standard source. This used to be the light of a candle, and standard flame sources were established in various National Laboratories to reproduce the old 'standard candle'. Today a new and easily reproducible standard is accepted internationally: the amount of light radiated from one square centimetre of a surface of melting platinum is defined as 60 'candelas'. The amount of light falling on a surface is measured in 'lumens' per square foot; the light intensity on a surface 1 foot from a standard candela is 1 lumen per square foot.

The aim of good artificial lighting is to supply sufficient light without direct glare from bright light sources, and if possible to emphasize important working points without producing too great a contrast. Glare is reduced by using diffusing bowls. In good factory lighting the light is directed as required by using correctly shaped mirrors to reflect the light rays, or by putting prisms in the glass or plastic light bowls to control the rays by refraction—that is, by bending them.

Good general lighting of large buildings is achieved if the spacing between lighting points is less than one and a half times their height.

Uniform general lighting can be obtained by concealing the lamps behind reflecting cornices or bowls, the light being directed to the ceiling which acts as the visible light source. The loss of light due to its being reflected many times makes this method inefficient, and so fluorescent lamps are now widely used for this type of lighting.

Only recently has it been practicable to have

British Thomson-Houston Ltd.

CENTRALLY MOUNTED STANDARDS, WITH THREE 80-WATT 5-FOOT FLUORESCENT LAMPS, LIGHTING THE PARADE AT LEAMINGTON SPA

indoor light intensities sufficiently high to avoid eye fatigue. A careful survey of many studies is summarized in the I.E.S. Lighting Code prepared by the Illuminating Engineering Society of Great Britain, from which has been taken the following table.

Condition	Minimum recommended intensity. Lumens per sq. ft.
Reading	7–25
Sewing	20
Inspection	50
Watch Repairing	100
Hospital Operating Theatre . .	300

The lighting of streets presents a special problem. Much work in this country has resulted in a recommended code of practice where, for main streets, lamps are mounted at a height of 25 feet, and the lanterns so placed that the road surface acts as a diffusing reflector to give broad streaks of light against which pedestrians or vehicles are silhouetted. Sodium and mercury vapour discharge lamps can be used most economically for this. Recently, fluorescent street lighting, introduced first in the world in Rugby and London,

British Thomson-Houston Ltd.

LIGHTING IN THE FACTORY OF BRYNMAWR RUBBER LTD., BRECKNOCKSHIRE

has given a light of good colour and low brightness at a cost little more than that given by discharge lamps (*see* Street Services, Section 2, Vol. X).

See also Vol. III: Light; Colour.
See also Vol. XI: Lighting, History of.

INDUCTION, ELECTRIC. 1. This is a natural force which creates Electric Currents in a loop of wire when the wire is moved near a Magnet (qq.v.). These 'induced' currents were discovered in 1831 by Michael Faraday, and it is by their means that electricity is produced in Electric Generators (q.v.). Fig. 1 shows a copper wire with its ends joined to a sensitive instrument for measuring current called a galvanometer. When the wire is thrust either down or up between the two ends of the horseshoe magnet, the needle of the instrument moves, which shows that an electric current has begun to flow along the wire. If the magnet is stationary, the current flows only when the wire is moving, but it can bc made to flow just as easily if the wire is held still and the magnet moved.

The direction of the current is governed by unchanging laws; if the wire and magnet are arranged as in the diagram, current flows from B to A when the wire is moved down, and from A to B when it is moved upward. This is determined by the relationship of the wire to the North and South poles of the magnet (*see* Magnetism, Vol. III). If the magnet were turned round so that the position of the poles was reversed, then a downward movement of the wire would send a current from A to B, and an upward one from B to A.

The actual cause of an 'induced' current in a wire is a change of any sort in the condition of the magnetism which surrounds the wire—that

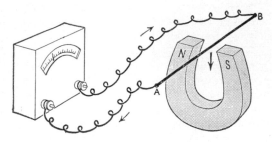

FIG. 1. PRINCIPLE OF INDUCTION

is, a change in the 'magnetic field'. If a magnet is moved near to, then away from, a wire, such movements obviously change the 'magnetic field'. It can also be changed without moving anything by switching magnetism on and off. It is not possible to switch on and off an ordinary magnet which is a piece of permanently magnetized steel; but it is possible to switch on an electric current, and every current behaves in some ways like a magnet: it can be used to create 'induced' currents in loops of wire which are brought near to its magnetic influence.

When a current is first switched on in any kind of electric circuit, a magnetic effect spreads out very rapidly from all wires which form part of that circuit, and this surging magnetic effect creates an 'induced' current in any other wire circuit which is near to it. This effect lasts only a tiny fraction of a second; once the surge is over, and a steady current has settled down to flow in the first circuit, no further current is induced in any wires near it. Yet when the first current is switched off, the dying down of that current for an instant of time causes a brief current to flow again in the neighbouring wire, for again a change in magnetism creates an induced current. Switching on causes the induced current to flow in one direction, and switching off in the opposite.

In circuits which carry ALTERNATING CURRENT (q.v.) the current is continually reversing its direction and is zero twice every cycle.

2. TRANSFORMERS. One single wire throws out only a very weak magnetic effect; therefore, to make the best use of electromagnetic induction, the wire of the first circuit is always coiled round and round a great number of times, like the cotton on a reel, which greatly increases the magnetic strength. The second circuit—the one in which it is desired to induce a current—also contains a coil with many turns, which magnifies the effect of induction. The principle of two circuits with two coils, one influencing the other, underlies the great range of electrical appliances known as TRANSFORMERS (q.v.).

3. CHOKE COILS. When a current flowing in a coil of wire is first switched on, each turn of the coil has its own magnetic effect, and as it spreads out it induces currents in all the other turns of the same coil. This effect is called self-induction and it is increased as the number of turns in the coil is increased. It is also increased if the coil is wound on an iron core, which itself greatly strengthens the magnetic effect. The self-induced currents act against the main current, opposing any changes in the strength of the main current; consequently 'choke' coils can be used to choke out, or smooth out, the fluctuation in the direct current produced by rectification of an alternating current (*see* RECTIFIERS).

See also ELECTRIC CURRENT; MAGNETS.

INFRA-RED RAYS, *see* Vol. III: RADIATION.

INSTRUMENTATION. The dictionary meaning of this word is, of course, 'the use of instruments'; but today instrumentation has come to have a special meaning: the application of instruments in manufacturing (particularly chemical manufacturing) processes, with the object of eliminating the human element in the process.

The most important instruments met with in practice are those for measuring length (*see* LENGTH-MEASURING INSTRUMENTS), weight (*see* WEIGHING INSTRUMENTS), volume, level, rate of flow (*see* HYDRAULICS), pressure (*see* PRESSURE GAUGES), temperature (*see* TEMPERATURE, MEASUREMENT OF), time (*see* CLOCKS AND WATCHES), and electrical properties (*see* ELECTRICAL INSTRUMENTS). There are also many special-purpose instruments for measuring more complex quantities, some of which are mentioned below.

The three basic types of instrument, in the order in which they were developed historically, are indicating instruments, recording instruments, and controlling instruments.

1. *Indicating instruments*. These are applied to a process to eliminate human judgement. You need judgement to bake a cake without using instruments, but with a THERMOMETER (q.v.) to tell you how hot the oven is, and a clock to tell you how long the cake has been in, you can produce a nicely browned cake without judgement, once you know the correct conditions for the process. The majority of chemical processes are surprisingly similar in principle to cake-baking; and indicating instruments, the simplest forms of instrumentation, were applied to chemical processes very early in the history of chemical engineering.

2. *Recording instruments*. These not only measure and indicate but also record what they have measured in the form of a GRAPH (q.v.). They are chiefly used because they make it possible to see quickly whether the quantity measured is varying from the normal. Perhaps the most familiar recording instrument is the barograph

I.C.I.

THE CONTROL ROOM OF THE ACETONE PLANT AT I.C.I.'S WORKS AT BILLINGHAM-ON-TEES

The dials on the walls are recorders, that is, moving pens tracing continuous records of temperatures, pressures, and rates of flow at various points on the plant. The operator at the desk can take further readings from points all over the plant by throwing operating switches on the keyboard that faces him

(see METEOROLOGICAL INSTRUMENTS) which records atmospheric pressure. The ordinary barometer (an indicating instrument) merely tells you what the pressure is when you are looking at it; but the barograph tells you at a glance whether the glass is rising or falling, and how quickly. Recording instruments are also used industrially because their records can be used to compare operating figures under different conditions—to compare, for example, the fluctuations in the demand of electricity from a power station during night and day, or in summer and winter.

3. *Controlling instruments.* These are the most recent and by far the most important class of instruments industrially. A homely example of a controlling instrument is the ordinary ball-cock on a water-cistern. The ball floats on the level of the water, and is connected by a lever to a control valve, so adjusted that the water is shut off when it reaches a predetermined level. This simple example brings home the important point that controlling instruments need neither indicate nor record—though in practice most controllers do indicate, so that their performance may be checked. The commonest controlling instruments are time controllers (for example, the time-clocks that switch on street lamps at lighting-up time); level controllers (the ball-cock, for example, and its innumerable industrial counterparts); temperature controllers or THERMOSTATS (q.v.); flow controllers; pressure controllers (the safety-valve on a boiler is a simple example), and various electrical controllers (such as the instruments used to maintain steady the voltage and frequency of a power-station's output).

The instrumentation of industrial processes has made great strides over the past 20 years, but the technique is still in its infancy. At present, what is done is to measure the 'key' physical quantities of a process when it is working correctly, and to install controllers to hold these quantities to the desired levels. For example, in fractional DISTILLATION (q.v. Vol. VII), the quality of the end-products for a given starting material depends on temperatures at various points in the distillation column; and it is not too difficult to install thermostats, which, by controlling the flow of heating steam and cooling reflux, can hold these temperatures steady.

But if there is any change in the quality of the starting material, the controllers cannot cope with this. They just go on holding the various temperatures to the old, now wrong, values until the chemist who does the routine analyses of the end-products notices that something is wrong and instructs the plant operator to reset the controllers to deal with the new operating conditions.

Instrument engineers are now trying to produce a controller that will do all this automatically. One recording instrument (the Metropolitan-Vickers Recording Mass Spectrometer), for example, can analyse a mixture of fifteen different gases and record the results on a graph. An electronic calculating machine is needed to decipher the graph and deliver the result in terms of ordinary percentages. It seems to be only a matter of time before complex plants will be completely automatic: before instruments will automatically analyse the products, and pass messages back to automatic controllers, that will in turn alter the operating conditions to keep the products up to specification. Then, using the language of the chemical engineer, we can truly say that such plants are 'fully instrumented'.

See also AUTOMATIC CONTROLS.

INSULATION, ELECTRICAL, *see* ELECTRIC CURRENT.

INTERNAL COMBUSTION ENGINE. As its name suggests this type of engine burns its fuel inside the working parts of the engine. The type includes petrol engines, diesel engines (more correctly termed compression-ignition engines), and GAS TURBINES (q.v.). Petrol engines are used chiefly in cars, aircraft, and light machinery: diesel engines in heavy machinery such as cranes, tractors, and locomotives, and ships up to about 20,000 tons, as well as in buses, lorries, and even some taxi-cabs; and gas turbines at present almost entirely in high-speed aircraft, though they have also been used for locomotives and for ships. This article deals only with modern petrol

and diesel engines; the article ENGINES, HISTORY OF describes earlier types of internal combustion engines.

1. BASIC PRINCIPLES. In any internal combustion engine, burning fuel heats air which consequently expands, and in expanding exerts a push (*see* HEAT ENGINES). Except in the gas turbine, the air expands in a cylinder and pushes a piston which, in turn, rotates the engine shaft through a connecting rod and crank. Because of this backwards and forwards action these engines are called 'reciprocating engines'. A mixture of air and fuel must be put into the cylinder, compressed, burnt, and the products of combustion (burnt gases) expelled, ready for a new charge of air and fuel to enter the cylinder. The piston drives the engine during only one part of this cycle, while the fuel mixture is burning. During the rest of the time the piston is moved by the energy stored in the revolving flywheel.

Petrol engines are called 'four-stroke' or 'two-stroke' engines according to whether there is one working stroke for every four strokes of the piston or for every two strokes. Engines using coal-gas as fuel (gas engines) follow precisely the same cycles.

2. THE FOUR-STROKE PETROL ENGINE. This is the commonest type of petrol engine, the type fitted to cars and some motor-cycles. It may have as many as eight or twelve cylinders, the pistons of which are connected to a single crankshaft, but for simplicity we shall consider a single cylinder engine. The inlet and exhaust holes or 'ports' are at or near the top end of the cylinder (Fig. 1a) and may be opened and closed by the movement of mushroom-shaped pieces of steel—the 'valves'. These valves are normally held shut

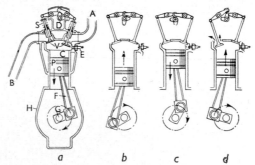

FIG. I. DIAGRAM OF A FOUR-STROKE ENGINE
A. Inlet port. B. Outlet port. C. Cylinder. P. Piston.
D. Cam. V. Valves. E. Sparking plug. S. Valve spring.
F. Connecting rod. G. Crankshaft. H. Crank case

by springs, but are opened by cams, operated by mechanical gearing, at the proper times.

On the inlet stroke the piston moves down the cylinder (Fig. 1*a*), leaving space above it and consequently reducing the pressure there. At the same time the inlet valve is open, and the pressure of the atmosphere pushes air along the pipe leading to the cylinder. On its way there the air passes through the carburettor, where petrol is sprayed into the air stream. The mixture of air and petrol passes through the inlet port into the cylinder. When the piston has travelled as far as it will go, the inlet valve is shut, thus trapping a quantity of the mixture in the cylinder (Fig. 1*b*). With inlet and outlet valves closed, the piston moves up the cylinder, compressing the gas. At the top of the compression stroke a spark is set off in the cylinder head by means of a 'sparking plug' screwed into the top of the cylinder, through which a high-voltage electric discharge is sent at just the right moment (Fig. 3). The spark fires the mixture (Fig. 1*c*).

The mixture, once fired, burns very rapidly— almost as an explosion. In a fraction of a second the heated air expands, and the pressure rises to about 500 lb. per square inch. This pushes down the piston and drives the engine. As the piston reaches the bottom of its stroke, the exhaust valve opens, and during the fourth stroke, the piston pushes the exhaust gases out into the atmosphere (Fig. 1*d*).

The exhaust valve and the inlet valve each open and close once only during the whole operation, which has taken two revolutions of the crankshaft. Therefore the camshaft carrying the cams that open and close the valves must rotate at half the engine speed, as must the contact-breaker shaft which causes the spark by suddenly cutting off the current. The carburettor in its simplest form is shown in Fig. 2. The petrol is fed through a pipe (A) into the float chamber (B), the level being kept constant by the float (C), which opens and closes the petrol inlet with the float needle (D) as necessary. At the same level as that of the petrol in the float chamber is the jet (E), from which, when air is drawn from the air inlet (F) through the carburettor, the suction causes petrol to flow in a fine spray—the harder the suction, the more petrol is supplied. The ratio of petrol to air, known as the mixture, is most important, for the fuel will not burn correctly in the cylinder unless the mixture is correct. Elaborate modern carburettors may incorporate as many as four jets to ensure that the mixture strength is correct under all running conditions, and they are always fitted with a 'choke', or device that causes the carburettor to deliver an extra-rich mixture for starting. On the simplest carburettor, the choke is simply a flap that blocks up the air inlet (hence the name 'choke'); while on others the choke control may lower the jet so that it gets more petrol, or may bring an extra jet into play. The inlet valve then closes, and as the piston travels back up the cylinder, the air-and-petrol vapour mixture is compressed.

The high-voltage current for the spark in the sparking plug is supplied by means of an induction coil (*see* TRANSFORMER). The current to the primary winding of the coil is stopped by opening the contacts (C) Fig. 3, a high-voltage current is induced in the secondary winding, and this causes a spark by leaping across a gap in the sparking plug. The contacts are opened by a cam driven by the crankshaft. On multi-cylinder engines, the contact-breaker camshaft also carries a rotating high-tension contact (the 'rotor arm') which ensures that the high-voltage current is led to the correct sparking plug of each cylinder in turn. The 'timing' of the spark is very important. For starting, it should occur just as the piston is at the top of the stroke; but at high speed, the engine delivers more power if the timing is

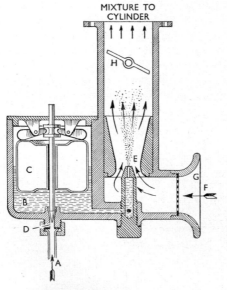

MIXTURE TO
CYLINDER

FIG. 2. DIAGRAM OF A CARBURETTOR WITHOUT SUPPLE-
MENTARY JETS FOR STARTING OR IDLING

A. Petrol inlet. B. Float chamber. C. Float. D. Float needle. E. Jet. F. Air inlet. G. Filter. H. Throttle valve

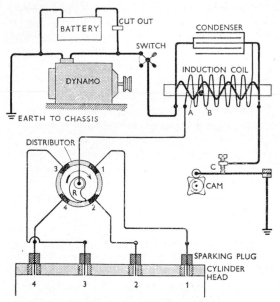

FIG. 3. ELECTRIC IGNITION SYSTEM FOR A SMALL
MOTOR-CAR ENGINE WITH FOUR CYLINDERS

A. Primary windings of induction coil. B. Secondary
windings. C. Contact. R. Rotor arm

'advanced'—that is, the spark occurs before the piston reaches the top of its stroke, giving time for the explosion to develop its greatest heat before the piston has travelled far down the cylinder. If the explosion occurs too soon, the shock on the cylinder causes a noise known as 'knocking'. The timing used to be arranged by a hand control, but today nearly all engines are fitted with an automatic device that sets off the spark sooner as the engine goes faster.

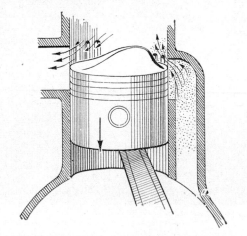

FIG. 4. TWO-STROKE CYLINDER SHOWING PISTON
NEAR BOTTOM OF STROKE

3. THE TWO-STROKE PETROL ENGINE. This has no valves; the inlet and exhaust ports are in the side of the cylinder near its open end, and are opened and closed by the piston as it slides up and down (Fig. 4). As the piston travels up on the compression stroke, the mixture is drawn into the space below it, the crank-case. During the firing stroke, the mixture in the crank-case is compressed by the descending piston. When the piston uncovers the exhaust port, the exhaust gases rush out; and then, as the piston continues to descend, it uncovers the inlet port on the opposite side of the cylinder. Compressed mixture from the crank-case sweeps up and in through the inlet port, filling the cylinder and pushing out the remainder of the exhaust gases. By this time the piston is on the way up again; it closes the inlet and exhaust ports, compresses the mixture for the remainder of the stroke, and as it reaches the top, the spark fires and the cycle begins again. Thus, in this engine, every downward stroke is a working stroke. The two-stroke petrol engine is not only very simple but gives nearly twice the power of a four-stroke engine from a cylinder of given size. But it is wasteful of petrol, as some mixture inevitably finds its way into the exhaust system on the combined inlet/exhaust stroke, and as there are always some combustion products left in the cylinder which reduce the rapid burning of the fuel.

4. DIESEL OR COMPRESSION-IGNITION ENGINE. Basically the same as the petrol engine, the diesel or C.I. engine has no carburettor or sparking plug. It may run on petrol (when it is sometimes known as a fuel-injection engine), but it usually runs on a heavier fuel, known as diesel oil. In the C.I. engine, air only is drawn in on the inlet stroke. On the compression stroke, the air is very highly compressed and its temperature consequently raised till it reaches the point at which oil-fuel will ignite (see GASES, PROPERTIES OF). At the top of the compression stroke (or just before, in practice) a fine spray of fuel is pumped into the cylinder through a nozzle called the 'injector'. The fuel burns at once, and from then on the cycle is completed as in the four-stroke petrol engine. The fuel pump is operated by a special camshaft driven at half-engine speed.

C.I. engines operating on the two-stroke cycle, unlike the two-stroke petrol engine, are very efficient, because there is no loss of mixture during the combined inlet-exhaust stroke—the only

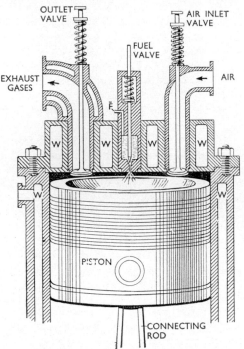

FIG. 5. COMPRESSION-IGNITION ENGINE SECTIONED TO SHOW
THE PISTON

The piston is at the top of its stroke and about to begin
its downward power stroke. Both the air inlet and exhaust
valves are closed by their springs and by the compressed
air in the cylinder. The fuel valve is lifted and combustion
begins. F. Fuel inlet. W. Water jacket for cooling cylinder

possible escape into the exhaust system being air.
In large engines of this type, the incoming air
is not compressed in the crank-case, but by a
separate rotary COMPRESSOR (q.v.).

5. OCTANE NUMBER AND 'PINKING'. In petrol
engines, compression causes the mixture to become hot, and if the amount of compression is
too high, the mixture will explode instead of
burning when the spark is fired ('pinking'), or
even explode spontaneously before the spark is
fired at all (pre-ignition or 'knocking'). The
amount of compression that a mixture containing a specified fuel will stand is known as the
'octane number' of the fuel, and is measured by
comparing the given fuel with a standard fuel
(octane) in a special engine.

The higher the compression ratio, the greater
the amount of air that can be got into the cylinder, and so the higher the power obtainable from
a given size of engine. Moreover, the higher the
compression, the hotter the air, and therefore
the more efficient the engine (see HEAT ENGINES).

Thus an engine running on high-octane fuel can
be made more efficient than one running on
ordinary fuel, and diesel engines, which have
very high compression ratios, are more efficient
still. The ordinary motor-car engine compresses
the mixture to about ⅙th of its original volume
(a compression ratio of 6 to 1), while racing engines may go up to about 9 or 10 to 1, and diesel
engines have a compression ratio of over 16 to 1.

6. SUPERCHARGING AND COOLING. The power
output of petrol engines may be raised if the mixture is forced or pumped into the cylinder instead
of being sucked in by the piston, because more
air and fuel can thus be got into the cylinder.
This is known as 'supercharging' (see p. 88).

All but the smallest engines would soon get
red-hot and 'seize-up' if they were not kept cool
artificially. The usual method is to surround the
cylinder with a water-jacket through which water
circulates, the water being cooled by an air blast
before being recirculated. In the motor-car, this
is done by the radiator and fan.

In small air-cooled engines, fins cast on the
cylinders help to transmit this heat to the outside
air. The cooling air is often kept moving by a fan,

COMPRESSION-IGNITION ENGINE SECTIONED TO SHOW THE
CYLINDERS AND PISTONS

A. Pistons.   B. Connecting rods.   C. Induction valves.
D. Crank-case coupling.   E. Cam shaft.   F. Exhaust

except on motor-cycles, where the movement of the machine itself keeps the air moving past the cylinders.

See also GAS TURBINE; ENGINES, HISTORY OF.

IRON AND STEEL. 1. Iron is an element (*see* MATTER, Vol. III); the symbol in chemistry is Fe (from the Latin *ferrum*). It is among the six most common elements, and makes up about 5% of the earth's crust. This means that a lorry-load of earth or rock (provided it carried a truly average sample of the earth's surface) should contain roughly a sackful of iron. Some plants extract from the soil minute quantities of this widely dispersed iron, which is indeed necessary to health and has medicinal properties. But in most soils iron is so thinly scattered that it is of no other than medicinal importance. It is only where it is concentrated in certain rocks or soils, so as to make up at least one-fifth, that it is of any importance to man as a source of metal. In a few places it is concentrated thickly enough to make up as much as two-thirds of certain rocks, and these are very useful indeed. This, however, is the richest concentration there is. Rocks or soils containing enough iron to make extraction worth while—that is, containing more than about 20 per cent. of iron—are called IRON ORES (q.v. Vol. VII), or more colloquially 'iron-stones'.

The iron in rocks and soils is not in a metallic form, as, for example, gold is. It is in the form of iron oxide; that is, atoms of iron and oxygen are joined together so intimately as to form a substance which is neither iron nor oxygen. (Rust is another variety of iron oxide.) A common form of iron oxide, haematite, is expressed as Fe_2O_3, or two atoms of iron to three atoms of oxygen; another is Fe_3O_4 (*see* CHEMISTRY, Vol. III).

There are eight different classes of iron ore, each with a characteristic set of impurities and iron oxide content. The richest ore, called magnetite because it is very hard and highly magnetic, contains up to nearly 70% of iron oxide. The biggest deposits of magnetite are in Sweden. The poorest ore in common use, a rather complex formation of ironstone, ranges from 20% to 30% or more in iron oxide content. Great deposits of ironstone like this stretch from Gloucestershire and Oxfordshire in an arc across Northamptonshire, Lincolnshire, and Yorkshire. The main ore fields throughout the world are shown on a map on p. 284 of Vol. III.

Apart from the earth and sand (mostly alumina and silica) mixed up with the iron oxide, the most important impurities in iron ore are sulphur and phosphorus. The proportions of these, especially phosphorus, have an important effect on later manufacturing processes (*see* STEEL-MAKING).

Iron in a very nearly pure state can be manufactured in the laboratory. Such iron is comparatively soft and flexible and can be shaped by hammering. It has no springiness, and no amount of HEAT TREATMENT (q.v.) will alter its character. In industry, however, iron always has a number of alloying elements mixed up with it, which affect its properties to a marked extent (*see* ALLOYS). The chief of these alloying elements is carbon, and the various manufacturing processes are largely the different methods of controlling the amount of carbon present in the manufactured product.

Three kinds of iron are used in industry: pig iron, cast iron, and wrought iron.

2. PIG IRON. This is the product of the BLAST FURNACE (q.v.), the function of which is to extract the iron from the ore. (A 'pig' is simply a slab or ingot.) Pig iron is an intermediate product; that is, although it is manufactured, it is only of use as a raw material for another process. It contains about $3\frac{1}{2}$% of carbon and up to about one-quarter of its weight is impurities. It is the raw material for cast iron, for wrought iron, and for steel. Pig iron itself is very hard and very brittle.

3. CAST IRON. For some purposes pig iron is remelted and poured into sand moulds to take its required shape (*see* CASTING). This remelting somewhat improves the mechanical properties of the iron, but cast iron objects are still very hard and brittle, though certain rather complex heat treatments can make certain sorts of cast iron tougher and less brittle. These irons are called 'malleable' iron, either 'whiteheart' or 'blackheart' according to the method of manufacture.

4. WROUGHT IRON, of which only about 100,000 tons a year are now made in the United Kingdom, is almost free from carbon. To make it, pig iron is remelted in a certain sort of furnace called a 'puddling' furnace, in which the metal is stirred to mix air with it, and from which it emerges in a pasty state, to be hammered and rolled into shape. The process by which it is manufactured extracts almost all the carbon, so

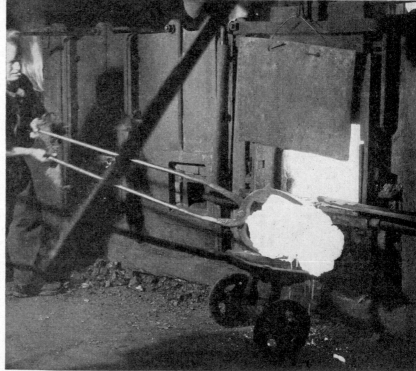

THE MANUFACTURE OF
WROUGHT IRON

Above: Puddling pig iron. The
first stage in the manufacture
of wrought iron. The furnace
hand is stirring the melt and
forming it into a spongy ball of
metal. *Below*: Puddled ball
withdrawn from the furnace
N. Hingley & Sons Ltd.

that the metal is, compared with pig iron and cast iron, soft and malleable. It also has a certain amount of slag (impurities) mixed up in it, which give it a characteristic streaky appearance. Wrought iron has very good resistance to CORROSION (q.v.), and is consequently still used for anchor chains, pier stanchions, and other marine purposes.

5. STEEL. When the carbon content in the iron is controlled by certain refining processes so that it falls within the range 0.1% to 1.5%, it has a remarkable effect on the properties of the metal, which is then called steel, and is hard or soft, brittle or ductile (easily pushed or drawn into shape), according to the amount of carbon still in it (*see* STEEL-MAKING). Steel's most remarkable property, however, is its responsiveness to heat treatment, its character being varied far more effectively than that of iron by fairly simple sequences of heating and cooling. Further, the responsiveness of the metal to heat treatment, as well as such mechanical properties as strength, may be affected by additions of small and carefully controlled quantities of alloying elements such as manganese, chromium, nickel, cobalt, silicon, and vanadium.

Some kinds of steel made for special purposes have relatively high proportions of alloying elements. Stainless steel, for example, may have 18% chromium, 8% nickel, and small quantities of other elements as well. Some of the heat-resisting steels used in GAS TURBINE engines (q.v.) have nearly half their weight made up of non-ferrous additions in this way.

Steel is thus a very versatile metal, which can be given exactly the qualities required for a particular engineering purpose. The toughness and hardness of railway lines; the springiness and lustre of a pen-knife blade; the amazing strength of a delicate piano wire or a violin 'string'; the reliability and endurance of the valve springs in a motor-car engine and the spokes on a bicycle wheel—all these and ten thousand other things demanding widely different properties and qualities are made from steel.

See also BLAST FURNACE; STEEL-MAKING; IRON AND STEEL INDUSTRY.
See Vol. III: METAL ORES.
See Vol. VII: IRON ORE.

IRON AND STEEL INDUSTRY, HISTORY OF.
The use of iron and steel goes back a long time in human history. As iron and steel rust quickly away (*see* CORROSION), there are few traces of their use left in ancient excavations. An iron blade, possibly 5,000 years old, was, however, found in one of the Egyptian Pyramids. Iron and steel were well known to the ancient Israelites, and are frequently mentioned in the Bible; and the epic poems of Homer mention the making and hardening of steel (an alloy of iron and carbon) in ancient Greece nearly 3,000 years ago.

Iron was first smelted by heating together a mixture of practically pure carbon, in the form of CHARCOAL, and IRON ORE (qq.v. Vol. VII) in a furnace provided with a vigorous blast of air. The oxygen in the iron ore combined with the carbon of the charcoal, and passed off as carbon monoxide gas; the sulphur, phosphorus, and other impurities also passed off as gases; the clay and stone portions of the ore formed a slag (mineral waste) around a core of soft semi-molten iron, which was withdrawn when the furnace was broken into. The soft core of iron was then hammered to knock out any fragments of slag sticking to it. This is how the Romans worked the native ores of Britain during their occupation of the country, but the Celtic inhabitants of Britain were fairly expert in working iron in the Iron Age before the Romans came (*see* PREHISTORIC MAN, Section 6, Vol. I).

These early iron-smelting furnaces were usually erected in exposed places where the wind would create a natural blast of air. Later on they were built by the sides of streams, where an artificial blast was provided by bellows worked by water-wheels. After the Romans left there is little written record of the British iron and steel industry until the 12th century, though the Anglo-Saxons certainly used iron. *Ferraria* (ironworks) were occasionally mentioned in the Domesday Book. In these early days steel making was an unreliable process. Iron of reasonable purity was first produced, and was then reheated in the presence of charcoal, from which it absorbed the necessary proportion of carbon to harden it.

As charcoal was one of the essential raw materials of the early British iron and steel industry, the industry was located in medieval times principally in the Forest of Dean in Gloucestershire and the Weald of Sussex and Kent, where there was plenty of wood for charcoal. For a long time the Forest of Dean was the chief iron-producing area; by 1282 there were sixty

Sir Alexander Gibb & Partners

COALBROOKDALE BRIDGE IN 1780, WITH IRON WORKS BEYOND
Painting by W. Williams

forges in the area, and the industry flourished there for many centuries: as late as the 17th century a considerable output was still coming from the Forest of Dean. As the local Gloucestershire ores were becoming worked out, ore was imported from Lancashire to supplement local supplies, and the half-finished material was sent to the Birmingham district, where it was worked up into various tools and implements. Towards the end of the Middle Ages the Forest of Dean area was losing its earlier importance, and the Kent and Sussex Weald came into greater prominence.

By the 16th century the supply of charcoal was getting short, for the forests had been cleared and timber was in increasing demand for ship building. In Tudor times the needs of the Navy were given preference, and laws were passed restricting the felling of timber for charcoal-burning; so a new kind of fuel had to be found. In 1621 Dud Dudley, a Staffordshire ironmaster, took out a patent for smelting iron by using coal as fuel instead of charcoal. But the iron smelted in this way absorbed so much sulphur and other impurities from the coal that Dudley's process was too unreliable to be of any use. The failure to find a practicable way of using coal in the smelting process led to a general decline in the British iron industry, until by the middle of the 18th century nearly twice as much iron was being imported into Britain from northern Europe as was being produced in Britain.

By that time, however, Abraham Darby had thought out the idea of first coking the coal (*see* COKE OVEN), and of thus transforming it into reasonably pure carbon before using it in the furnace. It is believed that Darby used coke as early as 1709, but it was not until the 1730's that his method became generally regarded as practicable and successful; 30 years later the erection of new and larger furnaces using coke ushered in a period of development and expansion in the British iron and steel industry. Expansion was greatly helped by the development of the steam engine, without which it would not have been possible to create the more powerful blast of air which was necessary if coke were used. Towards the end of the century the output of British-made iron had increased considerably, and the erection in 1779 of a cast-iron bridge over the Severn near Ironbridge in Shropshire (see BRIDGES, Vol. IV) marks the beginning of the modern age of iron.

But progress was still slow: even in 1788 nearly half the furnaces in Britain were still using charcoal. Within 20 years, however, there was a marvellous transformation: only eleven charcoal furnaces were working out of the 300 or so that

had existed 150 years before, and the industry was no longer located near the forest areas but was becoming concentrated around the coalfields of South Wales, Staffordshire, Shropshire, and Derbyshire. There had also been further important technical improvements. In 1742 Huntsman had perfected a method of making steel in a crucible furnace (like a large bowl made of strong earthenware) of his own design, and although his method was expensive it was extremely efficient: it is still used in Sheffield today for the making of special tool steels.

In 1784 Henry Cort invented the puddling furnace for making malleable or wrought iron (see IRON AND STEEL, Section 4). In the puddling furnace the crude and impure molten pig iron coming from the smelting or BLAST FURNACE (q.v.) was kept stirred and in constant motion, thus causing the excess carbon to disappear as a gas. The molten metal gradually became consolidated into a sticky mass, which could be removed in lumps to be hammered or rolled into

Steel Company of Wales

THE ABBEY STEEL WORKS, PORT TALBOT, WALES

Coal is brought to the building in the right foreground and carried by conveyor to the washery. The ore and limestone are brought in on the left and carried by conveyor to the blast furnace in the background

The Times

TAPPING THE BLAST FURNACE AT THE APPLEBY-FRODINGHAM STEEL WORKS, SCUNTHORPE
The furnace is capable of producing more than 6,000 tons of steel in a week

shape. The shortcomings of the hammering process led Cort to replace hammers by a rolling mill with grooved rolls, which squeezed the soft wrought iron into bars of the desired sizes and shapes. In 1828 Neilson, a foreman in a Glasgow gasworks, suggested the use of heated instead of cold air for the blast in the smelting furnace, a development which reduced the fuel consumption considerably. It was energetically adopted in Scotland, and later in England.

Even by half-way through the 19th century wrought iron was still the main product of the British iron industry and not a great deal of steel was made. In 1855 only about 50,000 tons of steel were home-produced, at the very high average cost of £75 a ton. But in 1856 Henry Bessemer invented a revolutionary method of producing steel by blowing a blast of air through a vessel (called a 'converter') containing molten iron. His method produced large quantities of good steel in a very short time, about 20 minutes only being needed for the 'blow'. It was extremely cheap, because the rapid combination of the impurities and excess carbon with the oxygen of the blast created considerable heat and reduced the amount of coal needed. Within 10 years the price of steel had been reduced to about one-fifth of what it cost to make by the Huntsman process. A few years after the invention of Bessemer's process the Siemens brothers patented a method of making steel in a regenerative furnace, and this became known as the 'open-hearth' method. Both the Bessemer and the Siemens processes worked by first purifying the molten iron put into the converter or the furnace, and then transforming the purified iron into steel by the addition of ferro-manganese, containing a known proportion of carbon (see STEEL-MAKING).

It was not until nearly the close of the 19th

century that these two revolutionary inventions caused steel largely to replace wrought iron as the chief product of the British iron and steel industry, and as the main engineering and ship building material. In many respects the new inventions helped other countries more than they helped Britain. With the exception of the ores of Cumberland and north Lancashire, most of the local British ores contained phosphorus, which made the ores useless for steel-making by the original Bessemer and Siemens processes—known as the 'acid' process. The new British steel industry, however, kept its place in world competition by importing large quantities of rich non-phosphoric ores from northern Spain.

In 1879 two cousins, Sidney Gilchrist Thomas and Percy Gilchrist, invented what became known as the 'basic' process. Their idea was to make possible the use of phosphoric iron by lining the converter or the open-hearth furnace with a material such as dolomite (*see* FIRECLAYS AND REFRACTORIES) which would absorb the phosphorus. This, incidentally, left behind a slag rich in phosphate, which could be sold to farmers as an ARTIFICIAL FERTILIZER (q.v. Vol. VI).

Production of iron and steel in Britain continued to expand, but not as fast as it did in the rest of the world. The Bessemer process was adopted on a large scale in the U.S.A., where Andrew CARNEGIE (q.v. Vol. V) built up the American steel industry. The Thomas process assisted France and Germany to build up important steel industries of their own, since each possessed extensive native deposits of phosphoric ores. By 1913 Britain was producing little more than one-tenth of the total world output of steel. The submarine war against shipping in the First World War reduced Britain's supplies of non-phosphoric foreign ores, and led to a considerable increase in the manufacture of steel from home-produced phosphoric ores by the basic process. But this war-time recovery of the British iron and steel industry was only temporary, and the industry went through a lengthy period of depression after 1920. The war had, however, led to much technical progress in the making of 'special' steels which were ALLOYS (q.v.) of nickel, chromium, molybdenum, vanadium, cobalt, and titanium. Between 1913 and 1934 British exports of iron and steel fell from nearly 5 million tons to about $2\frac{1}{4}$ million tons. By 1932, however, the industry was beginning to recover, largely as the result of the protection provided by import duties against foreign iron and steel (*see* INTERNATIONAL TRADE, Section 5, Vol. VII). A few years later the need for rearmament caused a further recovery. The high world demand for iron and steel continued after the Second World War; in 1952 the output of the industry was nearly half as much again as that of 1936. Moreover, by that time British steel had become the cheapest in the world.

See also IRON AND STEEL; BLAST FURNACE; METALLURGY.

IRRIGATION, *see* CENTRAL VALLEY PROJECT; LLOYD BARRAGE. *See also* Vol. VI: IRRIGATION.

ISOTOPES, *see* RADIOACTIVE ISOTOPES.

J

JET ENGINE, *see* Vol. IV: Aircraft Engines, Section 4.

JIG BORING MACHINES, *see* Drilling and Boring Machines, Section 2.

JIGS AND FIXTURES. 1. These are devices used in Production Engineering (q.v.) to save time and labour when a number of similar components has to be produced. If, for instance, twenty holes have to be drilled in a component, all accurately spaced in relation to each other, and several thousands of these drilled components are wanted, it would take a long time to mark out and drill each hole separately. By using a device, however, into which the component fits and is securely held, and which carries a plate in which the holes have already been drilled in exactly the right positions, the drill can be brought down through each of these holes and the holes on the component drilled without any marking-out at all. Such a device is known as a jig.

A fixture, similar in principle, is used, often in combination with a jig, to fix the components correctly for the various machining processes. These devices not only save time by making it unnecessary to mark out each component but also ensure that each component is sufficiently accurate and identical—an important feature now that interchangeability of the different parts has become so essential to mass production. Jigs and fixtures are normally used only where large numbers of a component are required, for they are usually costly to make.

The form of the jig or fixture is decided by the shape of the component, and a number of them may be needed to help in the different machining operations from the raw material to the finished product. For instance, various fixtures may be used to hold pieces of raw material—castings or bars of metal, perhaps—in Lathes and Milling Machines (qq.v.), and a whole series of drilling jigs may be used to drill holes or to cut slots.

Jigs or fixtures are normally devised by the tool designer and draughtsman before the work is put into production and, although their shapes and types vary, certain basic principles apply to all of them. There are hole-drilling jigs; bending jigs, around which a component can be bent to the required angle; slotting jigs, such as those used to cut slots in the heads of screws; filing jigs to allow work to be filed easily and accurately; reaming jigs for bringing holes accurately to size; and boring jigs which are used on the boring machine in conjunction with a fixture so that accurate holes (such as the cylinders of a motor-car engine) may be bored in a casting (*see* Drilling and Boring Machines).

There are also marking-out jigs or templets, which are laid over a component so that, for example, either the shape to which it has to be cut or the position of holes can be marked easily on it by a scriber and then followed by the cutter or drill.

2. Jigs. Fig. 1 shows the drawing of a simple component on which limits of accuracy have been set. These limits direct that the diameter of the larger hole may be as much as 0·5915 inches, but must not be less than 0·5905 inches. Similarly the smaller holes may be as much as 0·3945 inches, but not less than 0·3937 inches. Fig. 2 shows a drilling jig which could be used for this purpose. When the jig has accurately fixed the position of the component from an already machined edge, and the component has been clamped in position, the jig is put on the table of a drilling machine, and the drill is in-

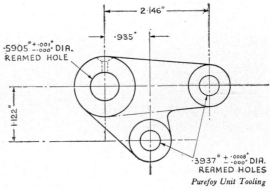

Purefoy Unit Tooling

FIG. 1. ENGINEERING DRAWING OF A COMPONENT

Purefoy Unit Tooling

FIG. 2. THE SAME COMPONENT AS IN FIG. 1 WITH THE JIG
USED FOR DRILLING THE TWO SMALLER HOLES

serted into each of the drill guides which direct it accurately on to the component. These guides are made of hardened and tempered steel and can be removed and renewed when they wear.

A common type of drilling jig for making groups of closely placed holes consists of an upper and a lower plate, kept in correct relation to each other by dowels or pillars. The alignment between the two plates must be maintained carefully, otherwise the drill would break and the component would be spoiled. The jig is also provided with one or more guides in which the work is placed and held accurately.

Where holes have to be drilled in more than one plane, a box jig (Fig. 3) is used; this has drill guides on two or more of its faces, and with these a number of holes can be drilled by the same jig in different directions without unloading the component from the jig.

Jigs must be designed so that the metal removed by the tool (the swarf) can be quickly cleared away to prevent its clogging the jig or interfering with the accurate placing of the component. The jig must also be easy to keep clean and so designed that the swarf does not prevent it from standing flat on the table of the drilling machine. The component must be firmly and accurately clamped in position in such a way that the clamping does not distort it but supports it firmly in the jig so that the cutting pressure applied by the drill or other tool does not shift it. Finally, many quick-clamping arrangements have been devised so that the operator can re-

move the drilled component and insert a fresh one with the least possible waste of time. If compressed air is available, it is often possible to incorporate a pneumatic clamping device, operated by a pedal, and this greatly speeds up the clamping and release of the component.

To speed up production, jigs are often made in duplicate, one operator loading while the other carries out the drilling. Where a hole requires enlarging (reaming) after drilling, a device, called a 'slip bush', is used so that the holes in the jig can serve either for the drilling or the final reaming which brings it to the finished size. After drilling, the slip bush is removed and the sizing reamer used.

In some cases, the jig is fixed to the table of the drilling machine to keep it in the correct relation to the drill; such an arrangement is common where a multi-spindle drilling machine is used to drill simultaneously a number of holes, perhaps of different sizes.

Where a series of holes has to be drilled around the circumference of a circle, a rotating drilling jig is often used, which is turned after a hole has

Purefoy Unit Tooling

FIG. 3. A BOX JIG FOR DRILLING HOLES IN THE TOP AND SIDES
OF A COMPONENT

The component is in place inside the jig

Purefoy Unit Tooling

FIG. 4. A COMPONENT HELD IN A FIXTURE WHILE THE SURFACE IS MILLED

been drilled, bringing the next drill guide under the drill. The correct position of the jig is fixed by means of a spring-loaded peg which fits into a notch cut in the movable part of the jig.

3. FIXTURES. On the same principle as that of jigs, fixtures are devices for holding work mounted on a machine in correct relation to a previously machined surface, so that the machining operation can be carried out accurately (Fig. 4). They eliminate the need to set up each piece of work separately. To enable the fixture to be placed correctly on the table of the machine tool, it has keys in its base which engage with slots in the table. Where it is used on a lathe, a peg, or 'spigot', is provided on the back of the fixture to correspond with a hole in the faceplate of the lathe.

As well as for machining, fixtures are widely used in connexion with assembling. They hold a number of components, in particular irregular-shaped pieces, in correct position while screws or rivets are inserted, other parts attached, or welding or soldering carried out. In modern production practice, transfer fixtures are sometimes used which not only hold the work but, in conjunction with a specially designed conveyor system, take the component automatically from one operation to another, often passing through a whole line of different machines.

See also PRODUCTION ENGINEERING.

K

KITIMAT HYDRO-ELECTRIC SCHEME (Canada). This vast scheme for the development of HYDRO-ELECTRIC POWER (q.v.), sometimes known as the Alcan project, is being undertaken to increase supplies of aluminium, the manufacture of which needs very large quantities of cheap electric power (*see* ALUMINIUM INDUSTRY, Vol. VII). Kitimat, where the new aluminium works have been built, is some 500 miles north of Vancouver. Work on the scheme began in 1951. The first stage was planned to finish in 1954, and to produce 450,000 horse-power. Ultimately over $1\frac{1}{2}$ million horse-power will be produced.

On the west coast of Canada the Cascade Range rises steeply from sea-level to heights of 5,000 feet and more. There is here a plateau with natural drainage eastwards, the fast-flowing rivers eventually finding their way into the Fraser River system. The Kitimat scheme makes use of three of these rivers—the Nechako, the Kemano, and the Kitimat. The basis of the scheme is the Kenney DAM (q.v.), on the Nechako River, forming a great reservoir with an area of 350 square miles. It will take 4 years to fill this with some 873,000 million cubic feet of water. The dam has a maximum height of about 317 feet, and is 1,550 feet along its crest. It has an impervious clay core, and contains nearly $3\frac{3}{4}$ million cubic yards of rock, clay, and gravel.

From this huge reservoir the natural flow of the water is reversed and carried westwards through two tunnels, each 10 miles long, to a power station placed on the banks of the Kemano River. The ships bringing the bauxite ore (from which aluminium is made) from Jamaica, some 5,000 miles away, cannot come up the Kemano River, and there is no suitable site there for the aluminium works. So a high-voltage transmission line carries the power 50 miles over a mountain and down into the valley of the Kitimat River where the aluminium works and a town for 50,000 workers and their families have been built.

The two water-tunnels, when complete, will be 25 feet in diameter and, as the rock is good, they do not need to be lined (*see* TUNNELLING). Each tunnel will normally take a flow of 3,500 cubic feet of water per second. The tunnels run on a gentle gradient through the mountains until they reach the Kemano Valley, high above the site of the power station. There, instead of carrying the water down the hillside in strong steel pipes, called 'penstocks', as is usually the practice, the tunnel never emerges from the mountain; steeply sloping shafts are driven through rock all the way to the power station, which is itself built in a cavern hollowed out inside the mountain.

The Kemano power plant, when complete,

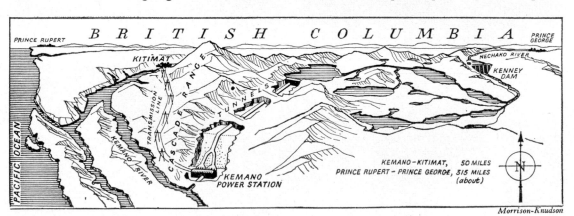

THE AREA OF THE KITIMAT HYDRO-ELECTRIC SCHEME

Canadian Ingersoll Rand Co.

DRILLING 10-FOOT-DEEP HOLES FOR ANCHORING THE TOWERS OF THE TRANSMISSION LINE CARRYING ELECTRICITY FROM KEMANO POWER STATION TO KITIMAT

will have sixteen turbines of the 'Pelton-Wheel' type (*see* WATER POWER), each rated at 150,000 horse-power at 327 revolutions per minute. They will be housed in an underground chamber over 1,000 feet long, 80 feet wide, and 135 feet high.

It will be the largest underground power plant in the world (*see* p. 77).

See also HYDRO-ELECTRIC POWER; POWER STATION; TUNNELLING.

See also Vol. VII: ALUMINIUM INDUSTRY.

L

LAND RECLAMATION. In many parts of the world there are large areas of potentially good land that cannot be used for agriculture because they are either too dry or too wet. But by engineering skill—devising efficient methods of IRRIGATION, DRAINAGE (qq.v. Vol. VI), or FLOOD CONTROL (q.v.)—and improved agriculture, it is often possible to reclaim such land. In Pakistan, for example, 5½ million acres of desert have been made fertile by a vast system of irrigation canals radiating from the LLOYD BARRAGE (q.v.) on the River Indus. Another spectacular example is the success of the TENNESSEE VALLEY AUTHORITY scheme (q.v.), which has transformed a derelict area of 42,000 square miles, devastated by SOIL EROSION (q.v. Vol. III) and alternate drought and flood, into one of the most flourishing areas in the world. In this instance the land was reclaimed mainly by vast schemes of flood control and irrigation and by terracing hundreds of miles of hills with trees and special plants to check erosion.

Thousands of acres of rich farmland have also been rescued from swamps and marshes and even from the sea. In reclamation schemes of this kind the area is first enclosed with high banks, or dykes, so that water, whether from a river or the sea, can no longer flow over it. If these dykes are inland they consist of shallow layers of specially selected earth, if possible a waterproof clay, thoroughly rolled and compacted. In the past,

cattle or sheep were driven over each layer as it was put down in order to make it compact, but today steam-rollers and tractors hauling heavy 'sheeps-foot' rollers (rollers fitted with 'spuds' like a sheep's feet) are used. If the soil available is not likely to be water-tight, a narrow core, about 2 feet wide at the top, of specially prepared clay called 'puddle clay', kneaded and puddled until it forms a watertight section, is built up in the centre of the dyke, from below ground-level to just above the highest regular flood-level (Fig. 1). In exposed areas the sides of the dyke are protected either by mattresses woven out of willows and reeds, or by stone, carefully packed but without mortar, called 'dry rubble pitching'. If a dyke is high enough and properly maintained, it should last for hundreds of years. In coastal areas, the land must be protected from the sea by building strong sea-walls of stone, concrete, or heavy timber (*see* FLOOD CONTROL).

When the dykes and sea-walls have been built, and the area protected from further flooding, the water must be drawn away before any crops will grow. This is done by digging drains at regular intervals all over the area. The water flows into these drains, and is then pumped out into the river or sea. In the past, windmills were used to work the pumps, but these have now been largely replaced by electrically driven pumping plants (*see* PUMPS).

Soil that has been covered with salt water cannot be cultivated until the salt has been washed out of it. Even soil on which fresh water has lain stagnant for a long time is full of salts, which the water has dissolved out of the chemicals that are naturally in the soil. So to obtain good crops from reclaimed land the soil has first to be washed. Fresh water is run on to the land, drained quickly from the top layers into the drainage channels and ditches, and then pumped away. This continues until the soil can grow some poor kind of crop. It may take several years of continual washing and cultiva-

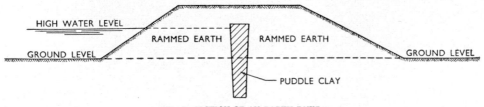

FIG. 1. SECTION OF AN EARTH DYKE

Tilbury Contracting & Dredging Co.

LAND RECLAMATION AT SURREY COMMERCIAL DOCKS, LONDON
Material dredged from the dock bottom is being pumped ashore to reclaim part of the dock area

tion before reclaimed land will yield the best crops.

For many centuries reclamation schemes of this kind have been carried out all over the world. In HOLLAND (q.v. Vol. III), over 2,000 square miles have been rescued from the North Sea and from inland lakes; the great ZUIDER ZEE PROJECT (q.v.) alone will account for more than 530,000 acres when it is complete. In Britain, the reclamation of the FENS (q.v.) has transformed more than 1 million acres of useless swamps into rich farmland. In Italy, the draining of the Pontine Marshes, which lie to the south-east of Rome, has been outstandingly successful: 500,000 acres have been reclaimed and repopulated and three new cities have been built. In the U.S.A., where there are nearly 65 million acres of swamps, vast schemes of reclamation have been carried out or are in progress: in the State of Minnesota, for example, $11\frac{1}{2}$ million acres have been reclaimed from the fringe of the Great Lakes. Successful reclamation schemes have also been carried out in Greece and Germany, but in BYELORUSSIA (q.v. Vol. III) apparently no attempt has yet been made to reclaim the vast expanse of the Pripet marshes.

See also FLOOD CONTROL; FENS, RECLAMATION OF; ZUIDER ZEE PROJECT.
See also Vol. III: SOIL EROSION.
See also Vol. VI: IRRIGATION; DRAINAGE.

LATHES. The lathe is the most widely used of machine tools and is also one of the oldest. Its development from the crude form in which it had existed for centuries is largely due to the work of Henry Maudslay in the early 19th century (*see* MECHANICAL ENGINEERING). In principle the horizontal lathe resembles a potter's wheel that has been turned on its side. Its function is to remove material from the workpiece by rotating it against a hardened cutting tool.

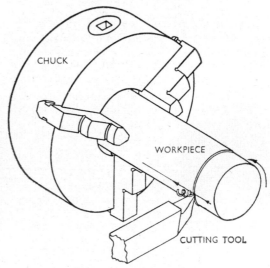

CHUCK

WORKPIECE

CUTTING TOOL

FIG. I. TURNING A CYLINDRICAL SURFACE ON A LATHE

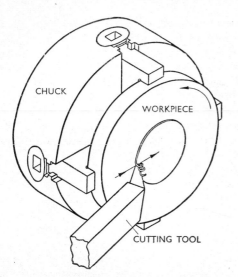

FIG. 2. FACING A FLAT SURFACE

The work is held in the machine and rotated, while the tool is moved slowly sideways parallel to the axis of rotation so that a continuous ribbon or thread of metal is peeled from the work. When the cutting tool is moved parallel to the axis of rotation, or along the work, producing a cylindrical surface, the operation is known as 'turning' or 'sliding' (Fig. 1); when the tool is moved at right angles to this, that is, across the work, it is known as 'facing' or 'surfacing' (Fig. 2).

A typical centre lathe is shown in Fig. 3. The main framework, or bed (A), is a rigid, cast-iron structure, along the top of which are two pairs of slideways. Permanently fixed to the left-hand end of the top of the bed is the headstock (B), while to the right of this slides the movable tail-stock (C) which can be clamped in any position along the bed. The headstock casting contains the main spindle which rotates the work, and in modern lathes it also houses a gearbox which provides a very wide range of spindle speeds. The tailstock acts as a support for the right-hand end of the work. Its centre height is the same as that of the centre in the headstock.

On the outer pair of slideways and between the headstock and tailstock slides the saddle (D). This carries the cross-slide (E), which enables the tool to make a cross movement. Both the length-ways movement of the saddle and the cross move-ment of the cross-slide can be operated by hand or driven mechanically through gears and con-trols carried in the apron (F), the part of the saddle which hangs down at the front of the machine.

Along the front of the bed are the feed-shaft (G) and leadscrew (H), both of which are connected to the workspindle through gearboxes so that they can be rotated at whatever speed is needed. In order to produce a cylindrical surface on the

Dean, Smith & Grace, Ltd.

FIG. 3. A CENTRE LATHE

A. Bed.   B. Headstock.   C. Tailstock.   D. Saddle.   E. Cross-slide.   F. Apron.   G. Feed-shaft.   H. Leadscrew.
J. Toolpost.   K. Four-jaw chuck.   L. Speed-change levers

workpiece, gears inside the saddle connected to the feed-shaft move or feed the saddle along the bed. When machining across the work—that is, carrying out a facing operation—the saddle is clamped to the bed so that it cannot move along it, and another set of gears in the apron transfers the feed-shaft drive to the cross-slide, thus making the tool move transversely across the workpiece.

The leadscrew is a very accurate and powerful screw to which the saddle is connected when a thread on the workpiece is to be made (see SCREW-THREADS). By means of gears, it is possible to rotate this leadscrew at whatever speed is wanted relative to the speed of the work spindle, so that the saddle is carried continuously along the work a fixed distance for each revolution of the workpiece. By selecting the right speed, the required pitch of thread is obtained, and the form of the thread is cut by a single-point tool in the toolpost (J), carried along the workpiece by the leadscrew while the work is being rotated by the spindle.

The workpiece must be held firmly during operations. Large diameter work is held by 'chucks', with jaws which move inwards towards the centre of rotation so as to grip the work, and reversed jaws for gripping work on its inside diameter (see Fig. 1). Smaller work is held in place by draw-in chucks or 'collets'. These consist of various sized cylinders split longitudinally, each of which can be pulled or drawn into the hollow main spindle by a special draw-in-bar. As the collet is pulled into the tapered nose of the lathe spindle by this bar, it contracts on the work and thus grips it.

For flat work, a faceplate is screwed on to the spindle, and the work is clamped to it. When work is mounted it is driven through a carrier or 'driving dog' clamped to the front centre end of the work by a slotted driving plate screwed on to the work spindle.

The cutting tool that removes metal from the workpiece must not only be considerably harder than the metal being cut but also be able to retain this hardness during the heat produced by the cutting action. A special 'high speed steel' containing tungsten and chromium (see ALLOYS) is used, as this does not lose its hardness, even when cutting at high speeds. For many operations this has now been replaced by tools tipped with a very hard material called tungsten carbide, which enables greater speeds to be used and a wider range of materials to be turned. The shape of the tool depends on the material to be cut and the operation to be performed.

Some time ago it was discovered that a stream of water directed on to the tool when it was cutting not only kept the tool sharp much longer, but also produced a better finish on the work. But the water caused both lathe and workpiece to rust badly, so soda was mixed with the water. Still there was rusting, so later mixtures of water and various kinds of oil were used. Today there are various brands of cutting oils, most of which are mixtures of mineral oil, soaps, and an emulsifying chemical which makes the oils mix

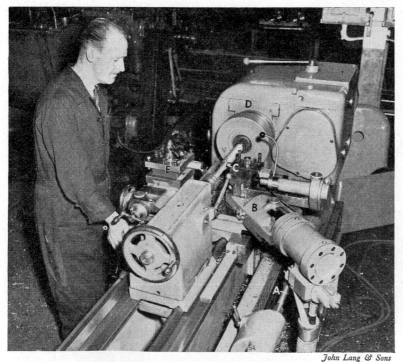

John Lang & Sons

FIG. 4. COPY-TURNING LATHE

A. Sample being copied. B. Profiling slide. C. Profiling tool cutting the workpiece
D. Headstock. E. Toolpost for normal turning

readily with water. These keep the tool and work-piece cool during the cutting operations, and so prevent excessive wear and distortion of the work. The 'coolants' also act as lubricants, resulting in better finish.

Lathes can perform other operations besides turning, facing, and screw-cutting. DRILLING AND BORING (q.v.) can be performed on the lathe and, by using special attachments, many other kinds of work can be done. Tapers may be turned either by moving the back centre slightly off centre or by moving the cross-slide against a templet which forces it to move gradually out-wards as it progresses along the work. Lathes can work at a wide range of speeds according to the kind of material being turned, its size, and the feed being used.

Turret or capstan lathes were designed to speed up production by avoiding the necessity of using a different tool or an adjustment to the tool for each operation. The turret lathe has its tool-rest in the form of a turret in which are mounted a number of tools, one for each operation. The turret can be rotated so that any tool can be pre-sented to the work in turn. The tools are fed in from the end of the work, and the conventional saddle and cross-slide are usually used for the parting-off operation, in which the completed workpiece is cut off from the bar. Though the turret lathe can be worked by comparatively unskilled operators, there must be an operator to work each machine.

To save labour and to speed up production the automatic lathe was evolved. There are various kinds of automatic lathes, but in all such machines feeding in of the work, carrying out all the operations on it, and cutting off and ejecting the finished product are all done automatically and continuously. One operator can look after a number of machines at once, for he has only to ensure that a supply of material is fed into the machine. The machine minder needs no special skill, but the initial setting and adjustment of an automatic lathe is a skilled and tedious task. This, however, is offset by the great saving in time and expense of the actual machining opera-tion in mass production. In the single-spindle automatic, a development of the turret lathe, the work rotates in the spindle and the tools advance in turn to carry out the various operations. The multi-spindle automatic operates on a number of workpieces simultaneously, each taking its turn in a sequence of operations until each has

Wadkin Ltd.

FIG. 5. A WOODWORKING LATHE
The operator is turning a cylindrical surface with the tool supported against the toolrest

had all the necessary operations performed on it. These lathes are built in both horizontal and vertical types and have so wide a variety of tool positions and motions that highly complicated parts can be produced in a very short time. The machines are extremely complex and very ex-pensive, and are not normally used except where a great many similar components have to be pro-duced on a mass-production basis.

The copy-turning lathe (Fig. 4), a compara-tively recent development, has a very wide field of application because it allows similar parts to be produced easily without the complications in-volved in setting up an automatic machine. Con-sequently it can be used to produce a much smaller number of parts than would be economi-cal with an automatic machine. Various types are built, all with the same basic principle: a finger or tracer 'feels' along a templet or pattern which is of the shape to be produced on the workpiece. Then, by various means, sometimes mechanical, sometimes electronic, and some-times hydraulic, according to the design, the movement of the tracer is translated to the slide on which the tool is mounted so that the machine automatically reproduces the shape of the pat-tern on the workpiece.

The wood-turner's lathe resembles the early type of metal-working lathe before the cross-slide was added (Fig. 5). It consists of a bed, to which is attached the headstock, tailstock, and toolrest. The work is either fastened to a face-plate or driven between centres by means of a 'butterfly', a front centre with four sharp projections which grip and rotate the work. The tool, which resembles a wood chisel, is supported on the toolrest and manipulated by hand against the workpiece in order to produce the required shape (*see* WOODWORKING MACHINERY).

The enormous variety of lathes built for various purposes ranges from huge machines for turning very large or unwieldy components to small and extremely accurate instrument and toolroom lathes. All these have special features of their own, though all are basically similar in principle to the types described.

See also MACHINE TOOLS; SAFETY DEVICES.

LENGTH-MEASURING INSTRUMENTS.

The measurement of length in nearly every case consists in comparing the length to be measured with a known standard length—the simplest example of such a standard being the ruler. Even the cheapest ruler must derive its accuracy at some remote stage from one of the fundamental standard lengths described in the article MEASUREMENT, UNITS OF.

The achievement of accuracy in the measurement of length is a cumulative process: it depends on the fact that a machine tool can always be used to make another machine tool more accurate than itself—otherwise we should never have achieved any greater precision than a skilled craftsman can manage with his unaided hands.

Each new increase in accuracy means that from time to time the standards themselves have to be improved. The inspection department of

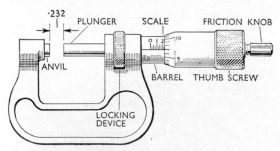

FIG. I. A MICROMETER

Each numbered division on the barrel represents 0·1 in. A complete revolution of the thumb screw withdraws the plunger by a quarter division, 0·025 in. The scale on the thumb screw is divided into 25 sections so that each represents $\frac{1}{25}$ of a revolution, that is, 0·001 in. The micrometer illustrated is thus reading 0·2+0·025+0·007 in., that is, 0·232 in.

any engineering shop contains length-measuring machines that are more accurate than the fundamental standards themselves were little more than 100 years ago. From the point of view of measurement, lengths can be roughly classified into:

Lengths less than one ten-thousandth of an inch;

Lengths between one ten-thousandth of an inch and (say) 1 yard;

Lengths above 1 yard (distances).

In measuring lengths less than one ten-thousandth of an inch, optical measuring methods must be used. Irregularities in a flat surface as small as one ten-millionth of an inch, for example, can easily be measured by covering the surface with an 'optically flat' block of glass—that is, glass so flat that any irregularities on it are no higher nor deeper than a known wavelength of LIGHT (q.v. Vol. III). We then examine the surface by this light, and measure the 'interference bands' (*see* WAVE MOTION, Section 5, Vol. III) formed by any irregularities. In this case, the standard is the wavelength of the light itself.

For measuring lengths between one-thousandth of an inch and, say, 6 inches, by far the commonest direct measuring instrument is the 'micrometer' (Fig. 1). This instrument is extremely simple in principle, being no more than a device for indicating how many times a screw of known pitch has to be rotated to withdraw a moving rod (the 'measuring plunger') the required distance from a fixed point (the 'anvil'). The object to be measured is placed between plunger and anvil. The accuracy of a micrometer depends on how accurately its SCREW-THREAD (q.v.) can be cut; with a modern micrometer fitted with the added refinement of a 'vernier scale' (*see* VERNIER), a skilled operator can measure small lengths with an accuracy of about one ten-thousandth of an inch, while an accuracy of one-thousandth can easily be achieved. The human factor enters into the measurement because the reading of a micrometer depends on how tightly the plunger is screwed up on to the object to be measured; but it is eliminated as far as possible by the provision of a friction device near the thumb screw, the plunger being screwed up until the friction drive begins to slip. A more elaborate form of micrometer, known as a measuring machine, is mounted on a bench for making more accurate

James Chesterman & Co.

FIG. 2. A SET OF SLIP GAUGES

The numbers represent thousandths of an inch, thus the one on the extreme right is 0·075 in. thick

measurements. For less accurate work the screw plunger is replaced by a sliding jaw fitted with a direct-reading vernier scale—an instrument known as a 'vernier calliper' (*see* p. 472).

As micrometers are both delicate and expensive instruments, they are replaced by gauges (*see* PRODUCTION ENGINEERING) for the routine measurement of fixed dimensions by unskilled labour.

In any large engineering works, there is a 'standards room' in which all gauges, micrometers, and callipers may be checked and reset if necessary. The standards room keeps its own set of reference standards—alloy metal blocks known as 'slip gauges' which are ground to an accuracy approaching one-millionth of an inch. A set of slip gauges is graduated, like weights, so that any required length can be built up by combining gauges. Their end surfaces are polished to an 'optical flatness' and are so free from irregularities that two slip gauges pressed together are held together by the pressure of the atmosphere and have to be prised apart (Fig. 2).

For measuring rather bigger dimensions, especially in the laboratory, a refinement of the micrometer known as the 'travelling microscope' is used. This is an ordinary microscope mounted horizontally on a travelling base worked by a screw-thread. The microscope is focused on one extremity of the length to be measured, and then made to travel along by rotating the screw until the cross-wires of the eyepiece line up with the image of the other end. The distance travelled is read off a cylindrical scale exactly as with the micrometer.

Longer distances up to about a mile are usually measured by direct comparison with a standard length, such as a surveyor's chain. Very long

distances are measured by triangulation (*see* SURVEYING).

See also MEASUREMENT, UNITS OF.
See also Vol. IV: MEASUREMENT, HISTORY OF.

LENS. 1. Lenses are the means commonly used to form optical images in the CAMERA, TELESCOPE, MICROSCOPE (qq.v.), and many other instruments.

A simple lens ordinarily consists of a disk of glass with its two opposing circular faces ground to either a spherical or 'flat' form, as shown in Fig. 1. The faces or 'optical surfaces' of the lens may be convex (bulging), making converging lenses, or concave (hollow), making diverging lenses, or one face may be plane (flat). This leads to six main types of lens, as shown in Fig. 1*a–f*. A lens is called 'thin' when the distance between its optical surfaces is small compared with their diameter (Fig. 1*g*); otherwise it is called 'thick' (Fig. 1*h*). The line joining the centres of curvature of the two spherical surfaces is called the 'axis' of the lens. The axis of a plano-convex lens is the line drawn perpendicular to the plane surface and passing through the centre of curvature of the curved surface.

2. SIMPLE CONVERGING LENS. Fig. 2 shows how a converging lens forms an image of a distant object AB. Some of the light rays which emerge in a fan or 'pencil' from each point of AB meet and pass through the surface of the lens, where they are 'refracted', that is, their directions are changed in accordance with laws of optics (*see* WAVE MOTION, Vol. III). They continue through the glass of the lens and, as they

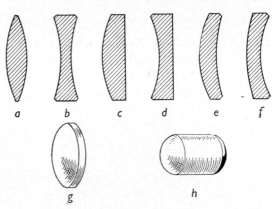

FIG. I. TYPES OF LENS

a. Biconvex. *b.* Biconcave. *c.* Plano-convex. *d.* Plano-concave. *e.* Converging meniscus. *f.* Diverging meniscus. *g.* Thin converging lens. *h.* Thick converging lens

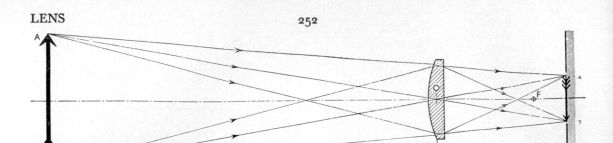

FIG. 2. REAL IMAGE FORMED BY CONVERGING LENS

AB is the object and A′B′ the image. OF is the focal length of the lens

emerge through its back surface, they are again refracted. The effect of the two refractions is to convert the diverging pencil of rays from the distant object-point A or B into a converging pencil of rays which all come together in an image-point A′ or B′. We say that the rays from A are 'brought to a focus' at A′. Each point of the object emits such a pencil of rays, and those rays which pass through the lens are brought to a focus at a corresponding image-point. The set of all the image-points formed in this way builds up the 'optical image' of the object by the lens. Rays parallel to the optical axis of the lens are brought to a focus at a special point F, and the distance between the optical centre O of the lens and F is called the 'focal length' of the lens.

If in Fig. 2 the object is brought nearer the lens, the image recedes. The positions of object and image in relation to the lens are governed by a mathematical formula. If u stands for the distance of the object in front of the lens, and v for the distance of the image behind the lens, and f is the focal length of the lens, then $\frac{1}{u} + \frac{1}{v} = \frac{1}{f}$. The focal length ($f$) is the value of v corresponding to an infinitely distant object. If $f = 2$ in.

and $u = 8$ in., then v will be $2\frac{2}{3}$ in. That is to say the image will be formed $2\frac{2}{3}$ in. from the middle of the lens on the opposite side from the object.

If the object is brought closer still to the converging lens until its distance from the lens is less than the focal length (as in Fig. 3), then the rays issuing from a point A of the object, and passing through the lens, are still divergent and appear to the eye as though they had originated in a point A′ on the same side of the lens as the object. A′ is called the 'virtual' image of A by the lens. Images which can be received on a piece of white paper or on a photographic plate are called 'real' images; the image shown in Fig. 2 is a real image.

3. SIMPLE DIVERGING LENS. Diverging lenses also form images. They can form real images only if supplied with 'virtual objects'—that is, if placed in the path of pencils of rays which are converging to form a real image (as in Fig. 4). When these rays are intercepted by the lens before coming to a focus, the real image A′B′ becomes a 'virtual object' which is re-imaged to A″B″ by the lens.

The image magnification produced by converging or diverging lenses depends on the relative position of image and object. The ratio of the

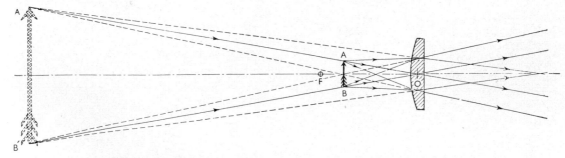

FIG. 3. VIRTUAL IMAGE FORMED BY A CONVERGING LENS

AB is the object and A′B′ the image

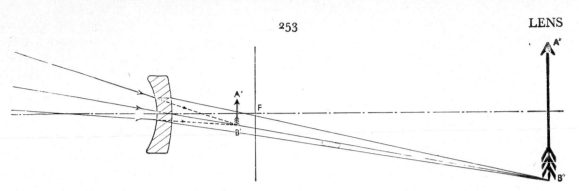

FIG. 4. REAL IMAGE FORMED BY A DIVERGING LENS
A′B′ is the virtual object and A″B″ the real image

size of the image to the size of the object is the same as the ratio of the distance of the image from the lens to the distance of the object from the lens.

4. POWER OF A THIN LENS. It is useful to define the power of a lens as $1/f$, where f is its focal length, because when two or more thin lenses are placed in contact, the power of the resulting compound lens is the sum of the powers of the individual lenses. The corresponding relation between focal lengths is less simple.

5. FOCAL RATIO AND F-NUMBER OF LENS. The brightness of the image of a distant object formed by a lens depends, other things being equal, on the ratio of its diameter to its focal length. Thus, suppose the lens-aperture (CD in Fig. 5) is doubled without changing the focal length f, then the area of its surface is multiplied by four; the lens, therefore, collects four times as much light from the object. The size of the image is not changed, since it depends solely on the distance OF $= f$. Hence the brightness of the image is multiplied by four. It is, in fact, proportional to the square of the aperture (a^2). On the other hand, if the focal length f is altered, while the aperture CD is kept fixed, the total amount of

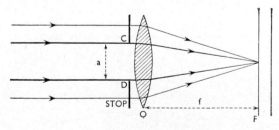

FIG. 5. FOCAL RATIO OF A LENS

light in the image remains constant; while its area is proportional to f^2. Therefore the image brightness varies as $1/f^2$.

It follows that, if the aperture CD and the focal length f can both vary, the image-brightness varies as $(CD/f)^2$. The quantity CD/f is called the 'focal ratio' of the lens for distant objects; its reciprocal f/a is called the F-number of the lens. The smaller the F-number, the brighter the image, and, if the lens is being used in a CAMERA (q.v.), the shorter the exposure needed for a satisfactory picture. On the other hand, the image becomes more and more spoilt by aberrations (*see* below) as the F-number is decreased. In practice, the aperture is increased (which lowers the F-number) until the image just begins to lose sharpness. In the less expensive types of camera lens, this occurs at about F/8; in more elaborate lenses at about F/3.

6. ABERRATIONS OF A THIN LENS. An actual lens, even one with surfaces accurately ground and polished to the desired spherical curves, does not form perfectly sharp images. The rays issuing from an object-point A do not come together again with complete accuracy in a single image-point A′, but are slightly disturbed by the so-called 'optical aberrations' of the lens. First there is the 'chromatic aberration'. Since the bending power of glass is slightly greater for light from the blue end of the spectrum than from the red end (*see* COLOUR, Vol. III), it follows that the power of a simple lens varies slightly for light of different wavelengths. In particular, the focal length of a simple biconvex lens is shorter for blue light than for red. The image of a point P on the axis of the lens is, therefore, not a single point but a tiny spectrum (as in Fig. 6a, b). The same effect occurs in the case of object-points which are not on the axis.

Even if we consider only light of a single wavelength, the imaging is not perfect. In the case of a real image formed by a converging lens, rays from the object-point which pass through the

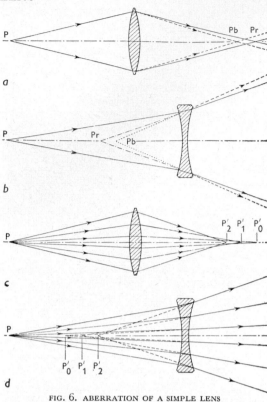

FIG. 6. ABERRATION OF A SIMPLE LENS

a, b. Chromatic aberration. P_b is the blue image point and P the red image point formed of an object point P.
In *a* the lens is biconvex and in *b* biconcave
c, d. Spherical aberration. P'_0, P'_1, P'_2 are the images of a point P formed by light passing through different parts of (*c*) biconvex and (*d*) biconcave lens

outer parts of the lens are brought to a shorter focus than those which pass through the central parts (as in Fig. 6*c*). The corresponding diagram for a biconcave lens is given in Fig. 6*d*. This disagreeable property, which affects the imaging of every point of the object in the same manner, is called 'spherical aberration'.

The other aberrations, called coma, astigmatism, field-curvature, and distortion, do not affect the image of a point on the axis but become worse and worse as the object-point P is moved sideways farther and farther from the axis. Thus their effect is to limit the 'useful field' of the lens, that is to say, the size of the object-area which can be satisfactorily imaged. Of the five kinds of aberration the last two, namely field-curvature and distortion, do not affect the sharpness of an image-point, but merely alter its position slightly. They pull the image out of shape without spoiling its sharpness.

Spherical aberration, coma, and astigmatism cause the image of a point to appear respectively as a small round disk (spherical aberration), a comet-shaped smudge (coma), and a small round or oval patch (astigmatism), according to the focal adjustment used. In practice, these aberrations all occur together.

7. 'CORRECTED' LENSES. By using compound lenses, made up of two or more simple lenses mounted together in a single cell, we can arrange for the aberrations of the component lenses to compensate each other to a considerable extent, and so obtain much better images than a simple lens of the same focal ratio could give. Lenses of this kind are called 'corrected lenses'.

The simplest example of a corrected lens is the 'achromatic doublet'. This consists of two lenses, of different glasses and of opposite powers, mounted close together in a single cell (*see* Fig. 7). One component, usually the front one, is a converging lens of crown-glass; the other is a diverging lens of flint-glass. The crown lens has nearly twice the power of the flint lens, so that the combination is convergent. But because the variation of refractive index with wavelength is more rapid for flint-glass than for crown-glass, the chromatic aberration of the weaker flint lens can be made to compensate that of the stronger crown lens, and the doublet brings all colours almost exactly to the same focus. Such a lens is said to be 'achromatic'.

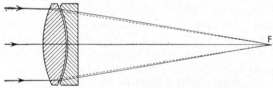

FIG. 7. BLUE AND RED RAYS BROUGHT TOGETHER TO THE SAME FOCUS WITH AN ACHROMATIC DOUBLET LENS

8. EYEPIECES. Ordinary telescope eyepieces consist of two simple plano-convex lenses, both of crown-glass, mounted at a suitable distance apart in a brass tube which can slide inside the main telescope tube.

The lens nearest to the eye is called the 'eye lens'; it may be said to supply the magnifying power. The other lens, called the 'field lens', partly compensates the aberrations of the eye lens and also gives the telescope a wider field of view.

The two best-known types of eyepiece are the Huyghenian and the Ramsden. In the Huyghenian (Fig. 8*a*) the focal length *f* of the eye lens is

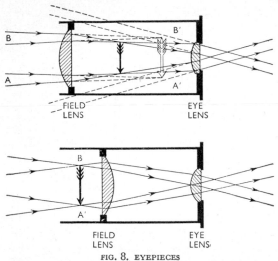

FIELD
LENS

EYE
LENS

FIELD
LENS

EYE
LENS

FIG. 8. EYEPIECES

a. Huyghenian eyepiece. *b.* Ramsden eyepiece

is acting as a pair of scales (Fig. 1*a*). If, however, one side of this arm is twice as long as the other, then the two equal weights will no longer balance each other; in fact, a weight of only one-half at the long end would be needed to balance the weight at the other end (Fig. 1*b*).

This illustrates the basic principle of leverage —that because the distance at one end is twice as far from the fulcrum as the other, only half the weight is needed to lift the weight at the other end. If it were four times as far from the fulcrum, only a quarter the weight would be needed. In other words, the force or effort required to overcome a weight, or any other force, resisting it at the other end in a lever system depends not only on the weight or force applied but also on the distance of both of them from the fulcrum. The tendency of the force to turn the lever is known as the 'moment', and is the product of the size of

one-third that of the field lens, and the distance between them is twice the focal length of the eye lens. The focal length of the eyepiece as a whole is $\frac{3}{2}f$.

In the Ramsden eyepiece (Fig. 8*b*) the eye lens and the field lens, though not of the same size, are of the same focal length f and are spaced a distance $\frac{2}{3}f$ apart. The focal length of the eyepiece as a whole is $\frac{3}{4}f$.

The eye lens, in order to give high magnification, is of short focal length; it has a sharply curved front surface and must, therefore, be small in diameter. Used without a field lens it receives light only from the central parts of the image. Used with a field lens, as in Fig. 8, it receives light from all parts of the arrow A′B′, so that the visible field has been enlarged.

Camera lenses are more fully described in the article CAMERA.

See also CAMERA; MICROSCOPE; TELESCOPE.

LEVERS.

LEVERS. A lever is a very important and ancient mechanism which makes it possible to move weights which would be impossible to lift by direct means. It does this by taking advantage of the mechanical power of leverage. It lifts more slowly than a direct lift, but for the same power it can lift heavier weights.

A simple lever consists of a rigid bar pivoted at a point known as the fulcrum (Fig. 1). If the fulcrum is exactly in the middle of the bar, and an equal weight is hung on each end, the ends will exactly balance each other, as if the whole

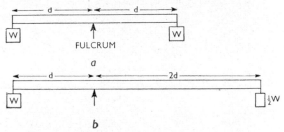

FIG. I. SIMPLE LEVER PIVOTED AT THE FULCRUM

the force and the perpendicular distance of the fulcrum from the line of action. In the first example, in Fig. 1, the turning moment required to keep the lever level can be expressed as $d \times w$. In the second case, the turning moment is $2d \times \dfrac{w}{2}$ which is exactly the same, but less force is required; and in the third case, $4d \times \dfrac{w}{4}$, even less force is required.

Levers with very long handles, therefore, need only a little force at one end to overcome a large force at the other end. This does not mean that a free supply of energy has somehow been obtained —it still takes as much energy to overcome a force at the other end, no matter how long the arm of the lever is, for the input energy always equals the output energy. But to lift a weight, the arm of the lever must be moved farther, and the speed at which the weight is lifted is slower. The force, therefore, though smaller at any one time, has to be exerted for longer. For example, if the lengths of the lever were arranged to give a mechanical advantage of 3 (that is, the weight at one end is three times the force at the other), the speed at which the weight is lifted would be only one-third the speed at which the lever arm is moved.

In many applications this does not matter at all. If the end of the handle of a carpenter's claw hammer has to be moved 6 inches to pull a nail only ¼ inch out of a piece of wood, that is a small price to pay for the mechanical advantage obtained (which in this example is 24), because it would have been very difficult to pull the nail out otherwise.

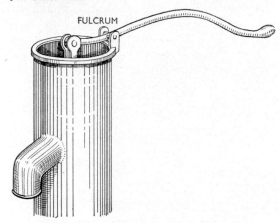

FIG. 2. PUMP HANDLE: A LEVER WITH THE FULCRUM
IN THE CENTRE

The effort and resistance need not necessarily be at opposite sides of the fulcrum; they can both be at the same side, and often are; but the moments are calculated in just the same way (Fig. 3). Further, levers may be bent and pivoted

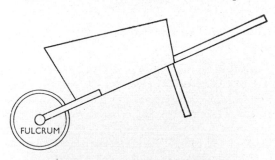

FIG. 3. WHEELBARROW: A LEVER WITH WEIGHT AND
FORCE ON THE SAME SIDE OF THE FULCRUM

at the bend, these being known as bell crank levers—the kind used for railway signals controls and formerly for bicycle brake controls (Fig. 4).

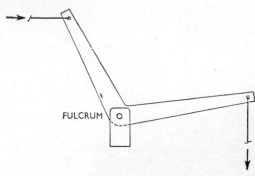

FIG. 4. BELL CRANK LEVER

Such levers are usually used to change the direction of a pull rather than to provide mechanical advantage.

There are numerous applications of the lever principle, and levers take many forms. The general principles described here, however, always apply.

See also MECHANICS.

LIFTS, *see* CRANES. *See also* Vol. IV: LIFTS AND ESCALATORS.

LIGHTING, *see* ILLUMINATION. *See also* Vol. X: STREET SERVICES, Section 2. *See also* Vol. XI: LIGHTING, HISTORY OF.

LIQUEFACTION OF GASES. The fact that all the substances we know as gases—such as air, hydrogen, and carbon dioxide—can be converted into liquids by being compressed and cooled was at one time a matter of purely theoretical interest, but today the liquefaction of certain gases is of great practical importance. Carbon dioxide, ammonia, and other gases are liquefied during REFRIGERATION processes (q.v.); solid carbon dioxide—'dry ice'—is widely used as a method of cooling both by the ice-cream and food industries and by engineers for cooling and shrinking metal parts for 'shrink fitting'; liquid air is used as a cooling agent in laboratories; and certain gases such as butane are liquefied and then 'bottled' to provide a portable gas supply for yachts, caravans, and country houses (*see* FUELS, Section 4). Oxygen, which is used in large quantities for cutting and welding, is generally transported in liquid form.

Some normally gaseous substances, such as ammonia and sulphur dioxide, can be liquefied at ordinary temperatures by compressing them to 100–200 lb. per sq. in. Others, such as oxygen, nitrogen, and hydrogen, remain gases even at many thousand pounds pressure, and consequently they were once thought to be 'permanent gases' which could not be liquefied at all. But experiments have since shown that for each substance there is a certain 'critical' temperature above which it cannot be liquefied whatever pressure is exerted on it. Below this 'critical' temperature moderate pressures only are needed for liquefaction, and as the temperature is further reduced, the pressure needed to liquefy the substance falls. It appeared, therefore, that the reason air and other 'permanent gases' were thought to be impossible to liquefy, or only at an unattainably high pressure, was simply that the temperatures at which liquefaction had been previously attempted were above the critical temperatures of these substances (*see* GASES, PROPERTIES OF).

Accordingly, in 1877, when attempts were made to liquefy 'permanent gases' by a combination of pressure with the lowest temperatures attainable, air was liquefied by French and Swiss scientists independently within a few weeks of one another. In 1898 a British scientist liquefied hydrogen, and 10 years later helium, the gas with the lowest critical point, was liquefied by a Dutchman.

Most gases can be cooled below their critical temperatures by means of other 'refrigerants'. Ammonia, for example, can be condensed at about 150 lb. per sq. in. at the temperature of ordinary cooling water. When its pressure is reduced, a part evaporates, taking the necessary energy from the rest of the liquid, which is thus cooled to its ordinary atmospheric boiling-point of −33° C. The liquid ammonia can then be used as a refrigerant for condensing a gas with a critical temperature below room temperature but above −33° C. Thus, ethylene can be liquefied at 260 lb. per sq. in., using boiling liquid ammonia as the cooling agent. When the pressure of the ethylene is in turn reduced, a part again evaporates, and the remainder is thus cooled to −103° C. Sometimes a whole series of substances is used in this way, such as ammonia to liquefy ethylene, ethylene to liquefy methane, and methane to liquefy air or nitrogen. The resulting arrangement, really a series of refrigerators, is called a 'cascade' (Fig. 1).

Hydrogen cannot be liquefied in this way as its critical temperature is lower than the boiling-point of nitrogen, and no intermediate refrigerant exists. Hydrogen can, however, like any other gas, be used to produce the low temperatures needed for its own liquefaction. In one method, the compressed gas, after the heat of compression has been removed by cooling water, is made to drive a reciprocating expansion engine or a turbine. In this way the gas expands and does work and is consequently cooled very considerably. If the cooled gas is returned to the compressor by

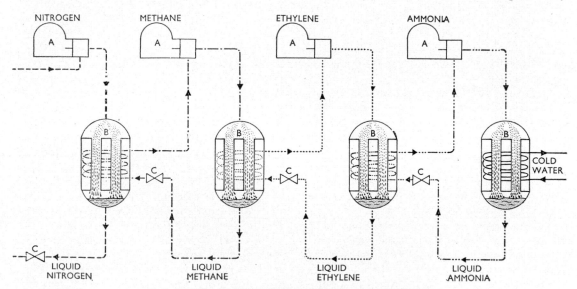

FIG. 1. DIAGRAM OF THE CASCADE PROCESS FOR LIQUEFYING GASES

A. Compressors in which gases are compressed. B. Heat exchangers and liquefiers in which gases are liquefied
C. Expansion valves at which pressure is reduced and gases evaporate

way of a heat exchanger, in which it cools incoming compressed gas and is itself warmed up, the engine becomes progressively colder until the gas begins to liquefy. To avoid liquid in the engine, the final step of liquefaction is generally taken by condensing a separate stream of gas under pressure in contact with the cold expanded gas leaving the engine (Fig. 2).

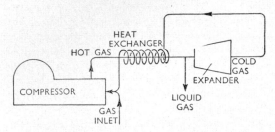

FIG. 2. DIAGRAM OF THE LIQUEFACTION OF HYDROGEN

Another method is to allow the compressed gas to expand through a nozzle without driving any machinery. With most gases this leads to a small temperature drop, which increases as the inlet temperature falls. By the inclusion of a heat exchanger this temperature drop can be made to cool the gas to liquefaction. An air liquefaction plant of this type consists of a compressor in which the air is compressed to about 3,000 lb. per sq. in., a 'scrubber' in which traces of carbon dioxide are removed from the air with a solution of caustic soda, a chemical drier for removing moisture, a heat exchanger, a throttle valve, and a vessel for collecting the liquid air. In this arrangement rather less than 10 per cent. of the air is condensed; the rest returns through the exchanger and serves to cool the incoming compressed air.

In the case of hydrogen and helium, if expansion starts at room temperature, the effect is to warm the gas instead of cooling it. But at low temperatures the effect becomes a cooling one again, and the method can be used successfully for liquefying hydrogen if the compressed gas is pre-cooled with liquid air or nitrogen. It can also be used to liquefy helium if the helium is pre-cooled with liquid hydrogen.

The principal industrial application of gas liquefaction is the production of pure gases by the DISTILLATION (q.v. Vol. VII) of liquid mixtures at low temperatures. All the oxygen used in industry is produced by the distillation of liquid air at temperatures around −190° C.

Small quantities of liquefied gases are stored and transported in double-walled vessels of glass or copper, the space between the inner and outer wall being evacuated to prevent conduction and convection of heat. A layer of silver is deposited on the glass walls and the copper is polished to reduce radiation—and consequently to reduce the rate of evaporation. A good, spherical, copper Dewar (as these evacuated vessels are called after their inventor Sir James Dewar) will lose about 4% of its liquid air content in 24 hours.

Liquid oxygen in quantities of several tons is stored and transported in large copper spheres in steel shells insulated with magnesium carbonate. As with increasing diameter the surface of a sphere increases much more slowly than its volume, evaporation losses from large vessels are not unduly high.

See also GASES, PROPERTIES OF; REFRIGERATOR.

LLOYD BARRAGE. This huge DAM (q.v.) in western Pakistan is one of several great engineering projects that have helped to solve the two most pressing problems of the sub-continent of India—the control of drought and flood—which in the past have cost many millions of lives. The Lloyd Barrage is built across the river INDUS (q.v. Vol. III) near Sukkur in Sind province; it is sometimes known as the Sukkur barrage.

Sind, for the most part a flat desert plain, has a small and uncertain rainfall, and its people depend for the IRRIGATION (q.v. Vol. VI) of their crops on the waters of the Indus, whose valley forms the backbone of the province. The river is fed by the melting snows of the distant Himalayas, which come down in flood during 4 months of the year; for the remaining 8 months the flow is small. Moreover, from year to year the floods vary in volume and in the time of their coming. The cultivation of the millions of acres of land dependent on this capricious water supply was always haphazard, and the people's hold on life precarious.

Schemes for some way of controlling the level of the river had been discussed since the middle of the 19th century, but it was not until 1923 that final approval was given for a plan to build a dam across the river. Work began at once; the barrage was opened by the Viceroy of India nearly 9 years later, and named after Lord Lloyd who, as Governor of Bombay Province, had done much to promote the project. Its construction was organized in stages, the area of each succes-

Ransomes & Rapier Ltd.

THE LLOYD BARRAGE

sive year's work being first enclosed in a Coffer-dam (q.v.). The river bed was excavated, at first mainly by Dredgers (q.v. Vol. IV), and then, after water had been pumped from the coffer-dam, by hand down to foundation level. Special broad- and narrow-gauge railways, 66 miles long, were laid to carry materials to the site, the narrow-gauge track being taken right into the cofferdams. Work went on day and night, a special generating plant providing electric light.

The barrage, which is nearly 1 mile long, is built of limestone with arches of reinforced concrete; it has sixty-six spans, each of 60 feet. Steel gates in each span, operated either electrically or by hand from a bridge above the barrage, control the flow of water. At a lower level the barrage carries a roadway from bank to bank. Water is drawn from the river above the dam by seven main irrigation canals, three on the right bank and four on the left, which branch out into minor canals to form a complicated distribution system (*see* Vol. III, p. 233). The total length of these canals is over 6,000 miles, and to build them about 5,500 million cubic feet of earth was excavated. This vast scheme, which cost £15 millions, irrigates some 5½ million acres, an area equal to more than one-sixth of all the land cultivated in the United Kingdom.

See also Dams.
See also Vol. III: Indus; India.
See also Vol. VI: Irrigation.

LOCKS, *see* Canal Building. *See also* Vol. IV: Locks and Weirs.

LOCOMOTIVES, *see* Railway Rolling Stock. *See also* Vol. IV: Locomotives.

LOGARITHMS. A logarithm is the name of a mathematical function which enables complicated multiplication and division to be carried out rapidly with the help of a book of printed tables of the logarithms of numbers.

To understand logarithms we must have in mind two kinds of numbers, natural numbers, the numbers in ordinary use (for example, 3 books, 14 chairs, 245 sheep), and logarithmic numbers, those which indicate the number of times some predetermined figure (called a 'base') must occur in self-multiplication to produce the natural number required. Let us choose 2 as our base. It takes three 2's multiplied together $(2 \times 2 \times 2)$ to make 8, so 3 is the logarithm of the natural number 8. Similarly, when 2 is the base, 4 is the logarithm of 16 $(2 \times 2 \times 2 \times 2)$ and 5 that of 32 $(2 \times 2 \times 2 \times 2 \times 2)$.

To write this down in a clear yet simple way we use index figures, small upper figures on the right-hand side which indicate self-multiplication of the large figure. Thus:

$$2 \times 2 \times 2 = 2^3 = 8$$
$$2 \times 2 \times 2 \times 2 = 2^4 = 16$$
$$2 \times 2 \times 2 \times 2 \times 2 = 2^5 = 32$$

or, if 7 is the base number, we might have:

$$7 \times 7 = 7^2 = 49$$
$$7 \times 7 \times 7 = 7^3 = 343$$
$$7 \times 7 \times 7 \times 7 = 7^4 = 2401$$

and so on.

We can quickly build a more complete table:

$2^2 = 4$	$2^7 = 128$
$2^3 = 8$	$2^8 = 256$
$2^4 = 16$	$2^9 = 512$
$2^5 = 32$	$2^{10} = 1024$
$2^6 = 64$	

These tables have great practical value. If we want to multiply 16 by 64, instead of doing a long multiplication sum, we find from the table that the logarithmic number of 16 is 2^4 and of 64 is 2^6. As the 2 is common to both, all we need do is to add together the index figures, or 'indices', thus $2^{4+6} = 2^{10}$. We consult the table and find that 2^{10} is the logarithm of 1024, and this is the answer we are seeking.

Division, let us say $512 \div 32$, is carried out as simply, by subtracting the index figures. As $512 = 2^9$ and $32 = 2^5$ so $2^{9-5} = 2^4 = 16$, which is the answer.

Most logarithms differ in two ways from the simple examples given so far. The base almost always used is the figure 10, which is found to be convenient because all modern counting is built on a scale of 10. And this base itself is never written down since everyone knows what it is: a logarithm is really an index figure written large, with the base omitted. Thus 10^2, 10^5, and 10^9 always appear in logarithm calculations simply as 2, 5, and 9. So long as the distinction between natural numbers and logarithmic numbers is remembered, this produces no confusion.

Logarithms to a base of 10, or common logarithms, are founded on this table:

Number	Logarithm
1	0
10	1
100	2
1,000	3
10,000	4
100,000	5
1,000,000	6

and so on.

If we want to multiply any two numbers together we look up the logarithms in the table and add them together. The decimals are so calculated that the result of this addition is the logarithm of the product of the two original numbers. An engineer or scientist engaged in laborious calculation will have on his desk a printed book containing tables of some thousands of logarithms, and so can carry out the longest operation of multiplication or division merely by simple addition or subtraction. The printed tables are saved from being unwieldy because, with the scale of 10, combinations of figures recur again and again; so by changing the number before the decimal point, the logarithm will be as valid for a number in the thousands as for one in the millions.

Suppose, for example, that the engineer wants to look up the logarithm of 20 (usually written for brevity 'log 20'). He knows that 20 is 10 times 2, and therefore that log 10 added to log 2 will give log 20. He knows that log 10 is 1, and he finds from his book that log 2 is 0·3010, so he adds both together and writes down 1·3010 without any further calculation. In the same way log 200 is 2·3010, and log 2,000 is 3·3010, and so on.

Since the logarithm of the natural number 1 is 0, that of a fraction must be less than 0. This is represented in a special way. Suppose that we want log 0·2. As 0·2 is 2 divided by 10, we need merely subtract log 10 from log 2. We have seen that log 2 is 0·3010, so we deduct 1 (the logarithm of 10) from it. But we do not write down the plain arithmetical answer, which would be

$$
\begin{array}{rr}
 & 0\cdot3010 \\
\text{minus} & 1\cdot \\
\hline
\text{equals} & -0\cdot6990
\end{array}
$$

Instead, the logarithm of 0·2 is written as $\bar{1}\cdot3010$, the symbol over the 1 indicating that the figure on the left of the decimal point is a minus quantity. This makes calculation much easier. A striking example of the logarithmic principle is the SLIDE RULE (q.v.), with which multiplication and division can be performed manually.

Some logarithmic tables and slide rules are designed to include figures which are in frequent use in special departments of engineering, such as the figures for angles in TRIGONOMETRY (q.v.), or those relating to calculations used in aeronautic engineering or electrical engineering. Sometimes, part of the information in a GRAPH (q.v.) is based on quantities calculated by natural numbers while another part of the information is based on logarithmic quantities.

See also SLIDE RULE.
See also Vol. IV: COUNTING, HISTORY OF.

LUBRICATION, *see* FRICTION AND LUBRICATION, Section 4.

M

MACHINE TOOLS. 1. These are the machines used in engineering to shape metals and other materials. Before the machine age this work was done with hardened hand tools—in particular, the chisel and hammer—and years of experienced craftsmanship were needed to obtain the necessary quality and accuracy. The metal was first given roughly its right shape by being either hammered when red hot or cast in a mould (*see* CASTING). Then the final shape was obtained by further hammering and by chiselling. A great advance was made with the introduction of the file, a hardened steel tool, roughened to form many tiny cutting edges, and used to smooth the relatively rough surfaces left by the chisel. Nowadays, these hand tools are normally used only for final FITTING (q.v.) and adjustment of parts made on machine tools.

The various complicated machine tools now used by engineers are designed to do the same jobs as the hammer, the chisel, and the file, but very much more quickly and efficiently, and with a much wider range of application. The vastly increased production of modern times would never have been possible without these machines to take the place of hand work, nor could the hand-worker ever produce the precision now needed. The machine tools which have replaced the chisel and file and which shape the metal by removing parts of it are shapers, planers, MILLING MACHINES, DRILLING AND BORING MACHINES, grinders, and LATHES (qq.v.); and those which have replaced the hammer and which press the metal into the required shape are steam hammers, FORGING AND PRESSING machines, and SHEET-METAL WORK tools (qq.v.).

Perhaps the most important of all machine tools is the lathe, which is described in a separate article. It can produce circular parts by bringing a cutting tool up against the part as it rotates, so that metal is cut away all the way round, thus leaving the finished piece of metal circular in shape. There is a great variety of different lathes for different purposes.

2. *Machining flat surfaces.* Metal is machined, that is, given a flat surface, by being moved under a cutter or, alternatively, by being kept stationary while a cutting tool is moved along it. The most important cutting tool is the milling machine, consisting, in its simplest form, of a horizontal shaft, or spindle, carrying a cylindrical cutter which is rotated over a table to which the workpiece is attached and which slices away metal from the work as it passes along underneath it.

The shaping machine, or 'shaper', also produces flat surfaces. The workpiece is fastened to the worktable of the machine, and an arm, with a sharp-pointed cutter at the end pointing down towards the workpiece, moves to and fro horizontally over it. At each slow outward stroke of the arm a strip of metal is cut away, and during the quick return stroke the table is automatically moved or 'fed over' a little, ready for the next cut. In this way, a series

Butler Machine Tool Co.

FIG. I. PLANING MACHINE CUTTING TWO SURFACES OF A WORK-PIECE SIMULTANEOUSLY

The operator is holding the electric control switch. A. Worktable. B. Cross-beam. C. Cutting-tools in between tool-posts. D. Workpiece clamped to table

of strips is cut from the work until the whole surface has been gone over. The cutting tool is mounted in a holder which lifts on the return stroke so as to avoid blunting its cutting edge. This holder can be moved upwards or downwards by means of a screw to vary the depth of cut. The length the arm travels is also adjustable. The shaper is used chiefly for machining single pieces of metal of relatively small size.

The planing machine, or 'planer' (Fig. 1), which is designed primarily for machining large objects, also has a to and fro motion like the shaper, but in this case the workpiece is moved instead of the tool. The work is clamped to a table (A) which is driven backwards and forwards between two rigid columns carrying a crossbeam (B). The beam, which can be moved up and down on these columns, carries the cutting tool (C). As with the shaper, the tool is automatically lifted at the end of each stroke and brought into contact again after the return stroke. It can be fixed so that either horizontal or vertical surfaces can be machined. Some planers are large enough to hold a motor lorry; and when a number of small but similar pieces of material have to be machined, these are arranged in line and all cut with one stroke—a method of setting out the workpieces known as 'ganging', and used also for other processes such as milling. To avoid waste of time, some planers have two tables, one in operation while the other is being loaded. For some types of work, an open-sided planer, with only one column to support the beam, is used, so that the work can overhang on the other side of the table.

3. *Making holes*. By far the commonest way of making holes in metal workpieces is with a drilling machine (*see* DRILLING AND BORING). The rotating cutter, that is, the drill, is brought down on to the work, cutting its way into it and, because it is rotating, producing a round hole. Drilling machines may vary from very small, single-spindle types, used to make one hole at a time, to extremely complicated multiple machines drilling a great number of different holes, often in a number of different sizes, simultaneously. Larger holes are made by boring mills, in which the work rotates instead of the cutting tool. For making holes to a high degree of accuracy and finish jig-boring machines are used.

Another way of making holes is by broaching. The tool is a long bar with a series of cutters all the way along it (Fig. 2). These have the same shape as the hole to be formed but start smaller than the hole and gradually get larger until those at the top of the broach are of the exact size required. This tool is either pulled or pushed through a preliminary hole, cutting progressively more and more metal away until, by the time the whole broach has passed through, the hole has been formed. This method is useful for producing holes of some irregular shape which could not be produced by drilling. The same method can also be used for shaping outside surfaces—known as external broaching.

4. *Grinding*. It is possible to remove metal not only by cutting it away but also by grinding it with a wheel made of an abrasive material. When the wheel rotates, the movement of the abrasive against the metal grinds it away much as sandpaper or emery paper smoothes a piece of wood. In fact, the earliest grinding machines used emery wheels. With the much more effective artificial abrasives the grinding machine has become one of the most important machine tools available to the engineer (Fig. 3).

Grinding is normally used where accurate and highly finished parts have to be produced. There is an almost endless variety of grinding machines. For the production of flat parts, a surface grinder is used, in principle like a milling

Lapointe Machine Co.

FIG. 2. VERTICAL BROACHING MACHINE WITH BROACHERS
ENTERING THE TWO WORKPIECES

Finished splined rings are shown in the foreground

Churchill Machine Tool Co.

FIG. 3. SIMULTANEOUS SURFACE GRINDING OF THREE WORK-
PIECES ACTING TOGETHER ON A MAGNETIC CHUCK

machine, except that a grinding wheel replaces the milling cutter. For grinding cylindrical parts, a cylindrical grinder is used, which works much as a lathe does, the work being rotated and brought against the wheel instead of against a cutter, as in a lathe. Cylindrical grinders may be used either for producing an external cylindrical surface or an internal one, such as a hole. Grinders could not at first be used to make very small holes because the grinding unit itself had to be so small that it was impossible to make it rotate fast enough. The development of special high-frequency ELECTRIC MOTORS (q.v.), however, has now made it possible for internal grinders to operate at speeds up to 100,000 r.p.m.

In the 1920's a new method of grinding was developed, called 'centreless grinding', in which the work, instead of being held while being ground, is merely supported on a rest, called the work-rest, and is kept in contact with the grinding wheel by a second wheel called the control wheel (Fig. 4). Instead of being on a moving table, the work is moved continuously along the work blade, parallel to the axis of the wheel. In this way, long pieces of material can be rapidly

ground to accurate dimensions or mass-produced parts can be fed through the machine continuously.

Another very important application is the thread or gear grinding machine in which a screw-thread or a gear can be cut in an already hardened steel part which could not, therefore, be cut with simple tools. One method of doing this uses a wheel formed to the shape of the thread to be ground, and another generates the gear-teeth (*see* GEARS and SCREW-THREADS.)

A special range of grinding machines, known as optical profile grinders, has been designed for very fine work of extreme precision; in some of which a greatly enlarged image of the work being ground is projected on to a screen so that the operator can see exactly what he is doing.

The cutters for modern machine tools have to be very carefully made, and there is a whole range of tool and cutter grinders designed specifically for grinding the cutters which are used on other machine tools.

5. *Forming metal by pressing.* All the tools so far described shape metals by cutting them; it is also possible to shape them by hammering or pressing them: indeed, this is much the older way. The wide range of machine tools which carry out this type of work are called presses, and all work on the same general principle. Very high pressure is applied to the metal, which is thus 'squeezed' into a given shape (*see* FORGING AND PRESSING.)

6. *Machine tools in modern industry.* The many other machine tools that have been devised for doing particular jobs in modern industry are

B.S.A. Tools Ltd.

FIG. 4. CENTRELESS GRINDING
A. Workpiece. B. Work-rest. C. Grinding wheel.
D. Control wheel.

all basically developments of one or other of the types described here.

The design of the machine tool today tends to become more and more complicated, but its object remains the same—to produce highly skilled work rapidly and with as little skilled labour as possible. In many cases, all the operator has to do is to start and stop the machine—the rest is automatic. Modern machines can carry out a whole series of operations, and can even inspect the finished product and reject those parts which are not right (*see* AUTOMATIC CONTROLS). In the future machine tools will almost certainly come to do more and more, and require less and less attention from the men who operate them, until a whole production line will virtually be able to operate itself.

See also PRODUCTION ENGINEERING; SAFETY DEVICES.

MAGNETIC MATERIALS. These are used to increase the magnetism produced by ELECTRIC CURRENTS and to make permanent MAGNETS (qq.v.). The magnetism produced by an electric current is increased many thousand times by passing the current through a coil of wire wound around a 'core' made of a magnetic material. The number of times that the core increases the magnetic effect of the current is called the 'permeability' of the material. The magnetic materials used for the electromagnets and armatures of ELECTRIC MOTORS and ELECTRIC GENERATORS, and for the cores of electric TRANSFORMERS (qq.v.), are alloys of steel and other metals in the form of sheets about $\frac{1}{50}$ inch thick.

One of the most used alloys is steel containing about $3\frac{1}{2}\%$ of silicon (a non-metallic mineral). This silicon steel is subjected to careful HEAT TREATMENT (q.v.) as it is rolled out into thin sheets by heavy steel rollers. The metal must be very pure, particularly it must be free from carbon, to obtain the best results. The maximum permeability of silicon steel is about 60,000, whereas that of certain alloys of iron and nickel, such as permalloy, is 90,000. A recent improvement on permalloy, called supermalloy, which contains small amounts of the rare metals molybdenum and manganese, has the exceedingly high permeability of 1,000,000—in other words the magnetism produced by an electric current flowing in a coil of wire is increased by one million times when a supermalloy core is placed inside the coil. The proportions of the different metals used in these alloys is shown in Table 1.

During recent years many new materials have been invented for making stronger and more lasting permanent MAGNETS (q.v.). The magnetic power of a material can be measured by first magnetizing a specimen of the material by placing it inside a coil of wire carrying an electric current, and then reversing the current by a switch so that its strength can be slowly increased until the magnetism of the specimen is just destroyed. The strength of the reversed current shows how strongly the specimen clings to its magnetism, and so measures its 'coercive force'.

The first permanent magnets were made of carbon steel; when the metals cobalt, chromium, and tungsten were added, the resulting alloy, 'kobalt 300', had five times the coercive force of carbon steel. There are now a large number of permanent magnet alloys containing cobalt: 'alnico', for example, contains also nickel and aluminium and has a coercive force fifteen times that of carbon steel. Many of the new alloys are such hard and brittle materials that it is difficult to manufacture them with ordinary machine tools. They can, however, be powdered and forced into moulds, using heat and high pressures to make magnets of any required shape.

Here are the compositions of the more common permanent magnet alloys.

TABLE 1

Alloy	Percentage of each ingredient				
	Iron	*Silicon*	*Nickel*	*Molybdenum*	*Manganese*
Silicon steel	$96\frac{1}{2}$	$3\frac{1}{2}$	..	..	..
Permalloy	$21\frac{1}{2}$	..	$78\frac{1}{2}$	..	..
Supermalloy	$15\frac{1}{2}$	..	79	5	$\frac{1}{2}$

TABLE 2

Alloy	Percentage of each ingredient								
	Iron	*Carbon*	*Cobalt*	*Nickel*	*Copper*	*Chromium*	*Aluminium*	*Tungsten*	*Titanium*
Carbon steel	99	1	..	..	..	..	..	..	..
Kobalt 300	51	1	35	..	..	9	..	4	..
Alnico	49	..	24	15	3	..	8	..	1
Cunico 1	..	..	29	21	50	..	..	..	..

Large numbers of small coils of wire are used in telephone and radio apparatus to carry the rapidly changing electric currents that correspond to the sound and radio waves (*see* TELEPHONE ENGINEERING). These coils are usually wound on a magnetic core, for less wire is then needed to produce the same magnetic effect. But the magnetic cores for radio coils cannot be made of the thin steel sheets used for the cores of electric motors and power transformers, for these would absorb far too much of the radio-frequency energy. Instead they are made from magnetic materials in the form of a very fine dust with each particle insulated from its neighbours in order to reduce the induced currents (*see* IN-DUCTION, ELECTRIC) that would otherwise flow in the core and waste energy.

There are two types of magnetic material suitable for this. The first is made by mixing fine metallic particles of iron or nickel-iron with a plastic material and moulding the mixture under heat and pressure as high as 100 tons per square inch. In radio apparatus the dust particles used are only 1/20,000 inch across. The second type is made by mixing magnetite (a magnetic oxide of iron) with the oxides of nickel, zinc, and manganese. The mixed oxides are moulded to the required shape in a hydraulic press and then fired in a kiln. The resulting material, called a ferrite, is like pottery, hard and brittle. Ferrite materials, which are relatively new, have permeabilities up to 3,000, whereas the highest permeability that can be reached with dust cores is about 200.

MAGNETS.

1. PERMANENT MAGNETS. The mineral lodestone is a natural magnet found in the earth (*see* MAGNETISM, Vol. III); but all the magnets now used in great numbers by electrical engineers are pieces of iron or steel that have been magnetized artificially by an ELECTRIC CURRENT (q.v.). The magnetic effect of a direct electric current is identical with that of the lodestone, but can be made very many times more powerful. It is increased when the wire carrying the current is wound into a large number of loops, and it can be increased several thousands of times more by winding the wire around a rod or 'core' made of iron or of one of the special alloys known as MAGNETIC MATERIALS (q.v.). When certain materials such as carbon steel are used, the rod remains strongly magnetized after the electric current has been switched off.

It is in this way that 'permanent magnets' are now made in a large variety of shapes and sizes for use in making ELECTRICAL INSTRUMENTS, in TELEPHONE ENGINEERING (qq.v.), and in magnetic COMPASSES (q.v. Vol. IV). The magnetic

material is formed into the required shape before it is magnetized by the electric current because permanent magnets lose their magnetism when they are struck, heated, or otherwise roughly treated. The two most common shapes of permanent magnet are horseshoes and long straight bars. The magnetic effects are strongest at two points near the ends of a magnet, and these points are known as its North and South poles. The region immediately around a magnet where its influence is felt is called the 'magnetic field'.

2. ELECTROMAGNETS. When the wire carrying the electric current is wound around a core of soft iron or silicon steel, the core's magnetism disappears almost completely when the current is switched off. This arrangement of a wire coil surrounding a core of soft iron is called an electromagnet. Electromagnets are very widely used in electrical engineering, for with powerful electric currents and many turns of wire extremely strong magnetic effects can be produced. Furthermore, the strength of an electromagnet can be easily adjusted by altering the strength of the current or can be made to vanish by switching the current off. Electromagnets are essential parts of ELECTRIC MOTORS and ELECTRIC GENERATORS, and slung from the hooks of CRANES (qq.v.) they are used for lifting scrap iron.

An important use of electromagnets is in the 'relays' employed in large numbers in telephone exchanges and in other electrical apparatus. A relay is simply an electric switch that is operated by an electromagnet. A typical relay (Fig. 1) consists of a body B, on the knife-edge of which is pivoted an L-shaped bar A, the 'armature'. These and a core C are made of soft iron. Round

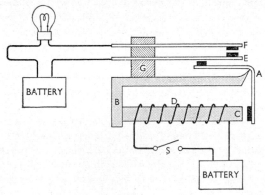

FIG. 1. DIAGRAM OF A RELAY

A. Armature. B. Frame. C. Core. D. Coil of insulated copper wire. E, F. Spring contacts. G. Insulating material. s. Switch

the core is wound a coil D of several thousand turns of insulated copper wire. The armature presses against the lower of two spring contacts, E and F, which are mounted on blocks of insulating material G fastened to the relay's body.

In Fig. 1 the coil is shown connected to an electric battery through a switch S. When the switch is closed, an electric current flows through the relay's coil, magnetizing the core, which then attracts the armature. As the armature moves towards the core it presses the lower contact E against the upper one, and so switches on a second electric circuit to light a powerful lamp. This example shows how a quite weak current in the relay's coil circuit can be used to switch on or off a much more powerful current in the relay's contact circuit. Relays often have several separate sets of contact springs, all operated by the one armature. In this way several independent circuits can be switched on and off together by means of one switch controlling the current in the relay's coil.

See also MAGNETIC MATERIALS.
See also Vol. III: MAGNETISM.

MARINE ENGINEERING. 1.

This is concerned with the design and construction of all the machinery which drives and serves a SHIP (q.v. Vol. IV)—the main propelling engines, boilers, dynamos for electric power, pumps, and many other pieces of auxiliary machinery. Marine engineering is a separate activity from NAVAL ARCHITECTURE (q.v.), which is concerned mainly with the design of the ship as a whole.

A reciprocating STEAM ENGINE (q.v.) was used in the 1800's to drive the paddle-wheels of the first practical STEAMSHIP (q.v. Vol. IV), and triple-expansion reciprocating engines still drive many of the older merchant ships. Nowadays most high-powered liners and naval vessels and many medium-powered cargo ships and tankers are driven by steam turbines. Ships may also be propelled by diesels, gas turbines, or electric motors.

2. STEAM-DRIVEN SHIPS. The steam for these engines, whether reciprocating engines or turbines, is generated in boilers burning fuel oil or coal. Cylindrical fire-tube, or 'Scotch', boilers are still used in many low-powered merchant ships, though not often for pressures above 250 lb. per square inch. For higher steam pressures and temperatures many different kinds of water-tube boiler are used. These are smaller,

lighter, and more efficient than comparable Scotch boilers, the smaller diameter drums allowing higher pressures to be developed. A modern marine boiler can produce 250,000 lb. of steam per hour at 650 lb. per square inch and at a temperature of 850° F. Most boilers are oil-fired, the fuel being pumped through steam heaters before being sprayed into the furnace. Air to burn the fuel is supplied under pressure by fans or blowers. The latest developments in boiler design include forced circulation of the boiler water by pumps, and fuel burning under very high air pressures (*see* BOILERS).

A marine turbine set usually consists of two or three separate turbines, the expanding steam passing from the high-pressure through the intermediate-pressure to the low-pressure turbine. These are installed beside one another and all drive on to the same main gear-wheel and propeller shaft. A separate turbine for developing astern power is fitted, usually on the low-pressure ahead turbine shaft. Turbines do not work efficiently unless their blade speed is high; PROPELLERS (q.v.) on the other hand work best at low speeds. As the early turbines were coupled directly to the propellor shafts, they had to be run slowly, and so turbines of very large diameter were built to give a high blade speed at a low number of revolutions. But even these big unwieldy turbines were still running more slowly than their ideal speed, while the propellers were

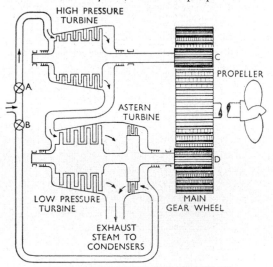

FIG. 1. LAYOUT OF A MARINE TURBINE SET

Steam from the boilers enters from the left and follows the direction of the arrows. A. Ahead throttle valve. B. Astern throttle valve. C. High pressure pinion. D. Low pressure pinion

Vickers Ltd.

THE CONTROL PLATFORM OF THE ENGINE-ROOM OF THE STEAM-DRIVEN P. & O. LINER *HIMALAYA*
Showing port and starboard ahead and astern steam valves and telegraphs

running too fast. Finally this difficulty was overcome by using various systems of speed reduction, such as gearing or electric transmission. GEARS (q.v.) were in common use by 1920, and in the following 30 years there were steady improvements in design, culminating in gearing sets that give a reduction of speed of about 30 to 1. These enable the ratio of speed of turbines and propellers to be very different and small turbines to be used with maximum efficiency.

Since 1945 'reaction' turbines, which were installed in most ships between the First and Second World Wars, have given way more and more to 'impulse' turbines. These have small alloy-steel rotors running at about 7,000 r.p.m., giving high blade speeds. The expansion of the steam can thus be carried out efficiently in very light and compact turbines (*see* STEAM TURBINE).

Steam turbines take up much less space in the engine-room than reciprocating engines or diesels, and cause less vibration.

3. DIESEL. The largest ship fitted with diesel engines is the *Dominion Monarch*, a quadruple-screw passenger vessel of over 26,000 tons. Many different types of slow-speed, two-stroke cycle diesel engines are used to drive higher-powered ships of this type. All are large, heavy engines which run at about 100 r.p.m. and have from three to eight cylinders arranged in line, developing up to 1,500 h.p. per cylinder. The same amount of power can be provided by high-speed diesels if several engines are connected to one propeller shaft, either by electric transmission or by mechanical gearing.

As diesel engines have a low fuel consumption they are much used for ships, such as small liners, coasters, and submarines, where only medium or low speeds are necessary. With these ships high-speed diesels may be used, in various

General Electric Co.

THE ENGINE ROOM OF THE TURBO-ELECTRIC TANKER *SAN SILVESTRE*

formations of eight or sixteen cylinders, arranged in line or in the shape of a **V**, and developing up to 3,000 h.p. at 1,000 r.p.m. Many modern diesels are also fitted with turbo-superchargers which make use of heat from the exhaust gas (*see* INTERNAL COMBUSTION ENGINE).

4. GAS TURBINE. The earliest marine gas turbine, first used in a motor gunboat in 1947, was essentially the same as an aircraft jet engine (*see* AIRCRAFT ENGINES, Section 2, Vol. IV), with exhaust gases driving a separate power turbine. With its high power and light weight, a gas turbine is an ideal engine for fast gunboats or as a 'boost' engine for giving high speeds when used with steam turbines or diesels. But it has a high fuel consumption and only a short working life owing to the destructive effect of its intensely hot gases. Gas turbines designed as long-life main engines for larger ships may carry blade-cooling equipment and heat-exchangers to transfer some of the heat of the exhaust gases to the incoming air, and may use several air COMPRESSORS (q.v.)

in a series driven by separate turbines. Gas turbines are also used for driving electric generators and other auxiliary machinery (*see* GAS TURBINE).

5. ELECTRIC TRANSMISSION. In ships with electric transmission, the main turbine or diesel engines drive electric generators which supply power to slow-speed ELECTRIC MOTORS (q.v.) which turn the propellers. Ships of this type are known as turbo-electric or diesel-electric ships (*see* ELECTRIC SHIP, Vol. IV). The advantage of electric transmission is that the main engines can be placed anywhere in the ship while the driving motors are right aft near the propellers, and long propeller shafts are unnecessary. The disadvantages are the heavy weight of electric machinery and the complicated SWITCHGEAR (q.v.) needed for manœuvring the ship.

6. NUCLEAR POWER. The U.S. submarine *Nautilus*, launched in 1953, was the first ship to be propelled by NUCLEAR POWER (q.v.). In this ship the atomic energy, produced by the nuclear power plant carried in the submarine, provides heat for a boiler and steam turbine. A few pounds of uranium is sufficient to drive the submarine many thousands of miles.

7. AUXILIARY MACHINERY. In addition to their main propelling engines, ships need ELECTRIC GENERATORS to provide power for heating and lighting and driving other auxiliary machinery. Numerous PUMPS (qq.v.) have to be fitted for bringing fuel and water from storage tanks to the main and auxiliary engines and boilers; for drinking water; for fire services; and for pumping away all waste, or 'bilge'. Fresh water for drinking and for feeding the boilers is made from sea water in evaporators, and REFRIGERATORS (q.v.) are needed for cooling food and cargo and for air-conditioning. Other machines include steering engines for moving the rudder, capstans for hauling in the mooring cables and ropes, and hoists and derricks for lifting cargo (see MECHANICAL HANDLING). All this auxiliary equipment may be driven by steam or gas turbines, diesels, or electric motors.

'Stabilizers', designed to counteract rolling in bad weather, are sometimes fitted in ships—as an aid to accurate gunnery in some warships or for the comfort of passengers in certain liners and ferries. They consist of fins, fitted amidships on each side of the hull near the bottom, which can be withdrawn into the hull when not in use. One type consists of two fins, each of them $12\frac{1}{2}$ feet long. Two GYROSCOPES (q.v.) automatically control the angle at which the fins must be tilted, and how long they must remain tilted, to counteract the ship's roll. The fins can move through about 40° in $1\frac{1}{2}$ seconds, and can produce a righting force of 700 tons when the ship is steaming at full speed. Hydraulic power, produced by a pump driven by a 50 h.p. electric motor, is used to tilt the fins.

See also NAVAL ARCHITECTURE; ENGINES, HISTORY OF.
See also Vol. IV: SHIP; STEAMSHIP.

MASONRY. 1. Stone is the finest of all building materials. In ancient times, if there were no local deposits of stone, it was often imported. The Babylonians, for example, living in the stoneless valley of the Euphrates, brought stone for their palaces from great distances, in spite of the difficulties of transporting such heavy materials. In the 13th century, Westminster Abbey was built of stone brought from Caen in Normandy, for there is no local stone near London and the sea

journey from the Continent was less difficult than the journey overland from the West Country or the Midlands. Stone can be cut accurately and given a smooth surface; it can be carved; and it is durable and weatherproof. Its quality varies from the hardest granite and the finest marble to soft chalky stones such as Clunch and Beerstone.

Of recent years STRUCTURAL STEELWORK and CONCRETE CONSTRUCTION (qq.v.) have been used more and more for large buildings, for the greater strength of these materials makes possible lighter walls and larger openings for doors and windows. But in order to have the fine surface finish of stone, the walls of 'frame' buildings of steel and reinforced concrete are often faced with stone (see BUILDING, PRINCIPLES OF). County Hall, Westminster, for example, is a steel-frame building faced with stone.

2. BUILDING STONES. The fact that most buildings have been built of local stone has given an individual character to the towns and villages of different parts of the country (see HOUSES, TYPES OF, Vol. XI). The most suitable building stones

ROUGH-HEWN STONE-WORK: A COTTAGE AT SWANAGE

are limestones, sandstones, granites, and marble (*see* STONE QUARRYING, Vol. VII). Limestones are divided into hardstone and softstone according to their texture and quality. A hardstone, such as the Portland stone used for St. Paul's Cathedral and many other London buildings, is close grained and weathers well, being not easily destroyed by the polluted air of cities. Bathstone and Painswick stone are examples of softstone, or 'freestone' as it is sometimes called because it is easy to work. It is now mostly used for the interiors of buildings. Limestones vary in colour from dead white to deep yellowish brown. In England they are found in a belt running from Dorset to Lincolnshire.

Sandstones are generally coarser than most limestones, and so cannot be given such a fine finish. They have a rich warm colour, are very durable, and can be split into thin slabs for window sills, steps, paving stones, and so on. In England they are chiefly quarried in the Midlands.

Granite, quarried in Devon, Wales, the Lake District, and Scotland, is very hard, and is used where great durability is needed, as, for instance, in DOCKS AND HARBOUR CONSTRUCTION (q.v.) and other heavy engineering works, and for the ground floor of buildings. It is very difficult to work, but its surface can be polished.

Marble was the chief building material used by the Greeks and Romans, and, later, by the Italians. It has a very fine texture and can be worked and carved with great refinement. Italian marble quarried at Carrara is pure white, Greek marble is a soft creamy colour, and others are veined with various colours. It is much used for lining interior walls and floors, as in Westminster Cathedral, London, thin pieces being cut and arranged so as to show the veining and colour to the best advantage. Purbeck marble, much used for columns and other details in 13th-century churches, is, in fact, not marble but a dark grey limestone which is very hard and takes a high polish.

3. TYPES OF STONEWORK. Building stone is either 'rough hewn', that is, roughly shaped with a mason's hammer, or 'dressed' (*see* STONE DRESSING, Vol. VII), that is, prepared by machinery or cut by hand into accurate, rectangular blocks. Walls may be built entirely of dressed stone, or they may be mainly of rough-hewn stone, called rubble walling, with the corners, doorways, and windows, which need to be accurately placed, of dressed stone.

Rough-hewn stone for rubble walling may be bedded in cement or in lime mortar, consisting of approximately 1 part of lime to 3 parts of sand or ashes. This type of walling varies from district to district according to the stone available. If the stone is thin and slatey the walls are made up of thin lines, or 'courses'; if it is rough and lumpy, they are built in small polygonal patterns or laid at random. Sometimes rubble walls are laced with bands of brickwork or flints. In East Anglia, where there is no local stone, flint is frequently used.

Dressed stone, which can be jointed very accurately, is always bedded in mortar, the face of the stone being perfectly flat ('ashlar' work), or rounded or patterned in a variety of ways. Medieval buildings were invariably built of ashlar, but in the Renaissance the stones were often 'rusticated', that is, the edges were bevelled to emphasize the joints, or the surface was roughened or patterned. Often the lower courses

ASHLAR: SIR WALTER SCOTT'S HOUSE IN EDINBURGH
The ground floor is rusticated and the basement has vermiculated rustication

of the building were rusticated to give an effect of strength and solidity, while the upper part was of ashlar.

The Greeks bonded the joints in their marble buildings with iron clamps instead of mortar. The marble was so accurately dressed that it was possible to design the buildings with great precision. Columns, for example, were smaller at the top than at the bottom to prevent their looking top heavy, and the vertical lines were slightly curved outwards to give an effect of straightness by an optical illusion. Similarly, horizontal lines were slightly curved to prevent an effect of sagging. The Romans used a very strong cement, and developed arched and vaulted structures which the Greeks had not used (*see* ROMAN ART, Vol. XII).

For dry stone walls, which may be of rough-hewn or dressed stone, no mortar is used, the stones being either bedded in dry earth or bonded together with great precision. In ancient Egypt and in Peru dry stone walls were built with large blocks so accurately cut that the joints fitted together perfectly.

4. BUILDING METHODS. A mason's hand tools have changed little since ancient times, though metals such as tungsten are now used to make the tools harder. All stones are cut with a chisel, which is struck with a hard wood mallet or with a metal hammer. The chisels may be wide or narrow with straight or toothed edges—the latter being called 'claw tools'. Granite masons use heavy hammers and thick heavy chisels tempered very hard to stand up to the hardness of the material. Softstones are worked with chisels similar to carpenters' chisels and small zinc alloy mallets. For working marble, light and delicate tools, tempered to cut hard material, and iron hammers are used. Pneumatic tools rather like miniature road drills, which can be fitted to all shapes of chisel, are used for hard stones such as granite and marble.

Nowadays most stone is worked by machinery, hand tools being used only for more intricate work. These machines include 'frame saws', which are used to cut the stone from its roughest state into slabs corresponding to the height of the courses in a building; 'diamond saws', circular saws of varying diameter which cut the slabs into smaller sizes; 'carborundum saws', which are used to cut the stone accurately into slabs of even smaller proportions; planing machines; and lathes which are used for 'turning'

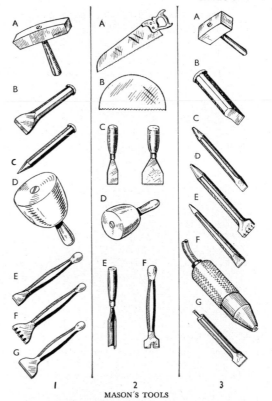

MASON'S TOOLS

I. HARDSTONE TOOLS. A. Hammer. B. Pitching tool. C. Punch. D. Mallet. E. 1 in. chisel. F. Claw. G. Boaster (E–G are mallet-headed tools). 2. SOFTSTONE TOOLS. A. Handsaw. B. Drag. C. Wood-handled chisels. D. Mallet. E. Gouge. F. Waster. 3. MARBLE TOOLS. A. Hammer. B. Pitching tool. C. Splitter. D. Claw. E. Chisel. F. Pneumatic hammer. G. Pneumatic chisel

circular-shaped stonework, such as balusters on columns.

When the dressed stonework is to be backed with a wall of concrete or brickwork, the stones are cut in heights corresponding to the main material; but for good proportion and ease of handling the length of each block should not be more than twice the height. Sometimes a building is faced with large slabs of stone only 2 or 3 inches thick, which are cramped to the wall like a veneer. The blocks of stone are bedded on mortar called 'mason's putty', usually sieved stonedust and hydraulic lime in proportions of 3 to 1. Each block is lowered on to a thin layer of mortar, and 'tamped' or beaten down with a wooden mallet until it is plumb on the face and firmly in position. The joints are 'pointed' and filled with cement 'grout', a type of liquid cement with stonedust added to it. During building, the stonework is protected from dirt by a coating of 'slurry', a mixture of water, stonedust, and plaster of Paris, which is scraped off when the building is finished, and the stonework washed to look new and clean.

Masonry arches, which consist of a number of mutually supporting wedges (*see* BUILDING, PRINCIPLES OF), are built on 'centres'—timber frames in the shape of the arch, which support the stones while they are being put in place. When the whole arch is complete and ready to support the wall above it the centre is removed.

See also BUILDING CONSTRUCTION.
See also Vol. VII: STONE DRESSING; STONE QUARRYING.
See also Vol. XI: HOUSES, HISTORY OF.

MASS, *see* Vol. III: MASS.

MATHEMATICS, *see* ARITHMETIC; ALGEBRA; GEOMETRY; TRIGONOMETRY. *See also* Vol. IV: MATHEMATICAL NOTATION; COUNTING, HISTORY OF; MEASUREMENT, HISTORY OF.

MEASUREMENT, UNITS OF. Measurement is the essence of scientific investigation and its interpretation; Lord KELVIN (q.v. Vol. V) once said that you do not really know anything about any natural phenomenon until you can measure it and express it in figures. The engineer equally must have convenient units to express the factors he is dealing with when, for example, he calculates how strong he must make a bridge if it is to stand up to its work.

1. FAMILIAR UNITS. The units with which we are constantly concerned in everyday life are those of mass, length, and time, and on these most other units—even electrical units—are now based. The units of mass and length used in the British Commonwealth are the British Imperial Units, the pound and the yard. On the Continent, and for scientific work generally, the International Metric System, with its corresponding units the kilogramme and the metre, is used. Since most of the units used to measure the quantities dealt with in science and engineering are derived from the units of mass, length, and time, it follows that there are two distinct sets of units to be considered.

The definitions which follow are not exactly in accordance with their formal specifications, which have to be very precisely worded for legal and other reasons.

(*a*) *Mass.* The MASS (q.v. Vol. III) of a body is the amount of matter of which it is composed;

this should not be confused with its weight, which is the force with which the mass is attracted to the earth by gravity. By an Act of Parliament of 1878 the 'pound' is defined as the mass of a certain cylindrical piece of platinum in the custody of the Standards Department of the Board of Trade. Every weight used by tradesmen is, in effect, corrected to agree with this standard. The International 'Metric' unit of mass, the 'kilogramme', is similarly defined as the mass of a certain cylinder of platinum-iridium alloy preserved at the International Bureau of Weights and Measures, at Sèvres in France. The relation between the pound and the kilogramme has been very accurately determined, and, to a sufficient degree of accuracy for present purposes, can be expressed as one pound = 0·45359 kilogramme.

(*b*) *Length.* The British Imperial 'yard' is defined as the distance between two specified marks on a certain bar of bronze, in the custody of the Standards Department of the Board of Trade, when the bar is at a temperature of 62° F. The International 'metre' is defined as the distance between two specified marks on a specially shaped bar of platinum-iridium alloy kept at the International Bureau of Weights and Measures. The yard is equal to approximately 0·91440 metre. An earlier set of British Imperial Standards of length can be seen on the north side of Trafalgar Square.

(*c*) *Volume.* The units of volume are derived from those of mass. On the British Imperial system the unit is the 'gallon', which is the volume occupied by 10 pounds of distilled water at a temperature of 62° F.; on the metric system the unit is the 'litre'—the volume occupied by one kilogramme of pure water at 4° C.

(*d*) *Time.* The unit of time is the 'second', which is defined as one 86,400th part of the average time it takes for the earth to rotate once on its axis.

2. MECHANICAL UNITS. There are two series of units to be considered. Those based on the British Imperial units of mass and length may be referred to for convenience as engineer's units. Those based on the metric system, the scientist's units, have in the past always been expressed in terms of the centimetre and the gramme instead of the metre and kilogramme, and are referred to as c.g.s. (centimetre-gramme-second) units.

(*a*) *Force.* The unit of force used by engineers is the force with which the earth attracts a mass of one pound—in other words, the unit of force is

VICKERS 'VISCOUNT' PROPELLER-TURBINE AIRLINER UNDER CONSTRUCTION AT HURN,
NEAR BOURNEMOUTH

The 'Viscount' has a range of up to 2,400 miles, a cruising speed of 325 miles per hour, and carries from 40 to 59 passengers

the weight of one pound, and force is expressed as so many pounds weight. But as the attraction of the earth varies a little from place to place, this means that this unit of force is not constant. An alternative unit is, therefore, preferred when this may be important; this unit is the 'poundal', which is the force which, acting continuously on a mass of one pound, produces an acceleration of one foot per second per second. A corresponding unit to this is used on the c.g.s. system: it is the 'dyne' (Greek *dunamis* = force), the force which, applied to a mass of one gramme, produces an acceleration of one centimetre per second per second.

(*b*) *Work, energy*. When a force of one pound weight moves its point of application through one foot—as, for example, when a mass of one pound is lifted through one foot—one 'foot-pound' of work is done. The corresponding unit in the c.g.s. system is the 'erg' (Greek *ergon* = work), the amount of work done when one dyne is exerted through a distance of one centimetre. This is so small a unit that for practical purposes a more convenient unit is used, the 'joule' (named after the physicist J. P. Joule), which equals ten million ergs. Whenever work is done, ENERGY (q.v.) is expended—more precisely, converted from one form into another—and energy is, therefore, expressed in the same units as is work.

(*c*) *Rate of work*. The rate at which work is done, in engineers' units, is expressed in terms of the 'horse-power', which is equal to the performance of 33,000 foot-pounds of work per minute. The corresponding c.g.s. unit, the erg per second, is impracticably small, and in practice the unit is the joule per second, which is known as the 'watt'. One horse-power is equal to approximately 746 watts.

(*d*) *Units used in the measurement of heat* (*see* TEMPERATURE, MEASUREMENT OF).

3. UNITS IN THE MEASUREMENT OF ELECTRICITY. All the quantities met with in electricity are measured in units based on recognized fundamental laws of electromagnetism (*see* INDUCTION, ELECTRIC) and electrostatics (*see* ELECTRICITY, Vol. III), expressed quantitatively in terms of the mechanical c.g.s. units, or of recent years in terms of units based on M.K.S. units (metre, kilogramme, second). For example, 'unit magnetic pole'—the unit of magnetic force—is such that two unit magnetic poles placed one centimetre apart in a vacuum repel each other with a force of one dyne; in 'unit magnetic field' a

unit pole experiences a force of one dyne; unit 'current' is that current which, flowing in an arc of a circle of one centimetre length, the radius being one centimetre, produces unit magnetic field at the centre. These are known as absolute electromagnetic (e.m.) units. Electrostatic units are based on the definition of the unit electric charge. These units are not in general of a convenient size for practical purposes; and another set of units, multiples and sub-multiples of the electromagnetic system, has been derived from them.

(*a*) *Current*. The practical unit of current, the 'ampere', is one-tenth of the absolute e.m. unit, as defined above.

(*b*) *Power, or rate of work*. Electrical energy can be converted to work, just as can heat, and the same practical unit for energy, or work—the 'joule'—is used in electricity as in heat. Similarly, the unit for measuring power, or rate of work in joules per second, is the 'watt'.

(*c*) *Electromotive force (e.m.f.), or difference of potential*. If unit current is flowing in a wire which as a result is giving out heat at the rate of one erg per second, there must be unit e.m.f. between the ends of the wire. In this case, all the electrical energy put into the wire is given out as heat. The practical unit here is the 'volt', which is the difference of electric 'pressure' between two points of a conducting wire carrying a constant current of one ampere, when the power dissipated between these points is one watt. It follows from this that the volt is a hundred million absolute e.m. units. It also follows that the product of voltage and current supplied by (say) a generator is equal to the power supplied, in watts. This is the familiar rule: VOLTS × AMPS = WATTS. But see also ALTERNATING CURRENT.

(*d*) *Resistance*. The unit is the 'ohm', which is the resistance through which an e.m.f. of one volt will maintain a current of one ampere. It follows that the ohm is a thousand million absolute e.m. units.

(*e*) *Quantity*. The unit is the 'coulomb', which is the quantity of electricity represented by a current of one ampere flowing for one second. It follows that it is one-tenth of the absolute e.m. unit.

(*f*) *Capacitance* (or 'storing power' of a condenser). The unit is the 'farad', which is the capacitance of a CONDENSER (q.v.) between the plates of which there appears a difference of 'pressure' of one volt when it is charged by a quantity of electricity equal to one coulomb. The farad is a very large unit, and in practice capacitances are usually expressed in terms of the 'microfarad', which is one-millionth of a farad.

(g) Inductance (see INDUCTION, ELECTRIC*).* The unit is the 'henry', which is the inductance of a closed circuit in which an electromagnetic force of one volt is produced when the electric current in the circuit varies uniformly at the rate of one ampere per second. In practice, the 'millihenry' —one-thousandth of a henry—is a more convenient size.

All the above definitions are based on the ampere—the unit of current—as recommended by the International Committee on Weights and Measures for legal and similar purposes; but an equally valid set could be based on the ohm or the volt, or any of the other quantities. The M.K.S. system of absolute units is being more and more used in place of the c.g.s. systems, and will doubtless in time supersede them altogether, but at present the c.g.s. systems are much the more commonly used.

The definitions of the electrical units given above are 'fundamental'—that is, they relate directly to the basic units of mass, length, and time. But for practical purposes, these definitions are not ideal, as they are difficult to reproduce experimentally with any accuracy. For this reason, 'secondary' and more practical standards have been established, which are related to the fundamental definitions by once-for-all experiments carried out extremely carefully at great trouble and expense. The volt is defined with respect to the e.m.f. of a 'standard cell'—a chemical battery constructed according to very precise rules; the ampere is defined with respect to the rate at which silver is deposited by an electric current on a silver electrode in a bath of a silver salt, and so on. This procedure is adopted with many different types of unit, the whole technique of establishing satisfactory practical reference standards being known as 'metrology'.

Other units are discussed in the articles SPECTROSCOPE, ACOUSTICS, ELECTRONICS, RADIO ENGINEERING, and ILLUMINATION.

See also WEIGHING INSTRUMENTS; LENGTH-MEASURING INSTRUMENTS; ELECTRICAL INSTRUMENTS.

MECHANICAL ENGINEERING.

The history of mechanical engineering might be said to go back to the time when man first tried to make machines to save himself work and to apply more

FIG. I. MODEL OF A HELICOPTER MADE IN ACCORDANCE WITH A DRAWING AND DESCRIPTION BY LEONARDO DA VINCI

If rapidly rotated such a device would rise into the air

power than human or animal strength alone could produce. The earliest ROLLERS, LEVERS, and PULLEYS (qq.v.), for example, could be called the work of mechanical engineers. LEONARDO DA VINCI (q.v. Vol. V), born in 1452, was a great mechanical engineer, with ideas far ahead of his time. He not only drew up plans for a type of aircraft and for a submarine, but also anticipated many of the machines and methods which modern mechanical engineers now use (*see* Fig. 1). The term 'mechanical engineering', however, was not used until the late 18th century, after the invention of the STEAM ENGINE (q.v.).

Most engineering in very early days was concerned with warfare. Then the term 'civil engineering' was used to distinguish such activities as bridge building from military engineering. Now engineering is divided into three main groups— civil engineering, mechanical engineering, and electrical engineering. Mechanical engineering, as we understand it today, stems from the INDUSTRIAL REVOLUTION (q.v. Vol. VII), and the first inventions were concerned principally with the textile trade—Kay's weaving shuttle of 1733, for example, and Hargreaves's spinning jenny of 1763. But the invention which really altered the whole outlook was Watt's steam engine of 1769. METALS (q.v.) became the main material of the engineer instead of wood, and STEAM (q.v.) gave man unheard-of reserves of power to drive not only railway engines and ships but also the machines which built them. Stronger materials were needed to withstand the new-found power that the steam engine was offering. Mechanical engineers had, therefore, to find ways of meeting these new problems. For instance, the development of Watt's steam engine was delayed 5 years because there was no machine that could bore the cylinders accurately enough until, in 1774, John Wilkinson built a boring machine which, although intended primarily for boring cannons, also served Watt's purpose.

To make steam engines, and the machinery which steam engines could work, men lacked MACHINE TOOLS (q.v.) which could shape metal, and methods of measuring to an accuracy hitherto unknown.

One of the pioneers who tackled these problems was Joseph Bramah, who was born near Barnsley in 1748. When he tried to make parts for his own inventions, his attention was drawn to the need for better machine tools; and finally, in 1802, he patented a design which was described as being 'for producing straight, smooth, and parallel surfaces on wood and other materials requiring truth'. This was the forerunner of the modern planing machine.

Bramah won such a reputation that other leading engineers were drawn to his works in Pimlico, London. Notable amongst these was Henry Maudslay—born in 1771—who was probably the greatest of the designers of machine tools for metal-working. He developed the prototype of the modern LATHE (q.v.) and laid the basis for both the metal-working planer and the slotting machine (Fig. 2). Each new tool invented was in most cases designed to meet a particular need: for instance, Maudslay invented a screw-cutting lathe in 1797 to help Bramah develop a hydraulic press on which he was working (see HYDRAULIC POWER TRANSMISSION). This lathe embodied a slide-rest, so that the cutting tool could be moved easily and accurately along the work without effort to the operator; eventually GEARS (q.v.) were also introduced so that different threads could be cut without making complicated adjustments. These two innovations had been foreseen by Leonardo da Vinci over 300 years before, but were applied now to the new requirements of turning metal instead of wood.

Mechanical engineering continued to develop as each engineer, learning from his predecessors, improved still further the tools for the job. Maudslay left Bramah and started on his own. Once again, the country's leading young engineers sought experience at a famous man's works. Amongst many who came to Maudslay was Joseph Whitworth, who became his most famous pupil.

Whitworth, born in 1803, laid the basis for modern precision engineering. With the growth

Crown Copyright, Science Museum

FIG. 2. MAUDSLAY'S ORIGINAL SCREW-CUTTING LATHE, c. 1800

FIG. 3. WHITWORTH 'MILLIONTH' MEASURING MACHINE, 1855

of industry, circumstances were changing rapidly. The old standards of accuracy—measured with a 2-foot wooden rule—were no longer adequate. Watt, in producing his first steam engines, had been satisfied with a fitting accuracy to within 'the thickness of an old shilling'. Now, with the advent of the high-pressure steam engine, and the growth of mechanical engineering in general, accuracies to within one-thousandth of an inch were necessary. But there were no means of measuring such small amounts.

Whitworth realized two fundamentally important facts. He must have a really flat surface (a 'true plane') as a basis of reference—obviously it is impossible, for instance, to measure the height of anything accurately if it is standing on an uneven surface. Secondly, he appreciated that the method of measuring by eye, by looking at a rule, could never be sufficiently accurate.

Whitworth produced his first true plane in 1830, and later he built an improved planing machine which could reproduce this plane at will. So accurate were the planed surfaces obtained from this machine, that two of them could be 'wrung' together—that is to say, if the two flat surfaces were pressed together, they would fit so tightly to each other that they could not be separated without considerable effort. Such precision for flat parts, badly needed for sliding

surfaces, was revolutionary. Whitworth also developed his 'workshop measuring machine', which was the forerunner of the modern micrometer (*see* LENGTH-MEASURING INSTRUMENTS) and could measure accurately to less than one ten-thousandth of an inch. In course of time he so improved his measuring machine that it could give accurate readings to less than one-millionth of an inch (Fig. 3).

Many famous engineers, such as Boulton and Watt, Trevithick (responsible for the high-pressure steam engine), Brunel, Nasmyth (inventor of the steam hammer), and others so revolutionized their age that, by about 1840, mechanical engineering had most of the basic tools it needed, as well as the means of measurement: there were engine-driven lathes, borers, planers, slotters, millers, shapers, and drilling machines, all capable of working in iron. By 1850 there were over 6,000 miles of railway line in Britain alone, and the Atlantic had been crossed and recrossed by steam power. Britain had become the centre of mechanical engineering in the world.

The next problem was to find methods of increasing production—in other words, to build machines which could turn out work faster. This in turn meant the development of better materials for cutting tools and stronger metals for the machines themselves. In particular, more steel was needed. The development of the Bessemer steel-making process, which was patented in 1856, went some way to meet this need (*see* STEEL-MAKING, Section 3). Mushet, in 1868, discovered that the addition of tungsten to steel gave it special properties, and this paved the way towards high-speed tool steel, a special steel eventually developed by Taylor and White and first demonstrated in 1900.

Electricity came into the factory towards the end of the 19th century, although it was some time later that the modern method of applying individual motors to each machine was generally accepted (*see* ELECTRICAL ENGINEERING, HISTORY OF).

In the 20th century the engineer has at his command many sources of power unknown in the 18th century. Now the mechanical engineer is concerned not only with the steam engine, but also with the ELECTRIC MOTOR, the INTERNAL COMBUSTION ENGINE, the STEAM TURBINE, and, latterly, the GAS TURBINE (qq.v.), and still further sources of power are on their way. Better materials to meet these new demands are constantly being developed, especially new ALLOYS (q.v.) for special purposes. As human labour becomes more expensive, machinery tends to become more automatic—indeed, in the U.S.A. a design has been produced for a completely automatic factory. ELECTRONICS (q.v.) have become important both for controlling production machinery and for measurement.

Today there is still the same problem of making materials and tools keep up to the demands of new inventions. Whittle, for example, when he invented the gas turbine (or jet engine) had to wait until special alloys were available which would be strong enough for the turbine blades. Engineers today are still actively engaged in finding better methods both of making and inspecting this vital part of the jet engine because, due to their awkward shape and need for exceptional accuracy, these blades raise special engineering problems.

It is a long stretch from Watt's early steam engine to today's supersonic aircraft, yet in fact it is less than 200 years. Never before in man's history had mechanical engineering developed at such a speed—a progress as much due to the pioneers of the Industrial Revolution as to the brilliant designers of our own time. The history of development is continuous, for in this modern industrial phase, each pioneer meets new requirements with methods of mechanical engineering out of which the techniques of the next period develop—for the mechanical engineer is constantly improving and adapting himself to new requirements as they arise.

Today it is less easy to define mechanical engineering, since it is necessarily combined with other types of engineering. Further, the whole field of engineering has become so complex that a high degree of specialization has become inevitable. For example, the making of aircraft is known as AERONAUTICAL ENGINEERING, that of making ships' engines as MARINE ENGINEERING, and that of building bridges or similar structures as structural or CIVIL ENGINEERING (qq.v.), and so on. But all of these branches are, of course, also concerned with mechanical engineering because, without it, they could not make their own particular structures. The civil engineer, for instance, depends on mechanical engineering for producing the metal parts he uses. Also, he must have a wide knowledge of mechanical engineering himself, as, indeed, must all other engineers.

Mechanical engineering, in fact, is the basis on which all other forms of modern engineering depend fundamentally. Even the electrical engineer uses machinery, machine tools, and so on, in the production of his electrical apparatus. An electric motor, for example, could not be built were it not for such mechanical equipment as presses (*see* FORGING AND PRESSING) to stamp the laminations, LATHES (q.v.) and other machines to form the shafts, grinding machines, and many other types of machinery. The mechanical engineer devises and makes the machinery with which metals can be worked into the variety of forms and shapes needed in modern industry, and devises machines which make automatic mass production with higher and higher outputs possible (*see* PRODUCTION ENGINEERING).

See also CIVIL ENGINEERING; ELECTRICAL ENGINEERING.

MECHANICAL EXCAVATOR, *see* EARTH-MOVING EQUIPMENT.

MECHANICAL HANDLING. 1. In factories, in building and civil engineering, in chemical works—and, in fact, everywhere where work is done—a surprising amount of time is spent in simply moving things from place to place. Moving things about, or 'materials handling' as the experts call it, received little attention when labour was cheap; but today the high price of even unskilled labour and the need to make every part of manufacture as efficient as possible have led specialist engineers to make a study of materials handling and to design many special pieces of equipment simply for moving things about.

Many of these advances are merely a matter of using existing equipment, such as CRANES, PUMPS, and CONVEYORS (qq.v.), more widely and more often. Concrete, for instance, is today often pumped to where it is wanted, whereas in the old days it would have been carried by a man with a wheelbarrow. Ash from POWER STATIONS (q.v.), too, is often pumped away as a watered slurry instead of being removed by railway wagons. Here, however, we are concerned with special items of equipment used in speeding up the movement of raw materials and components in factories—pieces of equipment which are often used with basic machines, in particular with cranes.

2. EQUIPMENT USED WITH CRANES. Cranes may be fitted with grabs or skips for handling bulk material and slings for lifting packages. All types of grab may be fitted with teeth to ease the grabbing of difficult materials.

(a) *Hook-on, self-dumping grab.* This can be attached to the hook of any crane. The grab is closed by hoisting, and is discharged in the air by pulling a trip line or by lowering the grab on to the point of discharge and then raising it so that the locking mechanism is automatically tripped, and the jaws open (Fig. 1). This grab has a limited holding power and is not used for lifting very heavy or very large objects.

(b) *Ring-discharge, single-chain type.* This type of grab is used where continuous grabbing is necessary with a crane fitted with only one hoisting drum. It is suitable for handling coal, coke, or sand, as well as for light excavation work where the grab can be opened at a predetermined height. The grab is opened when its discharging hook engages with a cage suspended below the jib head. The height of discharge may be altered by adjusting the cage suspension ropes (Fig. 2).

(c) *Double-rope grabs.* These are used on cranes fitted with two drums. One drum carries a closing and hoisting rope and the other a holding and lowering rope. The closed grab is hoisted up and opened at any desired height by braking the holding rope drum while at the same time paying out the hoisting rope. To lower the grab

both ropes are paid out at the same rate with the holding brake on. After the grab lands on the material, the holding brake is released and the hoisting rope is wound in to close the grab, care being taken to ensure that the holding rope is slack. Once closed, the hoisting rope lifts the grab to discharge its load, ready to repeat the cycle (Fig. 3).

The double-rope grab may be discharged at any height within the range of the crane, may be used to grab difficult materials, and, with heavy-duty ropes, may be used for general excavating work. A variation is used on DREDGERS (q.v. Vol. IV) for clearing mud and silt.

(d) *Skips and buckets.* These are made in a variety of shapes and sizes to suit particular duties, with one attachment for simple hooking on to cranes or with more where mechanical tipping is wanted.

(e) *Slings.* A variety of slings is available for handling cases, cartons, and other packaged goods, as well as materials such as bundles of tubing. According to the kind of load, each sling may connect directly with the load or be secured round it in choker or basket hitches. Sometimes attachments are used to carry a number of slings so that loads are held with great stability, while grapples and nippers have been developed to handle difficult loads such as tubes or sacks.

3. PALLETS AND LIFT TRUCKS. To avoid handling each package every time it is moved by a truck, pallets—wooden or metal platforms supported on bearers—have been developed. With these, several packages at a time can be lifted and carried by fork-lift or pallet trucks, the lifting forks of the truck being slid beneath the load. The pallets may be single or double-sided, with a superstructure of corner posts or sides to hold materials which either are not flat or must not be crushed. With the fork-lift trucks loads of up to 6,000 pounds are frequently lifted by one man to a height of 16 feet. In this way time is saved in handling materials, and the best use is made of the height available in storage spaces.

4. LORRY LOADERS. Time and labour can be wasted in loading lorries without efficient equipment. Various lifting platforms have been designed to reach the level of lorry floors, and recently hydraulic loading attachments have been fitted directly to the lorry. One type of lifting mechanism, which can handle, for example, six 3 cwt. sacks a minute, is driven from the lorry engine, and is automatically started by the weight

Priestman Bros. Ltd.

FIG. I. HOOK-ON DUMPING GRAB DISCHARGING SUGAR
FROM BARGES TO SHIPS IN TRINIDAD

Priestman Bros. Ltd.

FIG. 2. RING-DISCHARGE, SINGLE-CHAIN GRAB UNLOADING
PHOSPHATE FROM BARGES INTO LORRIES

Priestman Bros. Ltd.

FIG. 3. DOUBLE-ROPE 'ORANGE PEEL' GRAB DREDGING
LARGE BOULDERS

Conveyancer Fork Trucks Ltd.

FIG. 4. STACKING CRATES ON PALLETS WITH A FORK TRUCK

of a sack placed on the lifting frame. With the latest type the whole tail gate of the lorry forms a movable platform which can be lowered to ground level and then lifted vertically with the load.

5. HOISTS IN FACTORIES. Hoists and pulleys are described under CRANES (q.v.). They are widely used where raw materials come into or products leave a factory, and are useful for the movement of parts between operations in manufacture. Mounted on to overhead runway tracks, hoists can cover considerable distances and may connect up with other hoists or cranes by means of special latches.

See also Vol. VII: FACTORY ORGANIZATION.

MECHANICS. 1. This is the study of the speeds, accelerations, and energies of moving objects (dynamics) and of how stationary objects press and pull on each other (statics). The machines and vehicles that engineers design move themselves, or have parts that move, or have to resist the tendency of something else to move. A knowledge of mechanics enables an engineer to work out in advance how his machine will behave.

The part of mechanics that deals with moving objects is called 'dynamics'. The laws which form the basis for all calculations in engineering are those known as Newton's Laws of Motion. These three famous laws are:

1. First Law. Every body continues in a state of rest or of uniform motion in a straight line, except in so far as it is compelled by some force or forces to change that state.
2. Second Law. Change of momentum is proportional to the applied force and takes place in the same straight line in which the force acts.
3. Third Law. To every action there is an equal and opposite reaction.

These laws are discussed in MOTION (q.v. Vol. III). From them it is possible, for example, to predict the power of an engine needed to lift a load on a crane at a particular rate, the length of runway necessary to allow an aeroplane of particular weight and speed to land safely, or the exact length of pendulum to make a clock keep time.

2. WORK AND ENERGY. When a man or a machine raises a weight from the ground work has to be done, and the heavier the weight (that is, the greater its inertia) and the greater the height to which it is raised the more the work. In mechanics, whenever a force works against a resistance, the mechanical work done is the strength of the force in pounds weight times the distance moved in feet. Thus when a 10 lb. weight is lifted 4 feet, the work done is said to be $(10 \times 4) = 40$ foot-pounds.

When a lot of work is to be done, an engine is used, and the rate at which the engine does work is called its power. Power is usually expressed in horse-power, h.p., an engine of 1 h.p. being able to do 550 foot-pounds of work per second, which is about the maximum rate at which a strong and willing horse can work. An engine of 2 h.p. could, of course, do 1,100 foot-pounds of work per second, and so on. In order to do their work all engines consume ENERGY (q.v.) of one sort or another—electric motors, for instance, consume electrical energy, and steam turbines use the energy of hot and rushing steam. Energy can be described as stored-up work and is measured in foot-pounds. Mechanics is concerned with two sorts of energy—potential energy and kinetic energy. For example, when the 10 lb. weight in our example was lifted 4 feet above the ground, 40 foot-pounds of work was done; the weight in this position, consequently, possessed that amount of potential energy, for were the weight connected to a machine, that work could be recovered when the weight was allowed to descend again to its former level. The stored-up work in wound-up SPRINGS (q.v.) or stretched elastic bands are examples of potential energy. When the weight on the spring is released, its potential energy is converted into energy of movement or kinetic energy. The potential energy of the water at the head of Niagara Falls, for example, is converted into kinetic energy at the foot of the falls, some of it being used to drive water turbines (see WATER POWER); or the potential energy of a watch spring is converted into kinetic energy to make the watch go.

The relation of work to energy is most important for its enables engineers to design machines and the engines that drive them. The same amount of work is done, say 30 foot-pounds, when a force of 30 lb. acts over a distance of 1 foot, 10 lb. over 3 feet, or 360 lb. over 1 inch. Machines are used to change the proportions of force and distance that go to make up a given amount of work. Usually they exert a very powerful force over a short distance, when the man or engine working the machine exerts a

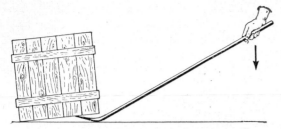

FIG. 1. A CROWBAR USED TO LIFT A HEAVY CASE

much weaker force over a long distance. A perfect machine does not waste any work, but gives out as much work as was put into it. Thus, with a simple perfect machine, such as the crowbar shown in Fig. 1, if a man presses down the handle with a force of 50 lb. weight and moves it through 3 feet, he does $(50 \times 3) = 150$ foot-pounds of work, all of which is available at the lifting end of the crowbar. But this is much shorter and so moves only 3 inches; it can therefore lift a heavy packing case weighing $(150 \div \frac{3}{12}) = 600$ lb. This simple machine has multiplied the man's force by 12 times and divided the distance moved by 12. The crowbar is an example of a machine called a LEVER (q.v.). In practice, however, machines do waste some of the work put into them because FRICTION (q.v.) resists the movement of the parts of the machine, even when the machine is well oiled. The proportion of the work put in that comes out again as useful work is called the efficiency of the machine. Perfect machines are 100% efficient, and simple practical machines have efficiencies of 30% to 90%.

3. MOMENTUM. When a body is acted on by a force it is said to have 'momentum'. This is the product of its MASS (q.v. Vol. III) and its velocity. If the motion is opposed by a force, the body will be brought to rest in a time that depends directly on its mass (roughly, weight) and how fast it is going. The same force would stop an object of half the mass in half the time. When two objects collide, the total momentum is unchanged. The same happens if two objects are forced apart (as, for instance, when a shell is fired from a gun) the momentum of the light shell in the forward direction is equal to the momentum of the gun in the backward direction (Newton's Third Law). Since the shell is very much lighter than the gun it moves away at high speed while the gun moves backwards much more slowly (see BALLISTICS).

4. STATICS. This is the part of mechanics that deals with the forces with which stationary bodies

push and pull each other. When a force acts on a body it causes the body to move unless it is prevented by an equal, balancing force acting the opposite way.

An important part of statics tells how to combine the effects of two forces acting together at the same point. Consider, for example, a sledge with two pulling ropes attached to the same ring, and two men pulling on the ropes with forces of 40 lb.-weight and 30 lb.-weight. When the men pull in the same direction, as shown by the arrows in Fig. 2a, their two forces add together and their combined, or resultant, pull equals $(40+30) = 70$ lb. If the men were pulling in opposite directions, as in Fig. 2b, the backward pull of 30 lb.-weight would partly cancel the 40 lb.-weight forward pull, and the resultant force would be $(40-30) = 10$ lb.-weight forward. In Fig. 2c the two men are pulling at right angles to each other. Their combined force can be worked out by marking off a distance OA of 40 units along the direction of the force of 40 lb.-weight, and a distance OB of 30 units along the direction of the

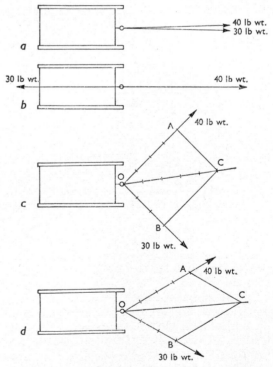

FIG. 2. RESULTANT OF TWO FORCES ACTING TOGETHER

a. Both forces pulling in the same direction. b. Forces pulling in opposite directions. c. Forces pulling at right angles. OC represents the resultant force. d. Forces acting at less than a right angle; OC represents the resultant force

30 lb.-weight force. If we complete the rectangle OACB by drawing AC parallel to OB and BC parallel to OA, the direction of the diagonal line OC represents the direction of the resultant force, and its length OC, which in our example would be 50 units, represents its strength, that is, 50 lb.-weight. This method can also be used when the two forces act at some other angle, as in Fig. 2d; only then the figure OACB produced by drawing parallels to OA and OB is a parallelogram called the 'parallelogram of forces', and not a rectangle. When more than two forces act at the same point of a body they can be combined together two at a time by drawing the parallelogram of forces until they are reduced to a single resultant force.

Another important part of statics deals with forces acting at different points of a body which tend to turn or twist the body around. The way of allowing for their effect is best illustrated by considering a beam with its middle point resting on a wedge, or 'fulcrum' as it is usually called. If equal weights of, say, 10 lb. are placed at equal distances, say 1 foot, on opposite sides of the fulcrum, as in Fig. 3a, the beam will balance. This is, of course, the ordinary method of weighing with a pair of scales. If the left-hand weight is

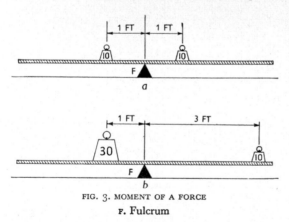

FIG. 3. MOMENT OF A FORCE

F. Fulcrum

increased to 30 lb., as in Fig. 3b, then in order to keep the balance the right-hand weight of 10 lb. has to be moved out until it is 3 feet away from the fulcrum. The strength of a force multiplied by the perpendicular distance of the fulcrum from its line of action is called its 'moment', and for balance the moments of the forces acting on each side of the fulcrum must be equal.

When several forces act on one side of the fulcrum their moments can be worked out separately and added together.

5. ANGULAR MOMENTUM. If an object is free to turn about some axis and is acted on by some force which has a moment about that axis, then

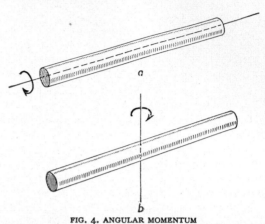

FIG. 4. ANGULAR MOMENTUM

a. Bar spinning about an axis along its length. *b.* Bar spinning about an axis perpendicular to its length

the object will spin. The longer the turning moment is applied the faster the object will spin. How quickly the spin builds up depends on the distance of the line of action of the force from the axis (i.e., on the moment) and also on the distribution of the mass of the object. It is very much easier to spin a long bar about an axis along its length than it is if the axis is perpendicular to the bar (Fig. 4a, b). The distribution of mass with respect to the axis is called the 'moment of inertia' and the product of this with the rate of spinning is called the 'angular momentum'.

See also ENERGY; LEVER.
See also Vol. III: MOTION.

METALLURGY. 1. Metallurgy is the science and technology of extracting METALS (q.v.) from the METAL ORES (q.v. Vol. III) in which they are found in the ground, of purifying them, and converting them into useful forms. Many metal ores are oxides (that is, metal combined with oxygen), some are sulphides, some carbonates, while some are more complex compounds; and the first task of the metallurgist is to separate the metal from the other ingredients of its ore, after it has been freed from purely earthy matter, such as clay. This first extraction process, known as smelting, produces metals of a moderate purity, usually as rough lumps, such as pig iron. As a rule the crude metals obtained by smelting must be further purified, and for almost every purpose the lumps of either smelted or purified metal must be converted into another shape according to the use to which the metal is to be put.

2. Smelting Ores. Most smelting is carried out at high temperatures, usually higher than the melting-point of the metal. The simplest type of smelting is that used for producing iron (*see* Blast Furnace)—the oxygen being removed from the iron oxide by heating the ore along with carbon (coke) at a very high temperature. For extracting zinc, carbon is again used to abstract the oxygen from the ore and set the metal 'free'. But since the boiling-point of zinc is only 907° C., the temperature used in smelting is high enough to evaporate the zinc as it is set free. The vaporized metal is thus removed from the mixture of ore and carbon by Distillation (q.v. Vol. VII) and is then condensed back into solid form by cooling. The lumps of zinc are rather impure and cannot be purified by the methods used for iron and steel. One process used for purifying zinc consists of making the crude metal one pole of an electrolytic cell (*see* Electroplating) and then of passing a small current through it. Very pure zinc will then be deposited on the other pole.

The extraction of metals by heating their ores with carbon is the oldest method of smelting, and has been used for many centuries for producing lead, tin, and zinc, as well as iron. But it cannot be used for every metal: some, notably aluminium and magnesium, cling so tenaciously to the oxygen in the ore that the carbon is incapable of detaching the oxygen from the oxide ores of these metals and so liberating aluminium or magnesium. This is why these two metals have only lately come into use in industry and commerce. Both aluminium and magnesium, as well as some of the rarer metals, are smelted by the method known as hot electrolysis. The metallic oxide is dissolved in a molten chemical compound, usually one which already contains some of the metal that is sought, and which is heated (for aluminium production) to a temperature higher than 700° C. in a vessel called a cell. A powerful electric current is then passed through the cell and the molten aluminium is attracted to one terminal under the influence of the current, and from time to time it is drawn off and poured into moulds, in which it solidifies.

The powerful attraction of aluminium for oxygen is used in smelting other metals which are difficult to liberate in any other way. Chromium and manganese, for instance, cling too tightly to oxygen to be easily smelted with carbon: but if their ores, reasonably purified, are mixed with powdered aluminium and heated, the aluminium extracts the oxygen and liberates the chromium or the manganese. This method is also used for obtaining some other rarer metals.

When these less plentiful metals are sought, the ores are purified and concentrated as much as possible before smelting in order to produce a material suitable for smelting. Most of the processes used in purifying are chemical, but concentration can also be achieved by violently shaking the powdered ores so that much of the earthy impurities fall apart from the ore.

For many industrial purposes, metals must be made as pure as possible; pure copper, for instance, is used in the electrical industry and pure tungsten for filament lamps. Most metallic materials in use, however, are Alloys (q.v.) that contain two, three, or even more metals. These alloys are nearly always made by melting together a mixture of metals. Thousands of different alloys are known, and the accurate control of their composition is a vital function of metallurgy.

3. Shaping Metals. Metals and alloys are given a useful shape either by casting when molten or by mechanical deformation when solid. In Casting (q.v.) the molten material is poured into a mould formed so that the metal takes approximately the shape of the finished article. When taken out of the mould, castings are sometimes sufficiently accurate to be used without further treatment, but for the majority of engineering purposes some parts of the castings have to be machined to make them more accurate (*see* Machine Tools). Those that are used in the most precise forms of engineering, such as aero-engines, are given very accurate dimensions by being machined all over.

About 90% of all the metallic materials used in engineering and elsewhere are shaped by the sheer pressure of mechanical force, various mechanical processes being employed. The shape and size of the ingot first cast varies with the shaping process: round, square, or octagonal ingots are used for Forging and Pressing (q.v.), round ones for extrusion, and flat ones for making sheets or strips.

Producing useful forms through mechanical deformation is the oldest of all shaping processes: for thousands of years blacksmiths have hammered metals by hand. Shaping by hammering is now carried out by power-driven plant, and large forgings approximating to finished shapes are widely used. Finished shapes are also produced in a single operation by extrusion; ingots of the softer metals are transformed directly into bars and sections of special shapes by being forced through a hole or 'die' made of hardened steel, much as toothpaste is squeezed from a tube. By this method enormous quantities of complicated sections for use in either aircraft or ship construction are produced in light alloys,

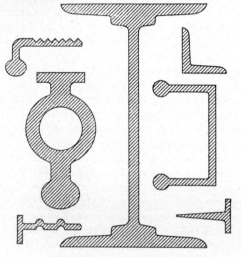

SOME SHAPES OF EXTRUDED METALS

and huge varieties of sections for engineering or other uses are made in brass and copper.

A very large quantity of mechanically shaped metals and alloys is produced by two-stage processes. In the first part of each of them the ingots are rolled between powerful rollers, either into sheets and strips or into bars and rods, all of standard dimensions. In the second part these semi-manufactured products are taken as the raw materials for further shaping operations. Sheets and strips may be rolled to thinner pieces, even into such thin foils as chocolate wrappings and the tops of milk bottles. Sheets may be pressed to shape between dies, as in the stamping out of a motor-car body in gigantic presses. They may be spun or be cut into pieces and joined by WELDING or RIVETING (qq.v.). Bars may be cut to suitable lengths and drop-forged into engine components for motor-cars, locomotives, or aircraft. Rods can be drawn into yet finer rods or into wire (*see* WIRE DRAWING). Large bars may be pierced and drawn into TUBES (q.v.).

In most of the main processes of mechanical shaping the metals are worked hot, since they are then softer and more malleable. Steels and wrought iron are heated to temperatures between 1,000° C. and 1,200° C., copper to 850° C. or 900° C., brass to about 650° C., and aluminium alloys to about 440° C. In the later stages of rolling or drawing the results are better if the metals are shaped while cold. Since the materials then are harder and less easily deformed, both the force applied and the amount of deformation must be regulated and, after they have been hardened as much as they can bear by the mechanical straining, the metals must be softened again by heating to moderate temperatures in preparation for further deformation. At some time during every mechanical-shaping process, therefore, metals and alloys are exposed to heat, and the temperatures they attain must be accurately related to the structural changes that occur in many alloys at temperatures below their melting-points. Because of these changes steels, for example, must not be hot-worked at temperatures below 750° C.; most aluminium alloys must not be worked at temperatures above 520° C.; and magnesium at temperatures below 250° C.

The relation between temperatures and the internal structures of alloys has been worked out for most combinations of metals. Further ingredients are constantly being added to known alloys in the search for improved materials.

These structural changes affect not only the temperatures used in shaping processes, but form the basis of all forms of HEAT TREATMENT (q.v.), such as hardening and tempering, some of which can double the strength of an alloy.

See also METALS; ALLOYS; HEAT TREATMENT; FORGING AND PRESSING.
See also Vol. III: METAL ORES.

METALS. 1. Of the ninety-six elements appearing in the Periodic Table of the Elements, which make up all known MATTER (q.v. Vol. III), more than sixty are classified as metals. The remainder—such as sulphur, chlorine, phosphorus, or nitrogen—are simply called non-metals. Many of these give rise to acids which might attack the metals and form chemical compounds with them. If such compounds are then broken up by electrolysis (*see* ELECTROPLATING) in a suitable cell, the metals go to the negative pole and the non-metals to the positive pole of the cell. This difference in behaviour provides a reasonable method of distinguishing metals from non-metals. In general the metallic elements can also be recognized by being essentially crystalline in structure, by possessing a lustre, by being conductors of electricity and heat, though in varying degrees, by being more or less elastic, malleable, ductile, and strong. Because of their behaviour in an electrolytic cell metals are usually called the basic—which is the opposite of acidic—portion of ordinary chemical compounds, of which many thousands are known. For example, common SALT (q.v. Vol. III) is a compound of the metal sodium, which is the basic component, and the non-metal chlorine. Some metals are plentiful, some less plentiful, and some are exceedingly rare. Unlike some non-metallic elements no metal at ordinary temperatures is gaseous, and only one—mercury—is a liquid.

The best known metals are iron, copper, zinc, tin, lead, aluminium, nickel, cobalt, magnesium, gold, silver, platinum, tungsten, chromium, manganese, and mercury, of which aluminium, iron, and magnesium are present in the earth's crust in the greatest quantities. Several other metals are far more plentiful than many of those mentioned—for example calcium, the metallic ingredient of limestone, potassium, and sodium —but these are rarely extracted from their ores and made use of.

Some metals that are present in quite minute proportions in the earth are valued because they possess unique properties. URANIUM (q.v. Vol. III) is used in the production of NUCLEAR ENERGY (q.v.); iridium is a hard-wearing metal and is present in nearly all good fountain-pen points; palladium is used in high-class jewellery alloys; thorium and cerium, from which are formed the oxides thoria and ceria, are used as the foundation for incandescent mantles in gas and oil lamps.

Most metals are found in nature as METAL ORES (q.v. Vol. III); only gold, platinum, a little silver, and less copper being found 'free'—that is, not combined with other elements. Metals are separated or 'set free' from their ores by various methods carried out at suitably high temperatures (see METALLURGY). When free, certain metals have characteristic colours, such as the yellow of gold and the red of copper, while the majority display a bright sheen or lustre, particularly on freshly broken surfaces, and this appearance is what is described as 'metallic'. Not all metals, however, are bright; platinum is dull,

tungsten is dark-grey, while sodium and potassium look greasy. Many even of the bright-looking metals rapidly become tarnished, rusted, or otherwise corroded when exposed to ordinary damp atmospheres (see CORROSION) and quickly lose their lustre.

The physical properties of metals differ greatly, chiefly in density (comparative weight), strength, hardness, elasticity, melting- and boiling-points under heat, and electrical and heat conductivity. In order to obtain the properties desired, metals are often blended with other metals, or even with non-metals such as carbon or silicon. These blended metals are known as ALLOYS (q.v.).

2. DENSITY OF METALS. Some metals, such as gold and tungsten, are very heavy, while sodium and potassium are actually lighter than water. The ratio of the weight of a certain volume of a metal to that of the same volume of water is called the density of the metal: the densities of some of the better known or more plentiful metals are:

Potassium .	.	0·86	Iron .	. .	7·86
Sodium .	.	0·97	Nickel	. .	8·9
(Water .	.	1·0)	Copper	. .	8·93
Calcium .	.	1·55	Silver	. .	10·5
Magnesium .	.	1·74	Lead	. .	11·37
Aluminium .	.	2·65	Tungsten .	.	19·3
Zinc .	.	7·1	Gold	. .	19·32
Tin .	.	7·29			

Difference in density largely explains why aluminium and magnesium and their alloys are used so extensively in aircraft construction, although they are not as strong as the alloys of iron.

3. MELTING-POINT OF METALS. This greatly affects the uses to which a metal can be put. The melting-points of different metals vary enormously: for example, mercury is liquid at the freezing-point of water, while tungsten remains solid up to a temperature as high as 3,387° C. The melting-points of several different metals in degrees C. are

Mercury	minus	39	Calcium	plus	780
Gallium	plus	30	Silver	,,	962
Potassium	,,	62	Gold	,,	1,062
Sodium	,,	97	Copper	,,	1,084
Tin	,,	232	Manganese	,,	1,210
Lead	,,	327	Nickel	,,	1,450
Zinc	,,	419	Chromium	,,	1,490
Magnesium	,,	635	Iron	,,	1,500
Aluminium	,,	657	Tungsten	,,	3,387

4. MALLEABILITY OF METALS. When pure, many metals, notably copper, gold, silver, lead,

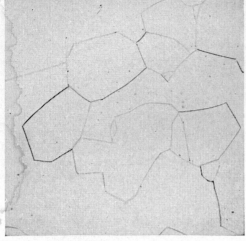

MICROSTRUCTURE OF A PURE METAL
Magnification 100

inch in cross-section. The load required depends upon the temperature of the metal. The breaking loads, at room temperatures, for some of the common metals are (in tons per square inch)

Lead .	. . 1·5	Zinc .	. . 12
Tin .	. 3	Copper .	. . 14
Aluminium	. 5	Iron .	. . 19
Magnesium	. 11		

All these values are low in comparison with the breaking loads of high-tensile steels, which may be as high as 100 tons per square inch or even higher.

The hardness of a metal is measured by the resistance which it offers to being indented with, say, a diamond point. The relative hardnesses of the better-known metals are

Lead .	. . 6	Zinc .	. . 50
Tin .	. . 10	Copper .	. 50
Aluminium	. 20	Iron .	. . 80
Magnesium	. 40	Nickel .	. . 110
Gold .	. . 40	Tungsten	. . 500

The hardness of different steels ranges from 125 to 800.

6. ELASTICITY OF METALS. All the mechanically useful metals possess the property of elasticity at air temperatures and even when heated moderately. If a metal is loaded as though to measure its breaking strength, the metal before reaching breaking-point stretches a little under the load—the amount of stretch being proportional to the load applied. If the load is removed well before the metal breaks, the metal—because it is elastic—returns to its original dimensions. With small loads this process can be repeated indefinitely. The amount by which the metal stretches when a load of, say, 1 ton per square inch is applied varies from metal to metal: aluminium, for example, stretches three times as much as iron, magnesium five times as much, copper one and a half times, and beryllium only three-quarters as much.

7. CREEP AND FATIGUE. Either a pure metal or an alloy (which is usually stronger and harder than a pure metal) may break under a load less than its normal breaking load if the load is applied to it continuously over a long period, particularly if the load is applied when the metal is at a moderately high temperature. Under this smaller but continuous burden the metal gradually deforms or 'creeps', and eventually breaks. The load required to produce fracture in this way varies from metal to metal and from one

aluminium, and iron, are both ductile (able to be pulled or drawn into another shape) and malleable (able to undergo a change of shape, without breaking, when hammered or pressed) at room temperatures. When cold they can be fairly easily beaten into new shapes or rolled into thin sheets. Others, however, such as zinc, antimony, beryllium, and bismuth, are so brittle when cold that they break easily if struck. Cold magnesium is less brittle than these latter, but much less malleable and ductile than aluminium, iron, and copper. Almost every metal becomes softer and more malleable when heated to a temperature somewhere between that of the atmosphere and the melting-point of the metal. Zinc and magnesium, for example, which are brittle at air temperatures, can be beaten, forged, or rolled at temperatures of 200° and 350° C. respectively. On the other hand, certain metals, notably iron, which are tough at air temperatures, become quite brittle if they are cooled considerably below the freezing-point of water.

5. STRENGTH AND HARDNESS OF METALS. Metals are widely used, on the whole, because they are strong and hard. But they vary greatly in their strength and hardness at ordinary air temperatures. Mercury, being a liquid at air temperatures, has neither hardness nor strength; sodium and potassium have the consistency of putty. The strengths of those metals which are of some mechanical use can be measured and expressed as the load in tons which will just fracture a bar of the metal measuring one square

alloy to another. Only those materials which can sustain large loads for long periods are suitable for use in the vital components of such highly developed machines as jet engines.

A fracture produced by applying, releasing, and reapplying a load less than that required to break the metal in one application, perhaps several million times, is called 'failure by fatigue', a term which suggests that the metal becomes tired of having loads applied and removed. A high proportion of the failures of engine parts and of breakages in aircraft and motor vehicles is the consequence of fatigue.

8. Conductivity of Metals. A characteristic which clearly distinguishes true metals from the non-metals is that metals are conductors to varying degrees of both electricity and heat. The differences between the conducting capacities of the commoner metals appear in the following values, which show electrical conductivity. Silver is taken as the basis of comparison.

Silver	.	.	100	Tungsten	.	.	33
Copper	.	.	94	Nickel	.	.	14
Aluminium	.	.	57	Iron	.	.	11
Magnesium	.	.	38	Lead	.	.	7

This table explains why copper (which is more easily produced and therefore cheaper than silver) has for long been used as the principal conducting metal in electrical engineering and why, in more recent years, it has been possible for some purposes to substitute aluminium (which is cheaper still).

Metals that have poor electrical conductivity are suitably used in resistance heating-units, because resistance wires of a good conductor, such as copper, must be very long or very thin to provide the sort of resistances needed in electrical equipment of this kind. Alloys containing both iron and nickel, often some chromium as well, are most commonly used to make the glowing elements in electric fires and furnaces. Though the conductivity of pure tungsten is not very low, its melting-point is extremely high, and therefore it is used as a resistor for special purposes. Drawn into very fine wires in order to increase as much as possible the resistance to the electric current, tungsten forms the filaments of many electric lamps. The metal can safely be heated to a white heat, emitting its bright light, without risk of melting.

The United Steel Companies Ltd.

A ROW OF CREEP-TESTING MACHINES

In each machine a metal specimen is heated in a cylindrical electrical furnace and stressed by a weighted lever. The extension after various periods of time is read by a travelling telescope

9. STRUCTURE OF METALS. All metals possess a crystalline structure, which means that any piece of metal consists of large numbers of very small units, or cells, in each of which the ATOMS

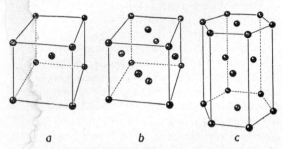

a   *b*   *c*

FIG. I. THE ATOMIC STRUCTURE OF METALS

a. Body-centred cubic (e.g. cold iron, chromium, tungsten). *b.* Face-centred cubic (e.g. copper, silver, lead, gold, white-hot iron). *c.* Hexagonal (e.g. magnesium, zinc, titanium).

(q.v. Vol. III) are arranged in the same definite geometrical pattern. Each metal has its characteristic pattern: in some, the atoms are arranged as though they were situated at the eight corners of a cube, with one atom lying in the middle of the cube. In other metals the atoms are placed in positions corresponding to the corners of the cube and in the middle of each face: in yet other metals the atoms are arranged as at the corners of a six-sided prism and at the other positions shown in Fig. 1c. Though the number of different patterns is limited, the actual dimensions of the unit cells vary greatly. By using an X-ray spectroscope these dimensions have been measured for all metals, and it has been shown that at any chosen temperature the size of the cell (of whatever pattern) in any metal is a characteristic and unique property of that metal.

In any metal the unit cells are extremely small, their dimensions being comparable with the wavelength of LIGHT (q.v. Vol. III)—in the region of one fifty-thousandth of an inch. By the assembly of a number of unit cells, each one fitting into its neighbours, a crystalline form is produced which grows into a grain. A piece of metal consists of multitudes of grains which, though rarely visible to the naked eye, can be seen when a polished section of a piece of metal is examined under a microscope.

See also METALLURGY; ALLOYS; HEAT TREATMENT.
See also Vol. III: METAL ORES.
See also Vol. VII: ALUMINIUM INDUSTRY; COPPER MINING; GOLD MINING; IRON ORE; LEAD; MAGNESIUM, EXTRACTION OF; MERCURY; NICKEL; PLATINUM; SILVER MINING; TIN; ZINC MINING.

METEOROLOGICAL INSTRUMENTS.

These are used to measure the pressure and temperature of the air, the amount of water vapour in it (humidity), the speed of the wind, the amount of rainfall and of sunshine, and all other things that go to make up the WEATHER (q.v. Vol. III). The instruments used work on the same principles as those used in laboratories, factories, or mines, but they have to withstand the weather and may be used by unskilled observers in different conditions. They have, therefore, to be specially robust and foolproof.

Continuous records of the weather are obtained from self-recording instruments. In a common form of these, a light lever carrying a pen at its free end is attached to the measuring device, for example, to the bellows of an aneroid barograph (*see* Section 2b) or to the bimetal coil of a thermograph. The pen presses lightly against a paper chart surrounding a drum which rotates by clockwork once per day or week according to the length and openness of record required. As the paper moves round, the pen moves up and down in response to the changes in the temperature, pressure, and so on to give a GRAPH (q.v.) of the quantity concerned.

1. ANEMOMETERS, derived from the Greek *anemos*, 'wind', are instruments for measuring the speed and direction of the WIND (q.v. Vol. III). The simplest is the 'vane anemometer', which is just a sensitive windmill, generally about 3 inches in diameter (Fig. 1). It must be set up to face the wind, and the number of rotations of the spindle in a given time, say 5 minutes, is then counted by a train of wheels, as in an electricity- or gas-meter. The larger the count the higher the wind

Negretti & Zambra Ltd.

FIG. I. VANE ANEMOMETER FOR MECHANICAL RECORDING MECHANISM

speed. The 'cup anemometer' (Fig. 2) is a more robust instrument which works no matter which

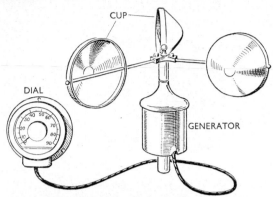

FIG. 2. CUP ANEMOMETER AND WIND-SPEED INDICATOR

way the wind blows, and so is more widely used. It has three—sometimes four—cups at the ends of arms mounted on a vertical spindle. This rotates because the wind presses more strongly when blowing on the inside of a cup than when blowing on the outside. The rotations of the spindle are counted by a mechanical or electrical counter, as with the vane anemometer, or the spindle may drive a small ELECTRIC GENERATOR (q.v.) whose voltage thus increases with the wind speed.

The 'pressure-tube anemograph' is a more elaborate, self-recording instrument that measures both the speed and direction of the wind (Fig. 3). The head is a refined kind of weathercock, the swinging of which is transmitted to a direction-recording pen at the bottom of the mast, on which the head is mounted. The wind speed is obtained from the pressure which the wind exerts on an opening in the head at the other end from the vane. This opening is connected by tubing down the mast to the inside of a float with an open bottom, which rides partly submerged in a closed tank of water. The float rises and falls as the wind speed varies the air pressure in the tubing. The movement of the float is increased by connecting the tank to small holes bored round the top of the mast. These provide a suction. The float and attached pen move about $\frac{1}{2}$ inch for 10 m.p.h. wind speed, and the record is generally one of continual change, representing the gustiness or turbulence of the wind.

2. BAROMETERS. These measure the PRESSURE (q.v. Vol. III) of the atmosphere.

(a) *Mercury barometers* are commonly of two

patterns, the Fortin barometer and the Kew barometer. Each consists basically of a glass tube closed at one end, filled with mercury, and inverted so that the open end dips into a small open bath, also containing mercury. The mercury in the tube runs down into this cistern, leaving a vacuum (*see* PRESSURE GAUGES) at the top of the tube, until the weight of the mercury column is balanced by the pressure (that is, the weight) of the atmosphere.

The atmospheric pressure is measured by the height of the top of the mercury column (visible in the glass tube) above the level in the cistern, allowance being made for the fact that the cistern level rises as the column falls, and vice versa. In the Fortin barometer (Fig. 4*a*), the allowance is made by raising or lowering the base of the cistern, which is a leather bag, by means of a screw until the surface of the mercury exactly coincides

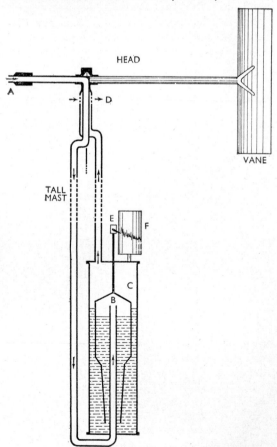

FIG. 3. PRESSURE-TUBE ANEMOGRAPH
A. Hole at which wind enters. B. Float. C. Enclosed tank. D. Holes providing suction. E. Pen. F. Revolving drum on which pressure is recorded

with the tip of a fixed, downward-pointing ivory marker pin. This tip is at the zero of the scale which measures the length of the mercury column. The level of the top of the mercury column is obtained by turning a screw until the lower front and back edges of a sheet-metal cylinder surrounding the barometer tube exactly coincide by eye with the top of the domed surface of the mercury. The level of the bottom of the metal cylinder is then read against the barometer scale by means of a VERNIER (q.v.), and the reading gives the length of the mercury column.

The Kew barometer (Fig. 4b) has a fixed cistern; the rise and fall of the mercury in it is allowed for by graduating the barometer scale with a 'false' scale of length, so that it does, in fact, read correctly when the setting of the top of the column—the only setting with this pattern—is made—as with the Fortin. The instrument-maker adjusts the scale according to the diameters of cistern and tube. Both the Fortin and

Kew barometers have thermometers attached to their cases so that the change of density of the mercury with temperature can be allowed for.

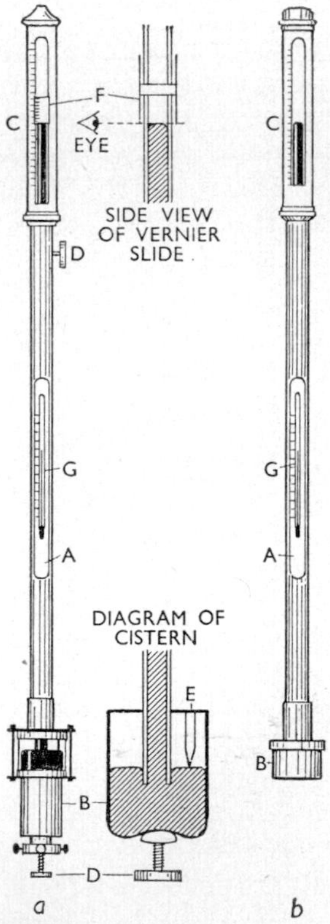

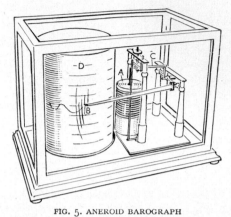

FIG. 5. ANEROID BAROGRAPH
A. Metal cylinders. B. Pen. C. Levers moving pen. D. Revolving drum on which recording is made

(b) *Aneroid (non-liquid) barometers*, frequently used as recording instruments (barographs), consist of a number of short, wide, metal cylinders placed top to bottom. Most of the air is pumped out of them, and compressed springs keep the circular faces of each cylinder apart. The cylinders then expand if the outside air pressure decreases, or contract if it increases. This moves a pointer or pen by levers (Fig. 5). The aneroid is less accurate than the mercury barometer, but more compact. Most homely 'weather-glasses' are aneroid barometers.

3. THERMOMETERS. Most of these instruments, used for measuring heat, are described in the article on THERMOMETERS (q.v.); here it is only necessary to mention the special designs used for meteorological purposes. The highest temperature reached by the air in a certain period is obtained from the 'maximum thermometer'. In this type of thermometer, there is a very narrow part in the bore just above the bulb. As the temperature rises, the expanding mercury in the bulb forces its way past this constriction and up the scale. When the temperature falls, the narrow bore of the constriction prevents the mercury in the column from running back, even though the mercury below the constriction has contracted back into the bulb. The mercury column, therefore, sticks at the highest level reached since the thermometer was last reset. To reset it, the thermometer has to be shaken to bring the column

FIG. 4. a. FORTIN BAROMETER. b. KEW BAROMETER
A. Glass tube. B. Cistern containing mercury. C. Height of mercury. D. Screw for raising base of cistern. E. Ivory marking pin. F. Vernier. G. Thermometer

of mercury back through the constriction, exactly as with a clinical thermometer. The 'minimum thermometer' gives the lowest temperature reached by the air between readings. An organic liquid ('spirit') replaces the mercury, and a small, dark, glass slider is inserted in the bore. This allows the spirit to flow past it when the temperature rises, but the surface film at the end of the column of spirit pulls it back when the temperature falls. After reading, the thermometer is temporarily up-ended so that the slider is left submerged at the end of the thread of spirit, that is, at 'present' temperature, and is ready for the next period.

4. HYGROMETERS (Greek *hugros* = wet). These measure the humidity, or amount of WATER VAPOUR (q.v. Vol. III) in the air. The one most commonly used, the 'wet-and-dry-bulb' thermometer, consists of two thermometers side by side, one of which has wetted muslin wrapped round its bulb. The drier the air and the quicker the water evaporates from the muslin, the colder the thermometer bulb becomes, and the greater the difference in the readings of the two thermometers. A printed table determines the humidity from the readings.

Recording hygrometers generally make use of human hair, for this, when free of grease, changes

Negretti & Zambra Ltd.

FIG. 7. CAMPBELL-STOKES SUNSHINE RECORDER

in length with changes of humidity. The changes in length are communicated to the pen by a special arrangement of levers that makes the indications greater than the changes in the hair itself.

5. RAIN-GAUGE. The rain falls on to a funnel with an upper opening of given size, generally 5 inches in diameter, and passes into a measuring jar, the graduations of which are adjusted to read directly the depth of rain that has fallen. In the recording rain-gauge, the water flows into a cistern which carries an airtight float and vertical rod to which a pen is attached. As rain continues, the pen rises up the revolving chart until the water in the cistern reaches a critical level. The cistern then tilts, and the water is siphoned away; the float and pen return to zero level, and the operation begins again (Fig. 6).

6. SUNSHINE RECORDER. The duration of bright sunshine on any day is obtained from a 'sunshine card', which is placed in a circular arc at the focus of a spherical lens of glass (Fig. 7). Bright sunshine burns a thin line along the card (which is marked with a scale of hours), and the total length of burn gives the total period of sunshine.

7. STEVENSON SCREEN. Accurate values of temperature and humidity can be obtained only if the sun is prevented from shining directly on the instruments; yet the air must be able to circulate freely round them. This is usually arranged by placing the instrument in a white wooden box with double walls, built like two Venetian blinds back to back.

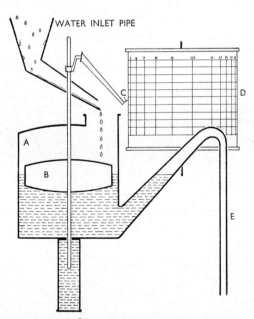

FIG. 6. SIPHON RAIN RECORDER

A. Cistern. B. Float. C. Pen. D. Revolving chart. E. Siphon tube. The tilting mechanism by which water is siphoned out of E is not shown

8. RADIO-SONDES. These special instruments are used for taking measurements in the upper atmosphere, for the weather can be understood only if observations of pressure, temperature, wind, and so on are made in the free atmosphere above the earth as well as at the earth's surface. Radio-sondes, therefore, are carried into the upper air by a hydrogen-filled balloon, and there make these measurements and signal the results to the ground (or ship at sea). A small aneroid measures the pressure, a bimetal thermometer the temperature, and gold-beater's skin (made from animal gut) the humidity. But instead of registering directly, these instruments transmit their readings in code to the ground by means of a radio transmitter also carried into the upper air by the balloon. If a metallic reflector, not unlike a bicycle rear-light reflector but many times its size, is hung beneath the balloon, it may be tracked by RADAR (q.v.) on the ground, and its horizontal and vertical movements measured.

The speed and direction of the wind may then be worked out at all heights, in or out of cloud, up to the level at which the balloon bursts, commonly 10 miles or more.

See also Vol. III: WEATHER.

METROLOGY, *see* MEASUREMENT, UNITS OF.

METROPOLITAN WATER BOARD. This PUBLIC UTILITY (q.v. Vol. VII), one of the largest organizations of its kind in the world, provides the WATER SUPPLY (q.v.) for the County of London and for parts of the surrounding counties. It was set up in 1903 as the successor to eight separately controlled water companies, the oldest of which was the New River Company, formed in 1619. This early system consisted simply of a long open channel leading water from large springs near Ware, in Hertfordshire, along the valley of the river Lea to Clerkenwell, which was then on the outskirts of London; the original

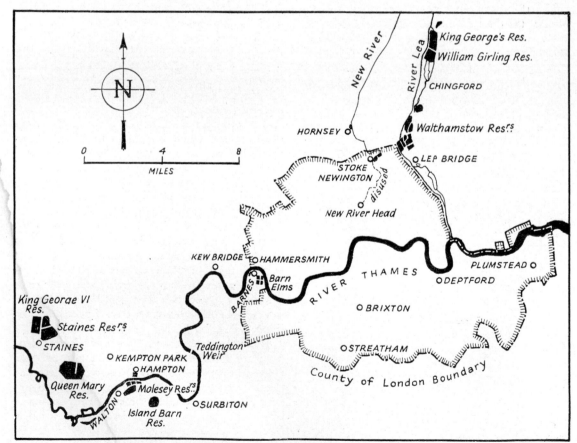

MAP OF THE DISTRICT SERVED BY THE METROPOLITAN WATER BOARD

Metropolitan Water Board

HAMPTON PUMPING STATION

There are eight steam turbines each driving two or three centrifugal pumps and, in seven cases, an electric generator

length of this 'river' was 39 miles. Most of this channel is still in use as part of the supply system to north London.

Today the Metropolitan Water Board supplies about 6½ million people, in an area of 540 square miles, with some 320 million gallons of water a day; in the summer it supplies even more. About one-third is used for trade and manufacture. The most important source of supply is the Thames, which provides about two-thirds of the total, the water being pumped out at various points above Teddington Weir (*see* Map). About one-sixth is taken from the Lea, and the remaining one-sixth from wells and bore-holes (*see* WELLS AND SPRINGS, Vol. III) in the chalk strata of the Lea valley and in Kent.

A distinctive feature of the supply system is a series of large open storage reservoirs holding in reserve water pumped into them during the winter when the river-flow is above normal. There are six large storage reservoirs and a number of smaller ones in the Thames valley, between Staines and Surbiton, the largest being the Queen Mary Reservoir, covering 723 acres and holding 6,750 million gallons. In the Lea valley there are two large reservoirs near Ching-

ford, and a group of smaller ones near Walthamstow. The largest is the William Girling Reservoir, which holds 3,493 million gallons.

Because the two rivers are liable to be contaminated by the large population living above the points where the supply is taken, the water has to be purified before it is suitable for drinking. A partial purification takes place naturally during the prolonged storage in open reservoirs, and the process is completed at special water-treatment works (*see* WATER SUPPLY, Section 3). In the Thames valley the principal works are at Kempton Park, Walton, Hampton, and Surbiton; in the Lea valley at Hornsey, Stoke Newington, and Lea Bridge. Supplies from wells north of the Thames, as well as those in the Kent district, are uncontaminated, but as a precaution they are chlorinated. At a large laboratory water samples from the treatment works and from all parts of the area are regularly tested.

The treated water is delivered by high-pressure pumping-plant from the various water-treatment works, either directly to consumers through the distribution mains or indirectly through nearly 100 service reservoirs.

One of the main pumping stations, at Kempton

Park, contains ten large pumping engines (*see* PUMPS). Some are used, under low pressure, to lift water either direct from the Thames or from the Queen Mary Reservoir for delivery to the adjoining water-treatment works; others pump the purified water under high pressure for distribution in north London. The two largest pumps, each about 62 feet high, are vertical triple-expansion engines of 1,000 horse-power which can deliver from 12 to 19 million gallons a day. The steam for working the engines is supplied by large coal-fired BOILERS (q.v.) next to the engine-houses.

See also WATER SUPPLY; NEW YORK WATER SUPPLY.
See also Vol. III: LONDON.

MICROMETER, *see* LENGTH-MEASURING INSTRUMENTS.

MICROPHONE. The purpose of this instrument is to turn sound into an ELECTRIC CURRENT (q.v.). The principle, which was discovered in 1876 by Alexander Graham Bell (*see* SPEECH, TRANSMISSION OF, Vol. IV), is applied both in an ordinary telephone mouthpiece and in the sensitive instruments in a broadcasting or film studio.

Fig. 1 shows the way a modern telephone works. When the waves of SOUND (q.v. Vol. III) from the speaker's voice strike the microphone, they cause vibrations to occur in a thin skin called a diaphragm, which works very much like a human eardrum. The diaphragm is a circular piece of some plastic composition, about one-thousandth of an inch thick, which acts as a lid or cover to a small circular space behind it, the whole resembling a pill-box turned on its side. The space is packed, moderately tightly, with tiny, dustlike grains of carbon, a mineral which conducts electricity. Attached to the centre of the diaphragm, inside the 'pill-box', is an electrical conductor linked by wire to the main telephone circuit; another conductor is attached to the inside back of the 'pill-box', also linked to the circuit. When an electric current is switched on, it flows steadily through the pill-box from one conductor to the other, making its way by passing from one carbon grain to the next. The amount of current which passes is limited because it can pass only at the points where each grain touches its neighbouring grain.

Now, when a sound is made near the microphone, the diaphragm vibrates; at each vibration the centre of the diaphragm presses inward, perhaps a thousandth of an inch, on to the carbon grains, then straightens again and bends outward from the carbon grains by another thousandth of an inch. There may be 3,000 such vibrations per second. When the diaphragm bends inward it presses the carbon grains slightly more closely together, making the electric current flow more easily from grain to grain; equally, each time the vibrating diaphragm bends outward, the contact between the carbon grains becomes a little weaker, and less current is able to flow through the microphone. Thus the vibrations of the diaphragm, actuated by the human voice or any other sound, become transformed into a series of variations in the strength of an electric current.

These electric variations, like the original sound-waves, have two characteristics—ampli-

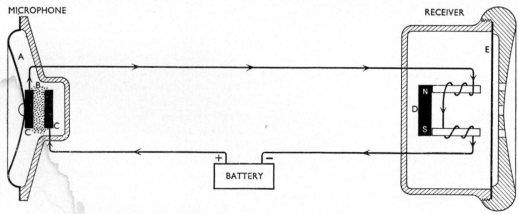

FIG. 1. PRINCIPLE OF THE TELEPHONE
A. Microphone diaphragm. B. Carbon grains. C. Conductors. D. Electromagnet. E. Receiver diaphragm

tude and frequency. Amplitude is concerned with the loudness or softness of the sound: a strong shout will make the diaphragm quiver violently, and the electric impulses which shoot along the wire will form part of a powerful current. Frequency concerns the pitch: a high-pitched girl's voice will make both diaphragm and electric current vibrate faster than a low-pitched male one, no matter whether the voice shouts or whispers.

The type of microphone just described is called a 'carbon microphone'; it is used in telephones because it produces quite a large electric current when someone speaks near it—that is, it is very sensitive. The carbon microphone, however, distorts the sounds slightly and so is not suitable for use in a broadcasting studio, especially for music programmes. 'Moving coil microphones' are mostly used for broadcasting; these have a small coil of wire attached to their diaphragm. As the diaphragm vibrates, the coil is moved between the poles of a powerful magnet, and an electric current, which matches the sound, is induced in it. Moving coil microphones are much less sensitive than carbon microphones, and valve amplifiers (*see* THERMIONIC VALVE) have to be used to magnify the tiny electric currents that they produce. This kind of microphone is very similar to the moving-coil loud-speakers used in most wireless sets—in fact, these loud-speakers can be 'worked backwards' and used as microphones.

During the telephone call the fluctuating electric current from the microphone, of precise amplitude and frequency, travels possibly hundreds of miles and responds to each change in a speaker's voice. At the distant end, the current reaches a telephone receiver or earpiece which contains a tiny electromagnet consisting of two stubs of soft iron, each wound with many coils of very fine copper wire. In front of the coils is a diaphragm made of flexible iron, and behind the electromagnet is a permanent magnet, which exerts a steady pull on the iron diaphragm. The electric current coming from the distant microphone passes through the coils of wire and causes a magnetic effect in the soft-iron stubs (*see* MAGNETS). As the current fluctuates, every change in it varies the magnetism, and increases or decreases the magnetic pull exerted by the permanent magnet on the iron diaphragm. Thus each change of frequency and of amplitude which occurs in the distant microphone is reproduced in the earpiece of the receiver, and as a result the

vibrating iron diaphragm gives out the sounds of speech.

See also TELEPHONE ENGINEERING; SOUND RECORDING; RADIO ENGINEERING.

See also Vol. IV: SPEECH, TRANSMISSION OF.

MICROSCOPE. This is an optical instrument for making small objects appear larger. Strictly speaking, the name includes the pocket lens or simple microscope, but in ordinary use it refers only to the compound microscope. In the simple microscope a converging lens held close to the

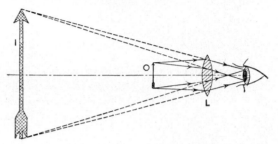

FIG. 1. HOW THE POCKET LENS (SIMPLE MICROSCOPE) WORKS
L. Lens. O. Object. I. Image

eye (Fig. 1) bends the light rays issuing from a small object o so that, on entering the eye, they appear to have come from a magnified object I. I is called the 'virtual image' of o by the lens. Simple microscopes magnifying up to 25 × are on sale, but they are most useful at magnifications from 8 × to 12 ×.

In the compound microscope, shown in Fig. 2, the object is magnified in two stages. First a small and very powerful lens L_1, called the 'objective',

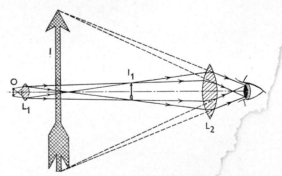

FIG. 2. HOW THE COMPOUND MICROSCOPE WORKS
L_1. Objective lens. L_2. Eyepiece lens. o. Object. I_1. Image formed by objective. I. Image formed by eyepiece

forms a magnified image I_1 of the object o. Then this image is looked at through a second lens L_2, called the 'eyepiece', which magnifies it still further to form the final image I. The objective L_1 and the eyepiece L_2 are shown as single lenses in Fig. 2, but in an actual microscope each is a group of lenses. The eyepiece usually consists of two lenses (Fig. 3a), while the best high-power objectives may contain as many as ten lenses (Fig. 3b), though a smaller number is more usual.

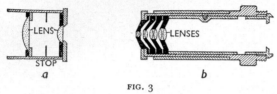

FIG. 3

a. Microscope eyepiece. b. High power micro-objective

A good modern microscope is provided with three or four objectives of different powers and three or four eyepieces of different powers. The objectives give a first magnification of from about $6 \times$ in the case of the lowest-powered to about $70 \times$ in the case of the highest-powered. The eyepieces give a further magnification of $5 \times$ to $20 \times$. Thus the combination gives magnifications ranging from $30 \times$ to $1,400 \times$. It is useless to construct microscopes giving magnifications

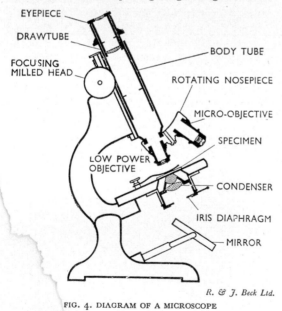

R. & J. Beck Ltd.

FIG. 4. DIAGRAM OF A MICROSCOPE

much greater than $1,400 \times$, because the light-waves themselves have a certain size (about $\frac{1}{50000}$ inch), and this prevents objects smaller than about $\frac{1}{50000}$ inch from being distinctly

seen, whatever lenses are used. If higher magnifications are needed, a microscope using ultra-violet light (which has a shorter wavelength) or an ELECTRON MICROSCOPE (q.v.) must be used.

As a rule, high-power microscopes are used to examine thin, partly transparent slices or specimens mounted between two glass plates. One plate (called the 'cover slip') is very thin, and this is on the side next to the micro-objective L_1 (Fig. 4). The other, called the 'slide', serves to support the specimen, which is usually immersed in canada balsam, a resinlike substance, forming a thin layer between slide and cover-slip.

Light is concentrated on the back of the specimen by means of a group of lenses (the 'condenser'); it then passes through the specimen and on into the microscope. The proper illumination of the specimen is very important in a high-power microscope.

See also LENS; TELESCOPE.

MILLING MACHINES. 1. In general these are designed to remove metal on flat surfaces or to produce an irregular shape by using a rotating cutting tool. In a very crude form they are among the oldest of MACHINE TOOLS (q.v.), a type of milling machine being in existence as early as the 16th century. The present-day milling machine, however, stems from the work of an American, Eli Whitney, in the early part of the last century.

There are two general types, the horizontal and the vertical milling machine. The general principle can be seen in the illustration of the horizontal type (Fig. 1). The worktable (A) moves horizontally at right angles to the horizontal spindle (B) which carries the cutter. It is mounted on a bracket, or knee (C), which can be raised or lowered by the same motor which rotates the cutter. Because of the knee-shaped bracket, machines of this design are known as knee-type machines. The table can also be moved sideways to allow the work, which is clamped on to it, to be fed crosswise under the cutter as well as moving lengthwise.

2. *Milling cutters.* For general milling, the worktable is moved under the cutter in the opposite direction to the cutter's rotation, the cutter having teeth all the way round its circumference. The cutting faces of the teeth are either made radial, that is, they all point towards the centre of the cutter (Fig. 2a); or else they are given a positive rake angle, that is, the cutting face

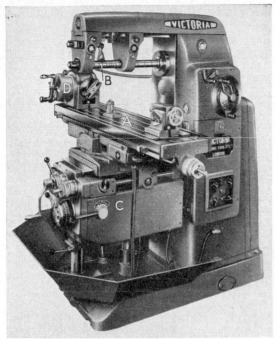

B. *Elliott & Co. Ltd.*

FIG. I. KNEE-TYPE HORIZONTAL MILLER

A. Worktable. B. Copper spindle. C. Knee. D. Dividing head clamped to worktable

slopes backwards from the tooth tip so as to form a wedge-shaped tooth (Fig. 2*b*). Recently, cutters have been made with teeth tipped with a very hard material called tungsten carbide and having a so-called negative rake-angle, so that the cutting face slopes forward from the tooth tip (Fig. 2*c*). Machining with this type of cutter is known as negative rake milling, for the metal is removed by a pushing rather than a cutting action. These cutters are more effective, but a very robust machine is necessary in order to provide the necessary rigidity. On the whole, however, tungsten carbide cutters with positive cutting angles are proving the most satisfactory.

In addition to machining flat surfaces, millers are used for many other operations, such as cutting spirals in the flutes of twist drills (*see* DRILLING AND BORING MACHINES) or the teeth of spiral gear-wheels. For work of this kind, the universal type of horizontal miller is used, the table being mounted on the 'knee' so that it can be swivelled horizontally about its centre and the work inclined at the correct angle to the cutter. The work, here cylindrical in shape, is mounted on a dividing head, which is rotated at the correct rate by the same mechanism which propels the

worktable, so that the cutter machines a spiral on the work.

A number of cuts can be made simultaneously by mounting a series of cutters on the cutter spindle and rotating them all at once—a procedure known as gang milling. Irregular shapes can be milled by using a special 'form cutter', which may have cutting edges of special shapes either on its edge or side or both.

The vertical type of miller is similar to the horizontal tool except that the axis of the cutter is vertical. The teeth are formed on the end and side of the cutter. This tool can cut blind slots, that is, slots which do not continue to the edge of the workpiece; and it can also cut irregular shapes, for the tool can be fitted to the required angle. Some cutter heads are made in which the cutter can be adjusted in both radial and horizontal directions. Some have rotary tables so that cylindrical work can be milled.

3. *Copying from a pattern.* An important development is the contour or copy milling machine where a tracer, or feeler, presses against a 'master' or templet of the shape to be produced and transmits this shape to the machine, so that the

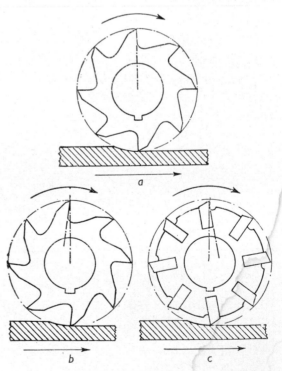

FIG. 2. UPMILLING

a. Teeth with radial cutting face. *b.* Teeth with positive rake cutting face. *c.* Teeth with negative rake cutting face

Ford Motor Co.

FIG. 3. MACHINING MOTOR-CAR CYLINDER HEADS ON A
MASSIVE TWO-SPINDLE VERTICAL MILLING MACHINE

cutter automatically follows the form of the templet. This method is obviously convenient for milling parts with complicated shapes or profiles since, once the templet has been made, a number of parts can be produced from it without the exercise of any skill by the operator. Some modern machines can control movement of this sort in both the horizontal and vertical directions, so that copying in three dimensions is possible. These devices are often operated hydraulically, but electrical or electronic methods are also used.

Machines where a high rate of production is required may have a fixed bed, the movement being obtained by sliding the cutter head on its column. Another type uses a rotating table, carrying fixtures on which the work is mounted, and moving each workpiece past the cutters as the table rotates. Alternatively, the work is sometimes mounted horizontally on a rotating drum, these machines being known as drum type millers. Both kinds are much used for mass-production work. Special universal millers are available for toolroom or other high precision work; and another special type, called a thread miller, can be used to cut threads and worms (*see* SCREW-THREADS). For very heavy work, a planer type milling machine, or plano-miller, is often used. This has the same general form as a planing machine (*see* MACHINE TOOLS), but instead of the lathe-type cutting tool on the planer, a rotating milling cutter, or series of cutters, rotates on a spindle at right angles to the table.

See also MACHINE TOOLS; SAFETY DEVICES.

MINERS' LAMPS, *see* SAFETY LAMPS.

MINING ENGINEERING. 1. The tasks which a mining engineer may be called upon to perform include PROSPECTING (q.v.), exploration of mineral deposits (*see* METAL ORES, Vol. III), opening, developing, and working of mines, and separating minerals from the 'gangue' or useless rocks with which they are generally associated. The last operation is carried out on the surface of the mine and is referred to as 'mineral dressing'.

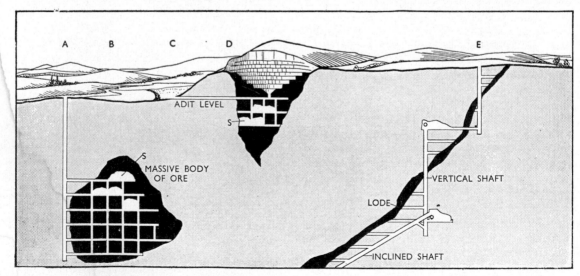

FIG. I. TYPES OF METAL MINES

A, E. Deep level mines. B. Placer mine in alluvial deposits. C. Adit mine. D. Open-cast mine. E. Shaft mine. S. Stopes

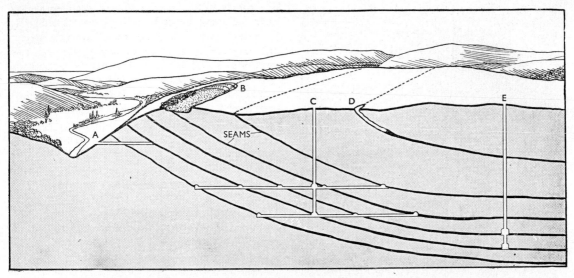

FIG. 2. TYPES OF COAL-MINE
A. Adit mine. B. Open-cast mine. C. Horizontal mine. D. Drift mine. E. Typical shaft mine

Mines are classified into alluvial or 'placer' mines, open-cast mines, adit and drift mines, and deep-level mines. The different types are shown diagrammatically in Figs. 1 and 2. Placer mining, which is done chiefly to obtain gold, platinum, and tin ore, is the most simple operation from an engineering standpoint. It is carried out on a large scale by dredging and by directing a powerful jet of water against the sides of a cutting in the deposit, so that the water performs the two essential functions of breaking down the gravel and washing away the lighter dirt from the heavier mineral particles (see GOLD-MINING, Vol. VII). Most of the tin ores are now obtained in this way from Malaya and other places in the Far East and from Nigeria.

Mining engineering problems become more difficult when minerals have to be extracted from solid rocks, but they are still comparatively simple providing the minerals are sufficiently near the surface to be extracted in open-cast mines (see MINING, Vol. VII). The operations are then very similar to those employed in QUARRYING (q.v.). Great mining engineering problems arise when the minerals lie far below the surface and have to be reached by deep-level mining. These involve:

1. Sinking shafts or driving tunnels from the surface to reach the mineral.
2. Driving roadways from the shafts to develop the mine.

3. Opening 'stopes' or working faces for the extraction of the mineral.
4. Providing means for breaking and loading the mineral at the faces, and arranging suitable equipment for transporting it to the shafts and for winding it to the surface.
5. Supporting the roof above the roadways and working places, and keeping the subsidence of the rest of the undermined strata under control so that agricultural land, roads, railways, and buildings on the surface are not damaged by uneven settlement of the ground.
6. Providing adequate ventilation in all parts of the mine.
7. Providing means for draining water from the mine.
8. Designing and building surface structures such as headgears, shaft-houses, gantries (cranes), screens (sieves), mill-houses, and washeries, and installing winding engines, fans, power plants, air-compressors, and equipping the workshops and laboratories.
9. Surveying the mines periodically and preparing detailed plans to show the exact positions of all underground roadways and working places.

Such a wide variety of tasks cannot be accomplished without drawing upon the resources of civil, mechanical, electrical, and chemical engineering to some extent, and when the work at

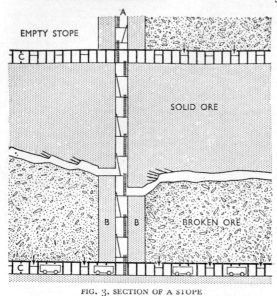

EMPTY STOPE

SOLID ORE

BROKEN ORE

FIG. 3. SECTION OF A STOPE

A. Manway with ladders to stope. B. Pillars of ore left to support manway. C. Haulage roadway supported by timber props. The broken ore is delivered from chutes into mine cars

a large mine involves any of these branches of engineering, it is carried out by specially trained departmental staffs under the general direction of the mining engineer in charge of the mine.

2. METAL MINING. Metallic ores are mostly found in the form of steeply sloping veins, lodes, or reefs, as shown on the right in Fig. 1; but the ores of some base metals, such as copper and iron, sometimes occur as massive bodies of irregular shape as shown on the left. The main underground roadways of a metal mine are driven horizontally at regular vertical intervals of about 100 to 200 feet and the ore is then extracted between one level and the next by drilling into it and BLASTING it (q.v.) with explosives. The broken ore falls into chutes which discharge it into mine cars on the level below as shown in Fig. 3. It is a fundamental principle in mining engineering that the methods adopted should enable as much as possible of the work to be done by gravity. The open spaces which are formed where the ore is extracted are called 'stopes', and the process of extraction is called stoping.

When a vein of metal ore lies within a hill or a mountain it is reached by driving horizontal tunnels, or adits, to it from the hillside, as shown on the left in Fig. 1. These adits are given a slight upward gradient so that water can drain out of the mine, and they are used as the main roads

for carrying ore in cars drawn by electric or diesel locomotives, or by belt CONVEYORS (q.v.). In the example shown, the ore is being extracted underground in an adit mine and also on the surface in an open-cast mine. In some cases an opening is made at the bottom of an open-cast pit to let the broken ore fall into mine cars on an adit level below the pit. This type of open-cast mine is called a 'Glory Hole'.

In Fig. 1 on the right the inclination of the lode is such that the mine develops in a downward direction and may eventually become very deep. Several mines of this type in South Africa and elsewhere have reached depths as great as 10,000 feet, involving many special engineering problems. In the first place, since ore cannot be raised to the surface in a single lift of much more that 6,000 feet without the lifting ropes breaking under their own weight, there have to be two or more stages of lift as shown in Fig. 1, where two of the shafts are vertical and the third is inclined.

A serious problem in deep mines is to get rid of heat, for the temperature of the rocks increases with depth, and the ventilating air is also heated by compression as it descends through the downcast shafts (see COAL-MINING, Section 4, Vol. VII). High temperatures and humidity would make it impossible for miners to work at a greater depth than 8,000 feet in South Africa and about 4,500 feet in Britain without artificial cooling of the ventilating air. In Britain few coal-mines are more than 4,000 feet deep, but powerful REFRIGERATORS (q.v.) with cooling capacities equivalent to 2,500 tons of ice a day are installed in many deep metal mines. Another great problem in deep mining is the enormous pressure exerted on the rocks by the weight of the strata above them, which may cause the rock face to burst into the mine with disastrous consequences. No certain way of getting over this difficulty has been found, and at present this is the factor which more than anything else limits the depth to which any mine can go.

The shafts of a large metal mine are usually rectangular in shape and up to 45 feet by 10 feet in section. They are divided into several compartments for skips, cages, and service pipes and cables. The ore, on arriving at the surface, is first crushed into pieces of less than 2 inches in size, and then reduced to a very fine powder in ball mills or tube mills to facilitate the separation of the mineral particles from useless materials by physical or chemical processes. The product is called a concentrate of the mineral or minerals in the ore, and this is the final state in which it leaves the mine for the smelters (*see* BLAST FURNACE).

3. COAL-MINING. The difference between the engineering problems in coal-mining and metal-mining are due mainly to the fact that coal lies in extensive flat layers or seams, whilst metal ores are generally in irregular lumps. A coal seam which has not been disturbed from its original position forms a flat or slightly inclined bed of uniform thickness extending in some coalfields over several hundred square miles. The main roadways and working faces of a coal-mine, therefore, spread outwards from the shafts and are more or less on the same level (Fig. 4).

The appearance of a large modern British coal-mine on the surface is shown in Fig. 5. The winding engines (*see* MINING MACHINERY) are placed in the two high towers which stand directly over the shafts, one over the downcast shaft, and the other over the upcast shaft. The one on the right, over the upcast shaft, is connected to the ventilating fan in the small building in the foreground, with the two openings above it for the discharge of the used air from the mine into the atmosphere. Coal is raised through both shafts, but that which comes through the upcast has to pass out through an air-lock at the top of the shaft, which prevents air being drawn into the fan directly from the atmosphere.

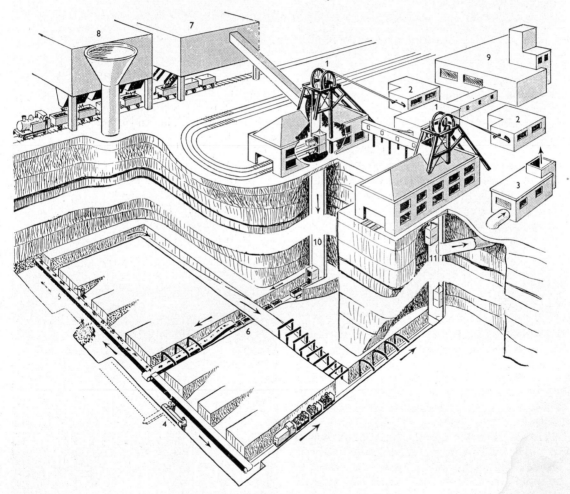

FIG. 4. DIAGRAM OF A COAL-MINE

1. Head-gears. 2. Winding-engine houses. 3. Fan house. 4. Cutting machine at coal face. 5. Conveyor. 6. Mine cars at loading-point. 7. Screens. 8. Washery. 9. Pithead baths and canteen. 10. Downcast shaft. 11. Upcast shaft. Arrows show the direction of the flow of air through the mine

National Coal Board

FIG. 5. SURFACE VIEW OF A MODERN COAL-MINE IN GREAT BRITAIN
Model of Rothes colliery, Fifeshire

A colliery of this size would work all the available seams under an area of from 10 to 15 square miles, and its reserves would amount to about 150 million tons. The colliery would be planned for an output of about 5,000 tons a day and would therefore have a useful life of nearly 100 years. The cost of sinking and equipping with machinery such a colliery would be about £7 millions, and it would take 5 years to complete the shafts and another 5 years to bring the colliery into full production. On reaching this stage it would give employment to about 3,500 men.

See also PROSPECTING; BLASTING; MINING MACHINERY; SAFETY LAMPS.

See also Vol. VII: MINING; COAL-MINING; GOLD-MINING.

See also Vol. III: METAL ORES; MINERALS.

MINING MACHINERY.
Mining machines may be classified according to whether they are used for (1) rock-drilling, coal-cutting, and loading at the working faces of the mines, (2) hauling and conveying on roadways, (3) hoisting or winding in shafts, (4) pumping, ventilating, and cooling.

1. COAL-CUTTING AND LOADING MACHINERY. (a) *Rock drills.* A steam-driven rock drill was invented in 1813, but as steam was found to be unsuitable for this purpose, no real progress was made in mechanical rock-drilling until percussive machines operated by compressed air were used successfully in the construction of the famous Alpine tunnel at Mont Cenis in 1861.

The pneumatic percussive drill (Fig. 1) is still the most suitable machine for boring in hard rocks, but rotary drills are now often used for boring in coal, shale, and other comparatively soft rocks.

(b) *Coal cutters.* About 90% of the deep-mined coal produced in Great Britain in 1953 was undercut by machines so that it could be easily extracted by explosives and picks (*see* COAL-MINING, Vol. VII). The standard type of machine used for this purpose (Fig. 2) consists of an endless chain carrying sharp pick points round an

Holman Bros.

FIG. 1. ROCK DRILLING WITH A HOLMAN 'DRIFTER'
This is a pneumatic percussive drill

oblong steel frame, or jib, which projects about 4 to 8 feet into or under the coal seam. An undercut about 6 inches high is taken right across the coal face, as the machine is hauled along under its own power by a wire rope anchored at the far end of the face and wound in by a winch attached to the machine. A driving motor of about 50 h.p. and the gearing through which it is connected to the chain sprocket are enclosed in the steel casing of the machine. These machines may be operated by compressed air or electricity supplied by a trailing hose pipe or cable. Electric motors must be made flame-proof to avoid any danger of causing an explosion by igniting firedamp (*see* SAFETY LAMPS). The rate of undercutting, which depends on the hardness of the coal, varies from 1 to 5 feet per minute.

(*c*) *Cutter-loaders.* With ordinary undercutting the coal has to be broken down by explosives or by picks before it is ready to load into mine cars or on to CONVEYORS (q.v.), but the Meco-Moore machine (*see* Vol. VII, p. 112) does all these things simultaneously. It consists of one vertical and two horizontal jibs and a short transverse conveyor. The three jibs acting together cut out of the seam a rectangular block of coal, which disintegrates as it falls and is gathered by a combing device on to the conveyor; this delivers it to the face conveyor running parallel to the face on the other side of the machine. The largest Meco-Moore machine weighs about 10 tons and is powered by two 50 h.p. electric motors. It can cut and load from 300 to 400 tons of coal in one shift of 8 hours in seams not less than 4 feet thick.

(*d*) *Coal ploughs.* When the coal is soft it can be ploughed off the coal face, a method developed in Germany during the Second World War. The plough is held against the coal face by the steel frame of the conveyor: the lower half of the plough is so shaped that it scoops up the broken coal into the trough of the conveyor as it travels along the face. The plough is pulled by a wire rope which passes over a pulley in the foreground to a winch on one of the gate roads leading to the face. Most coal seams in Britain are too hard for the German type of plough, but the Samson Stripper machine has been specially designed to shear off these harder coals. The plough of this machine is driven into the coal by a hydraulic ram, the ram cylinder being held firmly between roof and floor by a hydraulic jack. When the plough has reached the end of its working stroke

Jeffrey Mfg. Co.

FIG. 2. MACHINE UNDERCUTTING A COAL SEAM IN U.S.A.

of 2 ft. 7 in., the jack is released, and the cylinder is carried forward on the ram by hydraulic pressure into position for the next working stroke.

(*e*) *Continuous miners.* A variety of machines have been evolved, mainly in the U.S.A., for the continuous extraction of coal. The cutting heads for ripping the coal off the face may consist of chains with picks (Fig. 3) or of revolving chisels. The coal, having been broken into small pieces, is swept to the rear of the machine by revolving spirals underneath it or carried over the top by conveyors. The trade name 'Colmol' given to this type suggests that these machines act much

Joy-Sullivan Ltd.

FIG. 3. THE CONTINUOUS 'MINER' DIGGING AND LOADING
COAL SIMULTANEOUSLY

Joy-Sullivan Ltd.

FIG. 4. JOY LOADER DELIVERING COAL INTO A SHUTTLE CAR AT THE FACE

as a mole does, digging its way through the ground and throwing the loose earth back as it advances.

(*f*) *Mechanical loaders*. Fig. 4 shows one of the main types of deep-mine mechanical loaders. The 'Joy loader' has a tapered head which is forced under the heap of broken coal on the floor as the machine moves forward on wheels or on caterpillar tracks. The claws driven by the rotating disks on this head sweep the coal on to the conveyor running along the centre of the machine, and this delivers it into a mine car or a roadway conveyor. The tapered head can be raised or lowered and swung from side to side as required by means of hydraulic rams, and the machine, together with the hydraulic pump, is driven by an electric motor supplied by a battery of accumulators. This loader is specially designed to work under a low roof, but as it is over 20 feet long, it is too large for most English coal-mines. In American coal-mines, however, the system of working out large areas, leaving pillars to support the roof, allows the Joy loader room to move about. The 'duckbill' loader, which requires even less headroom than the Joy loader, consists of a broad shovel at the end of a shaker conveyor. The shovel is lowered slightly during the forward stroke and then raised sharply during the return stroke, jerking the coal along the trough of the conveyor until it reaches the far end and falls into a mine car. The 'shovel' loader and the 'scraper' loader or 'slusher' need more headroom and have been mainly designed for tunnelling and development work.

2. HAULING MACHINERY. (*a*) *Mechanical haulage*. The 'main-rope' system is used on steep gradients for bringing the coal up, particularly in drift mines, where the rope to which the cars are hitched is sometimes more than 2 miles long. The empty cars drag the rope back down to the coal face. With the 'endless rope' system the rope moves continuously round, taking the full cars up on one railway track and bringing the empty ones down on another.

(*b*) *Locomotive haulage*. If the haulage roadways are level, or can be graded slightly in favour of the loaded trains, as happens more often in metal than in coal-mines, locomotives provide the most efficient mode of traction. The electric trolley-wire type of locomotive, widely used in metal-mines and in U.S.A. coal-mines, is prohibited in British coal-mines, except under special circumstances, because it is not absolutely flame-proof. The electric battery locomotive, however, can be made flame-proof and is therefore in general use. The diesel locomotive (*see* INTERNAL COMBUSTION ENGINE, Section 4), which is widely used in every part of the world, can be made flame-proof by fitting flame traps on the inlet and exhaust pipes of the engine.

(*c*) *Trackless haulage.* In some modern mines, particularly in the U.S.A., the haulage roadways have no rail tracks but only plain surfaces for rubber-tired vehicles. The shuttle car (*see* Fig. 4), specially designed for working in such mines under a very low roof, has a floor consisting of a movable platform or conveyor which enables the car to be loaded and discharged rapidly from either end without having to lift the coal over the sides or to tip the body. It has battery-driven electric motors and can be steered in either direction without being turned round. Mechanical CONVEYORS (q.v.) of various types are now also widely used in mines.

3. WINDING MACHINERY. Minerals are brought to the surface through shafts in cars on cages or loosely in large hanging buckets called skips. With skip winding, the cars are emptied at the bottom of the shaft into the skip loading pocket and then returned to the workings. Two cages or skips are used so that one descends whilst the other is ascending—a system which not only doubles the winding capacity but, since the skips balance each other, reduces the strain on the winding engine. From 10 to 20 tons of coal or ore are lifted at a time in large mines from depths up to 6,000 feet. Deeper vertical shafts than this subject the rope to too great a strain from its own weight, and in very deep metal-mines winding from the lowest levels has to be carried out in stages.

Winders in mines usually have either two ropes coiling in opposite directions on a drum, or a single rope passing round a pulley with its two ends attached to cages or skips in the shaft (*see* Vol. VII, p. 297). The winder shown is sometimes fitted with a tapering drum to enable the ascending rope to coil on a smaller diameter at the beginning of the wind than at the end of the wind, and this reduces the effort required to start and stop the winding engine. In the Koepe system the drum is replaced by a grooved pulley which drives a single rope by friction. The cages or skips attached to this rope are also joined underneath by a balance rope hanging loosely in the shaft; this increases the pull in the descending rope to make it grip the pulley firmly and not slip. Winding ropes are made of special steel wires built up into a strong cable. The largest rope that can be coiled on a drum or bent over a pulley is about 3 inches in diameter and has a breaking strength of about 500 tons; the working load, however, is reduced to about one-seventh of this to provide a sufficient margin of safety. Winding engines are driven by steam or now more usually by electricity. The maximum power developed during the winding cycle may reach 7,000 to 8,000 h.p.

4. PUMPING AND VENTILATING MACHINERY. The workings of a deep mine are usually well below any water-bearing strata, but water often finds its way down through fissures in the rocks or through old workings at higher levels. Small ram PUMPS (q.v.), as well as centrifugal pumps, are used to clear water from the mine workings to the main pumping station at the bottom of the shafts. The main pumps are of the multi-stage centrifugal type, and can be connected in series to pump water to the surface against heads up to 5,000 feet.

The amount of air needed to ventilate a large mine is of the order of 500,000 cubic feet per minute, and the pressure required to overcome the resistance to flow varies from about 3 inches to 20 inches on a water-gauge (*see* PRESSURE GAUGES). About 6 tons of air is used for ventilation in the coal-mines of Great Britain for every ton of coal produced, and as much energy may be used in drawing air into a colliery as in bringing the coal out. Centrifugal (or radial-flow) and axial-flow fans (*see* COMPRESSOR) are used for mine VENTILATION (q.v.). The centrifugal fan (*see* Fig. 4, p. 88), one of the most powerful mine fans in the world, driven by a 6,000 h.p. motor, is capable of drawing 800,000 cubic feet of air a minute through the mine against a water-gauge pressure of 30 inches. The axial-flow fan, though more efficient in most ways, makes a noise like an aeroplane propeller. This is difficult to suppress.

5. MINE POWER STATIONS. Some important mining areas, such as northern Ontario in Canada, the Witwatersrand in South Africa, and the coalfields of Britain, are within sufficiently easy reach of large grid electricity systems to be able to take from the grid most of the energy they need to work the machinery. Other important mining areas, such as the Copper Belt district of Northern Rhodesia, are so remote that they must generate their own power. Mine power stations not only contain turbo-alternators to generate electricity but also turbo-blowers to supply compressed air. A rock drill requires an input of about 16 h.p. at the compressor, and since there may be as many as 2,000 rock drills in operation in a large metal mine, the demand from the turbines driving the compressors is often very great. Some mines, such as the gold-mines on the Rand and some collieries in South Wales, are supplied with compressed air as well as electricity on the grid system from central power stations equipped with turbo-compressors and alternators.

A large proportion of the coal-mines in Britain have their own steam-power plants, and in some collieries recently the methane gas present in the coal seams and their surrounding rocks has been drained and piped to the surface to be used as a gaseous fuel in the boilers and in gas engines and turbines. This new development in coal-mining is not only a great economy but also, by removing the methane from the mine, reduces the amount of firedamp and hence the danger of explosions.

See also MINING ENGINEERING; COMPRESSOR; CONVEYORS; PUMPS; VENTILATION.

See also Vol. VII: MINING.

MODEL ENGINEERING.

This can mean either the making of an experimental prototype by a professional engineer in order that he may study how it works before going on to make the real thing, or the making in miniature of models by amateur engineers as a useful and practical hobby.

Soon after the Industrial Revolution started in the last decades of the 18th century, people began to make models of the machines which were now beginning to play a greater part in their lives. With the rapidly growing variety of machines from which to choose, there was no difficulty in finding suitable subjects for reproducing in miniature, though the favourite prototypes have always been STEAM ENGINES (q.v.) of some kind.

Amateur model makers, scarcely less than fully trained mechanical engineers, have had difficult problems to solve in developing reliable and successful working steam engines, whether of the simplest or of more elaborate kinds; and the experience they gained proved valuable when, after the steam engine, came ELECTRIC MOTORS (q.v.), gas engines, oil engines, petrol engines (see INTERNAL COMBUSTION ENGINE), and STEAM

TURBINES (q.v.). All these types have been successfully reproduced in working models.

In 1898 the founding of the Society of Model and Experimental Engineers in London enabled model engineers to organize themselves for the first time on something like an official foundation. Other similar societies were formed—all strictly non-professional so far as the engineering industry is concerned, though an interest in every known branch of engineering is to be found among the membership. The meetings provide for lectures, discussions, and demonstrations upon all relevant subjects, and many societies have their own workshops where members can either carry out constructional work for which they have no facilities of their own, or receive instruction in the use of tools of all kinds.

The models they make can be classified, broadly, under two heads: the fully representative, exact-scale model, in which even the smallest detail of the prototype is faithfully reproduced; and the model intended to be primarily a working model, with only its external visible features as nearly as possible to scale. Examples of the former are to be found in technical museums and private collections, and they often have great historical interest and value, as well as showing craftsmanship of the highest class. Working models are, however, more representative of the hobby of model engineering; the most popular are MODEL SHIPS, MODEL RAILWAYS, and MODEL AIRCRAFT (qq.v. Vol. IX).

The reasons for research and experiment in the design of miniature engines arise from the fact that the conditions in which they operate are not the same as in the prototypes; that is to

The Model Engineer

1¼-IN. SCALE MODEL OF AN AGRICULTURAL TRACTION ENGINE OF ABOUT 1890 say, there are no such things as scale materials, scale fuel, scale water, or scale steam. All these, and other factors, remain constant, whatever the size of the model, and due allowance must be made for this. Therefore, there are difficult decisions to be taken upon such matters as cylinder sizes, diameter and arrangement of boiler tubes, hull dimensions, wing spans, and the like, all calling for care, ingenuity, and patience from the designer and builder. With stationary steam engines, such as mill engines, winding engines, and marine engines, the problem of design is, perhaps, not so severe because such engines, when reproduced in miniature, are not usually called upon to produce high-power outputs or particularly spectacular performances.

Miniature petrol engines and very small compression-ignition engines have now been brought to a high level of perfection. Model racing boats, capable of reaching very high speeds on the water, are usually powered by small petrol engines of high efficiency. The compression-ignition engine, of which the capacity may be as low as $2\frac{1}{2}$ cubic centimetres or less, is often used as a power unit for model racing cars and model aircraft.

The model engineer has often overcome what seem, at first, insoluble problems. For example, at the beginning of the 20th century, it was thought impossible to produce steam turbines small enough to be put into models and still to work efficiently. However, several model engineers persisted in making experiments until, in 1905, the subject had aroused so much interest that a competition was organized, and this brought to light some miniature turbines which would work properly, though with a very small output of power. About 30 years later, amateur experimenters succeeded in making miniature turbines with an output powerful enough to drive a 4-foot model boat, built externally to scale.

Let us now consider the part played by model engineering in engineering production and research. Often, some great project is evolved after a model or several models have been made, tested, and every source of weakness eliminated. A striking instance is to be found in the constant development of aircraft design, in which, from the earliest times in AERONAUTICAL ENGINEERING (q.v.), models have been constructed and thoroughly tested before a proposed new type of

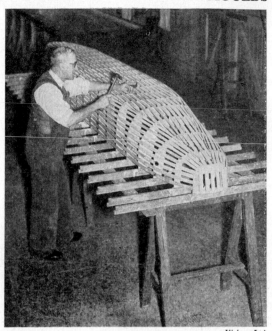

Vickers Ltd.
BUILDING THE MODEL OF A SHIP

aeroplane has been put into production. Most of the available information on the shapes of fuselage, and their effects on aeroplanes in flight, has been obtained by building scale models and testing them in WIND TUNNELS (q.v.) where their behaviour under varying rates of air flow can be studied.

The same sort of procedure has been applied in BRIDGE BUILDING (q.v.), the final design for a bridge usually being settled by making and experimenting with a model. In NAVAL ARCHITECTURE (q.v.), too, models are of great value in determining, for example, the best shape of hull or type of PROPELLER (q.v.) to meet certain specified conditions. There is, in fact, an almost unlimited scope for the use of models as an aid to the advancement of design and practice in the engineering industry.

See also ENGINEERING DESIGN.

See also Vol. IX: MODEL SHIPS; MODEL RAILWAYS; MODEL AIRCRAFT.

MOTOR-CAR, *see* INTERNAL COMBUSTION ENGINE. *See also* Vol. IV: MOTOR-CAR. *See also* Vol. VII: MOTOR INDUSTRY.

MOULDS, *see* CASTING, Section 2.

N

NAVAL ARCHITECTURE. 1. This is concerned with the design of a ship's hull and superstructure and of the general arrangement of spaces inside the hull; MARINE ENGINEERING (q.v.), on the other hand, is concerned with the machinery that drives the ship. The design and construction of both merchant SHIPS (q.v. Vol. IV) and NAVAL VESSELS (q.v. Vol. X) are supervised by naval architects; the naval architects responsible for naval vessels are members of the Royal Corps of Naval Constructors and are employed by the Admiralty.

2. DESIGN. The first step in designing a ship is to calculate its dimensions. These depend mainly on the amount of BUOYANCY (q.v.) which must be provided to carry the vessel's 'total load' —that is, its 'lightweight' (the weight of the main steel structure of the ship, the machinery, and all permanent fittings and equipment) and its 'deadweight' (the weight of everything the ship carries: passengers, cargo, fuel, fresh water, and so on). If he is to design a cargo ship, for example, the naval architect must know the weight of cargo that the vessel will have to carry. He must also know the speed at which the ship must usually travel, so that he can estimate the weight of the engines that will be needed to produce this power and the weight of fuel that the ship will have to carry for the length of voyage it will usually make. With these facts and from experience of existing ships of a similar type he can calculate fairly accurately both the deadweight and lightweight.

When the ship is floating, this total load will equal the weight of water which the ship displaces, called its 'displacement'. As the displacement equals the volume of the ship which is under the water multiplied by the density of the water (*see* BUOYANCY), the naval architect can thus deduce the underwater volume which must be provided to enable the ship to support its total load.

Now if the ship were a rectangular box, its underwater volume would be equal to the length multiplied by the beam (the maximum width at the waterline) and by the draught (the depth of the keel below the surface). Though no ship is rectangular, it is possible to imagine that its form has been cut out of a rectangular block with dimensions equal to the overall dimensions of the ship. The ratio of the underwater volume of the ship to the volume of this imaginary block is called the 'block coefficient'. The underwater volume, therefore, equals the length of the ship, multiplied by the beam, by the draught, and by the block coefficient. Thus, knowing the volume of the block coefficient for similar ships, the naval architect can deduce from the known underwater volume the length, beam, and draught of a new ship.

When the main dimensions have thus been settled, the form of the ship is well defined, and the naval architect can make a detailed check of his original estimates. He must then examine the following aspects of his design:

(*a*) *Stability*. This is largely governed by two things: the ship's underwater form, in particular the ratio of the beam to the draught, and the distribution of the weight vertically in the ship.

Here the naval architect works to the practice followed in other similar ships. The maximum draught to which a merchant ship can be loaded is governed by law (*see* SAFETY AT SEA, Vol. IV), and depends in a complicated way on the length

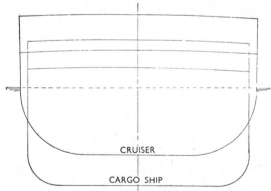

FIG. 1. COMPARATIVE SECTIONS OF A CRUISER AND CARGO SHIP

and depth of the ship. In merchant ships the ratio of the beam to the draught is usually 2:5 or more; in warships, which have to carry heavy weights such as guns high up, the ratio is usually about 3:5 (Fig. 1). If the designer has to improve the stability of a new ship design, he can do it either by slightly increasing the beam or by ballasting, that is, by adding weight low down in the ship; the former is more usual.

(*b*) *Strength.* The naval architect can check the strength of his design by calculating the stresses in the deck and the keel when the ship is in waves as long as itself. The waves are considered

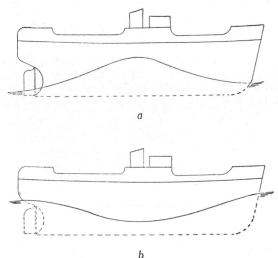

FIG. 2. *a*. SHIP 'HOGGING' ON WAVES. *b*. SHIP 'SAGGING' ON WAVES

in two positions relative to the ship, one in which the ship is said to be 'hogging' (Fig. 2*a*), and the other in which it is 'sagging' (Fig. 2*b*).

From these calculations, and by comparison with similar ships, the naval architect knows if the steel structure he proposes to provide is strong enough. If the stresses are high, he usually reduces them by putting in more steel structure.

(*c*) *Resistance.* The resistance experienced by a ship as it passes through the water is due partly to the waves it creates on the surface ('wave-resistance') and partly to the friction of the water moving past the underwater surface of the ship ('skin friction').

Wave resistance, which is greater at high speeds, depends to a large extent on the length and fineness of a ship. Thus warships, being faster, are longer and finer than merchant ships (Fig. 3). 'Skin friction' resistance, which is greater in merchant ships, increases with the increased roughness of the underwater surface of

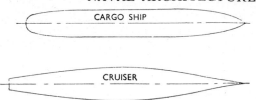

FIG. 3. COMPARATIVE WATERLINES OF CARGO SHIP AND CRUISER

the ship, for example, when it has become 'fouled' with marine growth. To reduce this resistance all ships are docked at least once a year so that their bottoms can be cleaned and painted (*see* SHIP REPAIRS).

The total resistance of a ship is usually found from experiments on a model of the ship towed at various speeds in a long tank of water (*see* MODEL ENGINEERING). The results of these experiments are compared with those on other ship models to see if the form can be improved; the models are made in paraffin wax so that their shape can be easily altered until the most satisfactory form is obtained. Experiments are also carried out in the testing tank on models of the PROPELLERS (q.v.) which the ship will use.

When all model tests have been completed, the naval architect is supplied with an estimate of the horse-power required to propel the ship at the design speed. With a marine engineer he can then make a more accurate calculation of the weight of machinery and fuel which the ship must carry.

3. GENERAL ARRANGEMENT. The naval architect now prepares detailed drawings of the 'general arrangement' of the ship, that is, the position and proportions of holds, cabins, and all other spaces inside it (Fig. 4). In a cargo ship, the engine-room and all fuel bunkers are usually placed amidships. Forward and aft of this space are holds for the cargo; at the extreme ends, called respectively the 'forward' and 'after' peaks, which are inaccessible for cargo, water ballast is carried. All ships are divided below deck into watertight compartments across their breadth by steel bulkheads. In a cargo ship, these bulkheads are so placed that if one compartment is flooded the ship will remain afloat; in a passenger ship, two or even three compartments may be flooded without the ship sinking. In addition, most modern ships are fitted with an inner bottom, running the length of the cargo holds and machinery space. The space between this and the outer bottom is sub-divided across the breadth of the ship and fore and aft by other divisions, forming a large number of tanks in which fresh water, oil fuel, and water ballast can

breadth of the ship. These tanks are about 30 to 35 feet long, and all are connected by pipes to the pumping machinery.

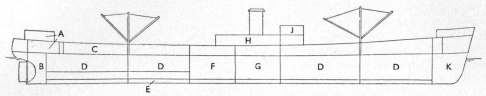

FIG. 4. GENERAL ARRANGEMENT OF CARGO SHIP

A. Crew. B. Aft peak. C. Deck; also used for cargo. D. Cargo holds. E. Double bottom used for oil fuel, fresh water, or water ballast. F. Machinery space. G. Cargo hold or water ballast. H. Offices. J. Bridge. K. Fore peak

be carried. The ship may have one or more decks, the spaces between them also being used for stowing cargo. Ships' officers live in deckhouses placed amidships above the uppermost deck, and the crew may be accommodated aft or amidships. The navigating bridge, from which the ship is controlled, is also amidships, but the steering gear is now almost always carried aft in a special compartment. A large passenger ship, such as the QUEEN ELIZABETH (q.v. Vol. IV), has much the same layout, except that a large superstructure is built up amidships containing cabins, dining-rooms, and so on.

Cargo ships built for carrying special kinds of cargo are sometimes laid out very differently. In an oil tanker, for example, the machinery space is always aft so that the main portion of the ship can be given up to the oil cargo, which may weigh as much as 30,000 tons. The oil space is divided into a number of small tanks by oil-tight bulkheads, running fore and aft as well as across the

It is in the preparation of these general arrangement drawings, and in ensuring that all space within the ship is economically and suitably used, that the bulk of the work in designing a new ship lies. When this stage is complete, the drawings are passed to the shipbuilder who prepares the many detailed plans and drawings necessary for building the ship.

4. LINES PLAN. As well as plans showing the general arrangement, the naval architect also prepares a 'lines plan' showing the outside form of the ship under and above the waterline. This consists of a number of horizontal and vertical sections taken through the ship at intervals of a few feet (Fig. 5). Not only must the underwater form give the correct displacement, but it must also be shaped in smooth curves to give the least resistance to motion through the water. These curves are used later in the SHIPBUILDING yard (q.v.) where the form of the ship is drawn full size on the floor of the 'laying-off loft'.

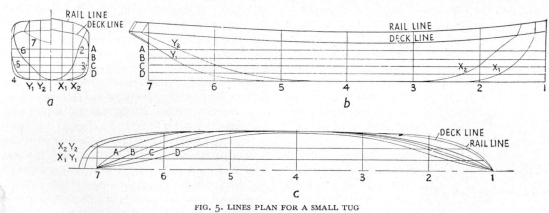

FIG. 5. LINES PLAN FOR A SMALL TUG

a. Body plan. 2–7 are vertical half-sections of the ship, forward on the right and after on the left. b. Profile. X_1, X_2, Y_1, Y_2, called 'bow' and 'buttock' lines, are vertical projections on the middle line plane. c. Half-breadth. A–D are horizontal sections, known as waterlines. The positions of the sections are shown on all the drawings

Vickers Ltd.

MARKING OUT TO FULL-SIZE DETAILS OF A SHIP'S PLATES IN A LAYING-OFF LOFT

5. SHIP SURVEYORS. Many naval architects are employed as ship surveyors by Classification Societies, such as Lloyd's Register of Shipping (*see* LLOYD'S, Vol. IV). These societies issue rules or standards of construction, which are recognized by most ship owners, ship builders, and government authorities; Lloyd's 100 A1, for example, means that a ship has been built to the highest standards. It is the duty of ship surveyors to see that a ship is built to these rules, and that its standard is afterwards maintained (*see* SHIP REPAIRS). The Ministry of Transport also employs naval architects to see that various safety regulations are complied with in a ship. They must make sure, for example, that there are sufficient lifeboats and proper means for launching them; that fires can be detected and extinguished easily; and that water can be pumped out quickly if a ship is damaged.

See also SHIPBUILDING; BUOYANCY; HYDRAULICS.
See also Vol. IV: SHIP.

NAVIGATIONAL INSTRUMENTS (Air), *see* Vol. IV: NAVIGATION, AIR.

NAVIGATIONAL INSTRUMENTS (Marine), *see* Vol. IV: NAVIGATION, MARINE.

NEW YORK WATER SUPPLY. NEW YORK City (q.v. Vol. III), with its population of nearly 8 million, has the largest WATER SUPPLY (q.v.) system in the world; the average daily supply being about 870 million gallons. Nearly all this water is obtained from rivers and streams in the mountains to the north of the city where a series of DAMS (q.v.), forming large reservoirs, has been built. From the reservoirs the water flows to the city, without need for pumping, through many miles of aqueducts consisting partly of deep tunnels driven through solid rock (*see* TUNNELLING).

There are three separate supply systems, the first of which, the Croton, developed between 1842 and 1911, uses the flow of the Croton River, a tributary of the Hudson (*see* Map). The water, collected in twelve reservoirs and six natural lakes, supplies about 275 million gallons of water a day. The largest reservoir, Croton Lake, holds about 23,400 million gallons and is 20 miles long.

Two large aqueducts carry the water 45 miles to service reservoirs in New York, where part is pumped to supply high-level districts.

The second system, the Catskill, developed between 1905 and 1928, supplies just over half the city's total demand. The water from two rivers in the Catskill Mountains, about 100 miles from New York, is stored in two main reservoirs. The Ashokan reservoir, a gigantic construction larger than all the Croton reservoirs put together, holds as much as 108,000 million gallons, or 125 days' supply for the whole city. The Schoharie reservoir holds 16,300 million gallons. Water from the Schoharie is carried through an intervening mountain range by a tunnel 18 miles long to join the Ashokan. The main aqueduct from this reservoir to the service reservoirs near the New York boundary is 92 miles long. The greater part of it consists of a covered-in channel, but at many points the route is shortened by driving tunnels through high ground; it passes under the Hudson River through a deep tunnel about 1,000 feet below the surface. Nearer the city the aqueduct is connected to the Kensico reser-

voir, with a capacity of 25,500 million gallons, also formed by a dam, which holds a reserve of water in case the supply from the Catskill Mountains is interrupted. One of the important advantages of the Catskill system is that it delivers water at a much higher level than the Croton, so that on arrival nearly all the Catskill water can be supplied without pumping.

The third system, the Delaware, was begun in 1937, and was still under construction in 1953, though completed parts had been brought into service. It consists of three large reservoirs, also in the Catskill Mountains, with a single aqueduct to the city about 130 miles long. The aqueduct is a deep tunnel under high pressure, driven under hills and valleys; part of it runs in a straight line for about 45 miles. It is connected to the Kensico reservoir, and thus forms an additional reserve. When complete, this system will supply about 470 million gallons a day.

In New York itself an unusual feature of the distribution system is the construction of two tunnels, each about 20 miles long, at depths of 200 and 750 feet below the streets. At intervals

Dept. of Water Supply, New York

CROTON DAM

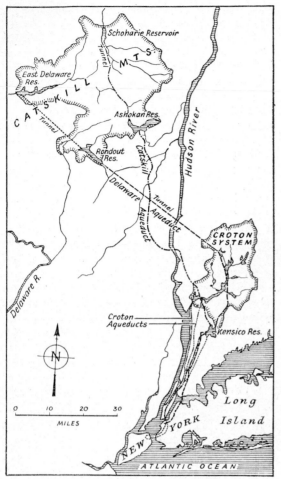

MAP OF THE NEW YORK WATER SUPPLY SYSTEM

vertical shafts bring the water to the surface, where they are connected to the ordinary mains.

See also WATER SUPPLY; DAMS; METROPOLITAN WATER BOARD.

NUCLEAR ENERGY. This is a form of energy which comes from breaking down or joining together the nuclei of ATOMS (q.v. Vol. III).

When energy is produced by burning a fuel, such as coal, the nuclei of the atoms in the fuel are not affected in any way. And, so far as can be measured, the total mass (roughly, weight) of the substances concerned seems to remain the same. For instance, when coal is burned in air (see COMBUSTION) it forms carbon dioxide, water, and ashes, the total mass of which at the end appears to be the same as the mass of coal and air used up. Facts like this led chemists to formulate the

Law of Conservation of MATTER (q.v. Vol. III). It was also found that when energy was changed from one form to another, for instance from electrical energy to heat, the total amount of energy remained the same, and this fact is expressed by the Law of Conservation of ENERGY (q.v.). EINSTEIN (q.v. Vol. V) found that neither of these laws is exact, but that, in fact, whenever energy is released in any process, a small amount of matter disappears, and that whenever energy is absorbed, a small amount of additional matter appears (see RELATIVITY, Vol. III). For chemical reactions, however, the amount of matter that disappears is very small indeed. For instance, when one ton of pure carbon is burned it uses up about three tons of oxygen out of the air, and produces carbon dioxide; according to Einstein's calculations the carbon dioxide should weigh about one hundred-thousandth of an ounce less than the original 4 tons of carbon and oxygen. This is so tiny a difference that in dealing with chemical changes the Law of Conservation of Matter is quite sufficiently accurate.

It is quite different, however, when we are dealing with the reactions between the nuclei of atoms. Suppose, for instance, that the nuclei of hydrogen atoms could be put together to make helium nuclei; the helium made from one ton of hydrogen would weigh about 250 ounces less than one ton, and the difference would be detectable. The energy given out for this loss of matter would be about twenty million times more than that obtained by burning one ton of carbon in air. Nobody knows how to turn ordinary hydrogen completely into helium, although it is believed that this happens in the SUN (q.v. Vol. III) and is partly responsible for keeping it hot. Nuclear physicists have discovered how to release part of the energy to be obtained by making helium out of lighter elements, but the only practical use to which these discoveries have been put, so far, is in designing the hydrogen bomb. It is hoped that a method may be invented for using these enormous amounts of energy for more constructive purposes, such as driving machinery.

Nuclear energy can also be obtained by breaking up the nuclei of the heaviest atoms, such as those of URANIUM (q.v. Vol. III). Uranium has various isotopes: that is, it contains several different kinds of atom, the most important being uranium-235 (or ^{235}U) and uranium-238 (or ^{238}U). The numbers 235 and 238 stand for the number of particles, protons, and neutrons in the nuclei. Natural uranium is mostly ^{238}U; less than one-hundredth part of it is ^{235}U. In 1939 the German chemists Hahn and Strassmann, and the Austrian physicists Meitner and Frisch,

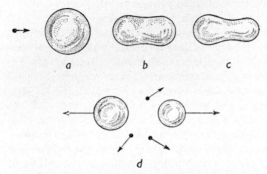

FIG. 1. DIAGRAM OF NUCLEAR FISSION

a. A neutron enters the ^{235}U nucleus and is captured. *b.* This imparts energy to the nucleus and makes it vibrate, rather like a drop of liquid. *c.* The protons in the nucleus repel each other because of their positive electric charges, causing the nucleus to elongate, becoming a dumb-bell shape. *d.* The nucleus splits into two parts which fly apart at great speed (about 5,000 miles per second), and eventually form two lighter atoms which are radioactive. Some neutrons are released at the same time

discovered that the nucleus of uranium can be split into two almost equal parts after it has captured an extra neutron. This process, shown diagrammatically in Fig. 1, is called fission. Fission occasionally happens by itself without any outside cause, and is then called spontaneous fission. The sum of the masses of the two smaller nuclei produced by fission is less than the mass of the original uranium nucleus, which means that a great deal of energy is given out, and the two parts of the uranium nucleus fly apart with great speed. A ton of uranium undergoing fission gives out about three million times as much energy as would be obtained by burning a ton of coal.

In the process of fission some neutrons are released. The average number of neutrons produced in uranium fission is 2·5 per nucleus, and they are travelling very fast when they are released. Scientists immediately searched for ways in which these secondary neutrons could be used to cause more fissions, and so set up a chain of processes by which more and more energy could be obtained from the uranium. During the Second World War two methods for releasing the energy of fission were discovered. The first resulted in the Nuclear Reactor, or Pile, which is described

in the article on NUCLEAR POWER (q.v.); the second in the atomic bomb.

The bomb dropped on Hiroshima in Japan at the end of the Second World War was made of pure ^{235}U which had been obtained from natural uranium. A small piece of ^{235}U is quite safe, but a large piece, which is above the so-called 'critical mass', explodes. The exact critical mass is kept secret, but most guesses set it at a few pounds. The reason for there being a critical size is illustrated in Fig. 2*a*. A few neutrons, resulting from spontaneous fission, are always present in uranium. If one of these enters a nucleus of ^{235}U and causes fission, two or three secondary neutrons are released and, in a small piece of uranium, almost certainly escape; in a large piece, however, they strike other ^{235}U nuclei, producing more fissions and still more neutrons. The way in which this process, which is called a chain reaction, can build up is illustrated in Fig. 2*b*. The figure looks rather like a family tree, but in an atomic bomb each generation takes only about one hundred-millionth of a second. If each fission produced

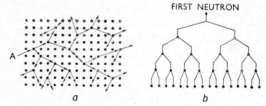

FIG. 2. TWO WAYS OF LOOKING AT A CHAIN REACTION

a. A neutron enters a uranium nucleus at A, produces fission, and releases secondary neutrons, which collide with other nuclei, produce more fissions, and so on. *b.* If each generation of the chain reaction contains twice as many fissions as the previous generation, the number grows very rapidly

two fissions in the next generation the number would grow, almost instantaneously, so that by the 80th generation—that is, in less than one millionth of a second—there would be more than 1,000,000,000,000,000,000,000,000 (10^{24}). In the first atomic bombs only a fraction of the ^{235}U was used before the bomb had blown itself apart and the chain reaction stopped. Nevertheless the explosive force was said to equal that of 20,000 tons of the well-known chemical explosive T.N.T.

Only large countries can afford the enormous factories which are required to produce atomic weapons. The United States, Great Britain, and Canada have released nearly all the scientifically interesting information about nuclear energy, but the exact methods of making and setting off the bombs are still kept secret. Various writers in newspapers and journals have suggested two possible methods. The first is to prepare the bomb in two parts, each of them below the critical size, and then, when the explosion is desired, to fire the two parts together as quickly as possible, thus making a lump which is above the critical size. The other is to prepare the ^{235}U in the form of a hollow sphere, which is not critical, and to surround it with an ordinary chemical explosive which, when set off, would crush the ^{235}U into a solid sphere above the critical size.

The only naturally occurring substance used as fuel for nuclear power is the ^{235}U, which makes up less than 1% of ordinary uranium; therefore, though uranium is a fairly common element, if there were very many factories using nuclear power, it might well run short. There are, however, two methods of making artificial nuclear fuels. The uranium atom ^{238}U, which will not sustain a chain reaction by itself, can be allowed to capture neutrons and so be changed into ^{239}U, a short-lived RADIOACTIVE ISOTOPE (q.v.). This decays just as natural radioactive substances do, and turns eventually into an isotope of plutonium, called ^{239}Pu, which is an even better nuclear fuel than ^{235}U, because it gives off more neutrons in fission. It is radioactive, but its average life being about 25,000 years, for all practical purposes it is a stable substance.

Artificial nuclear fuel can also be made from thorium, or ^{232}Th. When thorium captures neutrons, the isotope ^{233}Th is formed, and this finally decays into ^{233}U, which can be used as a nuclear fuel.

Plutonium is already being prepared in considerable quantities in very large nuclear reactors which use natural uranium for fuel. However, these reactors use up the ^{235}U faster than they produce ^{239}Pu. Thus, although they produce nuclear fuel in a more convenient form, they actually decrease the total potential quantity in the world. Nuclear engineers are trying to make efficient reactors which, as well as producing power, will produce nuclear fuel from ^{238}U or from ^{232}Th faster than they use up their own fuel. If they are successful, this process, which is called 'breeding', will do away with the danger that the supply might become exhausted.

See also NUCLEAR POWER.
See also Vol. III: ATOM; MATTER.

NUCLEAR POWER.

This is generated from the heat energy produced by nuclear fission. Nuclear fission is described in the preceding article NUCLEAR ENERGY (q.v.), which should be read before this article can be properly understood.

When nuclear fission takes place, a large amount of energy is given out, and some fast-moving neutrons are released. If these neutrons can be captured by other nuclei of uranium, and so cause further fissions, more neutrons will be released—and so on, setting up what is called a 'chain reaction'. The first chain reaction was started in Chicago in 1942 by the scientist Fermi, using natural uranium, which consists mainly of the isotope uranium-238 with less than 1% of uranium-235. The fast neutrons released in fission are not readily captured, but slow neutrons are easily captured by uranium-235 (though not by uranium-238). The neutrons can be slowed down by making them collide with the nuclei of light elements, for they lose more speed in collision with a light nucleus than when bouncing off a heavy one. Light elements which slow down neutrons without capturing them are called moderators, and the two best known moderators are heavy hydrogen in the form of heavy water and carbon in the form of very pure artificial graphite.

A chain reaction cannot be started in a mixture of natural uranium and graphite or heavy water because too many of the neutrons are captured by the uranium-238 nuclei without causing fission. The capture of neutrons by uranium-238 can be prevented by using the uranium in the form of concentrated lumps or rods, and not mixing it evenly with the moderating graphite. A large pile of pure graphite blocks was therefore built at the University of Chicago, and lumps of uranium metal or uranium oxide were packed in it at regular intervals to make the first atomic pile, or 'reactor' as it is now usually called.

Unless the uranium-graphite pile exceeds a certain 'critical size', the chain reaction will not go on in it for much the same reason as a piece of uranium-235 will not explode unless it is big enough (*see* NUCLEAR ENERGY). A natural uranium pile of critical size, however, consists of tons of uranium and hundreds of tons of graphite. When the chain reaction is going on in the pile, large numbers of neutrons are present and heat is released. The reaction can be slowed down or stopped by inserting material, such as cadmium

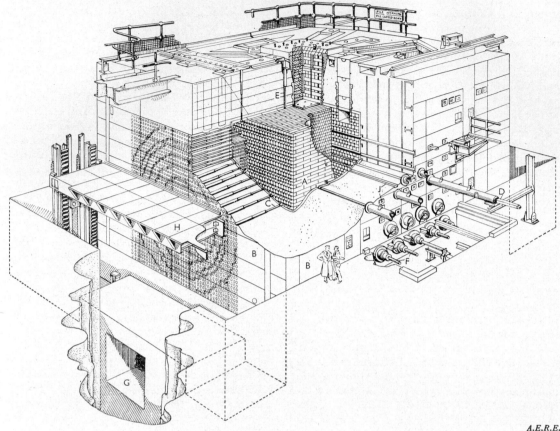

A.E.R.E.

FIG. 1. DIAGRAM OF THE BRITISH EXPERIMENTAL GRAPHITE PILE AT HARWELL (BEPO)

A. Graphite blocks with channels for uranium rods. B. Shield. C. Holes through shield for loading and unloading uranium. D. Control rods. E. Safety rods. F. Rods supporting ionization chambers. G. Inlet tunnel for cooling air. H. Hoist used when loading or unloading uranium. J. Holes through shield, used for experiments

or boron, which absorbs slow neutrons. In the first pile built at Chicago strips of cadmium were pushed into and out of the pile as needed.

A number of natural uranium piles (or reactors) are operating in various parts of the world. One of these is the large experimental reactor, known as BEPO, at Harwell in Berkshire. This reactor (Fig. 1) consists of a large stack of graphite blocks (A) in the shape of a cube about 20 feet across. Channels are cut in the blocks, and short rods of the uranium metal, carefully sheathed in aluminium, are put into the channels. When the reactor is running, heat is released equivalent to several thousand kilowatts of power. The reactor is cooled by powerful currents of air which are blown through the channels containing the uranium. The graphite core is surrounded by a shield (B) made of 6 inches of iron and about 7 feet of concrete, which is

needed to protect the operators against the harmful rays released in fission and against the intense radioactivity which accumulates after the pile has run for a time at high power. Two of the walls of this shield are pierced by hundreds of holes (C), one opposite each of the channels in the graphite, which are used for loading the uranium rods into the reactor. All the holes are closed when not in use by plugs that have steps in them so that narrow beams of radiation cannot escape through the cracks. When the used uranium rods are taken from the pile they are so dangerously radioactive that they have to be transported in very thick lead containers.

The reactor is controlled by several rods (D) made of steel containing the element boron. These rods enter horizontally through one of the faces of the shield, and absorb any extra neutrons not required for the chain reaction. If the power

A.E.R.E.

FIG. 2. THE EXPERIMENTAL FACE OF THE HARWELL PILE (BEPO)

In this face there are a number of holes through which beams of neutrons come out. Scientific apparatus for several experiments in which these beams are used is clustered round the centre of the pile face. There is nearly as much of the pile below the floor as above, so that the most intense beams are at a convenient height

of the reactor is increasing too much, these rods are pushed a little farther in, and are withdrawn slightly if it is decreasing. If the operators wish to increase the power of the reactor they withdraw the rods a little to allow the chain reaction to build up, and then push them in again until the power is steady at the new level. The pile can be shut down by sending the rods right in. A set of safety rods (E) can be dropped rapidly into the core of the reactor if the power is getting out of control. The power is measured by instruments called ionization chambers (see RADIOACTIVITY, DETECTION OF), which count the number of neutrons in the pile.

BEPO is used for preparing RADIOACTIVE ISOTOPES (q.v.), which are of great value to

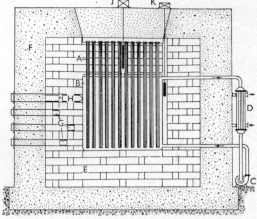

FIG. 3. CROSS-SECTION OF A SMALL HEAVY WATER
MODERATED REACTOR IN FRANCE

A. Uranium rods sheathed in aluminium. B. Heavy water
in aluminium tank. C. Pump. D. Heat exchanger to cool
heavy water. E. Neutron reflector made of graphite blocks.
F. Shield. G. Specimens being irradiated by neutrons.
H. Ionization chamber. J. Safety mechanism. K. Control
mechanism

scientists and engineers. There are much more
powerful reactors which use natural uranium
and graphite to make plutonium, but little is yet
generally known of their construction. Heavy
hydrogen, in the form of 'heavy water' (*see* ATOM,
Vol. III), has also been used as a moderator in
some natural uranium reactors (Fig. 3).

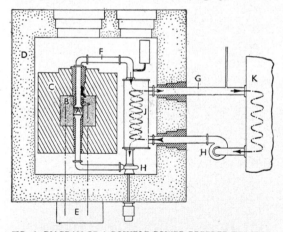

FIG. 4. DIAGRAM OF A POSSIBLE POWER BREEDER REACTOR

A. Core of plutonium, uranium-233, or uranium-235.
B. Thorium or uranium. C. Inner shield. D. Outer shield.
E. Control and safety mechanisms. F. Circuit for radioactive liquid metal which carries heat from the core.
G. Circuit for second fluid. H. Pumps. J. Heat exchanger.
K. Boiler and steam plant. The reactor could be controlled
by moving a portion of the thorium or uranium surrounding the core. If this were moved out, leaving a space,
fewer neutrons would be scattered back into the core and
the chain reaction would cease

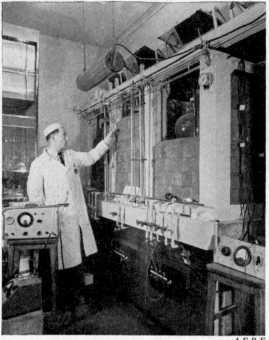

FIG. 5. CHEMICAL OPERATIONS BEING CARRIED OUT IN
A FUME CUPBOARD IN A RADIOCHEMICAL LABORATORY

The fume cupboard has lead walls to give protection
against gamma rays, and all the controls for the apparatus
are outside these walls. Great care is taken that no one is
exposed to too much radiation. There is apparatus for
measuring the amount of radioactivity in the laboratory,
on the scientist's hands, and on the special clothing which
he wears

The energy released from reactors like BEPO
is not of very much use, because the cooling substance is not hot enough when it emerges. To
produce steam at the right temperature for the
most efficient turbines the reactor would have to
be above 800° F. When steam or a gas is used to
extract the heat a high pressure is necessary, and
therefore the whole reactor has to be inside a
large pressure shell which is as strong as a boiler.
The uranium-graphite reactors at Calder Hall
in Cumberland, started in 1953, have pressure
shells about 35 feet across. Compressed carbon
dioxide is used to extract the heat, and raise
steam. The steam drives dynamos and delivers
electric power to the grid. By using uranium en-
riched with extra uranium-235 the diameter of
a reactor can be reduced to a few feet, and it is
then small enough for driving a ship or submarine. The United States submarine *Nautilus*,
launched in 1953, was the first vessel to be driven
by nuclear power. No matter how small and

light the reactors are made, however, they still need heavy shields, and this will always be a serious reason against using them in aircraft.

Another proposal is to use fast neutrons for causing fission, in which case no moderator would be needed, and plutonium, uranium-233, or nearly pure uranium-235 would be the fuel (*see* Fig. 4). The core of such a reactor might not be more than 1 or 2 feet across, and enough heat to drive a power station might be developed in this small space. The most likely method of removing so much heat would be to circulate a liquid metal such as liquid sodium through the core. The liquid metal would become very radioactive and might, therefore, be made to give up its heat to another fluid inside the shield. This second fluid could be used in a heat exchanger (*see* Heat Pump) to raise steam. If the core of a reactor of this type were surrounded by uranium-238 or by thorium, it might be possible to capture most of the neutrons escaping from the core, and thus form plutonium or uranium-233 (*see* Nuclear Energy). It might even be possible to prepare a greater quantity of nuclear fuel in this way than was being consumed in the reactor. Such a reactor would be called a power breeder reactor. An experimental power breeder reactor was run for the first time in the United States in 1951, and a small amount of electric power was actually generated from it.

Nuclear reactors cost several million pounds apiece to set up. Moreover, a number of large subsidiary factories, such as uranium and thorium refineries, plants for separating plutonium from uranium, and so on, have to be built before the reactors can be run. Because of the high cost of these plants, nuclear power could hardly be

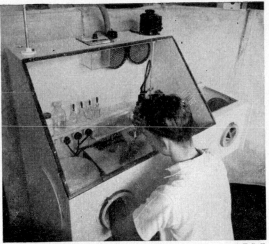

A.E.R.E.

FIG. 6. WORKING IN A SEALED GLOVE BOX WITH A RADIOACTIVE SUBSTANCE EMITTING ALPHA-PARTICLES WHICH ARE DANGEROUS TO HEALTH

The worker puts his hands into long rubber gloves fixed to the holes in front. Air is drawn into the box and passes out through filters so that if there were any leaks in the box nothing could escape

cheap, even though so much heat is obtained from so small a weight of fuel. It is a very difficult engineering problem to design powerful reactors which run at a high temperature, and they may not be widely used for a number of years.

Very great precautions have to be taken for the safety of the workers in all these plants. Figs. 5 and 6 show some of the work in ordinary chemical laboratories where radioactive substances are used (*see* Safety Devices).

See also Nuclear Energy.
See also Vol. III: Atom.

O

OWEN FALLS SCHEME (Uganda). This great scheme for the generation of HYDRO-ELEC-

TRIC POWER (q.v.) and IRRIGATION (q.v. Vol. VI) came into operation in April 1954 when the main DAM and POWER STATION (qq.v.), two of the most spectacular civil engineering works to be constructed in Africa, were opened by Queen Elizabeth II. Situated at the head of the White NILE (q.v. Vol. III), where the waters of Lake Victoria start their 3,000-mile journey to the Mediterranean, Owen Falls will not only produce electric power for development in Uganda and Kenya but will enable a vast quantity of water to be stored for use in the Sudan and Egypt. Lake Victoria, the third largest lake in the world, is over 26,000 miles in area, the same size as Ireland. The Owen Falls dam will enable

Sir Alexander Gibb and Partners

THE OWEN FALLS DAM NEARING COMPLETION

an extra 3 feet of water to be stored in the lake—the equivalent of no less than 127 years' supply for London's Metropolitan Water Board.

The concrete dam, which took 4 years to construct, is of the gravity type, 2,500 feet long and with a maximum height of 100 feet above foundations. The power station, built alongside the dam, has space for ten vertical-shaft Kaplan turbines and alternators, each of 20,000 horsepower (*see* WATER POWER). Four turbines were in operation in 1954, and the remainder will be installed as demand develops. The work was designed by British engineers, and carried out by a labour force of British, Danish, Dutch, Italian, Asian, and African workmen.

Although nine dams and barrages have been built during the last 50 years for FLOOD CONTROL (q.v.) and irrigation purposes on the lower reaches of the Nile, the Owen Falls Scheme is the first stage of a very large project for conserving water in the upper reaches of the river. Many other civil engineering works are proposed, including dams on the Blue Nile, which rises in Ethiopia, and the construction of a canal through a swampy region in southern Sudan (*see* Map). These will enable large new areas to be irrigated in Egypt and the Sudan, while the risk of drought and flood will be almost eliminated.

In addition to irrigation, many sections of the upper Nile as well as the dams and barrages on the lower Nile can be used to generate electric power. Between Lake Victoria, for example, which lies 3,716 feet above sea-level, and Lake

MAP OF EGYPT SHOWING THE NILE DAMS

Albert, about 234 miles downstream, there is a fall of 1,700 feet. This fall, with its average flow of 17,700 cubic feet per second, can yield over 3 million h.p.

See also DAMS; HYDRO-ELECTRIC POWER; POWER STATION.
See also Vol. III: NILE.
See also Vol. VI: IRRIGATION.

P

PATTERN MAKING. Before any Casting (q.v.) can be made in a foundry, it is necessary to make what in engineering is called a 'pattern'. In very general terms, this pattern has to be the same shape as the object to be cast, and is used to make the mould into which the molten metal is poured. In sand casting, the sand is packed round this pattern, which is then removed, leaving a firm impression of its own shape in the sand. This impression is then filled by the molten metal. Patterns are commonly made of wood, but for mass production they are often of metal. White pine is a suitable wood to use, as it does not splinter, is easy to work, and does not readily distort when exposed to the damp sand in the

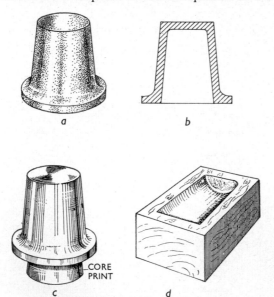

FIG. 1. *a.* CASTING. *b.* SECTION OF CASTING. *c.* PATTERN
d. CORE-BOX

The length of the core-box is equal to the internal height of the casting plus the core print. Two identical halves of the sand core are made in the core-box

mould. Patterns must be able to stand up to rough handling in the foundry, because making castings is heavy work.

The pattern-maker's job is highly skilled and one unlikely ever to be replaced by machinery. He must be able to make complicated shapes out of wood. In addition, he must know a great deal about foundry technique, and something about the nature of metals; for example, he must know enough about the particular metal to be used in the casting to be able to calculate how much allowance he must make in his pattern for the shrinkage, or contraction, which takes place in all metals as they cool. Brass, for example, contracts as much as $\frac{1}{8}$ inch per foot from the hot, liquid stage to the cooled, solid, casting stage, and the size of the pattern must allow for this. The pattern-maker has 'contraction rules' marked to show the allowance for contraction necessary for each metal. With metal patterns this contraction has necessarily to be allowed for twice, once in the metal pattern and a second time in the casting itself.

The pattern-maker must ensure that the pattern can be easily lifted out of the mould without scraping the sand surfaces or breaking corners (Fig. 1). All upright surfaces, therefore, are made slightly sloped in the pattern so that it can be more easily withdrawn from the mould. This is called 'draft', and may amount to as much as $\frac{1}{8}$ inch on all sides of a pattern a foot deep. Certain corners in the pattern must be rounded so that the metal will flow smoothly (Fig. 1*b*), and these are shaped by inserting leather pads or 'fillets' into them. As the surface finish of the casting depends largely on the surface of the pattern, the latter must be as good as possible. Therefore the wood of the pattern is glass-papered all over and then receives several coats of a shellac paint.

On the face of the pattern which does not come into contact with the sand there is a rapping plate into which a spike is usually driven or an eye-bolt screwed. The spike or bolt is rapped gently to loosen the pattern in the sand, and is then used to lift the pattern from the mould.

For the internal parts of hollow castings 'cores' are used, made of tightly rammed sand which has been baked to remove the moisture. The baked cores are fixed in the moulds on impressions left in the sand by 'prints' or blocks on the outside of the pattern. When the molten metal is poured into the mould it thus fills only the space

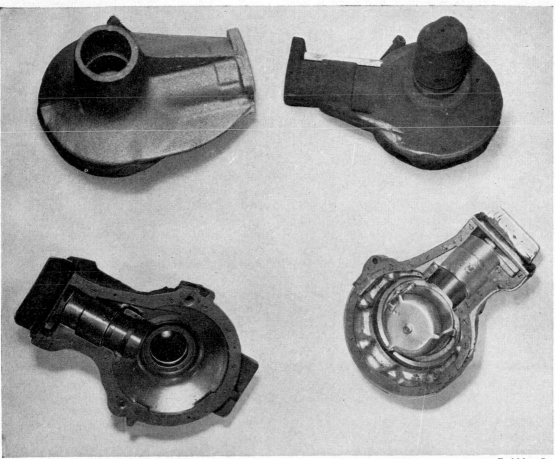

Ford Motor Co.

BELOW: TWO CORE-BOXES. ABOVE: RIGHT, THE CORE MADE FROM THEM, AND LEFT, THE CASTING

Sand is rammed into the core-boxes to make the two halves of the core, which are then brought together. The hole in the casting is made by the protruding part of the core, which in turn is made by the depression in the middle of the left-hand core-box

between the mould and the core. Cores are made in 'core-boxes' which are the internal equivalent of patterns and are made by the same craftsmen.

The pattern-maker has to visualize the finished casting from engineering drawings and to understand what the casting process can and cannot do. For example, on looking at the drawings, he may realize that it would be easier and more satisfactory if some parts of the component—such as a very sharp edge—were finished afterwards by ordinary machining methods instead of being cast. In this case, the pattern must leave sufficient metal on that particular edge of the casting for the machining to be done, and the working drawings indicate that subsequent machining will be needed.

See also CASTING.

PAWL, *see* RATCHET.

PERMANENT WAY, *see* RAILWAY CONSTRUCTION.

PERSPECTIVE, *see* ENGINEERING DRAWING, Section 2. *See also* Vol. XII: PERSPECTIVE.

PETROL ENGINES, *see* INTERNAL COMBUSTION ENGINE.

PHOTOCELL. This electrical device, known as a photo-electric cell or 'phototube', is based on the discovery that small particles of negative electricity called electrons are emitted from the surface of a metal plate when light falls on it. The light waves make the ATOMS (q.v. Vol. III) in the metal vibrate so strongly that some of their outer electrons fly off and escape from the surface of the plate. This happens with all metals to some extent, but certain metals such as caesium produce electrons more freely than others. The plate that emits the electrons is called the cathode, as in the case of a THERMIONIC VALVE (q.v.). Near the surface of the cathode, but not

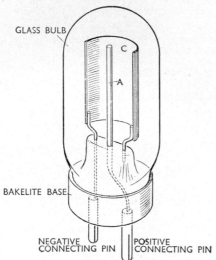

FIG. I. DIAGRAM OF A PHOTOCELL
A. Anode. c. Cathode (sensitive to light)

touching it, is a wire called the anode (Fig. 1), which is connected to the positive terminal of a battery, the negative terminal of which is connected to the cathode. The electrons emitted from the cathode, being charges of negative electricity, are attracted to the (positive) anode. This stream of electrons forms an electric current, called the emission current, which flows only when light is falling on the cathode. The stronger the light, the greater is the number of electrons emitted, and the stronger the current. Changes in the strength of the emission current caused by changes in light intensity can be amplified by using thermionic valves to operate switches or other electrical equipment.

In making a photocell the surface of the cathode is covered first with a thin layer of antimony or oxidized silver, and then with a very thin film of one of the alkali metals, usually caesium. The caesium layer must not be exposed to the air, at it would then instantly combine with the oxygen to form caesium oxide. It is therefore prepared inside a glass bulb from which all the air has been pumped. The bulb is sealed

either with a vacuum or filled with an inert gas such as argon or neon which does not combine with the caesium layer. In a gas-filled photocell the electrons emitted from the cathode collide with the atoms of the gas, knocking extra electrons from them. These electrons also travel to the anode, so that more electrons reach the anode than started from the cathode, and can increase the current in the circuit by about ten times.

Photocells can be made to respond to other RADIATION (q.v. Vol. III) besides light. Some cells respond to infra-red or to ultra-violet radiation, but cells sensitive to ultra-violet radiation require bulbs made of fused quartz instead of glass, which is opaque to such radiation.

The commonest use of photocells is for the reproduction of sound in cinemas. The sound is recorded in a narrow strip or track of the film alongside the pictures (see SOUND RECORDING). When a narrow beam of light is projected through the sound track on to a photocell, the light varies in intensity according to the sound; the corresponding variations in emission current in the photocell are then amplified by thermionic valves to operate loudspeakers.

The photocells which are used to operate burglar alarms are arranged so that an intruder has to pass through an invisible beam of infra-red radiation; this, by preventing the ray from falling on the cell, stops the emission current, and that starts an alarm-bell ringing. Photocells can form part of an electric circuit to open garage doors. When the returning motorist directs his headlights on to the cell, the change in emission current is amplified to control a small electric motor, which swings the doors open.

'Multiplier phototubes' can detect light which is much too faint to be seen by the human eye. In these tubes the electrons on their way to the anode bounce between sets of metal plates called targets. The targets, being coated with caesium like the cathode, release new electrons at each impact, so that the current which reaches the anode can be many million times the original current leaving the cathode, and so may easily be detected (see p. 356).

PHOTO-ELASTICITY, see POLARIZED LIGHT APPARATUS.

PHOTOGRAPHIC EMULSION. A photograph is taken by opening the shutter of the CAMERA (q.v.) for a time and 'exposing' the photographic plate or film. While the shutter is open, light is focused by the Lens (q.v.). This forms an image on the film or plate, which is sensitive to light because of a thin coating of a mixture of gelatine and chemicals—the photographic emulsion—carried on it. The light-sensitive chemicals ordinarily used are silver halides—chemical compounds of silver and one of the elements iodine, chlorine, or bromine (called halides).

The silver halides are in the form of very small crystals. When light falls on them, that is, when the exposure is made, they become 'developable'. What happens is still not fully understood, but when the film is later put into a developing solution, a picture slowly appears as the film is developed. The crystals that have been affected by the light are changed to grains of dark metallic silver; the rest are not affected by the developer. Where the image in the camera was bright, many crystals are made developable. In places where the light was faint few crystals are affected. The result is that, as the developer acts on the emulsion, a black silver layer appears where the image was bright, and a thinner layer where it was dull. The picture so formed is called a negative because the light appears as dark, and vice versa (see Fig. 1).

The negative is then 'fixed'—that is, it is put in a bath containing another chemical substance, sodium thiosulphate, a chemical formerly thought to be sodium hyposulphite, and the word 'hypo' is still used to describe it. This dissolves the undeveloped crystals out of the gelatine so that they will not change if the negative is brought into strong light. The negative is then washed thoroughly in clean water and dried.

To get a positive print—that is, a print in which the bright parts of the camera image are bright in the picture—the whole process is repeated. Light is made to shine through the developed negative on to paper coated with photographic emulsion. If the paper is in contact with the negative, a print of the same size as the negative, called a contact print, is produced. If sunlight is used, the print is made on 'printing out paper', but for artificial light 'gaslight' paper is used. If a bigger or smaller print is needed, an image of the negative is projected by an 'enlarger' on to some coated paper, which is then developed and fixed in the same way as for the negative.

Photographic emulsions are affected by ultra-violet and X-rays and can also be made sensitive to infra-red (see RADIATION, Vol. III). They can also be affected by the passage of charged particles, such as protons and electrons, through them. Indeed, this is one way of finding out how these particles move and of studying COSMIC RAYS (q.v. Vol. III). They leave a track of developable silver halide crystals in the emulsion, and this appears when the negative is developed. Particles such as these are given out when radioactivity takes place (see ATOM, Vol. III). People who work where there might be dangerous amounts of radioactivity carry small pieces of photographic film. Although the film has not been exposed to light, if the person has been where there is much radioactivity, the film has many black grains in it when it has been developed.

FIG. 1. LEFT: NEGATIVE. RIGHT: POSITIVE PRINT FROM THE NEGATIVE

FIG. 2. PHOTOGRAPHS TAKEN ON ORTHOCHROMATIC FILM (LEFT) AND PANCHROMATIC FILM (RIGHT)

Photographic emulsion is made by mixing a solution of silver nitrate and a potassium salt (iodide, bromide, or chloride) in gelatine. Potassium nitrate and the halide, silver iodide (or bromide or chloride), are formed. Potassium nitrate, being soluble in water, is washed out of all except 'printing-out paper' emulsions at this stage. After further processes to make the emulsion more sensitive, it is melted and coated on to its support—transparent glass or film for negatives and paper for positives. In photolithographic printing (see PROCESS REPRODUCTION, Vol. VII) the emulsion, silver halides in egg albumin (white of egg), is spread on zinc plates.

The sensitivity and speed of the emulsion depend on the silver halide used and the size of the crystals, fast emulsions having big silver halide crystals. A mixture of silver bromide and silver iodide is used for fast negative emulsions. Emulsions for papers can be slower: gaslight papers are coated with a silver chloride emulsion, and others contain a mixture of silver chloride and silver bromide. Enlarging paper emulsions contain silver bromide. If the negative is enlarged too much when making the positive the individual grains of the negative become apparent, and an unpleasant 'grainy' effect results. Graininess can be reduced by making the silver halide particles smaller—but the emulsion is then slower.

Ordinary photographic emulsion is normally sensitive to ultra-violet and visible violet-blue light, which is sufficient for contact and enlarging papers and for some negative emulsions. These are rather insensitive to yellow and orange light and can be handled in it. To make negative emulsions sensitive to green and yellow, dyes are added to the emulsion. This makes orthochromatic material which is insensitive to red. Further dyes can be added to make emulsions sensitive to all colours, including red, and these are called panchromatic emulsions (see PHOTOGRAPHY, HISTORY OF, Vol. VII). They can be handled only in darkness or in a dim green light. Fig. 2 shows how the same subject is rendered by orthochromatic and panchromatic emulsions. Since emulsions are unduly sensitive to ultra-violet and violet-blue light, filters over the lens are sometimes used to reduce this.

The choice of the right emulsion for a particular purpose is a compromise depending on the type of work, the type of camera, the size of the negative, and the degree of enlargement required.

See also CAMERA; LENS.
See also Vol. VII: PHOTOGRAPHY, HISTORY OF.
See also Vol. IX: PHOTOGRAPHY.

PHOTOGRAPHY, *see* CAMERA; PHOTOGRAPHIC EMULSION. *See also* Vol. VII: PHOTOGRAPHY, HISTORY OF. *See also* Vol. IX: PHOTOGRAPHY.

PIPES, *see* TUBES.

PLANING MACHINES, *see* MACHINE TOOLS, Section 2.

POLARIZED LIGHT APPARATUS. 1. Several scientific instruments make use of the natural phenomenon of the polarization of LIGHT (q.v. Vol. III). An ordinary ray of light consists of vibrations which are wavelike except that the crests and hollows of the waves move not only up and down, but also from side to side, and in every intermediate direction as well. Fig. 1 shows, in an extremely simplified way, the waves 'rising and falling' in two different directions at once. In fact, there should be an infinite number of lines of waves instead of two, each one vibrating at a slightly different angle from the others.

There are various devices that will reflect the light vibrating in all but one direction. The light that passes through them, which can be imagined as vibrating in one direction only, is called 'polarized' light, and the devices that filter ordinary light to produce it are called 'polarizers' (Fig. 1b and c). One form of polarizer consists of a double prism made from two pieces of tourmaline or Iceland spar cemented together. The angles of the two parts of the prism, and the 'refractive index' (*see* LIGHT, Vol. III) of the cement used are very important. Another form of polarizer is a manufactured material called 'polaroid', consisting of a very thin layer of specially shaped microscopic crystals cemented between glass.

A polariscope is the basic type of all instruments using polarized light. It contains optical condensers and LENSES (q.v.) of a kind common to most optical instruments. Their task is merely to focus the light and keep it in the right path. The essential parts are two polarizers, one at each end (Fig. 2); the one through which the light enters the instrument is fixed, and the other, called the analyser, can be moved to any angle.

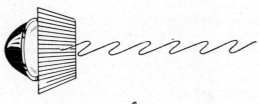

FIG. 1. POLARIZATION OF LIGHT

a. Beam of light with waves at two angles. *b.* Vertical crystal polarizer transmitting vertical light waves. *c.* Horizontal crystal polarizer transmitting horizontal light waves

If the polarizer and the analyser are set to pass a vertical wave, all the light admitted by the polarizer will pass out through the analyser and be clearly seen on a screen. If the analyser is revolved through 90° (a right angle), so that it passes a horizontal wave, the vertical wave is completely blocked, and no light, therefore, emerges from the instrument (*see* Vol. III, p. 259, Fig. 2c). If the analyser is set obliquely, half-way between vertical and horizontal, only a portion of the light will reach the screen. The quantity of light will be related to the angle at which the polarizer and analyser are set.

The object whose light-transmitting properties are to be examined is placed between polarizer and analyser. The light from the analyser may be focused on to a screen.

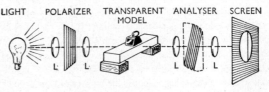

LIGHT   POLARIZER   TRANSPARENT   ANALYSER   SCREEN
MODEL

FIG. 2. PRINCIPLE OF THE POLARISCOPE
The model is stressed by the heavy weight. L. Lenses

2. PHOTO-ELASTICITY. This term indicates the connexion between light (Greek *phos*) and the bending of a solid object. The STRESS AND STRAIN (q.v.) of an object, such as a railway wheel, can be observed and measured by making a model of the object from a transparent material (glass or a plastic such as celluloid), placing it in a polariscope, and applying pressure to various parts of the model.

A polarized ray, on passing through certain kinds of transparent material, becomes separated into two rays, each polarized in a different direction. One of these rays takes longer to pass through the plate than the other, and its waves lag behind the waves of the other by some millionths of an inch. To measure the amount of retardation the two rays are passed through the analyser; if they are exactly out of step complete interference will result, each eliminating the other, and a black band will be seen on the screen. If pressure is applied to the transparent model, those internal parts of it which are under stress become a little more squashed, and this alters the angle at which the polarized ray is separated inside the model: consequently the degree of lag between the two groups of waves is altered, and so is the size and position of the black 'interference' band in the patch of light on the screen. Thus by passing a beam of light through various parts of a model, and carefully measuring the changes in the black band, the engineering designer can gain exact information about the location and degree of stress, and sees where he must alter his design.

Apart from this method of measurement, a whole model can be illuminated by polarized light and photographed while pressure is applied to certain parts. The photograph will show dark lines and circles spreading from the points of pressure. Special plastic materials reveal pressure by changes of colour, the increasing intensity of the pressure being shown by yellow, orange, red, brown, and green bands, in that order, and these also can be recorded by colour photography (*see* Colour Plate, opp. p. 368).

3. POLARIMETER. Light can be polarized not only by certain crystals but also by being passed through liquid solutions containing sugar or starch. Exact measurements of the quantity of sugar in a liquid can thus be made in a polarimeter, the liquid being placed between polarizer and analyser. Any variations from the normal in the kind of beam thrown on the screen indicate the strength of the polarizing material in the liquid. These are used in manufacturers' laboratories, and also in medicine for analysing fluids taken from the body.

4. POLARIZED HEADLIGHTS. Experiments have been made with polarized light in the hope of reducing the dangers caused by dazzling headlights on the roads. The proposal is that the light from the main headlights of cars should be polarized at the angle of this stroke \ by a polaroid screen, and that drivers should wear spectacles of polarizing material adjusted to the same angle, so that all drivers would see clearly objects illuminated by their own beams, or by the beams of other cars travelling in the same direction. All such headlights would be invisible to drivers travelling in the opposite direction, for to all drivers the headlights of an oncoming car would be polarized at the angle of /, and so be shut out by spectacles at the angle of \. Naturally, all cars would still need small lamps showing ordinary unpolarized light; otherwise oncoming cars would not be seen at all.

Although the theory is attractive, practical difficulties are very great.

See also STRESS AND STRAIN.
See also Vol. III: LIGHT.

POWER, *see* WIND POWER; WATER POWER; HYDRO-ELECTRIC POWER; POWER STATION; STEAM ENGINE; INTERNAL COMBUSTION ENGINE; GAS TURBINE; NUCLEAR POWER; ENERGY.

POWER STATION. Modern power stations are vast engineering units in which ELECTRIC CURRENT is produced. The machines which actually make the current are ELECTRIC GENERATORS (qq.v.). Most of the power now used is generated as ALTERNATING CURRENT (q.v.) or A.C., and A.C. generators are called alternators. The larger power stations in Britain, with which this article is principally concerned, are commonly driven by STEAM TURBINES (q.v.); but in many parts of the world power stations use water power (*see* HYDRO-ELECTRIC POWER).

The general arrangement of steam power stations, which are often very large, is illustrated in Fig. 1. Usually sufficient coal for about 6 weeks' winter use is stocked in a dump outside the power station. This coal is lifted by a CONVEYOR belt (q.v.), and is automatically weighed before being fed to the mechanically stoked chain fire grate of the BOILER (q.v.). The smoke and flue gases from the boiler fire, before they enter the chimney stack, are passed through a dust extractor, where they are washed with fine sprays of water; then they are passed through a grid of wires connected to a high-voltage electric supply where the last remaining particles are electrified, and thus easily drawn away by electric attraction. Only clean gases, therefore, are allowed to escape into the air. The ash from the boiler fires falls from the chain grate into a large hopper, and then on to a special conveyor. A large power station produces some 500 tons of ash each day, so that its disposal is a difficult problem. It is usually dumped out at sea, or on waste ground.

The steam at a very high temperature and pressure produced by the boiler is led away through a heavily wrapped or 'lagged' steel pipe to drive the steam turbine.

The used steam from the turbine passes into a condenser (see STEAM ENGINE) to increase the power of the turbine. The condenser needs a constant supply of cold water to cool the steam. The cold water obviously becomes heated in the process of cooling the steam, and must either be cooled again for further use, or a continuous supply of cold water must be provided. When the power station is built on a river bank, a continuous supply of cold water is drawn from the river and the hot water pumped back. But as a large

power station may need as much as 12,000,000 gallons of cold water every hour, only a very large river can supply so much water at all seasons. When no such river is available, the hot water from the condensers is cooled in large concrete cooling towers, by being trickled over a series of large trays or 'baffles'. A tower 250 feet high and 170 feet in diameter can cool 3,000,000 gallons of water an hour, so four such towers are needed to serve a large power station. Where a power station can be built near a large river, not only is the cost of the cooling towers saved, but also coal can be brought to the power station very cheaply by water, and the ash can be carried away in barges for dumping in the sea. Some experiments are now being made to make use of the hot water from condensers by pumping it through lagged pipes to nearby housing estates and using it to carry out schemes of 'district heating' (see HEATING).

The steam turbine together with the alternator which it drives is called a turbo-alternator. At modern British power stations the larger turbo-alternators generate 60,000 kilowatts of power at 11,000 volts (see ELECTRIC CURRENT). This immense amount of electric power corresponds to about 80,000 horse-power and is sufficient to supply the needs of a large town of about 200,000 inhabitants, such as Plymouth.

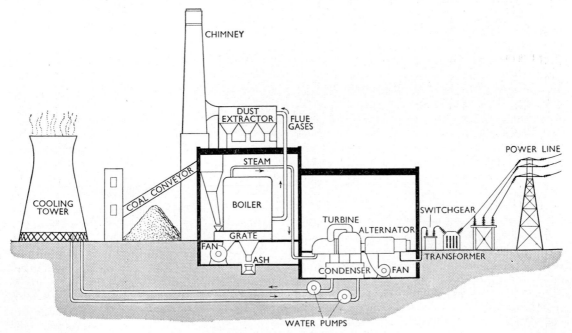

FIG. I. DIAGRAM OF A POWER STATION

C. A. Parsons & Co. Ltd.

TURBO-ALTERNATORS IN A LARGE POWER STATION

The alternator is carefully designed to change the mechanical power of the turbine into electrical power with the maximum efficiency and least possible waste; yet even the small fraction of power that is wasted, perhaps only one-thirtieth, makes the alternator so hot that it has to be kept cool by blasts of air from powerful fans. The air, after cooling the alternator, is itself recooled by being passed over cold water pipes and used again. In this way the air can be kept clean and dry and is not the means of introducing dirt and damp into the alternator. The newest high-power alternators are cooled with hydrogen gas, which is a more effective cooling agent than air, and the risk of fires and corrosion caused by sparking is less than when air is used.

The electrical power from the turbo-alternator is controlled by large switches (see SWITCHGEAR), which are often placed outside the power station because they may cause fierce sparks, and operated by remote control from the main control board. This control board is also fitted with measuring instruments, with indicators for the main switches, and also often with a diagram of the main electrical connexions of the power station. It may be arranged in a semicircle around a central desk for the control engineer, who can then see at a glance the state of all the equipment in the power station. The control engineer, whose job it is to keep the whole process of generating electricity going at the greatest possible efficiency and to deal promptly with any emergencies, has telephones so that he can speak directly to the men in the boiler and turbine houses. The power from the turbo-alternators may pass through the switchgear at 11,000 volts; its voltage is then increased to 132,000 volts by a TRANSFORMER (q.v.) before it is connected to the power line of very high voltage which carries the power wherever it is needed (see GRID SYSTEM).

The essential requirement of the design and operation of a large steam power station is to ensure that as much as possible of the energy stored in the coal is converted into electrical energy. It is not yet possible to make a steam boiler and turbine that can convert more than about one-quarter to one-third of the coal's energy into mechanical power. Almost all of this mechanical power, however, can be converted into electrical power.

Since large power stations are usually more efficient than small ones, the major part of the electric power required in Britain is now supplied by very large power stations. A typical station of this type has two turbo-alternators, each generating 60,000 kilowatts, and each turbine has two boilers to supply it with steam. About 1 lb. of coal is burnt for each 'unit' of electricity generated (1 unit = 1 kilowatt hour); so the station uses about 420,000 tons of coal every year. A power station of this size costs about £6,000,000 to build and equip, and about 150 men are needed to keep its valuable machinery working in good condition.

It is interesting to see how the cost of the electricity generated is made up. The cost of the coal used and of capital charges are about equal, and together make up 90% of the total cost. Capital charges, that is, the repayment, with interest, of the money borrowed to build the station, can be looked upon as representing the money that must be saved to replace the power station when it is worn out. The remaining 10% of the total cost is divided, almost equally, between the wages of the power station staff (6%) and the cost of various materials and supplies needed to keep it in good order (4%).

See also GRID SYSTEM.

POWER TRANSMISSION, *see* GRID SYSTEM; HYDRAULIC POWER TRANSMISSION; GEARS; BELT AND CHAIN DRIVE.

PREFABRICATION. There is nothing new about the principle of prefabrication, although the technique has become more widely known and applied in recent years—particularly in the building of houses. It is, in general, a development of fabrication.

Fabrication may be defined as the building up of frames or structures from a number of individual parts, which are then bolted, riveted, or welded together. A typical example of fabrication is the main frame or body of many machines, which is built up from steel sheets and sections welded together, instead of being cast in one piece.

In prefabrication, the same method is used to build up complete sections for a complicated structure, so that the sections can be brought to the site complete, instead of each having to be built up on the site. This has allowed many different kinds of structures, including houses and parts of ships, to be factory-built instead of being constructed laboriously on the actual site. The advantage of this is obvious. The prefabricated units can be made in factories where all the facilities exist for building them as quickly and efficiently as possible. If necessary, different prefabricated units, all intended for the same structure, can be made in a number of different factories and then brought together when the structure has to be put up.

This, once again, increases output, because each factory can plan to mass-produce the particular prefabricated sections they are responsible for producing, since it will be making these in large quantities (*see* PRODUCTION ENGINEERING). In prefabricated houses, not only can the framework, floor, roof, and accessories such as kitchen equipment, cupboards, and so on be prefabricated in this way, but even complete walls or complete rooms can be factory-made

'Prefabrication'

FIG. 1. BUILDING A PREFABRICATED VILLAGE HALL
A wall panel is being placed in position

and then just dropped into position on the site (Fig. 1).

In prefabricated building, a great deal of the work has, therefore, been finished before the house starts to go up at all, and consequently the actual erection time is very small indeed. All the pre-fabricated sections arrive on the site one day, and the house may have its roof on only a few days later.

During the Second World War, the use of prefabrication was applied extensively to the building of ships, and resulted in their being pro-duced much more quickly than had ever been possible before. Prefabricated welded units, some of them very large, were made in engineering plants and then taken to the site where the ship was to be built and launched. Instead of the ship having to be built up laboriously on the stocks, these prefabricated parts were simply assembled together, and the actual work on the stocks became one of final assembly. The 'Liberty' ships, for example, which did so much to keep the vital sea traffic going during the war, were actually put together from these large prefabri-cated units in a very few days.

The technique of prefabrication is not confined to houses and ships, although these are two of the most spectacular examples. Prefabricated units are used in aircraft, and sub-assemblies, which are, in fact, complete units, are used through-out engineering. There is a tendency in modern engineering to employ unit construction to an increasing degree, making use not only of stan-dard parts but even of standard pre-assembled or prefabricated units (see ENGINEERING DESIGN). A typical example is the special multiple machine for work in a motor-car factory. This is made up from standardized units, which can simply be joined together as required. Thus, a special machine can become an economical pro-position, whereas if it had to be designed from the beginning and built in the normal way, it would probably be too expensive. This use of standard prefabricated parts also makes it pos-sible to change the machine round easily or to convert it into another one for some other pur-pose—thus allowing far greater elasticity in the organization of production.

It is probable that in many fields standardized prefabrication will become increasingly used, as designs become more and more complicated and faster and more economical output is demanded.

See also BUILDING CONSTRUCTION.

PRESSING, see FORGING AND PRESSING.

PRESSURE, see Vol. III: PRESSURE.

PRESSURE GAUGES. These are instruments for measuring PRESSURE (q.v. Vol. III). The earliest pressure gauge was the mercury column of Torricelli, the 17th-century Italian, which measured the pressure of the atmosphere by balancing it against the pressure at the bottom of a column of mercury (see Vol. III, p. 353).

Pressure is defined as Force ÷ Area. This defi-nition holds good no matter whether we are dealing with solids, liquids, or gases. For ex-ample, if a post supporting a heavy load rests on the ground, the pressure on the ground is equal to the weight of the load plus the weight of the post, divided by the area of the base of the post. In this case, we can easily find what the pressure is by weighing the post and the load, measuring the area of the base of the post, and dividing the weight by the area. As we might expect, the larger the area of the base of the post, the smaller the pressure on the ground for a given load.

If we have a liquid or gas under pressure, it is not quite so easy to see what we must measure in order to calculate the pressure. But the principle is exactly the same as in the example of the post. Imagine a box-shaped vessel filled with a liquid or gas under pressure. Theoretically, all we have to do is to measure the force on one of the sides of the box, and divide it by the area. We could do this by making a box with a sliding end (Fig. 1), and putting the gas in that. We could measure directly the force on the sliding end with a spring-balance; this divided by the area of the end would be the pressure of the gas inside the box. Thus, if the end of the box was 2×2 inches and

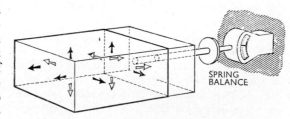

SPRING BALANCE

FIG. 1. MEASURING THE PRESSURE OF A GAS

the force on the balance was 112 lb. weight, the pressure in the box would be $\frac{112}{2 \times 2} = 28$ lb. per square inch.

So far we have tacitly assumed that we are

doing this experiment in a vacuum; if we did it in air, the ATMOSPHERE (q.v. Vol. III) would press on the outside of the sliding lid at about 14 lb. per square inch, and since it has 4 square inches to press on, it would exert a force of $4 \times 14 = 56$ lb. in the opposite direction; therefore the spring balance would read only 56 lb., a pressure of 14 lb. per square inch inside the box. This, of course, is the difference between the actual (or 'absolute') pressure in the box and atmospheric pressure. Since all practical pressure gauges do work in the atmosphere, and are affected in just this way, they all indicate absolute pressure minus atmospheric pressure, and this value is known as 'gauge' pressure. In any technical report may appear the expression 'so many pounds per square inch (gauge)', and that is what it means.

In practice, we can carry out the above operation more simply by connecting the gas or liquid to a cylinder and piston, and measuring the

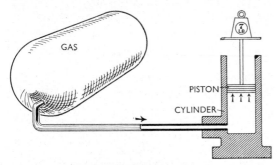

FIG. 2. PISTON PRESSURE GAUGE

The gas just balances the piston in the cylinder. If the area of the piston is 1 sq. in. the pressure of the gas is 7 lb. to the square inch (gauge)

force exerted by the piston (Fig. 2). In the example illustrated, the gas pressure is 7 lb. to the square inch (gauge). This is the sort of equipment used for checking other types of pressure gauge for accuracy.

We can now consider the chief types of pressure gauge used in practice.

(a) *Tire pressure gauges*. The pocket type works on the principle already described. The cylinder of the gauge ends in a rubber ring that fits on the valve tube of the tire. A plunger in the middle depresses the tire valve and so admits air to the cylinder. This pushes up the piston B until the tension of its retaining spring exactly balances the force of the air pressure in the tire acting on the piston. An indicator rides loosely

on the top of the piston and, when the gauge is applied, projects to show the exact degree of pressure (Fig. 3).

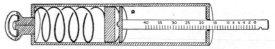

FIG. 3. DIAGRAM OF A TIRE PRESSURE GAUGE

(b) *Liquid-column gauges*. These, of which there are several variations, consist essentially of a column of liquid in a glass tube, against which the pressure to be measured is balanced.

The column may be single with a vacuum at the top, as in the mercury barometer (*see* METEOROLOGICAL INSTRUMENTS), in which case it measures absolute pressure—usually that of the atmosphere. It may be bent into a U, with one end open to the atmosphere and the other connected to the pressure to be measured (Fig. 4a). In this case the gauge pressure is equal to the weight of liquid in the section h of the column divided by the area of the column. The weight of liquid is the area of column $\times$ length h $\times$ density of liquid (*see* DENSITY, Vol. III); so the area of column cancels out when the division is performed, and we are left with gauge pressure $= h \times$ density of liquid. With this type of gauge, a high-density liquid, usually mercury, is used for pressures up to about the pressure of the atmosphere, and for vacuum measurements, in which case A is below B and the value of $h \times$ density gives the amount by which the pressure is below atmospheric (that is, the 'degree of vacuum'). A low-density liquid, usually water, is used for measuring smaller pressure variations —in particular the 'draught' or degree of vacuum in boiler chimneys. In this case the draught is usually referred to in terms of 'inches of water'—

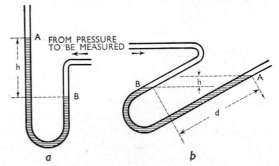

FIG. 4. LIQUID-COLUMN PRESSURE GAUGE

The pressure is h times the density of the liquid in the column just as we commonly talk of atmospheric pressure in terms of 'inches of mercury'. U-tube gauges can be made more sensitive by tilting the U (Fig. 4*b*), so that the distance *d* between the ends of the column changes by a large amount for small variations in *h*.

(*c*) *Aneroid gauges*. These are used almost exclusively for measuring atmospheric pressure, and are described in METEOROLOGICAL INSTRUMENTS (q.v.).

(*d*) *Bourdon gauges*. These are by far the commonest and most generally useful type of gauge, being simple, robust, and suitable for measuring a wide range of pressures from absolute vacuum

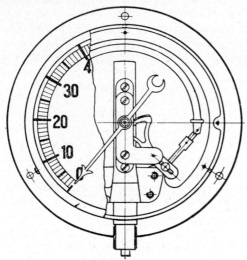

Budenberg Gauge Co. Ltd.

FIG. 5. A BOURDON GAUGE

The dial has been cut away to show the Bourdon tube

up to several tons per square inch. The Bourdon gauge is, however, less accurate than column-type gauges. It is also not a 'fundamental' instrument—that is, it has to be 'calibrated' or scaled by reference to an instrument of the type shown in Fig. 5. The basic working part of the Bourdon gauge consists simply of a metal tube of elliptical section bent into an arc of a circle and closed at one end. The other end is connected to the pressure to be measured. As the pressure increases, the tube tends to 'blow up' like a balloon—it tends to become more circular in cross-section and consequently to straighten out. The straightening-out movement drives a small gearwheel attached to the pointer.

It so happens that, for reasonable pressure changes, the straightening-out movement is almost exactly proportional to the change in

pressure, so that Bourdon gauges have an evenly spaced scale.

(*e*) *Crusher gauges*. For measuring the very high pressure impulses met with in gun barrels, for example, or other very high pressure measurement, a very simple type of gauge known as a 'crusher gauge' is used. This consists simply of a piston, which, under the pressure impulse, squashes a short alloy bar known as the 'crusher'. Previous tests determine how much the crushers are deformed by known pressures, so that by measuring crushers before and after the application of the unknown pressure, its value is easily determined.

See also METEOROLOGICAL INSTRUMENTS.
See also Vol. III: PRESSURE; DENSITY.

PRODUCTION ENGINEERING. This is the special branch of engineering that is concerned with mass production. Originally, production engineers were interested only in the mass production of engineering products, such as motor-cars or typewriters; but today many of the techniques of production engineering are used in the large-scale manufacture of a whole range of commodities from clothing to furniture.

The object of large-scale production is to produce goods in large quantities so that their cost can be kept low. In mass production the saving of a second or so of time or a fraction of labour cost in any one operation may add up to a considerable saving when thousands of a commodity are being made, involving a great many different operations.

Two main methods of cutting manufacturing costs in mass production are to replace manual work as far as possible by machinery, and to break down the manufacturing operations so that what manual work has to be done can be done by unskilled labour. Two further methods can be applied to all manufacturing operations even on the smallest scale; these are to plan manufacture to avoid waste of time and labour, and to ensure that all manual work is done as efficiently and with as little wasted effort as possible. These four fundamental points are the special study of the production engineer, and when put into practice, affect every single aspect of manufacturing, from the design stage to the selling stage.

1. USE OF MACHINERY. There are three main types of MACHINE TOOLS (q.v.)—fully automatic, semi-automatic, and hand-operated. Standard

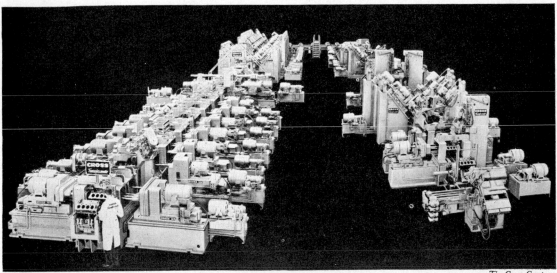

The Cross Company

A MODERN AUTOMATIC PRODUCTION LINE

This production line is 350 ft. long and carries out 555 different operations on motor-car cylinder blocks. As each machine in the line finishes its cycle of operation the cylinder block is automatically transferred to the next

fully automatic machines are available that will produce, for example, a complete bolt, screw, or similar component entirely on their own, feeding themselves with the material and delivering the finished part into a box. They are extremely adaptable, and one machine may be made to produce a wide variety of parts by adjusting its operating cams and by fitting different cutting tools, drills, and guides into its tool-holders. But such machine tools are so expensive that they are generally used only for manufacturing components that are common to a wide range of products and therefore required in vast numbers, such as nuts and bolts. In some kinds of production, such as the making of motor-cars, it may well justify enormous expense to lay down a line consisting almost entirely of special machinery in order to use as little skilled labour as possible, since, in the long run, the speed in output and saving in labour cost will more than pay for the initial cost of installing the special machinery. The production engineer must decide whether the use of a fully automatic tool is justified for the production of a particular part. He also designs the special cams and cutting tools for use in the machine, and he issues the instructions to the machine 'setter'—the skilled man who prepares the machine.

Three other problems are also involved in the question of machine tools—design for produc-

tion; standardization; and inspection. When designing a component that is going to be mass produced on a machine tool the designer must consider not only whether it will work efficiently, but also whether it can be made efficiently. A casting, for example, may be designed with a projection which forms no part of the finished component and, indeed, is later machined off. At one point in the production, however, this projection is gripped in the jaws of a semi-automatic lathe. It is in matters of this kind that the production engineer is concerned in the design of the product.

If a product is held together by nuts and bolts, it is clearly impossible in mass production to try each nut on to its bolt to see if it fits, still less to try each bolt on the product before assembly. Similarly pistons cannot be tried in cylinders, shafts fitted into individual bearings, and so on. Therefore, every component that is mass produced must conform to 'standards' of measurement so that it will be certain to fit its opposite number in the assembly. A certain fit could be achieved by making every measurement to the highest possible degree of accuracy; but this would not be efficient production because time and expense would be wasted in achieving a degree of accuracy which is often not needed. The production engineer and designer must therefore decide what accuracies are needed on each component, so that as much accuracy as necessary is called for without wasting production time. The dimensions required are shown on the working drawing as limits or 'tolerances' (*see* ENGINEERING DRAWING), indicating how far the measurement can vary from the 'nominal' dimension.

Standardization has another advantage, in that parts such as ball-bearings or nuts and bolts, which are common to a wide range of different products, can be mass produced and bought from other manufacturers rather than be made by each individual firm, and will be certain to fit where they are intended.

'Inspection' is the business of ensuring, by measurement, that a component is within the specified tolerances, that is, sufficiently accurate. The four fundamental points mentioned above as applying to production engineering in general apply equally to inspection in particular. Thus, much modern inspection is carried out with the help of automatic or semi-automatic measuring machinery, and much more can be carried out by unskilled workers by the use of gauges.

It is the production engineer's business to help draw up standards, and to design the gauges and

AN INSPECTION MACHINE

This machine checks nine dimensions at once on the cylinder liner A. Errors are shown by indicator lamps on the panel B

Alfred Herbert Ltd.

plan the inspection procedure for whatever products he is manufacturing.

2. UNSKILLED LABOUR. If a job is broken down into simple operations, it can often be done by unskilled men or women just as quickly and efficiently as by skilled workers. This is obviously more economical and, since there is usually a shortage of skilled men, it also means greater productivity.

In the engineering field, two of the greatest mechanical aids to the use of unskilled labour are capstan and turret LATHES (q.v.). Further aids to the use of unskilled labour are JIGS AND FIXTURES (q.v.). For example, if a number of holes are to be drilled in specified positions in a part, a drilling jig can be clamped round the part so that holes in the jig guide the drills to the correct positions. A semi-skilled man using a multi-spindle drill can then drill the holes. The use of gauges, enabling inspection to be carried out by less skilled men, has already been discussed. There are many similar examples in every branch of mass production.

3. PRODUCTION PLANNING. The qualities required by the successful production planning engineer are experience, organizing ability, and common sense. He must so plan all the operations in production that time and labour are not wasted in moving things from place to place or in waiting for tools or parts. Work can be made easier and time saved by using MECHANICAL HANDLING methods (q.v.) instead of manhandling work round the factory. This also often makes it possible to use women operators instead of men, even for heavy work.

4. WORK STUDY. The idea of work study is not to make people work harder, but to get the maximum results from their work. The job of making people work harder belongs to the personnel manager, who is responsible for working conditions, productivity bonuses, team spirit, and the other factors which go to determine how hard the employees work (*see* FACTORY ORGANIZATION, Section 4, Vol. VII). The production engineer's job is to study every manual operation of the workers and to break it into its simplest components—each a single motion taking no more than a very few seconds. He then concentrates on removing all wasted time, movement, and effort out of it.

Suppose that a man has to do a job of bolting two plates together. He stands at a bench with a box of nuts and bolts and a pile of plates.

Ford Motor Co.

SIX-SPINDLE FINE BORING MACHINE FINISHING BORE CYLINDERS ON CYLINDER BLOCKS

The cylinder block is loaded from the moving belt on to a fixture which is then inclined into the working position by hydraulic power

The work study engineer checks him with a stopwatch and produces a record something like this:

		sec.
1.	Reach out right hand for bolt . . .	1
2.	Pick up first plate and thread it on bolt .	1½
3.	Return left hand for second plate . .	½
4.	Pick up second plate and thread it on bolt .	1½
5.	Reach out left hand to box of bolts and nuts	¾
6.	Fish around for nut.	1
7.	Shift weight from left foot to right foot .	1
8.	Offer nut to bolt	1
9.	Attempt to engage thread . . .	1
10.	Screw up nut by hand	1½
11.	Return hand for spanner	½
12.	Offer spanner to nut	½
13.	Tighten nut	1½

Total 13¼

This table shows the work study expert that a lot of unnecessary effort is going into this apparently simple and straightforward operation. For a start, he can eliminate items 7 and 9 altogether by giving the man a chair and asking the produc-tion department to specify pointed bolts so that the thread will engage easily. By the time he has finished the operation sequence will be more like this:

		sec.
1.	Reach out right and left hands for two plates simultaneously	1
2.	Slip plates into slot on assembly fixture .	½
3.	Reach out right and left hands for bolt and nut from respective boxes	½
4.	Thread bolt through plates with right hand and engage nut with left hand . .	1½
5.	Reach out right and left hands for box span-ners	½
6.	Offer box spanners to bolt and nut . .	1½
7.	Tighten bolt and nut simultaneously . .	2

Total 7½

As a result of work study, the man is producing nearly twice as fast, but certainly working no harder.

PROPELLERS, AIRCRAFT. The purpose of the aircraft propeller is to induce a flow of air through the propeller disk, and it is the reaction from accelerating this stream of air backwards which provides the forward thrust. The propeller, therefore, has much in common with the jet propulsion system (*see* GAS TURBINE). However, because it handles a much larger mass of air accelerated to a slower velocity, it is better suited to the lower flight speeds and is still the best choice for aircraft with maximum speeds below about 450–500 m.p.h. Up to speeds of about 450 m.p.h., propeller efficiencies of about 85% are attained, but beyond this speed propellers are less efficient.

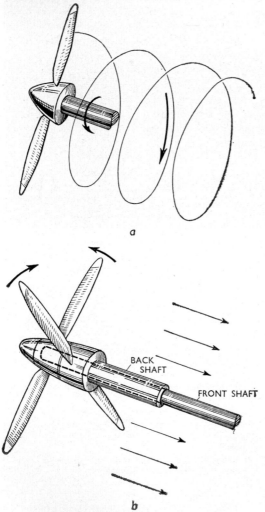

a

b

FIG. 1. SLIPSTREAM PRODUCED BY PROPELLER

a. Single rotation propeller which produces a spiral slipstream and tends to twist the aircraft in the opposite direction to that of the propeller. *b*. Contraprop. The propeller blades rotate in opposite directions so that there is no twist to the aircraft and the final slipstream is straight

According to whether the propeller, or airscrew, is mounted at the front or back of the aircraft, it is said to be of the 'tractor' or 'pusher' type, the former being almost universal today. Modern aircraft propellers have two to five blades fitted to a single hub rotating on one shaft, the larger numbers of blades generally being used with the higher powered engines. For the highest powers of all, dual rotation propellers ('contraprops'), having six or eight blades, are often used, the twin hubs each carrying half the total number of blades rotating in opposite directions on separate shafts (Fig. 1*b*).

The advantage of contraprops is that they produce a straight stream of air in contrast to the more turbulent spiral slipstream produced by a single propeller; they also eliminate the tendency of the propeller to 'twist the aircraft' (an inevitable fault of single propellers), because, since the halves of the contra-rotating system tend to twist the aircraft in opposite directions, the two effects cancel out.

Except for the simple examples fitted to light aircraft, such as trainers, nearly all aircraft propellers are now of the 'variable pitch' type—that is, the angle of the blades to the propeller disk can be varied in flight to suit changing conditions of speed of flight, air density at different altitudes, engine power, and revolutions per minute (r.p.m.). The r.p.m. are kept constant at any desired value, whatever the aircraft is then made to do, by an automatic governor device set by means of a cockpit control. The governor controls the pitch-change mechanism in the propeller hub, altering the blade angle as required. This means that when the pilot gives the engines more throttle, the pitch of the blades automatically becomes coarser, so that they take a bigger 'bite' of air, imposing a heavier burden on the engine, which thus continues to rotate at the same speed as before though it is delivering more power and the plane is moving faster.

These pitch-change mechanisms, which are of complex design, are usually operated either by oil pressure or by electric motors. Also the pitch-change mechanism on multi-engined aircraft is usually made capable of 'feathering' the blades, that is, turning them edge-on to the direction of flight so that, in the event of engine failure, their drag is reduced. The blade angles can also be turned back to a negative value during the landing run, a feature called 'reversible pitch', thus producing a considerable braking effect (Fig. 2).

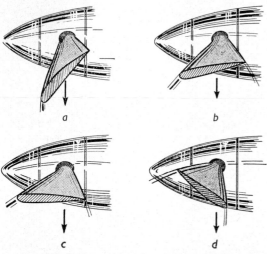

FIG. 2. VARIABLE PITCH PROPELLER

a. Fine pitch for take-off. *b.* Coarse pitch for flying fast. *c.* Feathered pitch to reduce propeller drag when engine has failed. *d.* Reverse pitch to give backwards thrust on landing. The propeller is cut to show the angle of the blade section. The arrows show direction of rotation

The great majority of aircraft propeller blades are now made from solid aluminium alloys, though some are still made in 'improved' or 'compressed' wood (that is, layers of wood veneers impregnated with plastics) which is stronger than natural timber. For the largest propellers (with diameters exceeding about 15 feet) hollow steel blades are often used because, in these sizes, they are lighter and so require the least effort for pitch change.

See also AERONAUTICAL ENGINEERING.
See also Vol. IV: AIRCRAFT ENGINES.

PROPELLERS, MARINE. The usual method of propelling a SHIP (q.v. Vol. IV) is by a 'screw' propeller. This consists of a heavy circular 'boss', to the outside of which are attached three, four, and occasionally five blades (Fig. 1). The boss and blades, which are usually cast in one piece, used to be made of cast iron, but are now generally made of manganese bronze, an alloy so strong that the blades can be made thinner and given a finer finish, thus reducing their drag through the water.

The propeller is connected to the main engines by a steel shaft, extending from the engine room, which is generally amidships, to the after-end where it emerges underwater. The section of the shaft projecting from the hull, called the 'tail-end shaft', is tapered slightly to fit a

similarly tapered hole in the boss. The boss is 'keyed' on to the shaft and further secured by a large nut. The tail-end shaft passes out of the ship through the 'stern tube', the after end of which is lined with strips of very hard wood. The action of sea water on these strips produces a lubricant for the shaft. The forward end of the tube is fitted with a 'stuffing' box, a steel cylinder packed with greasy hemp to prevent water entering the ship. Immediately behind the section of the shaft connected to the main engines is the 'thrust shaft'. This is fitted with a number of steel collars, which transmit the thrust of the propeller to thrust blocks connected to the main steel structure of the ship. In this way the whole thrust of the propeller is directed away from the main engines on to the ship itself.

The propeller is the link between the engines and the ship. It absorbs the engine power at a certain number of revolutions per minute and so moves the ship forward at a certain speed. Modern propellers are usually of aerofoil section (*see* AERONAUTICAL ENGINEERING). As the propeller turns, the back of the blade, that is, the side nearer the ship, exerts a negative pressure or suction, and the face of the blade exerts a positive pressure or thrust, the ratio between the two

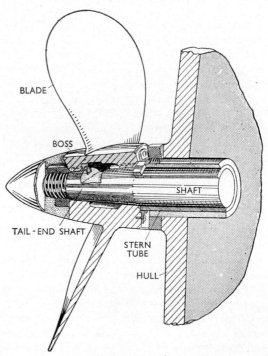

FIG. 1. DIAGRAM OF A SHIP'S PROPELLER

J. Stone & Co. (Charlton)

THE PROPELLERS OF THE QUEEN MARY

would go forward during one revolution if it were working in a solid and the distance it actually travels forward through the water in any given conditions. Slip increases as the ship becomes more difficult to drive—as the speed increases, for example, or in worsening weather.

Many types of ship are now fitted with 'controllable pitch' propellers. With these, while the propeller itself is moved at constant revolutions by the main engines, the pitch angle of the blades is altered to manœuvre the ship ahead or astern at different speeds.

Much valuable information about propeller design is obtained from the full-scale engine trials carried out on completed ships (*see* SHIP-BUILDING), during which engine power, the corresponding revolutions of the propeller, and the speed of the ship through the water are all measured. The designer is also helped by experiments with model propellers (*see* MODEL ENGINEERING), in which various features, such as pitch, blade area, and so on, are systematically varied. By relating model experiments to full-scale trials the designer can calculate the diameter, pitch, blade area, and the number of

being about 3 to 1. This is similar to the action of an aircraft wing, where the heavy suctions on top of the wing, and the smaller pressures underneath, enable the aircraft to rise into the air and to remain there (*see* HYDRODYNAMICS). The ability of the propeller to convert the engine power into useful thrust is governed to some extent by the angle at which the blades are set on the boss. This angle is known as the 'pitch' angle. Generally speaking, for a given rate of revolutions, the greater the pitch angle the greater is the power absorbed. If the engine power is too great to be absorbed by one propeller, two or more propellers, each fitted to a separate shaft, may be used.

The efficiency of a propeller may be limited by what is known as 'cavitation'. A propeller blade is capable of producing a certain maximum suction on the back. If there is a tendency to exceed this maximum, small cavities or water vapour bubbles form on the blade, leading to a breakdown in the flow of water over the blade and to a loss in efficiency. Eventually these bubbles collapse with intense force, allowing the water to hammer the blade and in time to cause considerable damage. The speed of advance (or forward speed) of the propeller is also affected by another factor, called 'slip'. Slip is the difference between the distance which the screw

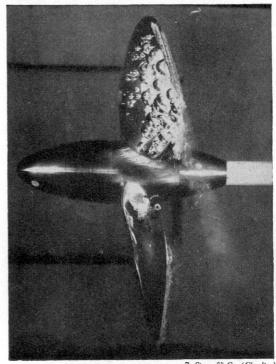

J. Stone & Co. (Charlton)

A MODEL PROPELLER IN CAVITATION
Ph. Karlstad Mekaniska Werkstad

propellers necessary for certain speeds, engine power, and revolutions.

See also MARINE ENGINEERING; PROPELLERS, AIRCRAFT. See also Vol. IV: SHIP.

PROSPECTING. Most of the valuable MINERALS (q.v. Vol. III) in the earth's crust are haphazard in their geographical distribution. The men who search for them, called prospectors, ventured in the past into unexplored regions, sometimes for months on end, to search for minerals and particularly for gold. The rapid development of Canada, Australia, South Africa, and the western parts of the United States in the 19th century followed closely upon the discovery of gold in these regions by adventurous prospectors who were the true pioneers. Prospectors used to travel on foot, on horseback, in canoes, and sometimes with sledges and dog-teams, and usually took several years to cover an area which it is now possible to map in a few days by air photography. In the summer of 1952, for example, by taking photographs from helicopters, five scientists of the Geological Survey of Canada were able to map the topographical features of 57,000 square miles of territory in a period of 14 weeks. With maps such as these prospectors can go immediately to the places where mineral deposits are most likely to be found instead of wasting perhaps many years in fruitless journeys overland and by water.

Modern science also helps the prospector to determine by direct and indirect methods the position and extent of a mineral deposit hidden below the surface. Although the physical nature of the earth has been studied for many centuries, it was not until the second half of the 19th century that this knowledge was first applied to prospecting. The geophysicist's knowledge of the properties of ROCKS (q.v. Vol. III) and the chemist's power of tracking down even minute quantities of metallic elements, perhaps in the roots of plants and trees, are now at the service of the prospector. The rare metals are usually present only in very small quantities in their ores (see METAL ORES, Vol. III); but these ores are often to be found in rocks of certain types which can be located by geophysical methods from some characteristic property or properties which they may possess. Radioactive minerals such as uranium, for example, are easily found by such means.

Minerals possessing magnetic properties can

BORING FOR COAL IN KENT

The drill is rotated by the motor in the background. Additional lengths of hollow rod are screwed in as the borehole gets deeper. The rods are lifted out from time to time by means of pulley blocks attached to a rope which passes over a sheave in the tower to a winch on the ground

be located with the aid of an instrument called a magnetometer, which is sensitive to MAGNETISM (q.v. Vol. III). A massive body of IRON ORE (q.v. Vol. VII) can be detected by a magnetometer carried in an aeroplane, even when the ore lies buried in the ground at a depth of more than 3,000 feet. Electrical methods are based on observations of the resistance encountered by an electric current when it is sent in various directions through the ground. Minerals which oxidize in contact with water act as the poles of a primary BATTERY (q.v.) and set up currents in their neighbourhood which may give a clue to their position. Metallic ores are usually much heavier than the rocks around them, and highly sensitive instruments are available which will indicate these differences in density. The seismograph used for recording EARTHQUAKES (q.v.

Vol. III) is also used by prospectors. A small earthquake is produced artificially by firing a quantity of an explosive placed in a borehole, and the recordings of the waves sent out in different directions from the centre of explosion give some information about the nature of the strata below.

Before a mine is opened, further exploration is usually necessary in order to assess the commercial value of the deposit. This information may be obtained by core-drilling. A diamond core drill consists of a steel tube with rough pieces of black diamond studded into the cutting end so that, when the tube is held vertically and rotated, the diamonds cut their way through the hardest of rocks, leaving a solid core of rock inside the tube. This core is broken off at intervals and brought to the surface for examination and ASSAYING (q.v. Vol. VII). The drill is driven by power, and it is extended as it bores downwards by screwing extra lengths of tube to the top end. Such drills, when being used in borings for oil deposits, have penetrated to depths of over 3 miles (see OIL WELLS, Vol. VII).

See also MINING ENGINEERING.

PUDDLING, *see* IRON AND STEEL.

PULLEY, *see* BELT AND CHAIN DRIVE; CRANES.

PUMPS. These are machines for causing water or other liquids to flow through a pipe. Pumps for air or other gas fluids, which reduce their volume with increase of pressure, are called COMPRESSORS (q.v.). The resistance to flow, against which a pump works, is known as the head, usually measured in feet, and is the height to which the pump could raise the liquid.

The simplest device for raising water, used by the ancient Egyptians and still in use today, is the 'shadoof' (see IRRIGATION, Vol. VI). From this developed the endless chain of buckets driven by oxen, and later the water-wheel—a large-diameter wheel carrying buckets round its edge, which is driven by animal, wind, or water power, each bucket filling itself with water at the lower level and tipping the water out at the higher level. Many of the old Dutch and East Anglian windmills are really windpumps working on this principle.

The next development, the lift pump, is still widely used today (Fig. 1a). When the piston in the pump is raised, the water above it is lifted

and flows out of the spout, and at the same time water is drawn up from below through the flap valve A. On the down stroke of the piston this valve A closes and the valve B in the piston opens, allowing water to flow through to be discharged on the next up-stroke.

When the raising of the piston reduces the pressure in the pump, the pressure of the atmosphere acting on the surface of the water in the well forces the water up the pipe. The atmospheric pressure, as measured by a barometer, is equivalent to a head of about 34 feet of water, so this is the greatest possible height from which any lift pump could raise water; in practice it is usually much less.

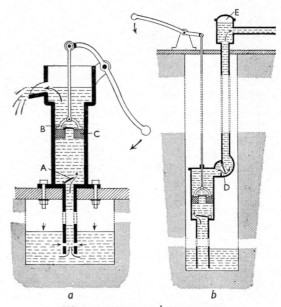

FIG. 1. *a.* LIFT PUMP. *b.* FORCE PUMP
A. Flap valve. B. Piston valve. C. Piston. D. Delivery valve.
E. Air bottle

A force pump, placed near the bottom of the well, acts in much the same way as a lift pump, except that on the up-stroke the water above the piston is forced past a valve D into the delivery pipe, which may be of any length. On the return stroke this valve closes to prevent the water flowing back. The water is delivered in a series of jerks, which might lead to a burst pipe were the flow not smoothed out by means of an air bottle E (Fig. 1b).

Force pumps may be made double acting, the ends of the cylinder each forming a separate pump, so delivery takes place both on the up and down strokes. The semi-rotary pump is a common example of this type (Fig. 2); a vane carrying the valves A and B is rocked like a see-saw

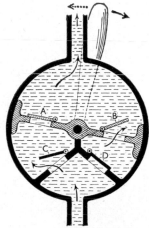

FIG. 2. SEMI-ROTARY PUMP

inside a circular casing, which is divided by a λ-shaped part carrying valves c and d. When the vane moves clockwise, valves A and D close and B and C open; water trapped between A and D is discharged through the delivery pipe at the top and at the same time water is drawn up from below through valve c. On the return stroke water trapped between valves B and C is discharged, and so on.

In the diaphragm pump the piston is replaced by a flexible diaphragm, the centre of which is forced to move to and fro, thus acting as bellows. This type of pump is widely used as a petrol pump on motor-cars, since there is no leakage past the diaphragm. It is also used by building contractors for pumping dirty water from excava-

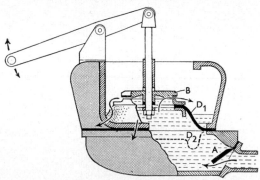

FIG. 3. DIAPHRAGM PUMP

The pump is shown at the end of the suction stroke. On the down stroke, valve A closes and water is delivered through valve B. Upper and lower positions of the diaphragm are shown at D_1 and D_2

tions, where an ordinary plunger pump would wear badly (Fig. 3).

Another common type of pump is the gear pump, used as an oil pump on engines of all kinds. It consists of two identical gear-wheels meshing together (see GEARS) and enclosed in a casing, with an inlet one side and an outlet the other (Fig. 4). There are no valves; the intermeshed teeth prevent the oil carried round between the teeth on the outer side of each wheel from returning.

All these pumps are 'positive displacement' types, a fixed quantity being delivered for each stroke or revolution of the pump. The action of a centrifugal pump is quite different. If an L-shaped pipe is filled with water and rotated at speed, the water, because there is no force acting inwards on it to keep it rotating in a circle, escapes continuously from the open end of the pipe. This draws more water up the vertical

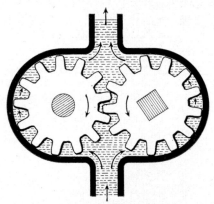

FIG. 4. GEAR PUMP

The driving gear is on the right

pipe (Fig. 5). The rotating part of the centrifugal pump, known as the 'impeller', consists of a number of curved passages leading from the centre outwards. The casing admits water to the centre of the impeller and collects the water which is shot from the outer edge into a spiral chamber leading to the delivery pipe.

The advantages of centrifugal pumps over positive displacement pumps are their mechanical simplicity, their smooth flow, and a large delivery for their size. On the other hand, they must be primed (filled with water) before they will function, and there is a limit to the head that can be developed in a single impeller. If the head is greater than about 500 feet, two or more impellers are used.

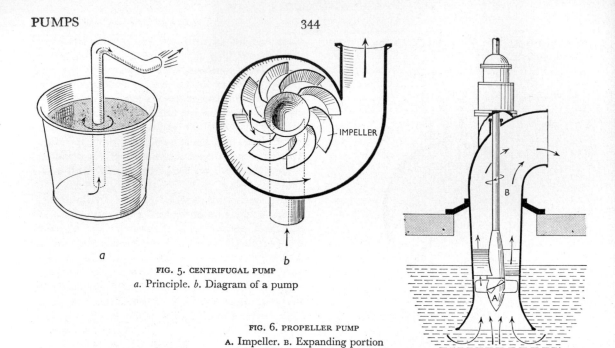

FIG. 5. CENTRIFUGAL PUMP
a. Principle. *b.* Diagram of a pump

FIG. 6. PROPELLER PUMP
A. Impeller. B. Expanding portion

The propeller type of pump is used to deal with large flows at low heads, below 20 feet, for which centrifugal pumps are not well adapted. It consists of an impeller very like a ship's propeller working inside a casing, followed by an expanding portion in which the water is slowed down gradually, thereby converting some of its kinetic energy (energy of motion) into pressure energy (extra delivery head) (Fig. 6). Some very large pumps of this type have been built.

Q

QUARRYING MACHINERY. The various methods of quarrying, or getting stone from open pits in the earth, are described in STONE QUARRYING and CHALK-MINING (qq.v. Vol. VII). Here we are concerned with the main types of machinery used in a modern quarry.

Whatever material is being quarried, the first step is usually to remove the topsoil or overburden, and for this various types of EARTH-MOVING EQUIPMENT (q.v.) are employed. Then the quarry face must be drilled for BLASTING (q.v.). For drilling down vertically into the face, a rotary drill is used. The drill is mounted on a tripod or a special wheeled trolley and worked by electricity or compressed air. A special type of 'churn' drill which bangs its way into the earth as it is alternately raised and dropped is used for drilling deep vertical holes into the top of the face.

The stone, or whatever is being quarried, having been broken down, has then to be transported from the quarry face. A narrow-gauge railway used to be used for this; but today mechanical shovels scoop up the stone and load it into diesel lorries holding up to 50 tons.

If the stone has to be crushed and screened, this also is done entirely by machinery. The stone, of many sizes, is usually first passed over a fixed sloping screen or sieve which allows the smaller fragments to fall through and so by-pass the first machine, the primary crusher. This crusher is usually set to take as large pieces of rock as can conveniently be lifted and loaded so as to avoid as far as possible having to break up large boulders by means of explosives in the quarry. The stone, having passed through the primary crusher, is usually raised by belt or bucket elevator either to a revolving cylindrical drum with perforations of several sizes, called a 'trommel', or to a series of flat, sloping, vibrating

I.C.I.

A LARGE MECHANIZED QUARRY SHOWING, AT THE TOP, MACHINES DRILLING HOLES FOR EXPLOSIVE CHARGES

Fraser & Chalmers

A MACHINE FOR SCREENING STONE

Cone Crusher, which is like a huge steel pestle and mortar. The product from this machine is then returned to the main screening unit for further sizing.

Frequently the stone has to be washed or sprayed with water to remove dust and small pieces of rock, and this spraying is usually done when the stone is being rolled over or vibrated in the screening unit. The uniformly sized stone is then conveyed to storage bins placed both near the plant and alongside a good road or railway for ease of loading and despatch.

If the crushed, sized stone is to be used for ROAD BUILDING (q.v.) it is sometimes further processed with pitch or tar to produce tarmac, a material that will bind when rolled to form a watertight road surface.

Again, the purest white LIMESTONE (q.v. Vol. III) is ground to a powder in special types of grinding mills, usually a dry grinding process, to produce ground agricultural limestone in powder form which the farmer uses to dress the land. This is packed into bags for delivery to the farms (*see* LIME, Vol. VI). Generally, however, quarry engineering deals simply with drilling, transport, washing, crushing, and sizing.

See also BLASTING; MINING MACHINERY.
See also Vol. VII: STONE QUARRYING.

screens. By either of these devices the stone is graded into the various sizes that are wanted. Some of the screened products are then ready for use, but often some oversized pieces have to be passed on to a secondary crusher. This is usually a gyratory crusher, such as the Symon's

QUARTZ CRYSTAL CLOCK, *see* TIME-KEEPERS, MODERN.

QUENCHING, *see* HEAT TREATMENT, Section 4.

R

RADAR. The name 'radar' (RAdio Detection And Ranging) is now generally given to the radio equipment specially used for the detection and accurate location of distant objects. Radio-location, as it was first called, was invented in Britain by Sir Robert Watson-Watt and a team of scientists working in secret, for the purpose of detecting the approach of hostile bombers, and was first used in operations during the BATTLE OF BRITAIN (q.v. Vol. X). It was developed from an earlier radio method used by Sir Edward Appleton to measure the height of the layers of electrified air many miles above the earth's surface which, by reflecting radio waves, enable them to pass round the curvature of the earth. Other countries had also developed similar equipment, but Britain was the first to use it on a large scale. Not only does radar detect the presence of distant objects such as aircraft and ships, but it indicates their exact position on a map as well as the speed and height of aircraft.

Radar detects the presence of distant objects by receiving an 'echo' from them—not the normal sound echo but an echo of radio waves. Sound echoes have long been used by sailors on board ship to detect the presence of cliffs in the dark or in fog. One method is to fire a shot, and then measure with a stop-watch the time that elapses between the shot and the echo—that is, the time the sound takes to go from the ship to the cliffs and back. This method simply depends on knowing the speed of SOUND (q.v. Vol. III). Sound waves travel 1 mile in 5 seconds, so an echo would take 10 seconds to return from cliffs 1 mile away.

This principle can also be used with radio waves. A powerful radio transmitter sends out a short burst of waves called a pulse, and a radio receiver picks up the feeble echoes returned from distant objects. With very sensitive radio receivers, the weak echoes returned from a small aeroplane 100 miles away can be detected. The time for the echo to return is much shorter than with sound, as radio waves travel about a million times faster—at 186,000 miles a second, or the speed of light. Time can now be measured in microseconds—millionths of a second—and a radar echo takes about 10 microseconds to return for each mile which separates the object from the instrument.

No ordinary watch or clock can measure such very short times, but it can be done by the CATHODE RAY TUBE (q.v.), as now used for TELEVISION screens (q.v.). The officer on a ship's bridge looks at the cloudy glass radar screen much as a viewer looks at the television set. Two spots of light are cast on the radar screen—one at the precise moment the transmitter sends out its pulse, and the other when the echo of the pulse comes back, and the distance between the spots enables the exact distance of the far object (say, an iceberg) to be measured. The spot of light is produced, as in television, by a beam of electrons projected on to the screen from a point inside the 'tube'. Let us say that the beam is adjusted to sweep continually and rapidly across the screen from left to right, making a very faint thin line of light on it. When the pulse is sent out the light suddenly increases for a moment into a bright spot. If the second bright spot, caused by another increase of light when the echo of the pulse comes back to the ship, is 3 inches away from the first on the glass surface (Fig. 1), and the scale of the instrument is, say, 1 inch for 5 microseconds (that is, 2 inches to the mile), the officer will know that the iceberg is 1½ miles away; if the bright spots are 6 inches apart, the iceberg will be 3 miles off, and so on. The straight line between the spots is called the 'time-base', because distances along this line correspond to echo times.

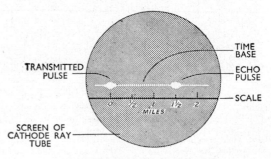

FIG. 1. DIAGRAM OF A RADAR SCREEN

If only one pulse were sent out by the radar transmitter then only one echo would be received from the iceberg, and the two bright spots on the radar screen would appear briefly and vanish. But a ship's radar transmitter usually sends out a continuous stream of pulses (about 1,000 per second), and a continuous stream of echoes is received, the bright spots being 'painted' again on the screen before they have time to disappear.

This very simple arrangement of two points would tell the officer only the distance of the object, and not its position in relation to the ship. On most radar sets, therefore, it is arranged that the 'time-base' line continually swings round in a circle, the first bright spot (the departure of the pulse) being always kept in the middle of the glass screen. The second spot (the return pulse) moved round and round it, nearer or farther according to the distance of the object detected. High up on the ship and keeping in exact step with this circular movement is a wireless aerial that produces a well-focused beam of radio waves, and continually turns round like a gramophone turntable. This beamed aerial both transmits the pulses and receives their echoes. It revolves fairly slowly, and about once every second it 'looks' right around the horizon—first North, then West, South, East, back to North, and so on. The revolving 'time-base' line on the radar screen is arranged so that the line points to the top of the screen when the rotating aerial 'looks' towards the bows of the ship. Thus, if there is an obstacle a mile away on the starboard (right-hand) quarter of the ship, a bright spot will show once every second on the upper right-hand side of the screen, 2 inches from the centre. To overcome the difficulty that the bright spot on the screen will occur only once every second, the screen is coated with a fluorescent material that continues to glow for several seconds after the electron beam has fallen on it; and consequently the spot lingers until the time-base line sweeps round again, and a stable picture appears to the ship's officer.

Instruments based on this rotating time-base line are called Plan Position Indicators (P.P.I.). A transparent sheet marked with 'range rings' showing distances in miles is usually placed over the P.P.I. screen. The effect of the system is that whenever the officer glances at the radar screen he sees on it a map or chart of the surrounding area, with the ship always represented by the white spot in the centre (Fig. 2). By using his radar screen, he can pick his way in a fog between ships surrounding him, or can find his way into harbour. Important harbours and estuaries, such as the Mersey, are equipped with land-based radar, and with its aid the harbourmaster can control the movement of all the ships in his area.

Special problems arise when a radar station is based on land, and has to distinguish the echo of an aircraft from echoes of objects on the ground. This is possible for two reasons: firstly, the signal strength from a short-wave transmitter close to the ground being weak, the echoes from objects on the ground, unless very close to the transmitter, are also weak; secondly, the earth being round, distant objects on the earth's surface lie below the horizon and are not 'in the beam'. Echoes are received, however, from surrounding buildings and trees near a radar station, and they do obscure the picture for the first few miles.

If the transmitter itself is high, as in an aircraft, the beam may be made to sweep over the

Decca Radar Ltd.

A SHIP'S RADAR AERIAL MOUNTED ON A SHORT MAST ON TOP OF THE WHEEL-HOUSE

The radar aerial is the oblong object on the left, and underneath is the electric motor which spins it round. The radar screen is inside the wheel-house, convenient to the helmsman. The circular object is the ship's radio direction-finding aerial

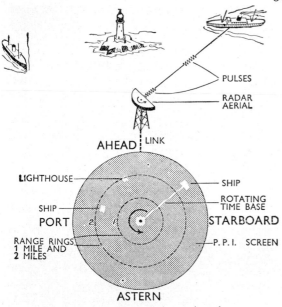

PULSES

RADAR
AERIAL

AHEAD | LINK

LIGHTHOUSE

SHIP

SHIP

PORT   STARBOARD

ROTATING
TIME BASE

RANGE RINGS
1 MILE AND
2 MILES

P. P. I. SCREEN

ASTERN

DIAGRAM OF A RADAR SCREEN (P.P.I.)

ground, and in this way a radar map may be produced showing outstanding features such as towns, lakes, and rivers. Towns show up as bright echoes, but lakes and rivers as dark patches, since water gives a very small echo. This is one of the most spectacular applications of radar, and by its means aircraft can find their way by night.

A very narrow beam of radio waves is needed to locate an object accurately, and therefore very short radio waves must be used if aerials of unwieldy size are to be avoided. In the early days of radar, wavelengths of a few metres were used, but no great advance could be made until, during the Second World War, valves were invented able to give high powers at wavelengths of only a few centimetres (10 cm. and 3 cm. were commonly used). These very short radio waves are called 'microwaves', and the high-power valves which produce them are called 'magnetrons'.

Unlike the longer waves used in broadcasting, which can be made to travel along wires, microwaves have to be piped along hollow copper tubes called wave-guides (*see* HIGH-FREQUENCY CURRENTS), and the aerial is usually a concave metal mirror rather like a searchlight's mirror, with, instead of the searchlight's lamp, a waveguide ending in a small horn pointing at the mirror.

Microwaves can penetrate cloud, fog, and rain and work just as well by night as day; one of the main uses of radar, therefore, is to extend the range of vision. Radar is a great help, for example, in enabling aircraft to land on a runway in foggy weather and is installed at most big airports for this purpose. It is found that heavy rain and also meteor trails give a strong radar echo, and so radar can be used for giving warning of the approach of thunderstorms and typhoons, for studying scientifically the process of rain formation in clouds, and for discovering new groups of meteors which come by day and so cannot be seen by the eye. Radar signals have also been sent to the moon and back.

See also Vol. IV: NAVIGATION, AIR; NAVIGATION, MARINE.

RADIOACTIVE ISOTOPES. 1. Many chemical elements contain more than one kind of ATOM (q.v. Vol. III), and the various kinds within any element are called 'isotopes'. It is now known that nearly all the chemical elements have some isotopes which are radioactive (that is, which shoot out rays or high-speed particles) and which can be artificially prepared. These have important uses in medicine, industry, and science.

The nuclei of all the atoms in any one chemical element contain the same number of protons with the same number of electrons circulating round them. The chemical properties of an atom depend upon the circulating electrons and are therefore almost exactly the same for all the isotopes of an element. The nuclei of the different isotopes, however, contain a greater or smaller number of neutrons, and consequently the different isotopes have different atomic weights (*see* Periodic Table of Elements, Vol. III, p. 278), and the properties which depend on the nucleus, such as radioactivity, are quite distinct. The naturally occurring radioactive isotopes were the first to be discovered, and were all found among the heavy elements with more than 80 protons in their nuclei. Later it was found that most elements had two or more stable (nonradioactive) isotopes, and radioactive isotopes of all the elements were eventually discovered.

The radioactive isotopes are usually prepared by putting ordinary chemicals inside a nuclear reactor or atomic pile and allowing them to capture some of the neutrons which are plentiful there (*see* NUCLEAR POWER). Two typical examples may be given.

To manufacture radioactive sodium, sodium carbonate (washing soda), which contains the only naturally occurring stable isotope of sodium, is placed inside an atomic pile. The nucleus of this isotope, which contains 11 protons and 12 neutrons, is called sodium-23. In the pile the sodium nucleus captures another neutron and turns into sodium-24, which is radioactive. This nucleus emits a fast electron, known as a beta-particle, and changes into magnesium-24. It also emits gamma-rays, which have the properties of very penetrating X-RAYS (q.v.).

To manufacture radioactive phosphorus, sulphur is placed in the pile, and when the nucleus of sulphur-32 captures a neutron and immediately afterwards ejects a proton, the nucleus phosphorus-32 is formed. The radioactive phosphorus-32 emits a beta-particle (but no gamma-rays) and turns back into sulphur-32. Fig. 1 shows radioactive isotopes being removed from the pile.

In the first example, the radioactive sodium is the same chemical element as the stable sodium isotope from which it is prepared, and therefore it cannot be separated from the rest of the sodium carbonate. In the second preparation, the radioactive phosphorus is made from sulphur and can be separated by chemical means.

There are some very useful radioactive isotopes which cannot be produced in the pile but can be made by bombarding nuclei with the fast particles from a cyclotron (see HIGH-VOLTAGE PARTICLE ACCELERATORS).

There are several hundred radioactive isotopes—too many to list them all here. This table shows some of the isotopes of a few of the more important elements:

A.E.R.E

FIG. 1. UNLOADING RADIOACTIVE ISOTOPES FROM 'BEPO'

The substances to be made radioactive are placed in aluminium cans and loaded into a train of graphite blocks inside the lead tunnel A. The train is then pushed into the pile. After a suitable interval the radioactive isotopes are withdrawn from the pile into the lead tunnel, which protects the operators from harmful rays. The cans are then shot down the hose B into a lead trolley C. Health monitors D detect the presence of radiations. The lead tunnel E contains one of the control rods of the pile

The 'half-life' is the time which elapses before one-half of the original radioactive nuclei have decayed. After two half-lives, one-quarter is left; after three half-lives, one-eighth is left, and so on. Most of the 90 or so elements have reasonably

| | Nucleus contains | | | Radioactivity | |
Isotope	Protons	Neutrons	Method of formation	Particle emitted	Half-life
Carbon-11	6	5	From boron in a cyclotron	Positive electron	20 minutes
Carbon-12	6	6	Found in nature	Stable	..
Carbon-13	6	7	" "	"	..
Carbon-14	6	8	From compounds containing nitrogen in a pile	Negative electron	5,000 years
Sodium-22	11	11	From magnesium in a cyclotron	Positive electron	2·6 years
Sodium-23	11	12	Found in nature	Stable	..
Sodium-24	11	13	From sodium compounds in a pile	Negative electron and gamma-rays	15 hours
Phosphorus-31	15	16	Found in nature	Stable	..
Phosphorus-32	15	17	From sulphur in a pile	Negative electron	14 days
Cobalt-59	27	32	Found in nature	Stable	..
Cobalt-60	27	33	From cobalt in a pile	Negative electron and gamma-rays	5·3 years

TABLE OF ISOTOPES OF SOME IMPORTANT ELEMENTS

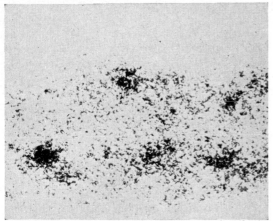

F. P. Bowden

FIG. 2. AUTORADIOGRAPH OF THE TRACK WHICH IS FORMED WHEN RADIOACTIVE COPPER IS SLID ONCE OVER A LUBRICATED COPPER SURFACE

A photographic film was pressed against the track for some time and then developed. The dark spots show where copper from the slider has been transferred to the other surface

convenient radioactive isotopes, but some of the elements with the lighter atomic weights have no radioactive isotopes with half-lives longer than 10 minutes—too short to be convenient for carrying out experiments. Of these oxygen and nitrogen are so important, especially in biological experiments, that the stable oxygen-18 and nitrogen-15 have to be used instead of radioactive isotopes, and quite different methods must be used for their detection.

The importance of the radioactive isotopes is due to the radiations which they emit, which are the same as those given out by the natural radioactive substances. They may themselves be useful for their effects upon matter, or they may be used to indicate the presence of a particular isotope, or to measure the amount of it which is present (*see* RADIOACTIVITY, DETECTION OF). The methods are astonishingly sensitive, and it is possible to make quite accurate measurements of 1/1,000,000,000th of a gramme of a radioactive isotope.

Radioactive isotopes are used in several ways in engineering problems.

(*a*) *Investigations of friction.* Isotopes are used as tracers to discover how much material is transferred from one surface to another when two similar surfaces are rubbed together so that there is FRICTION (q.v.) between them. If the friction of two copper surfaces is to be investigated, one piece of copper is made radioactive and may be,

for example, rubbed once, using a lubricant, over another piece which is not radioactive. The transfer of the material from the active to the inactive copper is then vividly shown by pressing a piece of photographic film against the surface. The film is affected by the radiations from the radioactive material transferred, and the amount of active copper can be measured: in the experiment illustrated in Fig. 2 it was found to be only 1/10,000,000,000th of a gramme per square centimetre. The radioactive copper in this experiment is called a tracer, because it is possible, by its aid, to follow the movements of atoms which are, for all practical purposes, identical with the atoms of ordinary elements.

(*b*) *Radiography.* The gamma-radiations emitted by radioactive isotopes penetrate matter and can be used for taking photographs in the same manner as X-RAYS (q.v.). No large and expensive X-ray machine is necessary, only a small capsule containing the isotope and a heavy lead casket in which to carry it about. A method of taking

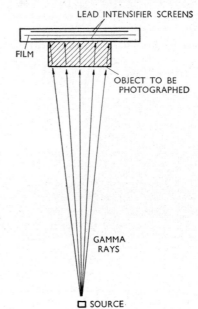

LEAD INTENSIFIER SCREENS

FILM

OBJECT TO BE PHOTOGRAPHED

GAMMA RAYS

□ SOURCE

FIG. 3. DIAGRAM OF GAMMA RADIOGRAPHY

The lead screens improve the quality of the photograph and shorten the exposure

the photographs is illustrated in Fig. 3, and a typical photograph is shown in Fig. 4.

(*c*) *Autoradiography.* The photograph in Fig. 2, a simple example of an autoradiograph, shows the distribution of radioactive material by photographic means. Autoradiography has important

FIG. 4. PHOTOGRAPH OF THE WORKS OF A WATCH, TAKEN WITH THE GAMMA-RAYS FROM A RADIOACTIVE ISOTOPE, THULIUM-170   *A.E.R.E.*

uses in biology: for instance, if a plant is fed on radioactive phosphate as a fertilizer, and the leaves are then pressed against a photographic plate, the developed photograph shows that the phosphorus first goes to those points of the plant where growth is taking place.

(*d*) *Thickness measurement.* The thickness of materials such as paper can be measured continuously, without contact (Fig. 5), by placing a source which emits beta-particles on one side of the layer of material and a detector on the other. The thicker the material, the greater the propor-

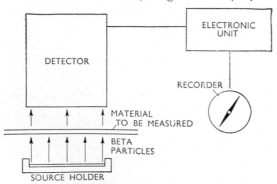

FIG. 5. DIAGRAM OF APPARATUS FOR MEASURING THE THICK-NESS OF A MATERIAL WITH BETA-PARTICLES

tion of beta-particles stopped. The more penetrating gamma-rays are used in the same way to measure materials such as steel sheet.

(*e*) *Elimination of electric charges.* In many industries using non-conducting materials, such as paper, plastics, cellophane, rubber, glass, and even cloth, much inconvenience is caused because the material becomes electrified by friction as it runs through the machinery. The material may become so highly electrified that the pieces repel or attract each other and cannot be handled properly, or electric sparks may even pass and cause fires. The electricity can often be discharged by using the radiations from radioactive substances to convert the air into a conductor, and so allow the unwanted electricity to leak away (Fig. 6).

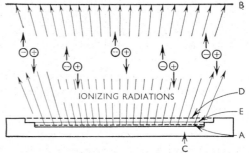

FIG. 6. HOW ELECTRIC CHARGES ARE REMOVED FROM A SURFACE BY RADIOACTIVE RADIATIONS

The radioactive source A causes positive and negative ions to be formed. The presence of these turns the air into a conductor which carries away the unwanted charge from the surface B. C. Earthed metal tray. D. Protective mesh. E. Protective foil

2. RADIOACTIVITY AND HEALTH. Many of the most interesting uses of radioactive isotopes are in biology and medicine. For instance, some are used in place of radium in the treatment of cancer (*see* RADIOTHERAPY, Vol. XI).

The radiations from radioactive isotopes, if they are too strong, are so dangerous to health that occasionally it is necessary to build a wall of lead to guard against gamma-rays or to interpose a sheet of plastic to stop beta-particles. Usually, however, it is sufficient if the operator keeps his distance and uses tongs. Radioactive isotopes are never touched by hand because they may damage the skin, or enter the body through small cuts, or be carried to the mouth on the fingers. Some isotopes are exceedingly dangerous because, if swallowed or breathed in, they can become permanently fixed in the body. Radium and several other elements, for instance, may be deposited in the bones, where they destroy the marrow in which blood cells are produced. In most applications of radioactive isotopes, however, the quantities used are so small that the dangers are no greater than those present in an ordinary laboratory.

See also X-RAYS.
See also Vol. III: ATOM; RADIATION.
See also Vol. XI: RADIOTHERAPY.

RADIOACTIVITY, DETECTION OF.

An important part of modern research in physics is concerned with detecting and investigating rapidly moving particles, such as electrons and the particles which make up the nuclei of ATOMS (q.v. Vol. III). Although these particles are far too small to be seen with any form of microscope, they can be studied by observing their effects upon the substances they pass through. The most important effect is ionization, in which the passage of a high-speed electrified particle removes electrons from some of the atoms of the substance, leaving them electrified with a positive charge. The positively electrified atoms (or the molecules of which they form a part) are called 'positive ions'. If the electrons which are removed from the positive ions attach themselves to other atoms or molecules, 'negative ions' are formed. Rapidly moving charged particles also emit light, form images in photographic plates, and have other effects.

There are four important sources of high-speed particles. The first is the radiation from radioactive nuclei, both natural and artificial (*see* RADIOACTIVE ISOTOPES). The second is COSMIC RAYS (q.v. Vol. III), which continually bombard the earth from outer space. The third is the artificial speeding-up of particles in machines called HIGH-VOLTAGE PARTICLE ACCELERATORS (q.v.), and the fourth is the nuclear pile or reactor (*see* NUCLEAR POWER).

An important instrument for detecting particles is the 'cloud chamber' (Fig. 1), invented by C. T. R. Wilson in 1911. This expands a damp gas very rapidly and so cools it and leaves it supersaturated—that is, containing so much vapour that a mist would form if there were something for the drops to condense upon. In normal air the drops condense round dust particles, but in the clean gas of the cloud chamber the only things on which they can form are the charged ions left by particles. Consequently, nearly all the drops are found in the tracks of

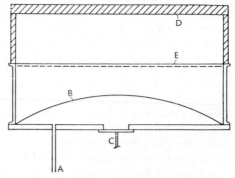

FIG. I. DIAGRAM OF A CLOUD CHAMBER

Compressed air enters at A and pushes up the rubber diaphragm B, compressing the gas in the upper chamber. When a picture is to be taken the valve C is opened. The compressed air rushes out, the diaphragm drops back, and the gas in the chamber is suddenly expanded. The tracks are viewed or photographed through the plate glass cover D. E. Perforated plate covered with black velvet

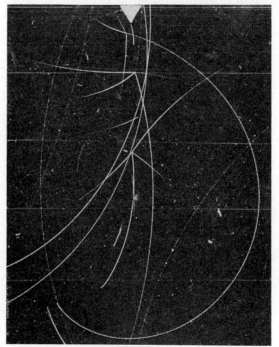

FIG. 2. A CLOUD-CHAMBER PHOTOGRAPH OF THE TRACKS WHICH ARE FORMED WHEN NEUTRONS HAVING AN ENERGY OF 90,000,000 ELECTRON-VOLTS PASS INTO A GAS

The neutrons, which enter through a thin window at the point marked by the arrow, do not themselves make any tracks because they have no electric charge. Most of the tracks occur when the nuclei of carbon or oxygen (from the alcohol and water in the cloud chamber) are disintegrated on being struck by a fast neutron. The chamber was operated in a strong magnetic field, which has bent all the tracks. (From Rochester and Wilson, *Cloud Chamber Photographs of Cosmic Radiation*, Pergamon Press. Photograph by K. Bruckner, W. Hartsough, E. Hayward, and W. M. Powell)

ionizing particles. Fig. 2 shows a photograph of these cloud tracks.

If the cloud chamber is placed in a magnetic field (*see* INDUCTION, ELECTRIC), these tracks can be bent into circles. By observing the curvature and density of the tracks and how far the particles go before they are stopped by collision with molecules of gas and water in the chamber, the masses, electric charges, and speeds of the particles can often be worked out.

When a fast particle passes through a photographic plate or film, the silver salt crystals in the PHOTOGRAPHIC EMULSION (q.v.) are changed and can be developed. Special, thick emulsions, which have the silver salt crystals small and close together, are used for detecting particles. After development and fixing, it is possible to trace with a microscope the path of a particle by a trail of grains of silver. The tracks can be followed only by the exercise of great skill and patience (Fig. 3).

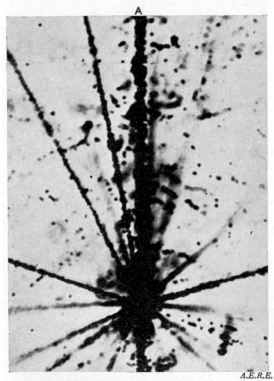

FIG. 3. NUCLEAR TRACKS IN A PHOTOGRAPHIC EMULSION

A small portion (highly magnified) of an emulsion which has been flown by balloon at about 100,000 feet to detect the cosmic radiation. A fast-moving nucleus of great energy, A, has struck the nucleus of an atom in the emulsion and shattered it, scattering particles in all directions

Particles can be detected by an 'ionization chamber'. The chamber, filled with a suitable

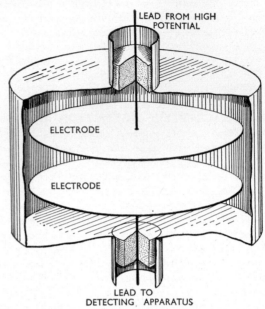

FIG. 4. A SIMPLE PARALLEL PLATE IONIZATION CHAMBER

Particles are detected if they ionize the gas between the electrodes

gas, contains two insulated metal plates known as electrodes, which are connected to a high voltage forming a circuit (Fig. 4). When a particle enters the chamber it produces ions in the gas, and these charged ions cause a very small electric current to flow through the chamber and round the electric circuit. This current can be amplified by a THERMIONIC VALVE (q.v.) and measured. With a sufficiently sensitive amplifier the effect of a single particle can be detected.

Another form of particle detector is the Geiger-Müller counter (Fig. 5). A very thin wire is surrounded by a cylindrical plate or electrode, and the space between is filled with a mixture of gases, usually argon and alcohol vapour. If the voltage of a battery connected between the wire and the cylinder is gradually increased, there comes a point when the electrons that any particle removes from the gas atoms are attracted so strongly towards the wire that they move with speeds high enough to produce more ions. The creation of these new ions may magnify the electric current a hundred times or more. The amount of current is still proportional to the number of ions first produced by the particle, and so the counter is known as a proportional counter. However, if the voltage is increased

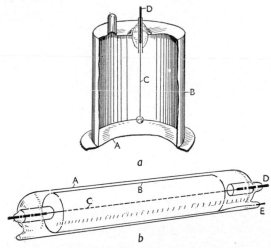

FIG. 5. TWO FORMS OF GEIGER COUNTER

(a) End window counter for beta-particles which enter through the thin window A. The metal can B acts as the electrode. C. Thin wire. D. Lead to detecting apparatus. (b) This counter is for gamma-rays which may knock an electron out of the walls into the counter. This secondary electron is detected by the counter. A. Glass envelope. B. Copper cylinder (electrode). C. Thin wire. D. Lead to detecting apparatus. E. Lead to high voltage

still further, an even larger pulse of current flows, but it is no longer proportional to the number of

ions first produced by the particle. In this condition the counter is said to be working 'in the Geiger-Müller region'. Proportional counters can deal with many more particles per minute than Geiger-Müller counters, and their current pulses can tell us something about the speed and mass of the particles; but their current pulses are much smaller, and consequently more sensitive amplifiers are needed. When it is only necessary to know how many particles are present, Geiger-Müller counters are simpler and easier to use; they can register several tens of thousands of particles per minute, and the current pulses that result are easily counted by electronic apparatus (Fig. 6). The Geiger-Müller counter is a standard piece of apparatus for work on NUCLEAR ENERGY (q.v.). If the current pulses from Geiger counters are connected to a loud-speaker after they have been amplified, the nuclear physicist can hear when particles are passing through the counter, each particle producing a loud 'tock' sound from the loud-speaker.

Neutrons are not electrically charged particles and so do not produce appreciable ionization or any other obvious effects as they pass through matter; they can be detected, therefore, only by indirect means. For example, if high-speed neutrons strike hydrogen nuclei (protons), the latter recoil at high speed and, being charged,

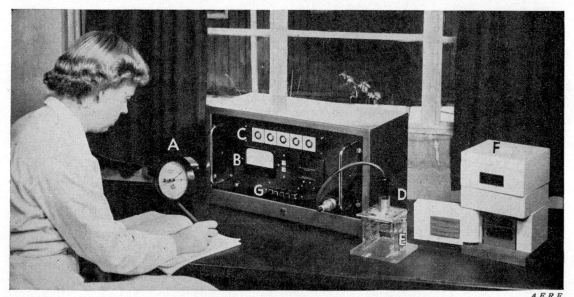

A.E.R.E.

FIG. 6. APPARATUS FOR COUNTING RADIOACTIVE SOURCES

A. Stop clock. B. Voltmeter, recording voltage on counter. C. Lights which record number of counts. D. End-window beta-particle counter. E. Plastic stand for holding specimens which are to be counted. F. Lead 'castle'. The counter is usually inside this; the lead reduces the 'background' count. G. Switches for controlling electronic apparatus

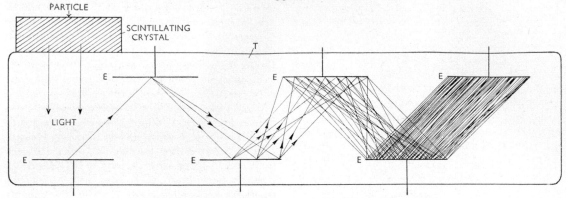

FIG. 7. THE PRINCIPLE OF THE SCINTILLATOR AND PHOTOMULTIPLIER
E. Electrodes. T. Tube from which all air has been removed

can be detected. Slow neutrons are detected by allowing them to be captured by the nuclei of the isotope boron-10; this immediately splits, and the parts fly apart at high speed and, being charged, can be detected.

Radioactive particles can also be detected by making use of the light which is emitted when fast, charged particles pass through certain substances known as scintillators. The most familiar example is the luminous paint used for watch dials, which consists of a mixture of radium and zinc sulphide, and appears to glow with a continuous light. The light really consists of a very large number of tiny flashes caused by the individual alpha-particles from the radium as they pass through zinc sulphide. An instrument known as a photomultiplier is used to detect the small flashes of light and so count the individual particles. Some of the light from the scintillator falls upon a sensitive plate, causing electrons to be emitted, which are made to bounce from one electrode to another inside a vacuum tube (Fig. 7). The electrodes are made with metal surfaces which give off extra electrons, in the end producing an electric current large enough to be measured.

Various crystals and solutions are used as scintillators. Zinc sulphide is especially suitable for alpha-particles, and anthracene for electrons and to detect fast neutrons through the recoiling nuclei of its hydrogen atoms. Sodium iodide is suitable for gamma-rays, and lithium iodide for slow neutrons, because the lithium nucleus disintegrates after capturing a neutron.

See also NUCLEAR ENERGY; HIGH-VOLTAGE PARTICLE ACCELERATORS.
See also Vol. III: ATOM.

RADIO ENGINEERING. This is concerned with the sending of signals through space by electromagnetic waves on 'wireless' principles—that is, without any wire or other electrical conductor linking the transmitter with the receiver. The radio engineer is responsible for WIRELESS TELEGRAPHY (q.v. Vol. IV), for wireless speech when used between TELEPHONE subscribers, for TELEVISION and sound broadcasting, as well as for the navigational instruments known as RADAR (qq.v.). All these depend on the same principles and general methods of transmitting and receiving high-frequency electromagnetic waves.

Radio signals are carried by waves which travel through space a million times faster than sound, and which differ from light waves only in having a very much longer wavelength; there are about 50,000 light waves to the inch, whereas anything from an inch to a mile or more may separate the crests of radio waves (see WAVELENGTHS, Vol. IV).

Radio waves are produced when a radio transmitter is joined to an aerial. The transmitter consists of electrical circuits and THERMIONIC VALVES (q.v.), so arranged that they generate a very powerful electric current which continually oscillates—that is, swings forwards and backwards, regularly reversing its direction, rather like the balance-wheel in a watch or clock.

A typical aerial is a vertical wire suspended

FIG. I. RADIO TELEGRAPH SIGNALS FROM A RADIO STATION TRANSMITTING MORSE CODE

from a high mast, in which the transmitter makes an electric current surge backwards and forwards many thousands, or even millions, of times a second. These 'high-frequency' oscillations, as they are called, cause electromagnetic waves to spread out into space in all directions from the aerial, just as waves spread out over a pond when a stick is dipped in and out of its surface. The radio waves from the transmitting aerial travel through space, and when they reach a receiving station they strike another aerial, causing an oscillating electric current to flow in it. This current, though vibrating in step with the one in the transmitting aerial, is naturally much weaker. The receiving aerial is joined to a radio receiver, which uses valves and circuits of its own to magnify the signals carried by the extremely weak aerial current until they are strong enough to work a loudspeaker.

When there are two or more transmitters, each sending different messages, the signals can be kept separate by arranging for the transmitters to work on different wavelengths, which is another way of saying that the currents in the aerials oscillate at slightly different rates. The number of to-and-fro surges made by the current in each second is its frequency, and each receiver can be adjusted to vibrate only in response to radio waves having the frequency of the selected transmitter. The process of adjusting a radio transmitter or receiver to work at one particular frequency is called 'tuning'.

A simple tuned circuit consists of a coil of wire joined to the plates of an electric CONDENSER (q.v.). If a tuned circuit is connected to a thermionic valve in a certain way, high-frequency electrical oscillations are generated (*see* HIGH-FREQUENCY CURRENTS). This arrangement, known as a thermionic valve oscillator, forms the heart of every radio transmitter.

A thermionic valve oscillator can be turned into a very simple radio transmitter by connecting an aerial to the tuned circuit and by connecting a switch or morse key to turn the oscillations on and off according to the dots and dashes of the MORSE CODE (q.v. Vol. IV). High-power radio telegraph transmitters, though naturally more complicated than this simple arrangement, work on exactly the same principle.

The signals sent out from a simple radio telegraph transmitter are shown in Fig. 1. Telephone signals can also be sent by varying the amplitude (strength) of the oscillations in sympathy with

B.B.C.

CHANGING A HIGH-POWER VALVE IN A RADIO TRANSMITTER
The valve is wheeled into position on a small trolley

the speech sound waves falling on a MICROPHONE (q.v.). The simplest way of arranging this is by connecting the microphone into the grid circuit of the oscillator valve; the signals then sent are shown in Fig. 2. The process of varying the amplitude of the oscillations in sympathy with sound, which is in general use, is called amplitude modulation or A.M. Another method of

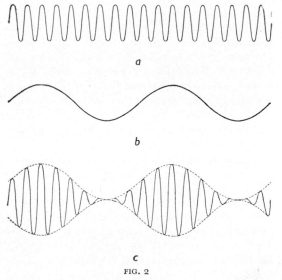

FIG. 2

a. High-frequency oscillations before being modified   *b.* Sound waves reaching microphone at radio transmitter. *c.* Transmitted signals carrying the shape of sound waves

modulation is to keep the amplitude constant and to vary the oscillation frequency in sympathy with the speech or telegraph signals. This process, called frequency modulation or F.M., has the advantage that it is less affected by atmospherics and interference; it is used in some countries for high-quality broadcasting on very short wavelengths, and is used for certain purposes by the B.B.C., and also by some British police forces (*see* TELEPHONES, MOBILE, Vol. IV).

The aerial at a radio transmitting station for medium and long wavelengths, say 500 to 1,000 metres, might consist of a horizontal 'hammock' of copper wires hung on insulators between two high masts and joined to the transmitter by a vertical wire. The high-frequency currents that

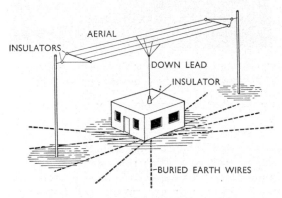

FIG. 3. DIAGRAM OF A RADIO TRANSMITTING STATION

flow in the transmitting aerial cause, by electromagnetic INDUCTION (q.v.), similar currents to flow through the ground beneath. If these 'earth currents' have to flow through the high electrical resistance offered by the soil they waste much of the transmitter's power, and so reduce the strength of its signals. A low-resistance path is, therefore, usually provided by burying a mat of copper wires beneath the aerial (Fig. 3) and connecting it to the transmitter.

Transmitting aerials for short wavelengths, say 10 to 100 metres, consist of a curtain of wires hanging on insulators between two masts. The wires are arranged in a pattern that is chosen so that the radio waves are concentrated into a powerful beam pointing in the direction of the distant place to which the signals are being sent (*see* SHORT-WAVE WIRELESS, Vol. IV).

Receiving aerials and earths are similar to transmitting ones, except that much smaller wires and insulators can be used, since currents

and voltages are very much weaker. Indeed, anyone living within a few miles of a powerful broadcasting station can receive its programmes with no aerial at all, for the circuit inside the set will act as an aerial. The signals, however, are usually rather weak, and reception may be spoiled by 'radio interference' currents produced in the circuits of the set by electromagnetic induction whenever electric currents are switched on or off in electric power wiring close by. These noises are swamped and are not troublesome when the signals are strong, and the simplest way to secure strong signals is to use a good aerial and a good earth connexion. Portable radio receivers use a different type of aerial; this consists of a large rectangular coil of wire inside the box containing the set, and no earth connexion is needed. Such an aerial, called a 'frame aerial', picks up signals best from stations in the direction in which the sides of the coil are pointing, and so the portable radio set is moved to face the way which gives the best reception from the station wanted.

When a receiving aerial is connected to a tuned circuit, the radio waves that are striking the aerial cause an oscillating current to flow in the tuned circuit; this current is very much increased when the circuit is tuned to the frequency of the radio wave, which enables the tuned circuit to select one particular frequency and reject the others. If the selected signals are amplitude-modulated by speech, a thermionic valve can be used to 'detect' these amplitude variations and to operate a loud-speaker to reproduce the original speech sounds. The circuit diagram of a simple one-valve receiver is shown in Fig. 4. The tuned

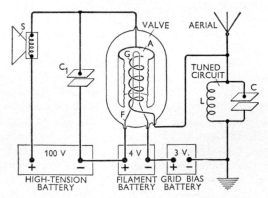

FIG. 4. CIRCUIT DIAGRAM OF A ONE-VALVE RADIO RECEIVER
L, C. Coil and condenser of tuned circuit. A. Anode, cut away to show grid G and filament of valve F. C_1. Condenser. s. Loud-speaker

circuit L, C is connected to the grid of the valve, and a negative grid-bias battery is connected so that the valve passes no anode current when no signals are being received. When oscillating signal voltages appear across the tuned circuit, anode current flows during the half-oscillations that make the grid voltage more positive, but not for those that make it more negative. The result is that the anode current flows as a number of impulses (Fig. 5b). These impulses are

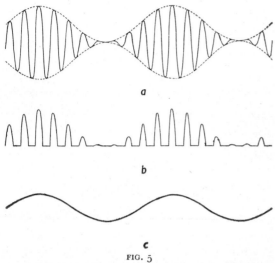

FIG. 5

a. High-frequency electric current (amplitude-modulated) in a receiver's tuned circuit. *b*. Impulses of anode current in receiver's detector valve. *c*. Smoothed current in loud-speaker winding

smoothed out by a condenser c_1, and the current that flows through the loud-speaker (Fig. 5c) produces sounds resembling those striking the microphone at the transmitter.

The whole process of sending and receiving speech by radio is illustrated in Fig. 6.

The simple type of receiver just described is called a tuned radio frequency (TRF) receiver, but, with many stations broadcasting, it cannot easily pick out stations working on wavelengths that are very close to one another. Most receivers therefore make use of the heterodyne method (*see* HIGH-FREQUENCY CURRENTS, Section 3), which alters the incoming frequency to a 'beat' or 'intermediate frequency', between the frequencies of wireless and of sound waves. This takes place in a thermionic valve known as a 'frequency changer', or 'converter'. The intermediate frequency signal, once produced by heterodyne methods, is amplified and detected as in the tuned radio frequency receiver first described.

A common type of mains receiver for broadcasting has five valves which are used as (1) frequency changer, (2) intermediate frequency amplifier, (3) detector, (4) loud-speaker amplifier, and (5) RECTIFIER (q.v.) for supplying high voltage power to the other valves. More expensive receivers have an extra valve to magnify the signals before they reach the frequency changer, and an extra intermediate-frequency amplifier valve—seven valves altogether. Four-valve receivers make do without an intermediate frequency amplifier valve. Receivers with several valves make it easy to pick up weak signals and magnify them until they are audible; but a skilful operator, using headphones and a good aerial, can receive signals in Britain from America with a set containing only one valve, such as that in Fig. 4. The valves used in radio receivers need

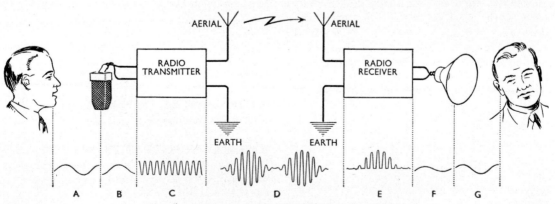

FIG. 6. DIAGRAM OF RADIO TRANSMISSION AND RECEPTION

A. Sound waves. B. Microphone current. C. High-frequency oscillations before being modulated by microphone current. D. Amplitude-modulated radio wave. E. Detector current (unsmoothed). F. Loud-speaker current. G. Sound wave

both high-voltage and low-voltage electric currents to make them work, and in mains sets the high-voltage direct current is provided through a rectifier valve. The low-voltage current for heating the cathode can be ordinary alternating current coming from a small TRANSFORMER (q.v.). Portable receivers and some others use BATTERIES (q.v.) to provide currents for the

layer. The air is electrified by the sun's rays, therefore the layers vary with the time of day and between winter and summer, and also at different times during the 11-year cycle of sunspot variations (see SUN, Vol. III). All of these variations have to be considered by radio engineers.

The range of wavelengths and frequencies

Type of wave	Typical wavelength and frequency*		Typical use
	metres	cycles per second	
Long waves or low frequencies . . .	3,000	100,000	World-wide telegraphy
Medium waves or medium frequencies .	300	1,000,000	Broadcasting
Short waves or high frequencies . . .	30	10,000,000	World-wide broadcasting, telegraphy or telephony
Ultra-short waves or very high frequencies .	6	50,000,000	Television
Microwaves	3/100	10,000,000,000	Radar

* Wavelength × frequency = the speed of light = 300 million metres per second.

TABLE OF WAVELENGTHS AND FREQUENCIES USED FOR DIFFERENT PURPOSES

valves, dry batteries being used for the high-voltage supply and accumulators for the low-voltage heater currents. These batteries must never be interchanged, as the high-voltage dry battery would fuse and destroy all the valve filaments.

Radio waves travel in straight lines, but are reflected by natural layers of electrified air high above the earth's surface to enable them to travel right round the earth. Fig. 7 shows a transmitter T and receiver R at stations some 3,000 miles apart. Were there no reflecting layers, the radio waves from T would travel into space along paths such as TAB and would never reach the receiving station R. There are sometimes three or more reflecting layers at different heights above the ground, ranging from 50 to 300 miles, but the most important is the Kennelly-Heaviside

used for different purposes by radio engineers is shown in the table above.

Long waves can be reliably transmitted all round the world. Medium waves are suitable for broadcasting over fairly short ranges—say, 100 to 200 miles by day and 400 to 500 miles by night. Short waves sometimes carry very well all round the world, but are more liable to be upset by variations in the reflecting layers than are long waves. Ultra-short waves and microwaves carry only to the horizon, say 30 to 60 miles, depending on the height of the transmitting aerial.

See also RADAR; TELEVISION ENGINEERING.
See also Vol. III: WAVE MOTION; RADIATION.
See also Vol. IV: WIRELESS TELEGRAPHY, HISTORY OF.

RADIOGRAPHY, see X-RAYS.

RADIO-SONDES, see METEOROLOGICAL INSTRUMENTS, Section 8.

RAILWAY CONSTRUCTION. 1. When a new RAILWAY (q.v. Vol. IV) is built, the preliminary work of the engineer roughly resembles that of the road builder. He has to survey large areas of country (see SURVEYING), carry out careful soil tests (see SOIL MECHANICS), and remove surface vegetation, buildings, ground irregularities, and

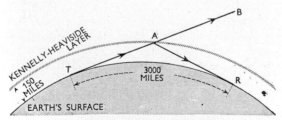

FIG. 7. THE REFLECTION OF RADIO WAVES BY ELECTRIFIED AIR ABOVE THE EARTH'S SURFACE

other obstacles with a great force of men and machines. Later, he may also have to make cuttings and tunnels through hills and mountains, erect embankments in valleys, and lay the foundations for bridges or viaducts over waterways, roads, and other railways. This work is described in the article ROAD BUILDING (q.v.).

2. DESIGNING THE TRACK. The engineer, having decided the route his railway is to take, must work out various features of the track itself. The ideal railway track is straight and level so that the locomotives do not have to pull their loads up steep gradients. For fast and heavy main-line expresses, gradients steeper than 1 in 150 are troublesome unless they are quite short, and a very steep gradient, such as the Shap bank (5 miles of 1 in 75) on the line from Crewe to Carlisle, creates special problems in locomotive design and in train operation. The 19th-century engineer and great railway builder, Isambard Kingdom Brunel, laid out the London–Bristol line with only two fairly short gradients of 1 in 100 between Swindon and Bath. In hilly country the engineer has to balance the advantages of a level track against the cost of TUNNELLING, BRIDGE BUILDING (qq.v.), and providing all the cuttings and embankments that such a line would entail. And he has to remember that the alternative, a 'cheap' line with heavy gradients and sharp curves, is costly to operate. Compromise is always necessary, and the decision is to a great extent governed by the amount of traffic the line is to carry. Only on a most important main line, for example, would the immense cost of constructing the FORTH BRIDGE (q.v. Vol. IV) be considered worthwhile.

Deciding the gauge of a railway, that is, the distance between the rails (see GAUGES, RAILWAY, Vol. IV), is also a very important calculation, for it governs not only the capital cost of the railway but also all future costs of operation and maintenance. Narrow-gauge railways are cheaper than those of wider gauge, because less land has to be bought and because the sleepers (blocks of timber which support the rails) and rolling stock are smaller. They can also have sharper, and therefore cheaper, curves, and are particularly suitable for mountainous or rugged country. On the other hand, wider gauge railways can carry heavier loads, and the LOCOMOTIVES (q.v. Vol. IV) can be designed for much greater speeds. The choice is usually governed, however, by the gauges of existing railways with which a

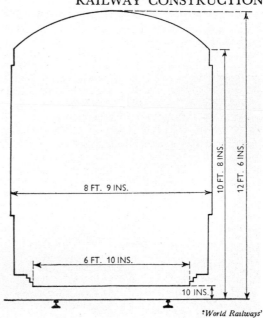

'World Railways'

FIG. I. BRITISH RAILWAYS LOADING GAUGE

new line has to connect. Most lines of British railways have a gauge of 4 feet 8½ inches, as have those of the U.S.A., Canada, and most European countries (Fig. 1).

The engineer also has to make allowances for safe clearance, that is, the space between the top and sides of vehicles and those of bridges, tunnels, and platforms. This is governed not only by the gauge and by the height and width of vehicles, but also by the vehicles' length and the curvature of the track. The body of a coach does not follow the curve of the track, but forms a straight line cutting across the arc: therefore the side of a bridge, for example, on the inside of a curve must be set back far enough to clear the side of the longest coach. The engineer must also overcome the natural tendency of a train to overturn when travelling at high speed on a curved track by raising the level of the outer rail, in the same way as 'banking' a road. This is called 'super-elevation'. To ensure smooth running at high speeds, and to avoid sudden tilts or changes of direction, both the curve and the super-elevation are generally made to start gradually, increasing to their maximum, and then 'shading off' again into a straight and level track.

3. THE RAILS. The type of rail is largely decided by the design of the locomotives, especially by the way in which the revolving and reciprocating masses of the driving gear (the connecting

FIG. 2. RAILWAY TRACKS AT ALNE, YORKSHIRE, ON THE NORTH EASTERN REGION
The left-hand track has flat-bottomed rails, and the centre track bull-head rails

FIG. 3. RELAYING A RAILWAY TRACK
The prefabricated track is being lowered into position

and coupling rods and so on) are balanced. These masses, when moving, can set up much higher impacts on the rails than the 'dead weight' of a stationary locomotive. In Britain, the 'bull-head' rail, 40 to 60 feet in length, held in 'chairs' by wooden 'keys' (Fig. 2), had a very long period of favour, though it was comparatively little used elsewhere. It is now being superseded by heavy flat-bottomed rails, 60 feet in length and weighing about 109 lb. to the yard. These are spiked to the sleepers, with a 'sole-plate' interposed between them. Pairs of 'fish-plates' are used to bolt the rails together. A small gap is left between the ends of rails to allow for EXPANSION AND CONTRACTION (q.v.) between summer and winter temperatures; the rhythmic beat of a train is caused by the wheels bumping over these gaps. In places where temperature conditions do not change very much, as in underground railways, or where the track can be held securely to resist the effect of expansion, rails are sometimes welded together in lengths up to one mile. This saves wear and tear on the rolling stock and goods and makes the train run more smoothly.

Most railway tracks have been laid by hand by large gangs of workmen. Mechanical track-laying, however, has been used for over 50 years in North America, and recently to some extent by the Eastern Region of British Railways. It is generally carried out by a special rail vehicle called a 'mobile layer', followed by one or more wagons loaded with rails, sleepers, and other parts, with a locomotive behind to push the whole unit forward after each new length of track is laid. The layer takes a number of rails and sleepers from the wagons behind it and feeds them forward roughly into position for the workmen to assemble and adjust (Fig. 3). Recently, prefabricated lengths of track have been handled in this way (*see* PREFABRICATION).

Other mechanical aids have been adopted to save labour and time while still maintaining high standards of safety. These include 'ballast cleaners' (if the ballast on which the track is laid becomes choked with dirt it will not drain properly); 'tampers' to consolidate the ballast; and smaller tools such as rail-carriers and track-jacks.

In Britain, sleepers are usually made of timber. Concrete and steel sleepers have also been tried, but concrete sleepers are generally too heavy and expensive, and steel ones are too easily corroded. Timber sleepers are preserved by being impreg-

British Railways

FIG. 4. POINTS AND CROSSOVER AT GRETNA JUNCTION, SCOTLAND, LOOKING NORTH

nated under pressure with creosote. The sleepers are laid about 2 feet 9 inches apart and are supported by a 9-inch layer of broken stone or clinker which forms the bottom ballast of the base (or 'formation') on which the track is laid. The top ballast of granite, slag, or limestone is added to fill up the space between the sleepers. Good drainage for rain-water all along the track is essential.

Points and crossings are usually prefabricated; to ensure sufficient accuracy they are first laid out and tested in a yard set aside for the purpose. Switches (or points) have movable 'tongues', which taper at one end to fit against the main 'stock' rail, and are joined together by tie-bars connected to the signalling gear; the signalling gear moves the tongues from one rail to the other, deflecting the train in the required direction. So that the wheel flanges of a train can pass through the junctions, gaps have to be left in certain places; if the angle between two crossing rails is very acute, these gaps are large (Fig. 4). To check the extra freedom thus given to the wheels, and to keep the flanges of the wheels to their proper path, 'check rails' are introduced. Check rails are also used on curves of less than about 600 feet radius in order to keep the wheels on the inner rail in place and to reduce the thrust on the outer rail.

In cold climates, where heavy drifts of snow can block the track, snow sheds are sometimes built over the track, or fences which create upward currents of air and so reduce the fall of snow. On railways built on mountain sides, more substantial snow sheds often have to be erected to protect the tracks from avalanches.

4. ELECTRIC RAILWAYS. The construction of ELECTRIC RAILWAYS (q.v. Vol. IV) is no different from that for steam trains, except that a conductor is necessary to transmit the electric power to the motors of trains. For lower voltages this conductor can be a third rail, generally outside the running rails, and mounted on insulated pedestals bolted to the sleepers. If the voltage is over about 800, an overhead wire is used. The pillars which support this wire need concrete foundations.

The return circuit is almost always effected through the wheels and running rails, the gaps at joints between rails being bridged with copper wire or strip to prevent a break in the electric circuit. An exception is the London UNDERGROUND RAILWAY (q.v. Vol. IV), where the return circuit is made through a fourth rail laid between the running rails.

See also ROAD BUILDING; RAILWAY ROLLING STOCK.
See also Vol. IV: RAILWAYS, HISTORY OF; RAILWAY SYSTEMS.

RAILWAY ROLLING STOCK. 1. As distinct from the constructional aspects of the permanent way, bridges, and tunnels, and the architectural work involved in building stations, warehouses, and offices (*see* RAILWAY CONSTRUCTION), the railway engineer is chiefly concerned with the design, manufacture, and maintenance of signalling and allied equipment (*see* SIGNALLING, RAILWAY, Vol. IV) and of rolling stock.

Broadly, this comprises LOCOMOTIVES, RAILWAY COACHES, and GOODS TRAINS (qq.v. Vol. IV) for both steam-operated and electric railways, and all the other equipment such as ballast and service vehicles, BREAKDOWN TRAINS (q.v. Vol. IV), inspection cars, and works CRANES (q.v.). It also includes the machinery needed for keeping all these vehicles in running order, such as turntables, wagon tipplers for coaling plant, water troughs, water cranes, special devices such as lifting tackle for locomotives and vehicles (*see* ENGINE-SHEDS, RAILWAY, Vol. IV). In addition,

there is the very extensive plant required for the building and periodic overhaul of both engines and rolling stock.

2. LOCOMOTIVES. In Great Britain these are usually built at the railway executives own workshops, though some may be built according to the railways' designs by private locomotive-building firms. Such firms, however, are mainly concerned with building locomotives, carriages, and wagons for export.

The design of a locomotive occupies several expert draughtsmen for many months, and when the detailed drawings are ready, they are sent to the various workshops for pattern-making and construction to begin. Locomotive construction follows a fairly well-defined sequence of operations. Machining of the frame plates and cylinders, connecting and coupling rods, and so on proceeds while the BOILER (q.v.) is being made in the boiler shop. Then all the items are assembled in the erecting shop. After completion, the engine goes to the paint shop. A trial run then follows, after which the locomotive is ready for traffic. When periodic repairs are needed, usually after a certain mileage has been completed, the engine is almost completely dismantled, and the components are returned to the boiler or machine shops for repairs.

A locomotive works, with all its extensive machinery, tool rooms, fitters' benches, erecting shops, and repair pits, takes a great deal of space. Many of the shops must contain overhead cranes for lifting engines, boilers, wheels, and heavy components. The boiler shop must have its own shears, rolls, and punching and riveting gear, as well as furnaces for heating the steel and copper plates for the fireboxes, smokebox doors, and so on.

3. RAILWAY COACH CONSTRUCTION. This needs nearly as much space as locomotive building because more coaches are needed than locomotives, and because coaches are so long (55–70 ft.). The underframes are usually of steel and need bending, drilling, and punching machines for their construction. The carriage works generally have their own wheel shops and axle bays. As a great deal of timber is used in the body-work, a sawmill with circular and band saws and tenoning and 'moulding' machines (*see* WOODWORKING MACHINERY) is an important part of the works. Adjacent to the body-building shop are the sections dealing with upholstery, arm-rests, luggage racks, and other fittings, and

LOWERING A LOCOMOTIVE ON TO ITS WHEELS AT THE LOCOMOTIVE WORKS, DONCASTER

British Railways

LOWERING A BODY ON TO BOGIES AT THE CARRIAGE WORKS,
DONCASTER

the departments for the lighting, dynamos, brakes, and steam heating. In the lifting shop the body and underframe assembly is placed on wheels and bogies; this shop is also used for the removal of bogies from vehicles needing overhaul. Besides all these workshops there is a carriage paint shop in which a constant temperature is kept to quicken the drying.

4. RAILWAY WAGON CONSTRUCTION. There are many different types of railway wagons, and as they are usually needed in far larger numbers than locomotives or coaches, mass-production methods are more easily used for making and repairing them. Apart from special-purpose vehicles, such as milk tanks or cattle trucks (*see* TRAINS, SPECIAL USES, Vol. IV), most wagons in Britain are of simple, open, four-wheeled patterns, and are of much smaller capacity than those in use in America or on the Continent. The latest British types have a capacity of 16 tons. There are also the box or closed wagons, normally fitted with side doors for hand loading, fish vans, refrigerator vans for perishable traffic, and flat wagons for carrying timber and other long articles.

In wagon construction the under-frame is assembled first; then the body is made ready and lowered on to it; the axle guards are attached; and the vehicle is then ready for wheeling. The stresses set up in shunting and in the starting and stopping of goods trains are very severe, especially in Britain where most of such trains have no continuous BRAKES (q.v. Vol. IV). Consequently the wagon bodies have to be very strong, and in recent years WELDING (q.v.) has become a recognized method of joining together the component parts.

5. ELECTRIC ROLLING STOCK CONSTRUCTION. The first important ELECTRIC RAILWAYS (q.v. Vol. IV), now over 60 years old in Britain, were the early Tube lines, the stock for which had to be built to smaller dimensions than ordinary railways, because of the restricted tunnel diameter. Separate locomotives, using direct current, were provided for the City and South London Tube (1890); the Waterloo and City line (1898) had electric motors built into some of the coaches, the other coaches being 'trailers'. In Britain 'built-in' motive-power units have proved more popular than separate locomotives. These have 'multiple-unit' control, that is, one driver can control the current supply and the braking throughout the whole train. The very heavy inner urban traffic of the London Transport Executive, and the dense suburban traffic of the Southern Region, are worked by multiple-unit types of trains taking direct current from a live rail. More recently the Liverpool Street and Shenfield line has been provided with multiple-unit trains collecting current from overhead conductors, a system used by the North-Eastern in 1905 for the Newport and Shildon line (now worked by steam locomotives). The 7,000-volt alternating-current overhead lines of the old London, Brighton, and South Coast Railway have long been abandoned in favour of the third-rail direct-current system. Alternating-current electric traction, however, is used in several countries on the Continent.

Much of the workshop equipment for the construction and repair of electric trains resembles that of locomotive and carriage works. No boiler shop is required; but numbers of men are needed for the rewinding of armatures, for the repair and testing of electric motors, and for such things as control equipment, current collectors, and air-operated doors. In large works, such as at Acton (London Transport), where a good deal of standardization has been carried out, a motor-car or a trailer-car is 'progressed' through the works in a very short time, many of the standard items of equipment being simply taken from stock.

6. Maintenance Work. In both steam and electric railways, much additional equipment is needed for the maintenance of the rolling stock in regular service. Steam locomotives need water cranes and water troughs and, nowadays, water-softening apparatus for these supplies. The coaling plant at running sheds needs its wagon tipplers to discharge the coal into the hopper forming the 'reservoir' from which incoming engines are replenished. Locomotives need vacuum apparatus for removing ashes from the smoke-box, and furnaces for drying the sand used for preventing wheel slip. The running sheds may also have wheel-drops—hydraulically operated platforms which enable a pair of wheels to be removed from a locomotive for servicing. Electric trains need special attention in respect of current collectors, control equipment, the testing of air-operated doors, renewal of brake blocks, checking of batteries for emergency lighting, and so on; in addition the lifts and escalators of Tube railways have to be maintained, and work on these often can be done only at night.

See also Vol. IV: Railways, History of; Locomotives; Engine-sheds, Railway.

RAIN-GAUGE, *see* Meteorological Instruments, Section 5.

RANGE-FINDERS. These are used to measure the range of distant objects—a ship at sea, for example, or an aeroplane. The principle of operation makes use of a right-angled triangle: if the length of the base is known and one acute angle can be measured, then the lengths of the other sides can be calculated. Thus in the triangle ABC (Fig. 1a), if the base length BC is known and angle C can be measured, then the length AB can be calculated by simple Trigonometry (q.v.). In optical range-finders the base BC is fixed, and the observer sees two views of the object at A, one by the direction BA and the other by CA. It is from the inclination of these two directions of view, that is, angle A, that the distance AB is derived. Such instruments are of two types, 'coincidence' and 'stereoscopic'.

The principle of the coincidence range-finder is shown in Fig. 1b. The observer uses one eye only to view with a Telescope (q.v.) the object A whose distance is to be found; by means of the four mirrors two images are seen in the field of view, and by suitably tilting one of the mirrors at B or C these two images can be superimposed so that one sharp image only is seen. The mechanism which tilts the mirror can be fitted with a scale to give the distance of the target on which the coincidence setting has been made. In more elaborate instruments, the two images are not formed on top of each other, but close to each other in separate parts of the field of view. In one type, an object such as a flagstaff appears to be divided into two parts by a line across the middle of the field: in measuring the range of the staff the mirror is tilted until the two halves are in line—that is, one continuous staff is seen. The coincidence range-finder can be used with accuracy after only a little practice, and is built into many Cameras (q.v.) so that the picture

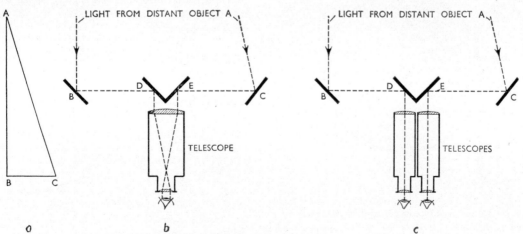

FIG. 1. *a.* RIGHT-ANGLED TRIANGLE. *b.* COINCIDENCE RANGE-FINDER. *c.* STEREOSCOPIC RANGE-FINDER
A. Distant object. B, C, D, E. Mirrors

may be sharply focused on to the plate or film without measuring the distance of the objects and setting the lens position on a scale. As the range-finder is operated, the lens is automatically set into the correct position to focus the object to be photographed.

The principle of the stereoscopic range-finder is shown in Fig. 1c. This is a binocular instrument, that is, each eye views the target through a separate telescope. When the instrument is pointed at a distant object, the eyes focus on the two images and converge so that the two images are fused into one. This is the normal process by which, without instruments, we are able to judge the relative distances of objects which we see (*see* STEREOSCOPE). By arranging in the fields of view of the telescope eyepieces suitable ranging marks, two of which are fused for each particular amount of convergence of the eyes, the distance of the target can be measured. There are, in principle, no moving parts in stereoscopic range-finders, and measuring distances can be a rapid process. They are difficult to use, however, and require considerable training before accurate measurements of distance can be made.

RATCHET. This is a toothed wheel or bar which, together with a 'pawl', a single tooth carried on a pivot, is used as a way of stopping a part of a mechanism when necessary. The pawl engages between a pair of teeth on the ratchet, so preventing its movement. For example, when a hand-winch lifts a bucket from a well (*see* CRANES, Section 2), the bucket is raised by a

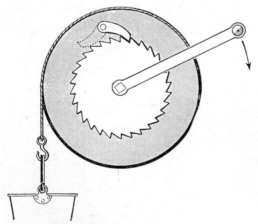

FIG. 1. RATCHET ON DRUM OF WELL

The pawl, which is fixed to the drum support, is holding the wheel. The dotted line shows its position when the bucket descends

rope coiled around a drum which is rotated by a crank handle. If the handle is released, however, the weight of the bucket will reverse the mechanism. To prevent this a ratchet wheel with teeth shaped like those of a circular saw is fitted at one end of the drum (Fig. 1). Whilst the weight is being lifted, the pawl trails loosely over the teeth, but immediately the turning is stopped it engages one of the ratchet teeth. Ships' capstans and windlasses are similarly equipped.

Sometimes the pivot carrying the pawl is itself able to rotate; for example, in the free-wheel of a bicycle the pawl is carried in a ring driven by the chain, while the ratchet is part of the spindle in the rear hub. When the bicycle is

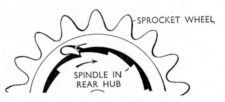

FIG. 2. BICYCLE FREE-WHEEL

pedalled, the pawl engages with a tooth in the ratchet, as in the 'stop' position of the well winch; but when the pedalling is stopped, the pawl rides loosely over the teeth (Fig. 2). In the screw-driver and hand-brace the 'free wheel' device is made reversible, the teeth being symmetrical, not sawlike, as the pawl has to engage in two directions.

The winding mechanisms of CLOCKS AND WATCHES (q.v.) make use of the ratchet and pawl, as does the household spring-blind, where the pawls disengage only when the blind is raised or lowered.

RECIPROCATING ENGINES, *see* INTERNAL COMBUSTION ENGINE.

RECTIFIER. This is an electrical device for converting ALTERNATING CURRENT (q.v.), or A.C., which flows to-and-fro in an electric circuit, into direct current, or D.C., which flows always in the same direction (*see* ELECTRIC CURRENT). Almost all the electric power generated today is produced as A.C., and rectifiers are used when D.C. is needed. Rectifiers operate by preventing electric currents from flowing freely in more than one direction, in this way converting the to-and-fro surges of A.C. into rather

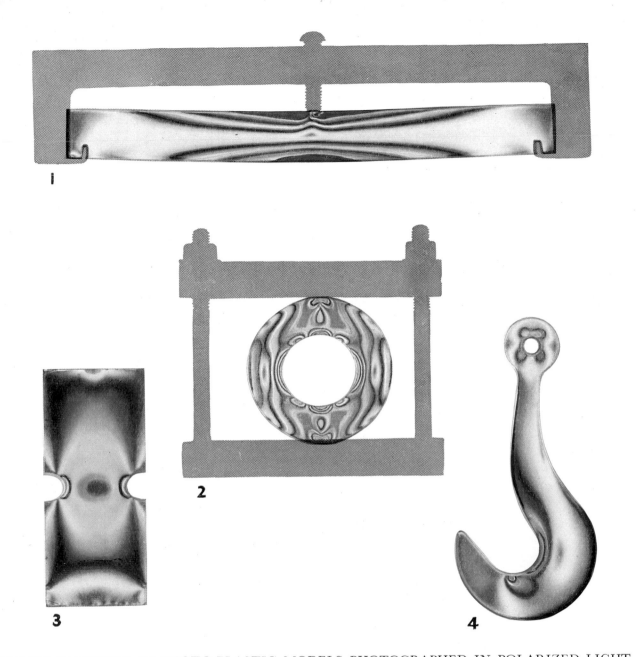

FRINGE PATTERNS IN PHOTO-ELASTIC MODELS PHOTOGRAPHED IN POLARIZED LIGHT

1. A bar in a straining frame under direct load from the screw in the centre. 2. A ring in a straining frame under direct load at the top and bottom. 3. A slice cut through a cylinder with a semicircular groove in which the stresses have been 'frozen' to render permanent the pattern obtained under load. The pattern shows that the cylinder is weakest near the groove. 4. A hook which had a weight hung from it and was then 'frozen'. In general, black regions represent regions of zero stress. Successive coloured fringes, crossed in the direction from red to blue (or from pink to green), indicate successive equal increases in stress, and regions in which the fringes are crowded and of pale colour represent regions of high stress. Thus in 1, starting from the black zero patch in the centre and moving downwards, we cross successively the first, second, and third fringes, representing 1, 2, and 3 units of stress; the stress at the bottom edge is about $3\frac{1}{2}$ units. On the inner boundary of the ring there are four points of zero stress, while the highest stresses are nearly 5 units at the side and nearly 6 at the top

fluctuating surges in one direction only. The most common type of rectifier is the diode valve (*see* Thermionic Valves), which is widely used to produce high-tension direct current supplies in Radio and Television transmitters and receivers (qq.v.).

The mercury-arc rectifier, a kind of diode valve used where high powers are wanted, has a pool of liquid mercury for its cathode or negative part (Fig. 1) and two or more metal anodes or positive parts, the whole being in a large bulb of glass or steel from which the air has been removed. When an alternating voltage is applied between the anodes and the cathode, an electric arc (a continuous spark of intense heat) occurs,

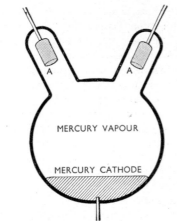

FIG. 1. DIAGRAM OF MERCURY ARC RECTIFIER

A. Anodes

and the current is able to flow through this arc from anode to cathode only, as in the ordinary diode valve. But this current is carried by electrified mercury atoms as well as by electrons, and so a much stronger current flows than in the ordinary diode. Mercury-arc rectifiers are used to provide direct current for the arc lamps in cinema projectors and for the motors of electric trains.

The simplest type of metal rectifier is made by heating a copper sheet in air, so that the air attacks the hot copper and, combining with it chemically, forms a thin film of copper oxide covering its surface. This film, when properly prepared, allows current to flow freely in one direction only. The rectifiers are made by bolting together a number of disks cut from the oxidized copper sheet, with soft lead washers between for good electrical contact (Fig. 2). Metal rectifiers

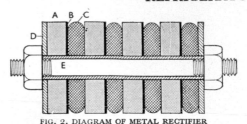

FIG. 2. DIAGRAM OF METAL RECTIFIER

A. Copper disks. B. Copper oxide film. C. Lead washers
D. Insulating washer. E. Insulating sleeve

are used, for example, in garages to charge car batteries and in dairies to charge the batteries of the milk delivery vans from the alternating current mains.

See also Electric Current; Thermionic Valve.

REFRACTORIES, *see* Fireclays and Refractories.

REFRIGERATOR. Refrigeration means, simply, cooling (Latin *frigidus*, 'cold'); but to an engineer it means cooling by machine. There is no natural way of getting something to become colder than its surroundings—in fact, heat will not of its own accord flow from a cool thing to another at a higher temperature. If we dip a red-hot poker into a bucket of water, the poker is cooled and the water is heated as heat flows from the hotter poker into the colder water. It would be against common sense as well as contrary to the Second Law of Thermodynamics (*see* Heat Engines) for the heat to flow the other way.

But the refrigerator does, in fact, make heat flow the wrong way, for it cools the things put into it below the temperature of their surroundings, the kitchen; and to do this it uses energy—in the case of the electric refrigerator, electrical energy from the mains. The ordinary domestic refrigerator makes use of the fact that when any liquid is evaporating (that is, changing into a gas) it always absorbs heat from its surroundings, which consequently become colder (*see* Liquefaction of Gases). If a liquid, therefore, in the refrigerator box can be made to evaporate continuously, the temperature in the refrigerator can be kept lower than the temperature outside. For this a special chemical is used which turns conveniently from a gas into a liquid and back.

The ordinary domestic electric refrigerator works in this way. An electric motor drives a small air Compressor (q.v.), which sucks in the

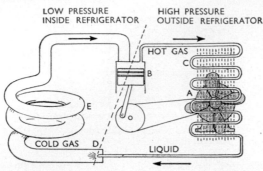

LOW PRESSURE INSIDE REFRIGERATOR   HIGH PRESSURE OUTSIDE REFRIGERATOR

HOT GAS

COLD GAS   LIQUID

FIG. I. DIAGRAM OF AN ELECTRIC REFRIGERATOR

A. Motor. B. Compressor. C. Condensing coils which liquefy gas. The coils are cooled by a fan on the motor. D. Expansion nozzle. E. Coils round frost-box

chemical in the form of a gas and compresses it. The compressor, which is rather like a bicycle pump in principle, heats up as it compresses the gas, much as the pump heats up if pumped hard enough—the energy of compressing (or pumping) turning to heat. This heat prevents the highly compressed gas from liquefying until it has passed through coils of piping in contact with the ordinary temperature of the kitchen; there its heat is dissipated in the kitchen, and the gas liquefies. At this stage the liquid is forced under its high pressure through a fine nozzle into a much larger pipe inside the refrigerator box which winds round the frost-box. The pressure in this pipe is so much lower that the liquid evaporates and becomes a gas again, at the same time absorbing the heat from whatever is in the frost-box and the refrigerator itself, so that these things are cooled down. The gas then passes back to the compressor to be used again, and the process continues. For the sake of clearness the diagram illustrates a rather old-fashioned type of domestic refrigerator—the modern ones have the motor and compressor combined into a single unit sealed into a metal casing to keep out air, dirt, and moisture.

If we consider how heat flows in a refrigerator, we shall discover something rather unexpected. In the evaporator pipe, the gas absorbs a certain amount of heat (h units) from whatever is in the refrigerator. At the compressor, the gas absorbs further heat (H units) from the pressure of the pump, originally derived from the mains as electrical energy. In the cooling coils, the gas liquefies and gives up all this heat ($H+h$ units)— partly H units as it cools down to kitchen temperature, and partly h units as it liquefies. The

actual values of H (energy) and h (heat) depend on the size of the apparatus and the working conditions, but the important thing is that all the energy from the mains, and any heat removed from the inside of the refrigerator, are going to warm up the air in the kitchen. This means that if we open the refrigerator door and switch on, the kitchen will get warmer, not colder as we might have expected. The practical use of this principle on a much larger scale for heating buildings is seen in the HEAT PUMP (q.v.).

In the household refrigerator, a THERMOSTAT (q.v.) starts and stops the compressor according to the temperature in the frost-box. Sometimes frost collects round the evaporation pipe. Frost is a bad conductor of heat, and interferes with the flow of heat from the inside of the refrigerator to the evaporating gas. Most refrigerators, therefore, possess a 'defrosting' switch, which allows warm gas from the condenser coils to pass into the evaporator pipe and thaw any frost.

All refrigerators, large and small, work on the principle described above and, with one exception, they all use a compressor with cooling and evaporator coils. In the exception, the 'mixed-vapour' type of refrigerator, the energy is supplied direct as heat—not as mechanical energy; so that domestic refrigerators of this type can run equally well on electricity, gas, or paraffin. They use an electric heating coil or a small gas or paraffin burner to supply the heat, and there are no moving parts. The heat flow is exactly the same as in the mechanical refrigerator, but more than one gas is used and the principle of operation is rather more complicated.

The special gas ('Arcton') used by domestic refrigerators is a complex chemical containing fluorine, chlorine, carbon, and hydrogen. It is non-poisonous, liquefies at a reasonable pressure at kitchen temperatures, and has a high 'latent heat'—that is, it absorbs a lot of heat when it changes from liquid to gas. Larger industrial refrigerators may use ammonia, sulphur dioxide, or carbon dioxide, ammonia being the most common. It is both safer and more efficient in these large plants not to circulate the evaporating ammonia liquid gas round the freezing pipes, but to use the ammonia evaporator coils to cool brine, which in turn is circulated in pipes round the meat storage room, or skating rink, or whatever it may be.

See also HEAT PUMP; LIQUEFACTION OF GASES; ENERGY; HEAT ENGINES.

RESERVOIR, *see* WATER SUPPLY; DAMS.

RESISTANCE, ELECTRICAL, *see* ELECTRIC CURRENT, Section 3.

RIVETING. This is a method of joining either metals or non-metals together by a form of permanent clamping. The rivets are inserted and hammered home, after which the joint cannot be undone except by cutting or in some other way destroying the rivets.

The simplest kind of rivet which is in common use is the paper-binding clip or staple used in binding exercise books and thin booklets with paper covers. The sheaf of paper (Fig. 1) is held together by the wire which is forced through it

FIG. 1. PAPER CLIP: A SIMPLE FORM OF RIVET

and then bent over on itself. The same general method is used in riveting together the edges of broken china ornaments with small wire insertions—a very skilled operation.

For heavier kinds of work the mushroom-type rivet (Fig. 2) is used. It may be made either of a soft metal such as copper or aluminium, in which case it is hammered home cold, or of steel, which is generally heated to a red heat before being inserted. Holes are first bored in the pieces to be riveted; the rivet is then inserted with the shank (the stalk of the mushroom) protruding through the holes and out on the other side. The head of the rivet is pressed firmly in while the end of the shank is either squeezed or beaten so that it swells outwards and forms another head on the opposite side. In this way the two pieces are securely clamped together.

The brake and clutch linings of a motor-car are secured to the 'shoes' by means of copper rivets which are easily put in cold and secured

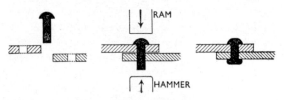

FIG. 2. DIAGRAM OF RIVETING

with a hand hammer as follows. Copper is a soft metal which is readily deformed with light blows, and when the linings have to be renewed it is a relatively simple matter to pull the old worn-out ones away, cut out the old rivets, and rivet fresh linings in their place. Cold riveting, using small, soft, metal rivets, is also widely applied to the manufacture of light machinery, electrical apparatus, and toys.

By far the most important application of mushroom-type riveting, however, is the hot riveting of steel plates with steel rivets in the shipbuilding and heavy engineering trades. The steel plates forming the hull of a ship are often riveted to each other and to the ship's frame (ribs); the plates of a locomotive boiler and firebox are riveted; and the heavy steel girders of bridges may often be made up of steel plates riveted one on top of the other to give the necessary thickness. The rivets are heated in a small furnace to a red heat, then passed up (or even thrown) to the 'catcher', who inserts them in the hole; the 'holder-on' then presses a ram firmly against the head, while the 'riveter', on the other side of the job, hammers the protruding shank with a small compressed-air machine to round it over and secure the rivet. As the hot rivet cools, it contracts, making the joint even stronger.

Steel rivets must be heated carefully and used at the right temperature. If they get too hot they may be 'burnt', in which case the shank may crack under the blows of the hammer; if they are put in too cold the steel may not be sufficiently soft to undergo the hammering treatment; or it may become slightly brittle, so that when it cools and contracts it is unable to withstand the stress and breaks in half.

Aluminium alloy rivets play an important part in securing aluminium alloy sheets in aircraft making. Many aluminium alloys tend to 'age-harden', that is, grow harder after a short period at an ordinary temperature, and to stop this happening to the rivets (which would make them too hard to hammer home) they are kept in a soft state in a refrigerator (*see* HEAT TREATMENT, Section 6). After riveting, the aluminium alloy rivets are allowed to age-harden and so strengthen the joint.

'Pop' riveting is also used in aircraft construction. A hollow rivet is used, and is secured by a device which holds it in position and causes it suddenly to expand and shorten, gripping the metal plates as if it had been hammered from

Holman Bros.

RIVETING A STEEL GIRDER WITH A PNEUMATIC RIVETING HAMMER
The 'holder on' can be seen behind the riveter

both sides. This avoids having to get at the inside of the joint, which, in the case of aircraft wings, for example, is often impossible.

'Explosive' rivets have also been used for 'blind' riveting; these contain a small explosive charge which goes off when the rivet is struck, and opens out the rivet on the inside of the hole.

See also WELDING; SHIPBUILDING; AERONAUTICAL ENGINEERING.

ROAD BUILDING. 1. This is the greatest contribution that CIVIL ENGINEERING (q.v.) has made to the history of civilization. From earliest times overland trade and communications have depended primarily upon roads. Some of the great ROADS (q.v. Vol. IV) of the Chinese Empire ran for over 2,000 miles; at the peak of its power the Roman Empire possessed more than 50,000 miles of excellent ROMAN ROADS (q.v. Vol. IV), radiating from the capital to its farthest dominions. Though built for military purposes, these roads of Imperial China and Rome spread culture and trade through parts of three continents, and accelerated the growth of the historic TRADE ROUTES (q.v. Vol. IV), which linked the nations. Today, the maker of roads is no less important, for with the development of the INTERNAL COMBUSTION ENGINE (q.v.) many types of traffic can move more cheaply and efficiently by road than by the great railways and waterways, which reached their peak of importance in the 19th century. In a highly developed country existing roads must be kept efficient and when necessary rebuilt; and the resources of a newly developed area cannot be exploited without first-class roads.

When opening up new territory, especially in mountainous districts, a road builder is often faced with tremendous tasks. In 1950, for example, work began on a new road in Venezuela, from the seaport of La Guaira to Caracas, the capital, which lies 3,000 feet above sea-level. This work will involve spectacular engineering feats, such as building three of the largest concrete bridges in the world (*see* p. 40), two twin-bore tunnels (one over a mile long), and cuttings some 300 feet deep. About one million cubic yards of material, 60% being rock, will be excavated per mile. The road will have four to six traffic lanes, and though only $10\frac{1}{2}$ miles long, it will cost about £20 million.

2. PLANNING THE ROUTE. When considering a project for a new road in undeveloped country it is advisable to find out by an economic survey the route which will best meet the agricultural and industrial needs of the community. The cost of constructing and maintaining a road, including bridges and other permanent structures, is repaid largely from the trade resulting from the traffic which uses the road.

The location of a new road used to be a most difficult and lengthy operation. Today, however, the development of aerial reconnaissance and photography has done much to simplify the work, particularly in wooded or mountainous country. Stereoscopic aerial photographs (*see* SURVEYING) enable the engineer to examine the ground over a wide area and to draw contoured maps on which he can plan various routes. With the help of these photographs and maps and personal reconnaissance over the ground he can select a route, at any rate provisionally, and can make some estimate of costs.

When the engineer's provisional plans are approved, a strip of ground is cleared along the route so that a team of surveyors can carry out a survey of sections of the ground, and a detailed investigation of foundations, called a soils survey, can be made (*see* SOIL MECHANICS). Generally, when the soil does not provide an adequate support for the weight of traffic, the work is more expensive, so that the direction of a road is partly governed by the suitability of the soil for foundations.

On this final survey the engineer's construction plans and designs are based. The placing of bridges, cuttings, and embankments, drainage problems, the final alignment and length of the route, and the radius of curves must all be considered in detail. Cuttings should be so planned that as much as possible of the excavated soil can be used for building embankments, so saving the expense of importing additional materials. The sharpness of curves and the steepness of gradients will decide the safe speed of the traffic. Safety largely depends on a driver's range of vision together with the distance within which he can pull up, and on modern roads drivers should be given a clear view 600 feet ahead. Another important factor is the tendency of a vehicle to overturn when going round a corner; to overcome this the road surface should be banked so as to help the vehicle to make the turn.

Crown Copyright

FIG. I. LEVELLING AND PREPARING THE SITE FOR A ROAD

Crown Copyright

FIG. 2. COMPACTING A ROAD WITH A PNEUMATIC-TIRED ROLLER

Crown Copyright

FIG. 3. SURFACING A ROAD WITH ASPHALT

Figs. 1, 2, and 3 by permission of the Road Research Laboratory of the Department of Scientific and Industrial Research

To prevent the underlying soil becoming waterlogged and embankments being washed away, drains must be provided to take away rain water. Bridges and culverts passing under the road are designed to allow water to drain away from both the road and the surrounding country-side. The engineer also tries to blend his route into the landscape, and he often plants trees, shrubs, and grass beside it.

These same principles are applied when improving or rebuilding an existing road. In such cases the preliminary examination is much more detailed than in open country, and there is a thorough examination of such things as land ownership, existing rights of way, cables, water-mains, and the levels of surrounding property.

3. BUILDING THE ROAD. When the engineer has finally decided on the most suitable route, a team of men and machines, including heavy EARTH-MOVING EQUIPMENT (q.v.), moves in to clear the ground of vegetation, trees, buildings, and other obstacles, and to level the surface ready for the foundations of the road. The ground is made more level and too steep gradients avoided by removing the soil in some places to make 'cuttings', and by building embankments in others to carry the road above the level of the surrounding country. Shallow cuttings are usually made by graders or skimmer excavators, but for deeper cuttings mechanical excavators or heavy scrapers are used, the material being carried away from the excavators in lorries or by light railways; if scrapers are used they can do the whole operation themselves. Ahead of this work, bridges and drains should be constructed so that the embankments may be built over the pipes. The embankments should consist of successive layers of earth, each 6 inches deep, consolidated and compacted by suitable heavy rollers. The most useful roller for this type of work is the 'wobbly wheel'; this consists of a heavily loaded superstructure running on a number of inflated rubber-tired wheels. The layers are further consolidated by the continual traffic of tractors and scrapers passing over them. A stable foundation (called the 'formation') for the surface of the road (the 'pavement') is fashioned by similar rollers and graders. Laboratory tests are conducted all the time to make sure that the materials used are satisfactory and that embankments and formation are sufficiently compact.

4. THE ROAD SURFACE. When designing the 'pavement' the engineer must consider the

A REINFORCED CONCRETE ROAD WITH PRECAST CONCRETE CURB AND PRECAST REINFORCED CONCRETE LAMP STANDARDS

weight and number of the vehicles which are expected to pass over it and the stability of the soil foundation. On these depend the strength, thickness, and method of construction of the pavement, which transmits the whole traffic load to the soil below.

In agricultural areas the pavement may consist simply of gravel or a similar natural substance. For heavier traffic, however, a layer of quarried crushed stone, rolled and bound with bitumen or tar, is provided; or, alternatively, concrete slabs reinforced to withstand the heaviest wheel loads. Whichever method is used, it is vital that the foundation is drained and protected from water. The verges or shoulders at the sides of the road are so constructed and drained that they do not suffer erosion by water draining off the pavement.

Gravel pavements, or those constructed with waterbound stone, as in MACADAM ROADS (q.v. Vol. IV), may be protected by tar or bitumen sprayed on the surface and covered with a layer of small gravel or stone chippings. Similarly, pavements constructed with suitably graded quarried stone can be bound and waterproofed by mixing the material with bitumen, asphalt, or tar. When laid and rolled, such a mixture is extremely hard wearing, and is more flexible than concrete. These types of pavements are supported along both edges by suitable kerbs, or haunches, able to withstand the outward pressure of the pavement and to prevent damage to the edges of the pavement by wheels or by erosion.

CONCRETE (q.v.) pavements are generally reinforced, and divided into short lengths to guard against EXPANSION AND CONTRACTION (q.v.) caused by changes in temperature. Such pavements are expensive to build, but they have a long life and are particularly suitable when very heavy traffic has to be carried; they have been much used for arterial roads, for example. Maintaining the expansion joints in the concrete is troublesome, however, and the movement of the joints makes it difficult to surface the road later on with asphalt. Concrete pavements scarcely ever appear in highly developed areas, though concrete is much used in preparing the foundations for an asphalt or bitumen surface. In this case the concrete is usually not reinforced as the road has to be opened from time to time for laying pipes, drains, cables, and so on.

See also Vol. IV: ROADS; ROADS, BRITISH; ROADS, MODERN; ROMAN ROADS.

ROCKET PROPULSION.

The rocket is an ancient device, originating in Asia several hundred years ago and finding some European military uses as far back as the Napoleonic wars. Early this century its serious scientific study was revived, and this system of propulsion is now becoming of increasing importance for SUPERSONIC FLIGHT and HIGH-ALTITUDE FLIGHT, for possible attempts at INTER-PLANETARY TRAVEL (qq.v. Vol. IV), and for GUIDED MISSILES (q.v. Vol. X) such as the German V2 used in the Second World War.

The rocket motor is a type of jet propulsion engine (see AIRCRAFT ENGINES, Section 4, Vol. IV), carrying within itself all the materials required to generate its propulsive jet—unlike other HEAT ENGINES (q.v.) which use the oxygen of the surrounding air. The rocket motor's forward thrust is the result of the mechanical reaction or 'push' which occurs when its exhaust gases are ejected backwards, and this is actually slightly increased in a vacuum because there is no atmospheric back pressure on its nozzle to slow down these exhaust gases.

The chemical substances used in rocket motors

Glenn L. Martin Co.

THE U.S. NAVY'S 'MARTIN VIKING' HIGH-ALTITUDE RESEARCH ROCKET

This Viking's liquid oxygen and ethyl alcohol rocket engine burned for 75 seconds, and in that time it had reached an altitude of 25 miles. Its impetus carried it without further power to a height of 135 miles, which it reached in 4 minutes 23 seconds

are called propellants. 'Solid-propellant' rockets have the advantage of greater simplicity, and are suitable for short burning times of a few seconds. The gunpowder used in simple firework rockets is a solid mixture of fuel and oxygen. Most modern rocket motors use 'liquid propellants', which are lighter, in general more powerful, and their thrust can be controlled by varying the flow of liquids. The various liquid propellant systems are, in the main, of the 'bi-propellant' type—that is, one of the liquids is a fuel (such as petrol, paraffin, or alcohol), and the other an oxygen-rich chemical known as the 'oxidant' (or 'oxidizer'), such as liquid oxygen, concentrated hydrogen peroxide, or nitric acid.

The liquid propellants are fed from tanks into the rocket combustion chamber, either by pressure (for example, from compressed nitrogen gas) or by mechanical pumps (usually driven by small gas turbines, themselves burning rocket propellants). In the chamber, they are burnt to generate gases, which are then expanded through a specially shaped nozzle to produce the exhaust; this emerges at a speed of well over 1 mile per second. The chamber and nozzle must be kept cool, and this is usually done by circulating one of the propellants around a jacket surrounding them. Remote-control valves regulate the flow of the liquid propellants, for starting and stopping the motor and varying its thrust.

Because a rocket motor must carry its own supply of oxygen as well as fuel, its fuel consumption is some fifteen times greater than that of a gas-turbine jet engine for the same thrust. For this reason, the rocket is suitable only for short runs. On the other hand, its extremely small size and weight for a large thrust to some extent offset its high consumption, particularly at great heights. Even at sea-level, however, the

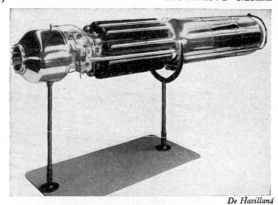

De Havilland

'SUPER-SPRITE' LIQUID PROPELLANT ROCKET MOTOR FOR ASSISTING THE TAKE-OFF OF AIRCRAFT, MOUNTED ON AN EXHIBITION STAND

Cylinders of compressed nitrogen gas are grouped in its centre. These are used to pressurize the tanks holding hydrogen peroxide and kerosene at opposite ends of the motor. The nozzle exit is at the left. Thrust is over 4,000 lb. for about 30 seconds, and the empty weight only about 600 lb.

rocket motor has its uses—in particular it is a compact form of added power for assisting the take-off of heavily-loaded aircraft (*see* AIRCRAFT TAKE-OFF, Vol. IV).

See also GAS TURBINE.
See also Vol. IV: AIRCRAFT ENGINES.

ROLLING MILL, *see* TINPLATE.

S

SAFETY DEVICES. In the early days of modern industry little thought was given to the well-being of factory employees. Apart from isolated cases of humane employers who considered themselves responsible for the welfare of their workers, conditions were bad, workers died of disease aggravated by their work, and there were many accidents due to unguarded machinery. In 1815 Sir Robert Peel stated that 1% of cotton operatives died yearly as the result of injury or disease. If the same percentage of deaths applied to the whole of industry today, there would be nearly 70,000 deaths annually instead of roughly 800, as in fact there are. As there was no social insurance as there is now, an injured person was left to fend for himself, although the accident might have been no fault of his own.

In 1833, when the system of factory inspection was started, legislation in factories became for the first time really effectual and influential. Primarily these laws applied only to textile factories, but after 1864 they were gradually made to extend farther. In 1901 an important Act consolidating all previous Acts was passed, and from that time on the Government has considered itself responsible for passing further Acts as the need for these become evident. Under the Factories Acts, though the worker has certain obligations, the main burden of providing a safe system of working for employees is placed on the owner of the factory.

The main hazard in factories which can be the cause of accidents is moving machinery. According to the Act all driving methods, either individual motors or shafting and pulleys supplying power through belts to machines, must be 'securely fenced'. Usually the shafting is enclosed in metal tubing and the pulleys and belts in wire mesh, thus preventing access to dangerous parts.

The machines themselves must also be guarded. Let us consider, for example, the safety devices necessary with MACHINE TOOLS (q.v.).

There is danger of trapped hands between the tools of a power press when they come together to form the work. This is guarded against chiefly by a fixed guard always in position, an automatic guard which will remove the hand from danger, or an interlock guard which must be closed before the machine will work. The guillotine, used for cutting metal or plastic, for example, has a knife which moves vertically. Fingers are prevented from going under the blade by a fixed guard which allows access for the materials being cut, but not for the fingers.

On LATHES (q.v.) the gear-wheels have to be covered by a solid metal guard, the rotating stock bar (that is, the bar from which pieces are being cut off) is guarded, and a telescopic type of guard is often provided for the revolving chuck which holds the work. DRILLING AND BORING MACHINES (q.v.) must have rotating parts (including the drill) protected to prevent clothing and even the hair being caught if the operator gets too close to the job. The cutter on a MILLING MACHINE (q.v.), which is very dangerous, is either covered by a fixed guard, or the cutter and table are surrounded by an interlock guard of a type which must be closed completely before the machine can be set in motion. Abrasive wheels, which run at high speed, have covers strong enough to stop any flying particles should a wheel burst.

In laundries, machines with rollers have arrangements to prevent fingers being caught. These guards are often automatic, that is, the machine is stopped if the guard is moved. Machines in which the water is removed from the clothes by a whirling drum can be very dangerous if the operator gets too close to them when they are working. The drum, therefore, is protected by an interlock guard which prevents the drum or basket moving when the cover is open (see LAUNDRY EQUIPMENT, Vol. XI).

The paper-cutting guillotine in printing works has a push-away guard to keep the operator from the danger zone; and the hand-fed platen printing machine has a guard which trips out the clutch if the hand stays in the danger zone (see PRINTING, Vol. VII).

Special regulations are applicable to WOODWORKING MACHINERY (q.v.) as the speed at which the cutting appliances run makes them extremely dangerous. Not only has each machine its own particular form of guard, but every operator has to be trained in safe and correct working methods.

Bakehouse machinery often has revolving rollers, blades, and mixing arms which must be protected. The dough brake or dough-rolling machine has a guard over the rollers which, if lifted up, reverses the mechanism, thus always protecting the in-running side. The revolving arms of the cake-mixer are interconnected with the cover of the machine, and other machines which work the dough are fed from a safe position (*see* BAKING INDUSTRY, Vol. VII).

Safety, Health, and Welfare Museum

INTERLOCKED GUARD ON A POWER PRESS
All the moving parts of the machine are protected

Safety devices to protect eyes are often necessary—for example, face screens usually of transparent plastic, visors in one piece across the eyes, and goggles of the close-fitting or spectacle type. For welding and flame-cutting processes fibre helmets with special glass are used. In some cases the body also must be protected, and special clothing may be needed as a safeguard against wet, dirt, oil and grease, extremes of temperature, corrosive fluids, irritant dust, hot metal, bursting bottles, and flying debris. Safety boots and hats prevent accidents from falling objects.

Precautions necessary to protect workers from various industrial diseases incidental to their work are vitally important. Lead, mercury, and benzine poisoning, and poisoning by aniline (in certain dyes), can all be caused by breathing in the poisonous vapour and dust, and in some cases by absorbing the poison through the skin. Various skin diseases can be caused by handling certain chemicals. Very serious ill effects can result from work with RADIOACTIVE ISOTOPES (q.v.) unless the greatest precautions are strictly enforced. Poisoning through inhaling vapour and dust is avoided by the application of exhaust ventilation to the job, and in special circumstances by the use of respirators of an approved pattern. In certain cases it may be necessary for

workers to enter a dangerous atmosphere. They must then wear breathing apparatus (which carries its own supply of oxygen) in order to overcome the risk of being gassed. Dermatitis (an inflammation of the skin liable to be caused by a variety of irritants) is another industrial malady. This, and contact with the poisonous substances mentioned, can be prevented by the use of protective clothing (*see* Vol. X, p. 207). The provision and use of good washing facilities is also essential. Dermatitis can also be controlled to some extent by the use of 'barrier' creams which are rubbed into the skin to prevent substances getting into the pores. In all cases there must be strict attention to proper methods of working.

See also Vol. VII: FACTORY ORGANIZATION.
See also Vol. X: INDUSTRIAL WELFARE.

SAFETY LAMPS. In the early days of mining the lighting of the tunnels and working places underground was very primitive. Early records indicate that miners even carried decaying fish into the mines because the phosphorescence of their skins provided a feeble light by which the men could work. Tallow candles were a common means of illumination. In the 18th century attempts were made to take daylight into the mines by using giant mirrors so placed as to reflect the rays of the sun down the shaft and along the tunnels. In 1740 Carlyle Spedding introduced his Spedding Steel Mill. If a flint were held in contact with the edge of this milled wheel when it was being rotated rapidly, usually by a small boy, the machine would emit a shower of sparks which provided a feeble light for the miner.

These methods, however, not only provided very inefficient lighting but were often the cause of explosions, especially in coal-mines. The coal and surrounding rocks in a mine give off continuously a gas called methane, generally known as firedamp, which, if ignited, can cause dangerous explosions. Early in the 19th century several such explosions occurred, causing attention to be drawn to the urgent need for some flame-proof method of mine lighting. The problem was to allow air to reach the flame without which it would not burn, and at the same time to prevent the heat from the flame reaching the outside air and igniting the gas. In 1813 Dr. Clanny of Sunderland invented a form of safety lamp worked by means of a bellows, but this was too cumbersome for general use. Two years later, in 1815, the famous Davy lamp, invented by Sir Humphry Davy, appeared (see Vol. V, p. 129). This is the forerunner of the modern flame safety lamp, and its invention was a turning-point in the fight to make the mines safer (see COAL-MINING, HISTORY OF, Vol. VII).

The flame in a safety lamp (Fig. 1) is totally enclosed by a fine wire mesh or gauze. This allows the air to reach the flame so that it can burn, but prevents the heat of the flame from escaping. Any firedamp present in the mine air, therefore, will burn inside the gauze, but as the gauze absorbs the heat of the flame, not enough heat can escape into the outside air to cause an explosion.

With the introduction of electricity the oil safety lamp has been largely superseded. However, it is still widely used as a means of detecting the presence of firedamp in a mine, for a skilled observer can estimate the percentage of firedamp present by observing the height of the cap of burning gas above the flame. The electric lamp now in common use in mines has a battery fitted on to the miner's belt and a headpiece on to his helmet. In modern mines many main tunnels are now lit by powerful 'flame-proof' electric lamps attached to the roof and sides. As the risk of damage is great, these lamps must be very strongly constructed and so designed to reduce to a minimum the danger of electric sparks initiating an explosion in the surrounding atmosphere. The lamp glass is frequently of a tough kind, and in addition some lamps maintain an air pressure inside the glass together with a device which automatically cuts off the power supply should the glass be broken and the air pressure reduced.

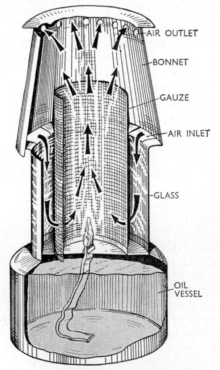

FIG. 1. DIAGRAM OF A SAFETY LAMP

AIR OUTLET

BONNET

GAUZE

AIR INLET

GLASS

OIL VESSEL

SCAFFOLDING. This consists of temporary platforms, supported by poles, which enable workmen to reach their work when building or repairing walls, chimneys, or any other high structures. It is impossible to build to any height without some form of scaffolding, and it is thought that the double walls of the Scottish fortified 'brochs', built in the 1st century B.C., may have been intended to overcome this difficulty—the workers standing on one wall while building the other.

A traditional bricklayer's scaffold consists of vertical timber poles, called 'standards', placed about 4 feet from the face of the wall and 8 to 10 feet apart. Horizontal poles, called 'ledgers', are fixed between the standards, parallel to the wall, at vertical intervals of about 5 feet, with diagonal bracings between the standards and ledgers to make the whole structure firm. Timbers, called 'putlogs', a little over 4 feet long, are then fixed at right angles to the ledgers, with one end supported by a ledger and the other resting on the wall in a niche left for the purpose. The working platforms, consisting of scaffold boards, are laid across the putlogs. These boards are 10 to 13 feet long, 9 inches wide, 1½ to 2 inches thick, and are bound at the ends with hoop iron. Guard-rails and guard-boards are fixed along the outside edges of the platforms for safety.

A mason's scaffold is similar to a bricklayer's but stronger, because it has to carry heavy stones and lifting tackle; it is also wider and is self-supporting. Two rows of standards are erected, with diagonal bracings between them. Each row carries ledgers, and the working platforms are laid, not on putlogs, but on timbers fixed horizontally between the two rows of ledgers. All the framework is made of stout, squared timbers bolted together, and the scaffold boards are lashed in place by lengths of wire rope called 'scaffold bonds'.

Modern scaffolding, used for all large buildings and many small ones, consists of metal tubes, usually of galvanized steel, about 2 inches in outside diameter, and similar in quality to those used for steam pipes. These are arranged in the same way as traditional timber scaffolding. If putlogs are used, their inner ends are flattened so that they can be built temporarily into the joints of the wall. All parts of the scaffold are joined together by 'couplings', usually iron forgings or malleable iron castings, with sockets into which the various parts are inserted and locked by wedges or screws. The wooden scaffold boards used for the working platforms are fastened to the tubular putlogs by special clips made of steel. Tubular scaffolding can be carried to a great height, with extra uprights to support the increased weight and with additional bracings. Sometimes tubes of aluminium alloy are used instead of steel, for these, though more expensive, are much lighter than steel tubes and less liable to corrosion.

Sometimes scaffolding has to carry CRANES (q.v.) and cage hoists for lifting materials up to men working at high levels. These hoists are provided with 'shafts' of tubular scaffolding braced to the main scaffold.

The outside decoration of a high building is

British Electricity Authority

FIG. I. BRICKLAYER'S SCAFFOLDING (TUBULAR)
A. Standard. B. Ledger. C. Putlog

sometimes done by men working not from a scaffold but from movable platforms suspended by 'block-and-tackle' hoists from the projecting eaves. So that the platforms can be used every few years for repainting the building, or by window cleaners, their attachments are sometimes left permanently in place.

See also BUILDING CONSTRUCTION.

SCREW-THREADS. The common screw-capped jar, the ordinary wood-screw, and the spindle of a water tap are everyday examples of the application of the screw-thread. The screw is of fundamental importance throughout the entire field of engineering.

Basically, a screw-thread is an inclined plane wrapped round a cylinder to form a screw-shaped line. If you wrap a piece of string round a stick so that it covers the stick from end to end without leaving any gaps, the spiral form made by the string, known as a 'helix', is, in fact, the basic form of the screw-thread. If you fix the string in position and hold the last turn of it between your fingers, and then turn the stick in the same direction as you wound the string, the string will feed through them, carrying the stick with it until the whole of the stick has passed through your fingers. This is what happens with the two mating parts of a screwed assembly, that is, the bolt, which is threaded externally, and the nut, which is threaded internally. The string represents the screw-thread on the bolt, while your fingers on it represent the nut.

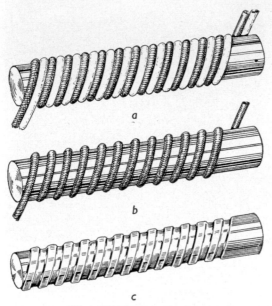

FIG. I. CUTTING A LEAD-SCREW

a. Two pieces of string wound round bore. *b.* One piece removed. *c.* Screw-thread cut

A modified version of the string and the stick was used to make the first lead-screws for lathes. Before precision instruments and manufacturing methods were available, these special screws, which are long and have to be very accurate, constituted a serious problem. Instead of one piece, two pieces of string, or some other material, were wound side by side round the bar or cylinder on which the lead-screw was to be cut (Fig. 1). One of them was then secured to the bar so that it could not move, and the other one was taken away, the screw-thread being cut in the gap left by the second string. In this simple way a true helical or spiral form was obtained.

This ability to make one part move lengthwise inside another simply by rotating one or the other, which is the important feature of screwed assemblies such as nuts and bolts, is invaluable for connecting pieces which have to be taken apart and put together again from time to time

without injury. The cylinder head of a motor-car engine, for example, which has to be removed periodically in order to reach the valves, is secured to the engine block by nuts tightened down on to 'studs' or bolts, fastened in the block. The joints of bridges are made by carefully fitted through-bolts—bolts with square or hexagonal ends which can be held by a spanner while the nut at the other end is being tightened, thus keeping the bolt still while the nut is screwed on.

The screw-thread principle is used for other purposes besides nuts and bolts. In the ordinary domestic mincing machine, winding the handle actually turns a screw. The material to be minced fills up the thread from the crest to the root and thus mates with it in the same way as a bolt would. As the handle is turned, therefore, the material must follow the spiral form of the thread and is thereby forced forward to the other end, where mincing takes place. In engineering, a similar principle is used in the screw extrusion press (*see* FORGING AND PRESSING) to force material through the die in the manufacture of, for example, tubes of lead or synthetic resin.

A major advantage of the screw is that a comparatively small force travelling a long way, such as that applied by hand to a spanner, can produce a lengthwise movement through a small distance which would otherwise require a much larger force. This might be called leverage, and is defined as the 'mechanical advantage' of the screw and its nut (*see* LEVERS). The ordinary screw-jack, for example, by making use of this mechanical advantage, can easily lift a motor-car off the ground.

The Archimedean screw, which operates in much the same way as a mincing machine, is used to move grains and liquids from one place to another. Here the spiral form of the screw-thread is made from a strip of plate metal which is wound round a central spindle, and the whole is embedded in the material to be moved. When the spindle is rotated, the material, acting the part of the nut, has to follow the spiral of the thread and therefore moves along it (Fig. 2).

In cases where a screw assembly has to be undone with only a small rotation or part of a rotation, but at the same time with a sufficient number of threads engaged, 'multi-start' threads are used. In these, the cylinder on which the thread is carried has several threads cut into its surface instead of only one. The breech block of a gun is an example of this type of thread.

Director, Science Museum

FIG. 2. AN ARCHIMEDEAN SCREW USED IN EGYPT FOR RAISING
WATER

In the last 100 years or so, a large number of kinds of thread have been designed to serve different purposes in engineering and industry.

Basically, the British Standard Whitworth thread, triangular thread (Fig. 3), named after the mid-19th-century engineering pioneer, Sir Joseph Whitworth, is the one commonly used for fixing purposes (*see* MECHANICAL ENGINEERING). However, such threads cut on the outside of a thin-walled tube would penetrate too deeply into the metal and so weaken it. The threads of Whitworth shape, but of much finer pitch and with correspondingly smaller triangles, were devised for pipes generally and for gas pipes in particular; these are known as pipe, or gas, threads. The still finer threads needed by the instrument industry were devised by the British Association for the Advancement of Science, and are known as B.A. threads. They are used, for example, in electric equipment such as switches. Another fine thread is the British Standard Fine, or B.S.F., used on nearly all British motor-cars. Other still smaller screws are needed in watch-making and for similar fine work. The smallest screw listed has 360 threads per inch on a diameter of 0·33 mm. The British Standard Whitworth thread is available in forty-eight different sizes, from 2·5 threads per inch on 6 inches diameter, down to 40 threads per inch on ⅛ inch diameter. Other screws and threads have been developed for the wood-screw, which, of course, needs no bolt, the thread forcing its way directly into the wood. In America there are different standard threads, and on the Continent there are metric ones.

Besides these standardized forms of screw-thread, there are many special shapes (Fig. 4).

The square thread is used in the lead-screw of modern LATHES (q.v.) and for bringing the punch down on to the work in screw-actuated stamping machines (*see* FORGING AND PRESSING). Where force has to be exerted in one direction only and a very strong thread is needed, the buttress-thread is used; and where close fit and accuracy are not necessary, as in the motor-car jack, the knuckle-thread, which is easy to cut or roll, is suitable.

Threads can be cut, rolled, milled, spun, moulded, or cast; the first being the most important since all the others depend on it as their origin. This is carried out on a screw-cutting lathe. As the work is rotated, the lead-screw on the lathe carries the cutter along the work, thus producing the spiral form. The internal thread on a nut can be produced in the same way.

For threading small diameters, taps and dies are used (*see* p. 164). A tap is a short piece of screw cut on a cylinder, and a die is a nut, both of which are gashed longitudinally to form cutting edges. The tap, when hardened by HEAT TREATMENT (q.v.), is rotated in a plain hole to cut an internal thread in it. Where high production is needed, a special tapping machine, an adaptation of the DRILLING MACHINE (q.v.), is used.

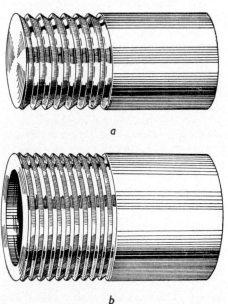

a

b

FIG. 3. BRITISH STANDARD WHITWORTH SCREW-THREADS

a. Ordinary thread. This is cut in 48 sizes from 2·5 threads per in. on a 6 in. diameter to 40 threads per in. on ⅛ in. diameter. *b.* Pipe thread. This is cut in 21 sizes from 8 threads per in. on a 12 in. bore tube to 28 threads per in. on ⅛ in. bore tube

The die rotates on the outside of a cylindrical bar to cut the external thread on it.

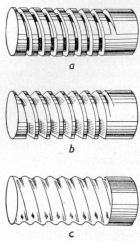

FIG. 4. SPECIAL SCREW-THREADS
a. Square thread. *b*. Buttress thread. *c*. Knuckle thread

Threads may also be cut on the Milling Machine (q.v.). In the process of spinning, applicable only to thin metal, a tool carrying the form of the thread to be produced is pressed into the metal while it is rotated. Grinding machines are used to produce highly accurate threads, the grinding wheel having a profile of the same shape as the thread to be made.

When plastic material is moulded or molten metal is cast (*see* Casting) external and internal threads can be formed by threads in the moulds themselves.

A comparatively new method is thread rolling. In this, the plain cylinder or 'blank' on which the thread is to be formed is placed between two rotating rolls of hardened steel which are of the form of the thread to be made. The rolls are forced towards each other by hydraulic pressure, and their threads continue to deform the metal surface of the blank until an identical thread is formed on it.

SERVO-CONTROLS, *see* Automatic Controls, Section 2.

SEWAGE DISPOSAL. For many centuries ignorance and neglect of any proper systems of Drainage and Refuse Disposal (qq.v. Vol. X) caused widespread ill-health and disease; Water Supplies (q.v.) were contaminated and caused epidemics of typhoid fever and cholera. Today, to prevent such outbreaks, all foul water is collected from drains and carried through underground pipes and sewers to some convenient point of disposal. On the coast the sewage is sometimes discharged into the sea at ebb tide. Most big towns and urban areas, however, have special sewage purification works. Here the liquids, having been separated from the solids, are purified to a state in which they can be harmlessly discharged into a river or stream for nature to complete the process; the solids are treated separately and, wherever possible, are made use of as farm Manures (q.v. Vol. VI).

A typical modern sewage works, for a town of perhaps 50,000 people, is situated beside a river. As well as the sewage tanks and filters, it also includes houses, a messroom, and baths for the workmen, an office, and a laboratory where samples of sewage can be examined at every stage of purification. It is often laid out attractively with trees and flower-beds.

When the sewage enters the works it passes through a kind of large underwater mincing-machine, which cuts up any refuse such as pieces of rag which might get entangled in the pumps and filters. Hard refuse, such as small stones, is raked out by a dredger and taken away to an isolated 'tip'. The sewage is then passed through a narrow gap so that the quantity coming into the works for treatment at any given moment can be measured. The amount of sewage which the works can deal with at a time is limited, so any surplus, usually caused by heavy rains, passes over a weir into storm water tanks. If the rains last for a long time, the storm water tanks overflow into the river. The solids, however, will have settled and been removed, and the liquid, though not as well purified as that from the main works, is usually not harmful because it is sufficiently diluted by rain water. The contents of the storm water tanks are passed back to the main works at a convenient time for full treatment.

The full treatment of sewage begins in a series of large open-air settling tanks, in which the greater part of the solids settle to the bottom as watery sludge. On the floor of each tank is a scraper, driven by an electric motor, which sweeps the sludge to a convenient point for pumping out into other tanks, called 'digestion' tanks.

Meanwhile the water from which the sludge has separated overflows continuously from the tanks on to filters, which are beds of stones or

AERATION TANKS AT A SEWAGE WORKS

other material up to 6 feet deep. The water is sprayed on to the filters from countless jets on moving tubular metal arms. In the filter beds are BACTERIA (q.v. Vol. II), tiny living organisms which feed on and remove the impure matter in the water as it passes continuously over the stones. The bacteria breed naturally where there is sewage, especially in warm weather; so to bring a new small filter bed to its highest efficiency quickly a few barrow-loads of stones from an old bed, with their microscopic inhabitants, may be added to it just before use. Beds should, if possible, be used more or less continuously to keep the bacteria alive.

Another way of treating the liquid from the settling tanks is to run it into another tank and force air into it. This aeration process causes more solid material to separate from the water and to settle as activated sludge; the water is then sufficiently pure to be discharged to the river. With this method the bacteria are carried away in the sludge; so to maintain the supply of bacteria some sludge has to be returned for mixing with the incoming water from the settling tanks before it is aerated. The sludge not needed for mixing is passed to the sludge 'digestion' tanks.

If the water from a sewage works is not pure it may poison the river water and kill the fish. Occasionally certain chemicals entering the

sewers in waste materials, from factories, for example, cannot be dealt with satisfactorily in the sewage works. These not only hinder purification, but also poison the river water. Laboratory tests should, however, disclose the presence of such chemicals, and damage can be prevented either by ensuring that they are discharged only in small quantities throughout the day rather than all at once, or by more elaborate means such as a separate pre-treatment works at the factory.

The solid matter, in the form of watery sludge, which has been pumped from the settling tanks to the 'digestion' tanks, is held there for about 40 days. This sludge, which is black or brown in colour, has a strong smell; but in a modern works this is not offensive because the sludge is drawn off under water. While it is in the tanks the sludge ferments, and a gas consisting mainly of methane bubbles to the surface. Methane is even better for burning than ordinary coal gas, and at many sewage works it is collected in floating gas-collectors, which look like steel roofs to the tanks, and is used to generate power for the sewage works and, in special gas heaters, to warm the fermenting sludge.

While the sludge is in the digestion tanks more water separates from it and is drawn off. At the end of the digestion period the sludge is much thicker and no longer offensive. It is then spread

SETTLING TANKS WITH SLUDGE SCRAPERS AT A SEWAGE WORKS

over open drying beds, where most of the remaining water drains off or evaporates. The dry sludge 'cake' is loaded into lorries and taken to farm land for use as manure. For market gardens the sludge is often further dried and ground into a fine powder.

See also Vol. X: DRAINAGE; REFUSE DISPOSAL.

SEXTANT, *see* Vol. IV: SEXTANT.

SHAPING MACHINES, *see* MACHINE TOOLS, Section 2.

SHEET-METAL WORK. The term sheet metal covers all types of metals which have been press-rolled into thin sheets, from which various useful shapes and components are formed. These range from tin cans to motor-car bodies. Until recent times sheet-metal work was mainly carried out by hand methods, the material being manipulated by skilled craftsmen into many complicated forms: medieval ARMOUR (q.v. Vol. X) is a typical example. Panelling for early motorcars was also manufactured by the same methods, as are special or 'coach built' bodies today.

Though there is still plenty of scope for the skilled hand sheet-metal worker, in almost every aspect of engineering production machinery is steadily being developed which can not

only do the same work much better and faster than the hand worker but which can also carry out work much too large and unwieldy to be done by hand.

1. *Hand sheet-metal work.* The essential principle of working up sheet metal by hand is often called panel beating. A sheet-metal bowl is shaped up by two methods, one called 'hollowing' and the other, 'raising'.

The hollowing process consists of beating the

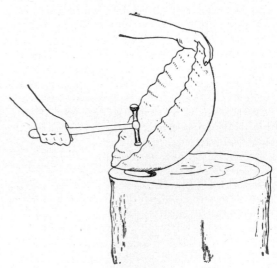

FIG. 1. HOLLOWING A SHEET-METAL BOWL

sheet metal with a round-faced hammer into a small recess or hollow in a wooden block (Fig. 1). A disk of sheet metal is held loosely in one hand over the recess and slowly rotated, while a number of blows are given round the edge of the disk. The beating over the recess forms a series of shallow hollows round the edge of the metal disk. The disk is then beaten again over the recess a little farther in from the edge, and then again yet farther in, until the middle of the bowl is reached. This procedure is repeated until the required shape has been reached.

For motor-car panel work, the beating up is usually carried out with a wooden mallet on a leather bag filled with sand.

Although it is quicker to carry out than raising, the hollowing process has the disadvantage that repeated blows tend to thin the metal too much, especially at the centre. The raising process is a reversal of the hollowing process; the work is shaped up from the centre by being beaten over

F. J. Edwards Ltd.

FIG. 3. SHAPING A CURVED SURFACE ON A WHEELING MACHINE

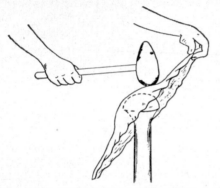

FIG. 2. RAISING A SHEET-METAL BOWL

a solid head (Fig. 2). This process puckers or wrinkles-in the metal until the series of beatings reach the circumference of the bowl.

The next stage after shaping up is to 'planish' or smooth the surface by hammering. The bowl is placed over a suitably shaped iron head or stake, and the metal lightly hammered all over its surface.

For many articles of double curvature form, a smooth finish can be obtained by the use of a wheeling machine (Fig. 3). In this machine two small, smooth wheels rotate tightly together, and the work is passed to and fro between them until a smooth surface is obtained. Panels of slight curvature can be shaped up on a wheeling machine by skilled craftsmen without any preliminary beating-up work being done. For large-scale pro-

duction, panels of double curvature are usually shaped up in dies by huge presses (*see* FORGING AND PRESSING).

The majority of sheet-metal articles are formed by rolling up blanks cut out to a 'templet' or pattern, several methods being used to draw, or lay out, the flat shape of an article on a piece of sheet material so that when it is rolled up it will be the correct shape and size.

Sheet-metal joints are made by RIVETING, WELDING, brazing, or SOLDERING (qq.v.), depending on the type of article and the metal used. A typical sheet-metal joint is made by forming the edges of the material into hooked shapes, which are then brought together and locked (Fig. 4), using a special tool called a groover. This, and similar types of joints, such as those used on a food tin can, are made very efficiently by machinery.

2. *Machine sheet-metal work.* As well as various bending, forming, and cutting machines designed to help the sheet-metal worker, a great deal of

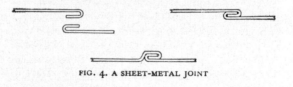

FIG. 4. A SHEET-METAL JOINT

specialized automatic machinery has been developed. For instance, specialized machines form and seal cans for food and other purposes completely automatically and at high speed.

In addition, modern machinery has been developed to make very large sheet-metal pressings, quite outside the capacity of the hand worker. For instance, the all-metal bodies of modern motor-cars need very large pressings compared with the panels produced by panel beaters for early cars. Today there are presses large enough to produce the roof of a motor body complete. Such presses are enormous; beds of 11 feet by 8 feet are not uncommon, and presses of much larger capacity even than this are being made. By producing what is effectively the whole of the top of the body in one pressing out of a single piece of sheet metal, a great deal of the welding which used to be necessary is eliminated.

The all-metal design of modern aircraft makes it necessary to produce sheet metal parts in batches at a rapid rate of production. By using the drop hammer method (*see* FORGING AND PRESSING) quite deep parts even can be pressed, or drawn, satisfactorily. Large hydraulic presses are also used, as in the motor-car industry, a number of different components often being produced at one time. One of the newest machines for metal forming, developed specially for the aircraft industry, is the stretching or stretch-wrap forming machine. This actually stretches the sheet metal to its limit and then wraps it round a die to give the shape required. Because it has been stretched, the metal stays in this shape instead of trying to spring back again. Special riveting machines are also much used in aircraft factories; some of these pierce the hole, insert the rivet, and close it, the operator only having to place the piece to be riveted in the correct position under the machine.

See also FORGING AND PRESSING.
See also Vol. VII: AIRCRAFT INDUSTRY; MOTOR INDUSTRY.

SHIPBUILDING. 1. Over $3\frac{1}{2}$ million tons of shipping were built in the world's shipyards in 1953; the British SHIPBUILDING INDUSTRY (q.v. Vol. VII) alone accounted for over a third of this vast total. Though some British yards build every type of steel ship, from small harbour and river craft to the largest merchant SHIPS, LINERS (qq.v. Vol. IV), and NAVAL VESSELS (q.v. Vol. X), usually they specialize in only one or

Vickers Ltd.

FIG. I. THE ORIENT LINER *ORCADES* UNDER CONSTRUCTION
The keel is lying on keel blocks with the centre girder, floors, side girders and tank margin plates in place

two types of ship. Craft with wooden hulls, such as yachts and rowing boats, are built in separate BOAT BUILDING yards (q.v.). Most large shipyards contain a number of building berths—wide, open spaces sloping towards the river into which the hull of a ship is launched; 'fitting out' quays, where the engines are installed and the superstructure built; all kinds of engineering workshops; and sometimes dry DOCKS (q.v. Vol. IV). CRANES (q.v.) and derricks, ranged along the sides of the building berths and quays, are used for lifting heavy steel girders and plating and large prefabricated parts, such as the ships' funnels.

2. *Preparing to build.* After a ship has been designed, much work has still to be done in the drawing office before building can start. Structural drawings of every part of the ship have to be made so that the right quantities of steel can be ordered, and working drawings have to be prepared for men at the building berth. Other draughtsmen work out details of accommodation and of the various items of equipment that will be needed, much of which is bought ready-made from other manufacturers.

When these detailed drawings are ready they are first passed to the 'laying-off loft'. Here the shapes of all the vertical and horizontal sections of the ship, from the keel to the top deck, are drawn full scale on the smooth, flat floor of the loft. These drawings are reproduced from the naval architect's 'lines plan' (*see* NAVAL ARCHITECTURE, Section 4), the scale of which is $\frac{1}{4}$ inch to 1 foot. As inaccuracies are almost certain to occur when working with such a small scale, the loftsmen have to check the lines carefully to ensure that they reproduce the smooth curves of the ship; this is known as 'fairing the lines'. Wooden 'templets' or patterns are then prepared for the main steel structure, and are used for cutting the steel parts and other materials to the right size and shape.

3. *Building a ship.* While work is going on in the loft, the keel, or backbone, of the ship is laid down on the building berth. The keel runs the full length of the ship and consists of a number of flat steel plates, each 20 to 30 feet long. The plates are laid on a series of 'keel blocks', pieces of timber 4 to 5 feet long and about 1 foot square, built up to a height of 5 to 6 feet. Two pieces of timber are first laid across the width of the berth, about 4 feet apart, and then another two facing fore and aft on top of them, and so on until the correct height is obtained. The tops of the blocks must lie in a straight line along the length of the ship and, as the keel lies at a slope along the launching berth, they must be at different levels.

When the blocks are in place, the keel plates are laid upon them and temporarily bolted together. Then the 'centre girder' is erected; this is a vertical line of plating, standing on the centre of the keel and extending the full length of the ship. It is shored or wedged in position by long pieces of timber, and temporarily bolted to the keel. Vertical plates, called 'floors', are attached to the centre girder, at right angles to it, and from 2 to 3 feet apart according to the length of the ship. To the floors are attached the plating forming the inner and outer bottoms of the ship (Fig. 1).

The 'side girders', small pieces of plate fitted in between the floors and parallel to the centre girder, are then put in position. Also placed parallel to the centre girder, and attached to the outside ends of the floors, are two plates, called the 'tank margin plates', which extend the full length of the ship. When they are in place, all the parts are permanently joined by RIVETING (q.v.).

While this is going on, the main frames, forming the ribs of the ship, are being prepared. These frames, made in steel sections, are attached to the tank margin plate on either side of the ship, and carry the side plating. The frames are spaced the same distance apart as the floors, and, like the floors, are set at right angles to the keel. The preparation of the frames demands great skill, for they must not only be cut to the correct length but must be bent to the exact shape of the outside form of the ship. This is done by heating the frame in a furnace until it is red hot and then bending it round a light bar of the correct shape. When the frame has cooled it is taken to the berth and attached to the margin plate by a steel bracket (Fig. 2).

The deck beams, which carry the deck plating, are put in place at the same time as the frames. These are also steel sections cut to the right length and given the correct camber or curve. Some of these beams extend right across the width of the ship and are attached to the frames by brackets. The deck girders, which run the length of the ship, and the watertight bulkheads,

Vickers Ltd.

FIG. 2. THE *ORCADES* UNDER CONSTRUCTION
The main frames with some of the plates in position

FIG. 3. THE BOTTOM HULL STRUCTURE OF THE *ORCADES* WITH BULKHEADS IN POSITION AND TUNNELS FOR THE PROPELLER SHAFTS

or partitions, which divide the ship into many compartments for reasons of safety, are also erected at this time (Fig. 3). The bulkheads are generally prefabricated, and if possible are lifted into position in one piece. The skeleton of the ship, consisting of floors, frames, beams, and girders, is then complete and ready for plating.

For a ship 500 feet long the steel plates, or 'strakes', are usually about 30 feet by 6 feet and about ¾ inch thick, and are bent to the shape of the ship. They are laid fore and aft, starting by the keel, and are joined together by riveting. At the same time the pillars, which support the deck girders and beams, and some parts of the superstructure, such as deck houses, are erected. After all the steelwork has been painted, the ship is ready for launching.

Within the last 20 years most shipyards have begun to use WELDING (q.v.) instead of riveting for joining certain parts. Welding not only reduces the weight of the structure but also ensures complete watertightness. It has also considerably speeded up and altered shipyard procedure as large portions of the ship can be prefabricated in the welding shop. The size of these parts largely depends on the cranes that are available for lifting them, but in most yards parts weighing from 30 to 60 tons can now be prefabricated.

4. *Launching.* Launching needs most careful preparation, for a structure containing thousands of tons of steel has to be transferred from land to water in little over a minute. Ships are usually built with their centre lines approximately at right angles to the river, and are launched stern first, sliding down two sloped 'launching ways' into the water. The launching ways are built on each side of the ship, about one-third of the breadth of the ship apart. Each consists of a sloped 'standing way', which is built up on blocks similar to the keel blocks and remains stationary when the ship moves, and a 'sliding way', which is attached to the ship and moves along with it. The sliding way rests on top of the standing way, with its under or sliding surface lubricated with tallow and oil. The space between the sliding way and the ship is filled by packing, wedged tightly into position. A 'trigger', which may be a simple wooden wedge or an elaborate locking device worked by electricity or hydraulic power, locks the standing and sliding ways together. When the ways are in position, the keel blocks and shores, which have so far supported the weight of the ship, are gradually

removed. When the ship is ready for launching, the trigger is released and the sliding way slips forward carrying the ship into the water. If the river is narrow, the ship as soon as it is water-borne must be checked by drags, piles of chain secured to the berth alongside the ship and attached to it by wire ropes. Sometimes anchors, laid on the bed of the river and attached to the ship by ropes, are used instead of drags (*see* Colour Plate, opp. p. 48).

5. *Fitting out.* After launching, the ship is towed by tugs to a 'fitting-out quay', where building is completed. Here the engines and other propelling machinery (*see* MARINE ENGIN-EERING) are installed, the various parts being lowered into the engine-room by cranes and assembled there. The boilers and funnels, which are now usually prefabricated, are lifted aboard complete (Fig. 4). Electrical equipment is installed, and the ventilation, heating, and water systems. Furniture is fitted, lifeboats and derricks brought on board, and the rest of the superstructure built and painted. If the PROPELLER (q.v.) has not been fitted before launching, the ship is

Vickers Ltd.

FIG. 4. INSTALLING THE FUNNEL OF THE *ORCADES*

taken to a dry dock for this before or after going to the fitting-out quay.

When the engines have been installed they are usually given a preliminary trial while the ship is still moored to the quay. The ship then goes out on a sea trial, during which the engines are tested for speed, COMPASSES (q.v. Vol. IV) are adjusted to counteract the magnetic effect of the ship, and the ANCHORS (q.v.), cable equipment, and steering gear are all tried out. With naval vessels particularly, a very extensive series of steering and circling trials is also carried out. When the ship has completed all her trials satisfactorily she is handed over to the owner and becomes his property, though the shipbuilder keeps a watch on the ship until the end of the guarantee period.

See also NAVAL ARCHITECTURE; MARINE ENGINEERING; SHIP REPAIRS; BOAT BUILDING.
See also Vol. IV: SHIP.
See also Vol. VII: SHIPBUILDING INDUSTRY.

SHIP REPAIRS.

Extensive repairs to a SHIP (q.v. Vol. IV) are usually carried out at special ship repair yards. These yards, often situated near a main SHIPBUILDING yard (q.v.), have numerous docks or quays where ships can be berthed, and sometimes dry DOCKS (q.v. Vol. IV) and slipways where the under-water parts of the hull can be examined. They are equipped with workshops, similar to those in a shipyard and engine-works, where any damage from the hull to the engine-room can be repaired, and with derricks and CRANES (q.v.) for lifting heavy parts of the main engines or other loads which may have to be taken to the workshops; for very heavy loads large floating cranes, which can lift up to 150 tons, are sometimes towed alongside the ship. Men of every trade are employed in these yards and, so that a ship can get to sea as quickly as possible, two or three shifts of men are continually at work each day and night.

Repairers get most of their work from the requirements of Ship Classification Societies (see NAVAL ARCHITECTURE, Section 5), whose surveyors must by law inspect certain parts of every vessel every 12 months and carry out a 'special survey' once every 4 years. This ensures that a ship is always seaworthy, and enables the owners to insure the vessel against different risks with underwriters such as LLOYD's (q.v. Vol. IV).

During a special survey, all holds and other spaces are emptied; water and oil tanks are drained and cleaned; the main and auxiliary engines and boilers are inspected in case bearings or other parts have become worn or corroded; the hull is examined in case the steel plates have weakened; and the steering gear and main pumps are tested. Underwater parts of the hull, the PROPELLER (q.v.) and its shaft, and the rudder are inspected in dry dock; if the vessel is small, it is hauled on to a cradle or slipway. Any repairs that are considered necessary are supervised by the owners and surveyors.

Apart from special surveys, most ships are drydocked once every 9 months so that the underwater parts of the hull can be cleaned. The barnacles and marine growths which stick to the plating and reduce the ship's speed are removed with steel scrapers and wire brushes. A coat of paint is put on to prevent corrosion, followed by another coating of special composition which discourages sea creatures from sticking to the ship. During these routine docking and painting jobs, which may take only 2 days, a look-out is kept for more serious defects.

Besides routine overhauls, ship repairers have to deal with damage caused by storms, or a fire, or by the ship's having collided or run aground. In most cases, if the damage is not extensive, the plating or other parts can usually be repaired with the ship afloat alongside a quay. A ship that has run aground, however, has to be drydocked for examination, for on hard rock the

Smiths Dock Co.

M.V. *BRITISH EARL* IN DRY DOCK FOR REPAIRS
The large hole in the hull was made by a mine

bottom plating and much of the inside structure may be buckled and torn. Special precautions have to be taken in bringing a fully loaded ship into dry dock, for its weight may be very much more than its usual docking weight. Extra keel blocks, side blocks, and cradles are carefully arranged on the dock bottom to take the extra load and to prevent the bottom plating, on which the ship rests, being 'set up' or permanently bent.

Often the damaged plating can be taken off, pressed or rolled to its original shape, and put back again. This is called 'removing, fairing, and refitting'. If the plating is only slightly buckled, strong steel bars are placed over the damage; long steel bolts, driven through the bars and the damaged plating and secured by nuts, pull the plating back into position. This is called 'fairing in place'. When the damaged plating has to be removed, it is usually burned through with an oxy-acetylene flame (*see* WELDING, Section 2*b*), this being much quicker than the old method of cutting out rivets, or laboriously cutting through the plate with hand tools. If the plates have been joined originally by welding, only the damaged part need be cut out; if they have been joined by RIVETING (q.v.), however, the whole plate has to be removed.

The repairs of a heavily damaged ship may be long and complicated. For example, a ship may have run aground and broken its back, that is, fractured the keel and deck plating right across the breadth of the ship, and buckled the plating down each side, so that the vessel can no longer float as a whole. If SALVAGE is possible (q.v. Vol. IV), the ship is cut in two along the line of the fracture and the two halves towed separately to a repair yard, the watertight bulkheads ensuring that each part floats. The two halves are then docked in a dry dock, a detailed examination is made, and the badly damaged parts of the structure trimmed off. The two halves are then refloated, the sides of the dry dock being marked

Smiths Dock Co.

AFTER END OF M.V. *BRITISH EARL* IN DRY DOCK
The ship was so badly damaged that she had to be cut in two. After the damage had been repaired the two halves were joined together again. Shores supporting the side of the ship can be seen on the left

off so that the two parts can be redocked in exactly the right position and alignment for joining up. The rest of the damaged material is then removed, and new plates, frames, and so on are riveted or welded on, joining the two parts together. Throughout the repair work precautions have to be taken to ensure that the halves of the ship do not move. This is done by placing sighting posts under the vessel and along the sides, at the bows, middle, and stern. Similar repairs are carried out if a ship's plating has been so buckled or fractured by a bad storm that the ship becomes 'hogged', that is, the stem and stern drop lower than the middle, or 'sagged', that is, the middle drops lower than the stem and stern.

During the 19th century, similar operations used sometimes to be performed on undamaged steamships and sailing ships in order to lengthen them, either to give them greater speed or to increase their cargo space. Between the First and Second World Wars several Blue Star passenger liners had their bows removed in dry dock and new ones fitted, each ship being lengthened by 15 feet in the process. This extra length, and the finer shape of the new bows, increased the ships' speed. A ship that has lost its bows in collision can also be dry-docked in a similar way for new bows to be fitted. The damaged plating on each side of the vessel is cut off, and the frames, beams, and parts of the deck plating which have suffered damage are also removed. When new plating has been bent to the correct shape, fitted, and lined up correctly, the parts are riveted or welded to the main structure, the 'fore peak' tank being filled with water to make sure that the plating is watertight.

A ship that has been holed or damaged beneath the waterline can be temporarily repaired at sea either by covering the hole with canvas or timber or by using a 'cement box'—that is, a wooden casing, open at the top, which is built inside the hull round the damaged part and filled with quick setting cement. Unless its back is broken, a damaged ship can usually reach a repair yard under its own steam or in tow with the help of temporary repairs of this kind, extra salvage pumps, and its own pumping machinery and watertight bulkheads. Even a ship which has lost its bows can often be saved if its forward watertight bulkhead is shored up and it is towed to a repair yard stern first.

See also SHIPBUILDING.
See also Vol. IV: SHIP; SALVAGE.

SHIPS' ENGINES, *see* MARINE ENGINEERING.

SHOCK ABSORBERS. These are, basically, devices fitted to machines to prevent either the whole machine or some part of it from bouncing. When an aircraft, for example, lands, the shock of landing is taken by strong springs in the under-carriage. But springs alone will not do; for springs simply store the energy of collision between the landing-wheels and the ground until they are fully compressed, and then expand again, causing the aircraft to bounce to rest in a series of jumps. Some device is needed that absorbs the energy of collision and dissipates it in some other way than in a rebound—usually as heat. This is what the shock absorber does. In an aircraft, a piston in the leg of the undercarriage is caused to force oil through a small hole; the oil is thus heated, and the energy of the collision is absorbed.

Shock absorbers or 'dampers' are used in vehicles to absorb or 'damp' the vibration of the SPRINGS (q.v.). After a wheel has passed over a hump in the road, its spring will oscillate for some time, making the vehicle bounce. If this vibration is not quickly absorbed, the passengers will have an uncomfortable ride. One expedient is to fit a pair of plates, clamped together by a bolt, nut, and spring washer, between the axle and chassis. The friction between these plates is sufficient to absorb the vibration.

In many modern vehicles the hydraulic method is used. A device like a perforated piston in a cylinder containing thick oil is bolted to the frame of the vehicle. Any violent movement is checked by the resistance of the thick oil in forcing its way through the small holes of the piston—sudden movements being far more quickly absorbed than slower ones (*see* p. 405).

See also VIBRATION, MECHANICAL.

SHORING AND UNDERPINNING. These are two ways of preventing 'movement' in a building, which may cause it to crack or threaten its stability. Movement may be due to several things: the foundations (*see* BUILDING, PRINCIPLES OF) may be disturbed by nearby excavations or by moisture in the subsoil draining away (*see* SOIL MECHANICS); or alterations may have to be made to the lower part of the building, which temporarily remove the support of parts above. For shoring, timber or steel props are used to provide temporary support for part of the building; underpinning involves some form of permanent building work beneath the structure, such as deepening the existing foundations.

Vertical, or 'dead', shores are used to support a wall that is in danger of collapse through overloading. Such shores are placed in pairs, one on either side of the wall, and are connected by a beam (called a 'needle') which passes through the wall either at an existing opening or through a hole made for the purpose. Folding wedges, driven in between the needle and the wall, enable the needle to take some of the load which is pressing down on the wall from above (Fig. 1*a*).

Horizontal or 'flying' shores, wedged in position between two buildings, prevent the buildings moving towards each other when, for example, another building between them has been demolished (Fig. 1*b*). 'Raking' shores, set at an angle to the building with one end secured firmly to the ground, are used to support a wall that has begun or threatens to bulge outwards (Fig. 1*c*).

Underpinning is a difficult process for it usually involves removing weak foundations and replacing them by new material carried down to a

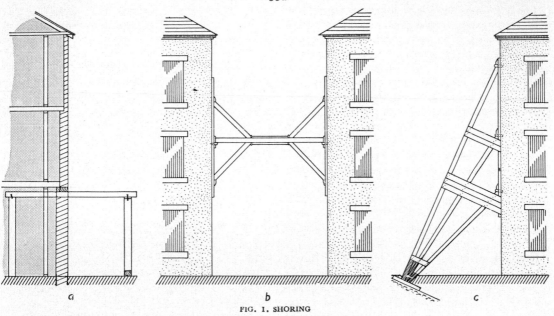

FIG. I. SHORING

a. Dead shore. *b.* Flying shore. *c.* Raking shore

greater depth or width, or both. If independent foundations are being replaced, the load must be supported by shores while the work is being done. For underpinning strip foundations, however, only the ends need be shored, and the old foundations can be replaced in short lengths of 4 to 5 feet.

See also BUILDING, PRINCIPLES OF; SOIL MECHANICS.

SLIDE RULE. This is an instrument for multiplying and dividing numbers. A scale (B in Fig. 1) is graduated from 1 to 100. The distance from 1 to any number is proportional to the LOGARITHM (q.v.) of that number. Scale B slides alongside an exactly similar scale A. To multiply 4 by 7, 1 on scale B is set against 4 on scale A, and the figure 7 on scale B is then seen to come opposite 28 on scale A. This is because log 4 + log 7 = log(4 × 7) = log 28. The lengths corresponding to log 4 and log 7 have been added to give a combined length corresponding to log 28.

For division, one length is subtracted from another. To divide 55 by 11, for example, 11 on the B scale is set opposite 55 on the A scale. 1 on the B scale then comes opposite 5 on the A scale.

When 3 numbers are to be multiplied together, the first pair are multiplied on the slide rule in the usual way, and then the cursor (usually a transparent slide with a thin line engraved on it at right angles to the scale) is moved along to mark the answer. The figure 1 on the B scale is then moved underneath it, and the answer is read from the A scale opposite the third number on the B scale. There is thus no need to write down any intermediate answers.

In the earliest type of scale rule, invented by John Gunter in 1620, lengths were measured on a single scale by dividers and transferred by them to make multiplications or divisions. Within 2 years it was discovered that a second scale was advantageous for transferring lengths, and the first true slide rule was made. A few years later it was realized that the scale need not be straight but could be engraved round the circumference of a circle. Circular slide rules were being used by 1627.

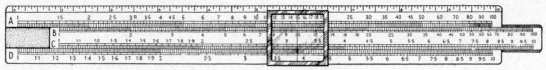

FIG. I. SLIDE RULE

The commonest modern slide rules are straight with scales about 10 inches long. Besides the A and B scales (1 to 100) they also have C and D scales graduated from 1 to 10 in the same length. This brings 1 on both A and D scales at the left-hand end but each number on the D scale is underneath its square on the A scale. Thus 3 comes under 9 and 10 under 100. With this, calculations involving squares or square roots are easily made. The numbers are transferred across the rule by the line on the cursor. Rules have been made with much longer scales (20 inches or even 40 inches) to get greater accuracy, but they are unwieldy. Special rules with the scales wrapped round cylinders have been invented to get long scales in a reasonable space.

Straight rules specially adapted for making calculations in engineering often have extra scales representing quantities such as electrical resistance or temperature. They may have extra sets of slides and more lines on the cursor. The accuracy of the answer given by most rules is about 1 part in 1,000. It can be slightly better if the rule is a long one and if the operator works extremely carefully.

See also LOGARITHMS.

SMELTING, *see* BLAST FURNACE; IRON AND STEEL INDUSTRY, HISTORY OF.

SOIL MECHANICS. This term describes the study of the strength, stability, and other properties of the soil. No important CIVIL ENGINEERING project (q.v.) can be planned without first finding out something about the ground on which it is going to be built.

Samples of the soil at different depths are obtained by means of special tubes, which are driven from boreholes into the ground and, when withdrawn, contain a 'core' of soil from the required depth. The samples are then tested to discover the amount of moisture in the soil, its strength, compressibility, and other properties. From this information the engineer, when planning, for example, the foundations of a building, is able to calculate the load that the soil will safely carry; in RAILWAY ENGINEERING (q.v.), he can discover the angle at which the slope of an embankment or cutting is safe against slipping; in planning methods of FLOOD CONTROL he can discover how quickly a river may wash away its banks; or, in DOCKS AND

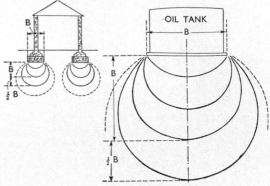

FIG. 1. DISTRIBUTION OF STRESS BELOW FOUNDATIONS OF DIFFERENT SIZES

Lines of equal stress produce what is known as the 'bulb' of pressure. B. Width of foundations

HARBOUR CONSTRUCTION (qq.v.), he can determine the stability of quays and breakwaters which are to be built on the sea bed.

Rocks, coarse sands, and gravels normally provide good foundations, but the finer soils, such as silts and clays, sometimes present considerable problems. Much depends on the amount of moisture they contain: for example, on fine, wet, sandy beaches stamping with the feet produces 'quaking' and a depression is formed; the sand becomes 'quick', in its worst condition forming a quicksand. Any vibrating load, such as an electric generator, founded on such material would settle or sink.

Silts and clays are also particularly sensitive to changes in moisture, shrinking and swelling according to whether they are dry or wet. Their strengths are highest when dry. On a muddy river bank, for example, the mud, when wet, is soft and will not support heavy objects; but as the mud dries, although the surface shrinks and cracks, it becomes hard and able to carry considerable loads. In order to make reliable tests, therefore, samples of such soils should be obtained and preserved in such a way that they are carrying the same amount of moisture at the time of testing as existed in the ground.

The shrinkage and swelling of the top few feet of a clay soil due to changes in moisture can cause the surface of the ground to rise and fall 2 or 3 inches between winter and summer. Similar, though smaller, movements occur in houses if the foundations are shallow, often causing these and other buildings to crack. A drop or 'settlement' of the foundations on clay soils is also caused by the moisture being gradually squeezed out of the soil by the weight of the building. This proceeds quickly at first but soon slows down, although some movement may continue for many years.

As the load from a building's foundations spreads deeper through the soil, the stresses it sets up gradually decrease (Fig. 1). The effect of the load, however, is still apparent to some extent at a depth of 1½ times the width of the foundations. Thus the wider the foundations the greater is the depth of soil affected.

See also BUILDING, PRINCIPLES OF; SHORING AND UNDERPINNING.

SOLAR ENERGY.

SOLAR ENERGY. Light and heat from the SUN reach the earth by RADIATION (qq.v. Vol. III) of waves. The total amount of solar radiation that falls on the Earth in one month is greater than the amount of heat that could be produced by burning the whole of the estimated coal reserves in the world. Only a small part of this energy can be put to useful work: about half may be used as heat at 160° F., and about a twentieth can be converted to mechanical power.

For ordinary heating purposes, where heat is needed only at a moderate temperature, the sun's radiant energy is trapped by allowing it to fall on to a device known as a 'flat-plate absorber' —a large metal plate with a matt black surface and an upper face covered with two sheets of plate glass. Copper tubing for circulating water is soldered to its underside. The flat-plate absorber depends for its effectiveness on two properties of radiation—that at low temperatures all wavelengths are absorbed but only very long wavelengths re-radiated by a matt black surface, and that glass will transmit short wavelengths, that is, those of light radiation, but is opaque to long wavelengths—such as heat radiation. The sun's rays pass through the plate glass and fall on to the metal plate, where they are absorbed and the energy converted to heat. As long wavelength radiations only are re-radiated, the energy of the sun's rays cannot get back through the glass plates, so is trapped by the flat-plate absorber and used to heat the circulating water be-

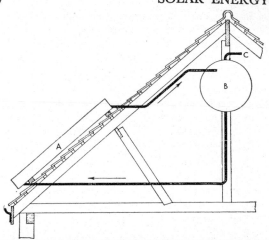

DIAGRAM OF A SOLAR WATER-HEATING SYSTEM ON THE ROOF OF A HOUSE

A. Flat-plate heat collector. B. Hot-water storage tank. C. Hot-water outlet

The arrows show the direction of the flow of water

neath it. Solar water-heaters are widely used in America, and special houses heated entirely by solar energy in winter have been built in the U.S.A.

Power production from the sun's energy is a more difficult matter. The efficiency with which heat is converted into power depends on there being a big temperature difference to work with (*see* HEAT ENGINES); therefore the supply of heat needs to be at as high a temperature as

Odhams Press

SOLAR ENERGY INSTALLATION AT MONT LOUIS, FRENCH PYRENEES
On the left is a huge concave mirror and on the right a flat mirror

practicable. In very sunny countries, plants have been built with huge concave mirrors to focus the sun's rays on to small boilers; these generate steam to drive steam engines. Such plants are, however, very expensive to build in relation to the output of power, the more so because the plant must be built on a movable frame to keep up with the movement of the sun.

Solar radiation may be very usefully employed to distill salt water for cattle-drinking in the semi-deserts in Australia, Africa, and the U.S.A. where fresh water is short.

Concave-reflector furnaces have also been built for melting metals, but again, the cost of the plant outweighs the fact that the sun's heat is free.

See also Vol. III: SUN; RADIATION; HEAT.

SOLDERING. This is a method of joining together two pieces of metal—usually copper, zinc, tin, lead, brass, bronze, and the material known as TINPLATE (q.v.), which is a thin sheet of steel with a very thin layer of tin on either side. The solder, a metal mixture used melted as a liquid, joins the metal pieces rather as glue joins wood. The metal pieces are made absolutely clean and free from grease so that the solder can spread evenly over the joint. The joint is then heated sufficiently to allow a little of the molten solder and of the metal to combine to form a thin layer of ALLOY (q.v.) between the solder and the metal. When these harden again the alloy makes

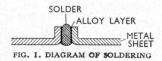

FIG. I. DIAGRAM OF SOLDERING

them adhere to each other, so making the whole joint firm (Fig. 1).

Many metals, when heated, become contaminated with oxide due to the chemical action of oxygen in the air (*see* CORROSION). To remove this oxide so that it does not weaken the soldered joint, borax or other chemicals known as 'fluxes' are spread over the surface of the metal before soldering. These combine with any oxide present to form an easily melted compound which runs off the metal surface, leaving it clean and ready for the solder.

Soldering is a low-temperature process, and solders are therefore mixtures of metals possessing a low melting-point. The commonest solder

is 'tinman's solder', an alloy of two parts of tin with one part of lead, having a melting-point of 180° C. This is the solder generally used for repairing pots and pans, and for securing copper wires to electrical contacts. It is simple to apply and can be conveniently used in the home. The metal is first cleaned and all grease removed. The joint is then smeared with flux and heated—either with the flame of a small blowpipe or by holding in contact with it a copper soldering iron which has either been heated over a flame or has an electrical heating coil built into it. When the joint is hot, the stick of solder is touched on the soldering iron, and some melts and runs down into the joint. It is then smoothed into position with the soldering iron (often called the 'bit') and allowed to harden. Tinman's solder melts and hardens instantaneously, with no intermediate semi-liquid, semi-solid stage.

Plumber's solder is an alloy of one part of tin and two parts of lead and is used for making 'wiped' joints around lead pipes and the lead sheaths of electric cables. It melts at 275° C. It does not melt instantaneously but when heated passes through a pasty stage. To make a wiped joint the melted solder is allowed to cool into this pasty condition, and then, with a thick cloth pad to protect the hand, the pasty solder is smeared and smoothed around the pipe or cable sheath to seal the joint.

Alloys in general use, especially in the manufacture of delicate electrical mechanisms, are the hard solders and silver solders made from various combinations of copper, zinc, silver, and sometimes cadmium. They melt at rather higher temperatures than the soft tin-lead solders. Silver solders are often applied by heating the metal pieces in a specially designed furnace to bring the joints up to the required temperature. Special fluxes are used.

A jointing operation carried out at an even higher temperature and applied to heavy copper pieces is brazing; in this a copper-zinc alloy is used. A blowpipe is essential for this operation, which is rather like fusion WELDING (q.v.), in which the metal is brought to melting temperature. Brazing may also be used for joining light steel or cast iron.

Until recently aluminium was regarded as a metal almost impossible to solder satisfactorily because of its tendency to oxidize when heated in air, and the difficulty of fluxing off the aluminium oxide satisfactorily. A method has now been devised, however, by which perfectly sound soldered joints in aluminium and aluminium alloys can be completed.

SOUND INSULATION. 1. Architects and building engineers in designing buildings have to concern themselves with the problems of noise—noise entering a building from outside, noise escaping from a building and disturbing neighbours, noise passing from one part of a building to another, and noise in a room distracting those who are working there. Apart from ensuring that equipment such as lifts is as quiet as possible, the defence against noise lies in planning wisely so that noisy places are isolated from those that need to be quiet, and also in using sound insulating and sound absorbing materials.

2. *Planning against noise.* When planning on a regional scale, noisy factories, for example, have to be sited away from dwelling houses, and aerodromes built in open places where the runways do not lead the planes over residential areas. On open sites trees often can be planted to break the sound: at London Airport walls have been built to protect surrounding houses from the noise of maintenance work on aircraft. In built-up areas buildings are often designed as tall blocks set well back from the street frontage, rather than lower buildings reaching to the street.

The arrangement of the rooms within a building has also to be carefully planned. In schools and colleges, for instance, workshops and practical rooms ought to be grouped together away from classrooms and libraries; in blocks of residential flats, bathrooms or kitchens should be placed next to noisy access corridors rather than sitting rooms or bedrooms. In factory rooms a noisy machine should, if possible, be placed as far as possible from other people working in the room, and the noise from it broken by a screen.

3. *Use of insulating and sound absorbing materials.* The insulation of a solid wall or floor against air-borne sound depends directly upon its mass; the heavier it is the more sound it keeps out. The light structures now often used for walls and floors are one reason why noise has become a greater problem of recent years in flats and houses: traditional load-bearing BRICKWORK (q.v.) is a much better sound insulator than a framed building with light panel walls (*see* BUILDING, PRINCIPLES OF).

But it is often uneconomical to achieve sound insulation by weight alone, so another principle —that of structural discontinuity—has to be used. If the paths by which sound travels through the structure are interrupted (by air gaps or by resilient material) the amount of energy transmitted is reduced. Double partitions, consisting of two 'leaves' with a cavity between; 'floating floors', in which the top surface is isolated from the structural floor by means of a resilient quilt such as glass wool; and independent or suspended ceilings are all forms of construction used for sound insulation. When very high insulation is necessary for a room, it may be built as a separate box inside the main structure and isolated from it at every point. Discontinuity is also the method of preventing 'impact sound'—such as vibrations communicated directly to the structure by footsteps.

The same methods are applied to doors and windows: they are made either very heavy or double, with an air space between; they are also made to close against strips of felt or rubber to seal the gaps round their edges. It is important to avoid all holes through an insulating partition, such as ventilation ducts and cracks between floorboards or around pipes; the conduction of sound along pipes and ducts also needs to be guarded against.

A good example of the use of all these methods of sound insulation is the Royal Festival Hall in London. The hall needed an exceptionally quiet background but, as its site immediately adjoins a railway bridge, the problem was acute. The following entirely successful means were adopted to overcome the noise:

1. The auditorium is placed in the centre of the building and entirely surrounded, except in its upper part, by other rooms where the need for quiet is not so important.

2. The auditorium walls are very heavy and in two independent leaves, each consisting of 10 inches of reinforced concrete, separated by a 10-inch airspace; the cavity is lined with sound-absorbent material.

3. The roof is also double, and the wall cavity continues between its two leaves. The inner leaf (6 in. thick) carries sleeper walls, leaving a 24-inch cavity, and between these and the outer concrete leaf (4 in. thick) is laid a glass wool quilt.

4. The auditorium doors are double with a wide lobby between them. These lobbies, and

also the surrounding foyers, have thick carpets and sound-absorbent ceilings. The windows to the foyers are of heavy glass.

5. The ventilation ducts are lined with absorbents to 'filter out' noise from outside and are carefully arranged to avoid making a connexion between the two leaves of the auditorium construction.

See also BUILDING, PRINCIPLES OF; BUILDING CONSTRUCTION; ACOUSTICS.

SOUND RECORDING AND REPRODUCTION.

The American inventor EDISON (q.v. Vol. V) can scarcely have foreseen the great industry he was founding by inventing the GRAMOPHONE (q.v. Vol. IX). Thousands of records are sold every day all over the world, but that is only one aspect of the sound-recording field. Without sound recording, sound films would be impossible, and broadcasting would be limited: the B.B.C. alone makes nearly 5,000 recordings each week—many of them lasting for 15 minutes or more.

The nature of SOUND is described in Volume III. A pure note causes the air to vibrate at some particular frequency, and the amplitude of the vibration determines the comparative loudness of the note. Most sounds are made up of mixtures of numerous pure notes, the number, frequencies, and relative amplitudes of which determine the pitch, loudness, and tone quality of the sound. A sound-recording system must be able to write down in some way the various notes and their amplitudes. The principal methods of recording are: engraving a wavy groove in suitable material, as for a gramophone record; photographing a track on to a film (see FILMS, PRODUCTION OF, Vol. IX); and varying the magnetism along the length of a steel tape or other magnetically sensitive medium.

In making gramophone records the sapphire-tipped cutting needle is attached to an electric vibrator; this is controlled by the MICROPHONE (q.v.), which picks up the sound vibrations and turns them into varying electric currents.

The simplest possible recording chain is shown in Fig. 1. A valve amplifier (B) makes the small currents developed by the microphone (A) powerful enough to drive the vibrator (C), thus making the cutting needle (D) engrave the record. The vibrator (called a cutter-head) is mounted on a carriage which travels on a rail from the outside to the inside of the disk upon which the record is engraved; the track, therefore, is spiral (starting at the outside and ending at the middle), with

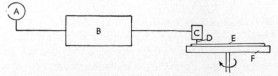

FIG. 1. DIAGRAM OF SOUND RECORDING
A. Microphone. B. Valve amplifier. C. Cutter-head. D. Cutting needle. E. Disk. F. Turn-table

sideways wiggles caused by the vibration of the needle.

Some idea of the way the needle cuts the wave-shapes can be obtained by resting the tip of a pencil on a piece of paper and moving the point from side to side so as to make a small line about a tenth of an inch long. If, while the tip of the pencil is still being vibrated, the paper is moved beneath it in a direction at right angles to that in which the pencil is moving, a wavy line will be produced on the paper. A gramophone record inspected through a magnifying glass shows similar wavy lines—but as the size of the vibrations is small, the waves in the record are also very small. The number of waves per inch is determined by the number of vibrations per second in the original sound, and the width of the wave is determined by the loudness of the sound.

The record is played back by reversing the process. A needle attached to a reproducing head (generally called a pick-up) is caused to follow the recorded groove and, consequently, to vibrate from side to side. This vibrational movement produces electric currents which are amplified and fed to a loud-speaker, which then re-creates the original sound.

The original record is often made on the surface of a soapy wax disk, or, if it has to be played back almost immediately, in a thin lacquer coating on an aluminium disk. The lacquer has to be soft enough to be easily cut away by the sapphire cutter, but hard enough to withstand the wear of a needle when the record is being played.

Copies of the original record, whether in wax or lacquer, are made by placing the record for a few hours in an ELECTROPLATING bath (q.v.), where a copper shell about $\frac{1}{32}$ inch thick is deposited on it. This shell, which has ridges where the original has grooves, can be used to stamp out duplicates in durable plastic material—the familiar gramophone records.

In recent years light-weight pick-ups have made it possible to produce such fine grooves that many more grooves to the inch can be recorded and, consequently, longer records made —some playing for 20 to 30 minutes. These records have to be played back by light-weight pick-ups, and so a softer material of finer grain, which greatly reduces background noise, is used for the records.

Nowadays the original recordings are generally made on magnetic tape or wire and copied on wax or lacquer. This makes it possible to remove unwanted clicks and bangs by cutting them out with scissors. The ease of making such recordings, the much reduced background noise, and the ability to erase the recordings so that the same tape or wire can be used again and again, have made this method popular for professional and amateur use.

The medium used in magnetic recording is either a steel wire or a plastic or paper tape coated or impregnated with a form of iron oxide. This has magnetic properties very like steel and can be easily magnetized. Electromagnets (*see* MAGNETS) make excellent magnetizers. The iron-oxide-coated tape is pulled steadily past three ring-shaped electromagnets, called 'heads' (Fig. 2). Into the first is fed a high-frequency electric current which demagnetizes the tape to erase any previous recording. The new sounds picked up by the microphone are led to the second electromagnet, called the 'recording head', and the tape, as it passes over the head, is magnetized in sympathy with the variations of the microphone sounds. The louder the sounds

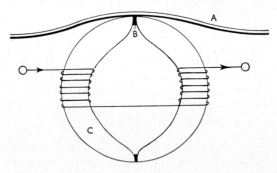

FIG. 2. RING-TYPE ELECTROMAGNET USED FOR ERASING, RECORDING, OR REPLAY HEADS IN TAPE-RECORDING MACHINES

A. Tape with oxide coating on the underside. B. Non-magnetic spacer. C. Core built up of thin sheets of soft iron

the stronger the microphone currents and, therefore, the greater the magnetization of the tape. The pitch of the sound governs the frequency of vibration in the microphone current, and this in turn governs the wavelike alternations in the magnetism induced in the tape.

The variations in the magnetism along the tape produce variations in the magnetism of the iron core of the third head, the 'replay head'. This causes electric currents to be induced in the coils surrounding the core, and these, amplified and fed to a loud-speaker, recreate faithfully the original sounds. Sometimes only two heads are used, the second one combining the functions of both the recording and the replay heads. For the best results the heads should occasionally be demagnetized.

Any unwanted part of the recording can be removed by magnetic erasure or by cutting and rejoining the tape—a simple matter.

See also Vol. III: SOUND; MAGNETISM.
See also Vol. IX: GRAMOPHONE; FILMS, PRODUCTION OF.

SPECTROMETER, *see* SPECTROSCOPE.

SPECTROSCOPE. This is an instrument for analysing substances by the light which they emit. LIGHT (q.v. Vol. III) travels in waves, its colour varying with the length of the waves. Most light is made up of a number of waves of different lengths, white light consisting of a mixture of almost all the light waves, while coloured lights contain only certain of them. The group of wavelengths emitted by an incandescent solid, liquid, or gas is characteristic of its chemical constitution. If, therefore, an object is or can be made incandescent (glowing with heat) its composition can be analysed by splitting up the light it emits into its constituent wavelengths. This may be done by means of a spectroscope (*see* COLOUR, Vol. III).

When light passes at an angle from one medium (such as air) into another of different density (such as glass) it is bent or refracted at a different angle to the surface of the medium (*see* WAVE MOTION, Section 3, Vol. III), and similarly on passing from glass to air it is again refracted. When passing through glass with two parallel sides the second refraction corrects the first, and the direction of light coming through an ordinary window is apparently unchanged. But if light passes through two sides of a triangular prism, the result of the two refractions (entering and leaving the glass) is to bend the light considerably, so that it emerges from the glass at a different angle from which it entered. Different wavelengths are refracted at different angles, and the light is, therefore, split up into its bands of different-coloured lights—its spectrum (*see* Vol. III, Colour Plate, opp. p. 96).

is made for this by first obtaining the spectrum of the arc alone.

The spectroscope thus provides a very efficient and sensitive means of detecting the presence of unknown elements in heated substances. Its development has also made it possible to determine the chemical composition of distant

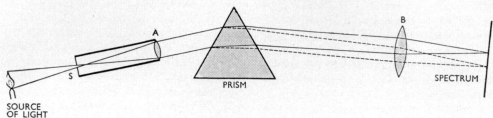

FIG. I. DIAGRAM OF A SPECTROSCOPE

A prism alone cannot give a clear spectrum as the different colours overlap and run into each other. In addition to a prism the spectroscope has two lenses or groups of lenses (Fig. I): one, the 'collimator' (A), which focuses the incoming light on to the prism as a straight beam, and another (B), which focuses the different waves of light from the prism so that they reach an eyepiece or photographic screen. Light can enter the spectroscope only through a narrow slit (S) in the collimator, which makes the beam a narrow strip so as to reduce the effect of overlapping. The ability of a spectroscope to show a clear distinction between the bands formed by light of two nearly equal wavelengths is known as its 'resolving power', and depends chiefly on the width of the slit, but also on the efficiency of the system of lenses, which may be very elaborate in really accurate instruments. The light which falls on the slit usually consists of a mixture of many hundreds of wavelengths, and the spectrum, therefore, shows an equal number of bands of colour.

Most incandescent solids give a continuous spectrum, that is, the bands merge into one another. This is useless for analytical work, but in the spectra of gases the bands are separated sufficiently to be distinguishable, and each gas gives its own particular pattern. The spectra of gases are obtained by passing an ELECTRIC CURRENT (q.v.) through them to make them glow; the spectra of solids and liquids are obtained by vaporizing them in the heat of an electric arc. This will, of course, give its own spectrum as well as that of the element in question, and allowance

STARS (q.v. Vol. III). This is done by comparing the spectrum of the starlight with standard spectra prepared with known elements.

Spectra obtained from light emitted from substances are called 'emission' spectra. It is not always possible to make substances incandescent, but valuable information can also be obtained by passing light of known characteristics through an unknown substance (usually a gas), which absorbs certain wavelengths of the light and leaves clearly defined blanks or black bands in its spectrum. Spectra of this type, known as 'absorption' spectra, are used to provide information about the atmospheres on the planets.

The prism produces spectra for comparison; it cannot be used to make absolute measurements of wavelengths. For this a different device known as a 'diffraction grating' is used instead of a prism. This is in principle a series of very fine slits very close together (the distances are of the same order as the wavelengths of light itself). As the light is split up by the slits it is diffracted or bent round them (*see* WAVE MOTION, Section 4, Vol. III). Waves of different lengths are diffracted by different amounts and thus are isolated to form a spectrum, from which the length of the waves can be calculated if the distance between the slits is known. The unit of measurement is a ten-millionth of a millimetre, called an Ångström unit after the Swedish physicist who introduced it in 1868. The wavelength of deep red light is 7,600 Ångström units and of violet light is 3,900 Ångström units; these are the limits of the visible spectrum.

For chemical analysis the spectrograph, in

which the screen is replaced by a photographic plate, is used so that records of spectra can be kept. In the spectrometer the instrument is adapted so that it can measure the angle of refraction of light and can thus be used to measure wavelengths.

See also Vol. III: COLOUR; LIGHT; WAVE MOTION.

SPEEDOMETER. This is an instrument for indicating the speed of a moving vehicle. For anything that runs on wheels, we must know how fast the wheels are rotating in order to know the speed. Since the vehicle moves forward a distance equal to the circumference of its wheels for each revolution of these wheels, we can tell how fast the vehicle is travelling per minute if we know what is the circumference of the wheels and how many revolutions the wheels make a minute. All speedometers are really revolution indicators or 'tachometers', with a scale reading in miles per hour instead of revolutions per minute.

All speedometers are driven indirectly from the wheels of the vehicle—in cars, the drive is usually taken from the gear-box; in some motor-cycles it is taken from the hub of the front wheel.

1. TYPES OF SPEEDOMETER.

(*a*) *Mechanical speedometer.* This type is driven by a flexible shaft which rotates a light framework called a 'spider', carrying two or more balance weights held in position by springs. As the spider's speed of rotation increases with that of the wheels, the weights fly outwards, and this movement is transmitted to a pointer on the scale of the instrument.

(*b*) *Electrical speedometer.* This type consists of two elements—the ELECTRIC GENERATOR (q.v.) and the indicator. The generator, usually mounted close to the point from which it is driven, is a small dynamo wound to produce a voltage proportional to its speed of rotation. This is connected to the indicator by a twin flex. The indicator is merely a voltmeter with a scale marked in miles per hour instead of electrical units. The advantage of this type of instrument is that the indicator is very small and may be mounted any distance from the driving point. It is, however, not so well adapted for recording mileage as it is for speed.

(*c*) *Magnetic drag speedometer.* This type of instrument, which is simple, cheap, and robust, is the type now most commonly fitted to motor vehicles (**Fig. 1**). It consists simply of a magnet,

A, rotated by the speedometer drive at a speed proportional to the speed of the wheels. Shrouding this magnet is an iron cup, B, which tends to be dragged round by the rotating lines of force from the magnet (*see* MAGNETISM, Vol. III), but is partially prevented by a hair-spring, C. A pointer D is connected to B and is dragged round

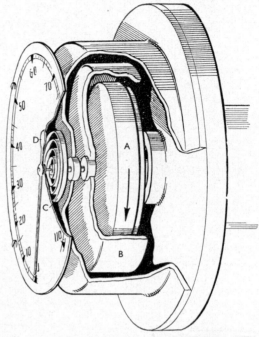

FIG. 1. DIAGRAM OF MAGNETIC DRAG SPEEDOMETER WITH PARTS CUT AWAY

A. Magnet. B. Iron cup. C. Hair-spring. D. Pointer

by the magnetic force to an extent proportional to the speed of rotation of A.

2. MILEAGE COUNTER MECHANISM. Most speedometers indicate mileage as well as speed—this is simply a matter of counting the number of revolutions made by the wheels. Fig. 2 shows a typical arrangement for doing this. The speedometer drive rotates a pair of gear-wheels known as a 'worm' and a 'worm wheel', which in turn drives a metal finger called a 'pawl'. The finger of the pawl connects with a toothed wheel called the RATCHET wheel (q.v.), and moves the wheel round by one tooth for each revolution of the worm wheel. The ratio of the worm and worm wheel, the number of teeth on the ratchet, and the gearing of the take-off for the speedometer drive are so arranged that the ratchet wheel is moved $\frac{1}{16}$th of a revolution for every mile the car travels (for every $\frac{1}{16}$th of a mile in some speedometers). The ratchet wheel drives a series of drums marked with figures, each occupying $\frac{1}{10}$th of the circumference. Normally,

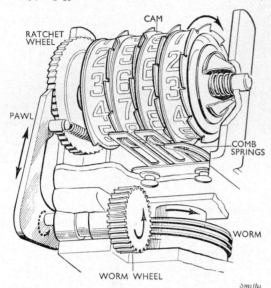

FIG. 2. DIAGRAM OF A MILEAGE COUNTER

This is seen from the back with the units drum on the left

all but the right-hand drum are prevented from rotating by comb springs, but once in every revolution a bump or 'cam' on this drum lifts the appropriate spring and allows the next drum to move round $\frac{1}{10}$th of a revolution before letting the spring snap back into place. Similarly the second drum controls the movement of the third, and so on—each drum rotating $\frac{1}{10}$th of a revolution (or one digit) for every complete revolution of the drum on its right.

See also Vol. IV: FLYING INSTRUMENTS.

SPRINGS. 1. The essential characteristic of a spring is its resilience—that is, its capacity of resuming its original shape after it has been pulled, pushed, or twisted out of it. The fact that a spring always tries to return to its normal shape can be made use of in endlessly different ways. For instance, when a mechanical toy is wound up, a certain amount of energy is stored in its compressed spring. Then, as soon as the spring is released, it will try to uncoil itself and, through various driving mechanisms, will cause the toy to move. In other words, it is giving back the mechanical energy which went to winding it up. This ability of a spring to store mechanical energy and then, when required, to give it back,

is the reason for its usefulness. When a watch is wound, for example, the wound spring gives the watch the energy to operate until the spring has run down, that is, has resumed its normal shape. When a diver jumps on a spring-board he pushes the board downwards and, at the moment he wants to leave it, the board, in trying to return to its usual position, gives him a good take-off. The spring on a door is another typical example. When the door is opened, the spring is compressed, but when the door is released, the compressed spring restores the energy taken in compressing it and, in returning to normal, closes the door. The energy stored in a spring is known as 'strain energy'.

2. SPRING MATERIALS. Many different steels and non-ferrous ALLOYS (q.v.) have been developed in order to provide the essential resilience needed for springs. Other properties also are essential, such as resistance to fatigue, that is, to the liability to breakage or failure due to repeated applications of load (see STRESS AND STRAIN), and resistance to CORROSION (q.v.) in situations where the springs have to operate under high temperatures. A very common metal is a steel alloy containing about 0·6% carbon and a certain proportion of other elements such as manganese or silicon; this alloy is very elastic and has a high endurance against fatigue. Springs, however, may be made from a number of other materials provided they satisfy the prime requirement of elasticity. Fuzed quartz and phosphor bronze are used in delicate ELECTRICAL INSTRUMENTS (q.v.) such as galvanometers. Rubber, either by itself or bonded to steel, is also used, particularly to form a cushioning under machinery and thus to absorb vibration (see SHOCK ABSORBERS). Compressed air in a cylinder, closed with a tightly fitting piston, is also used as a spring. Such arrangements are often known as resilient mountings. Small springs can be made without heating the steel; the spring is wound cold on to a rotating cylindrical rod, or 'mandrel', equal in diameter to the bore of the finished spring. Larger springs are forged hot by blacksmiths and are machined. All springs, however, need hardening followed by tempering (see HEAT TREATMENT) to make them tough enough for their purpose.

3. TYPES OF SPRING. One of the commonest types of spring, and the one most used to store energy, is the spiral or clock or watch spring (Fig. 1a). In this, the outer end is anchored, while

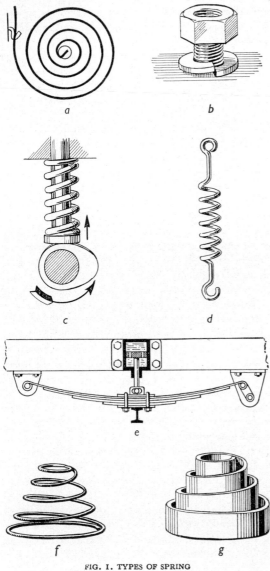

FIG. I. TYPES OF SPRING

a. Watch spring. *b.* Spring washer. *c.* Helical spring used in compression. *d.* Helical spring used in tension. *e.* Semi-elliptic spring with hydraulic shock absorber. *f.* Conical spring. *g.* Volute spring

the inner end is attached to a winding arbor. By means of this, the spring is compressed when wound and, to drive the watch or clock, the 'strain energy' is taken off through an escapement mechanism at a controlled rate (*see* CLOCKS AND WATCHES). The same type of spiral spring is commonly used for mechanical toys.

Apart from driving clockwork mechanisms springs have countless uses in engineering, one of the chief of which is to return a part of a mechan-ism to a given position after it has been displaced. Thus the valves of INTERNAL COMBUSTION EN-GINES (q.v.) are returned to their circular seats by helical springs in compression placed on the long stems of the valves (Fig. 1*c*). At regular inter-vals during the revolutions of the engine, each valve is lifted momentarily off its seat by a cam and then returned under the action of its spring.

Helical springs, as well as having uses when in compression, have numerous applications when in tension (Fig. 1*d*), for example, the familiar spring balance. Hooke's law states that the ex-tension of a spring is proportional to the force pulling it. Obviously, therefore, it is necessary only to mark the positions of a point on the free end of a suspended spring corresponding to each one of a series of loads, and an easy and fairly accurate method of weighing is obtained. Helical tension springs are also used to return some part to its original position, such as 'pull-off' brake springs. A helical spring derives its resilience from the twisting (or torsion) of the wire from which it is made.

For generations vehicles have been provided with 'suspension' springs to provide cushioning between the axle and the body of the vehicle. In modern vehicles, whether they be railway coaches or motor-cars, the form commonly adopted is the 'semi-elliptic', so-called because of its shape (Fig. 1*e*). It consists of a series of thin, wide beams placed one on the other, the top and longest one having holes or 'eyes' at each end to accommodate short rods or pins. The front pin passes through holes in a bracket bolted to the vehicle frame; the rear pin passes through holes in a 'shackle', which is connected by another pin to a second bracket bolted to the frame. The successive plates or 'leaves' of the spring are rigidly connected together at their centres and to the axle. Each leaf takes its part in carrying the load imposed between the axle and the vehicle. The plate spring and the watch spring derive their resilience from the bending of the strip of which they are made.

Among the many other forms of springs used in engineering is the conical spring, the simplest form of which is to be found in a jack-in-the-box (Fig. 1*f*). This is used for compression under light loads where compactness is an important feature. In circumstances where compactness is essential but there is a heavy load, volute springs are used (Fig. 1*g*). These are used, for example, under a railway wagon as well as a plate spring.

An important use of springs is to prevent the nuts in moving machinery from slackening. For this purpose a spring-washer is interposed between the nut and one of the parts the nut and bolt are holding together (Fig. 1*b*). The elastic force exerted by the compressed washer prevents the nut from turning.

See also SHOCK ABSORBERS.

STANDARDIZATION, *see* PRODUCTION ENGINEERING; ENGINEERING DESIGN; MEASUREMENT, UNITS OF.

STANDARDS, *see* MEASUREMENT, UNITS OF.

STATICS, *see* MECHANICS.

STEAM. Water, like all liquids, consists of molecules free to move relatively to each other, but bound into a coherent liquid by forces between them (*see* MATTER, Vol. III). If a dish of water is stood in a closed vessel empty of air, water molecules will leave the liquid and fly about the vessel, until a steady state is reached with molecules of water continually entering and leaving the liquid, and a steady concentration of free molecules moving about the inside of the vessel, above the water. The molecules leaving the surface constitute what we know as 'evaporation'; the molecules returning constitute 'condensation'; and the space in the vessel is filled with WATER VAPOUR (q.v. Vol. III) or steam. The free molecules banging about on the sides of the vessel produce a pressure, the amount of which depends on the temperature. This is known as the 'vapour pressure' of water at the given temperature.

This arrangement of water and water vapour in an otherwise empty vessel is, in fact, a steam BOILER (q.v.), used to generate steam pressure to drive a STEAM ENGINE or STEAM TURBINE (qq.v.). If a cylinder of water is covered by a piston, the pressure on the piston is that of the atmosphere. If we then start heating the water in the cylinder, nothing will apparently happen until the temperature is reached at which the vapour pressure of water equals that of the atmosphere. At this point, the water will suddenly begin to boil—that is, to evaporate 'from inside itself', so to speak. Bubbles of water vapour will form, and eventually a layer of steam will rise above the boiling water. The 'boiling-point' of water (and conversely the condensation temperature of steam) depends, therefore, on the outside pressure.

In our example the temperature rose as we added heat, until the water began to boil, the heat going to speed up the water molecules. But once the water begins to boil, however much heat we add, there will be no further temperature rise until all the water has turned into steam. During this process, the heat energy will go partly into pushing the piston up steadily against the atmosphere, but mostly into separating the water molecules against the natural forces trying to bind them together, as the water is turned into steam.

The total energy put into evaporating a pound of water at a given temperature is known as the 'latent heat of evaporation' of water. As long as there is some water left in the cylinder, the steam over the water will be at the temperature corresponding to the boiling-point of water at the given pressure, and in this condition it is known as 'saturated'. If we continue to add heat after all the water has evaporated, the temperature begins to rise again and the steam continues to expand. The hotter it gets, the more nearly the steam behaves like a 'perfect gas' (*see* GASES, PROPERTIES OF). Steam at a temperature higher than the boiling-point of water at the given pressure is known as 'superheated'. The points to remember are that superheated steam must be cooled or compressed before it will condense, and that saturated steam begins to condense at once if it is either cooled or compressed. When saturated steam is cooled or compressed, droplets of water form in it, and the steam is known as 'wet'. In our example, we have combined the boiler with the engine cylinder. In practice, of course, they are separate, but the work done by a steam engine or turbine is on the same principle as the work done by the piston.

See also GASES, PROPERTIES OF; STEAM ENGINE.
See also Vol. III: WATER VAPOUR.

STEAM ENGINE. The reciprocating steam engine has changed little in essentials since about 1870 (*see* ENGINES, HISTORY OF); it reached its highest development round about the turn of the century, when it was by far the most important HEAT ENGINE (q.v.) in existence. Large stationary steam engines then provided the power for factories and blast furnaces, while smaller, mobile engines drove tractors and locomotives.

Today, it has been largely replaced by the STEAM TURBINE (q.v.) and the diesel engine and petrol engine (*see* INTERNAL COMBUSTION ENGINE). It is now mainly used for railway engines (*see* LOCOMOTIVES, STEAM, Vol. IV) and for fairly small stationary power units where steam is available in any case—as in chemical works. Consequently the demand is now for convenient and reasonably low-priced small steam engines rather than for large ones of very high efficiency. The elaborate modifications, therefore, of the extremely efficient big horizontal engines of the 1890's are now no longer found.

All reciprocating steam engines consist of one or more sets of pistons and cylinders. The steam from the BOILER (q.v.) is admitted to the cylinder (A) by means of some kind of valve gear, and the piston (B), pushed by the steam, drives a crankshaft (C) through a piston rod (D) and connecting rod (E) (Fig. 1*a*, *b*). These features can be seen in a very simple form in the familiar toy steam engine with oscillating cylinder, in which a single hole in the end of the cylinder is brought opposite the steam inlet and the exhaust outlet in turn as the cylinder rocks back and forth.

Most steam engines are 'double-acting'—that is, the steam pushes alternately on both sides of the piston, in contrast to the petrol engine in which only the top of the piston is subjected to pressure. The connecting rod is, therefore, not fastened direct to the underside of the piston, as in a petrol engine. The steam is prevented from escaping round the piston rod when there is steam pressure in the lower half of the cylinder by an important device known as a 'gland'. In Fig. 1*c* (a cross-section) the gland prevents steam

escaping from the inside of the cylinder as the piston rod slides to and fro through the hole in the bottom of the cylinder. The gland nuts are tightened so that the cover (G) forces the packing against both the piston rod and the walls of the hole.

The way a steam engine works is most easily demonstrated by a simple 'slide-valve' engine.

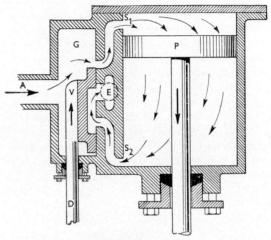

FIG. 2. DIAGRAM OF A SLIDE-VALVE ENGINE JUST BEGINNING ITS DOWNWARD STROKE

A. Steam inlet. G. Steam chest. s_1, s_2. Holes leading to cylinder. E. Hole leading to exhaust. V. Slide valve. D. Rod connected to crankshaft. P. Piston

Fig. 2 shows a cross-section of the cylinder and slide-valve as the piston is just beginning its downward stroke. Steam from the boiler is led through the pipe into a box on the side of the cylinder called the 'steam chest' (G). Two holes (s_1, s_2) lead from G to the top and bottom of the cylinder, while a third hole (E) connects with the exhaust pipe. The three holes are covered and uncovered by a sliding box (V), the slide-valve, which is moved up and down at the proper time by a rod (D) connected to the crankshaft. When the top hole is uncovered, steam from A enters the top of the cylinder and forces the piston (P) downward. Meanwhile, the bottom hole and the hole E are both uncovered on the inside of the valve, and so steam from the underside of the piston has a clear path to the exhaust.

When the piston has partly completed the downward stroke, the rod begins to move upwards, making the slide-valve cut off the top hole (s_1). The steam already in the top end of the cylinder continues to expand, pushing the piston farther down. The point at which the

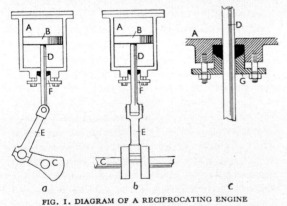

FIG. 1. DIAGRAM OF A RECIPROCATING ENGINE

a, *b*. Side and end views. *c*. Detail of gland. A. Cylinder. B. Piston. C. Crankshaft. D. Piston rod. E. Connecting rod. F. Gland. G. Gland cover

valve cuts off the steam inlet to the cylinder is known as the 'cut-off'. As the rod pushes the valve farther up, and just as the piston is approaching the bottom of its stroke, the bottom hole (s_2) is cut off by the bottom edge of the valve. Just before the piston begins to move upwards again, the valve, continuing its travel upwards, once more uncovers the bottom hole, this time to the steam supply, and at the same time uncovers the top hole on the inside of the valve, allowing the spent steam on the top of the piston to flow out through the exhaust pipe on the return stroke. This cycle of operations is repeated continuously and, of course, very much faster than it takes to describe it.

The valve rod moves up and down with the same frequency as the piston rod, but starts to move upwards when the piston rod is already half-way down. The engine would work, therefore, if the valve rod were worked by a crank about 90° in advance of the main crank (Fig. 3).

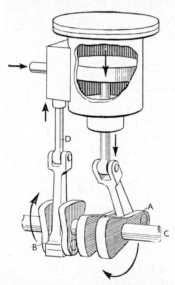

FIG. 3. PRINCIPLE OF THE SLIDE-VALVE ENGINE
A. Main crank. B. Valve crank, 90° ahead of main crank. C. Crankshaft. D. Valve rod

In practice, the valve rod is worked not by a crank but by a device, identical in effect, called an eccentric, which takes up less room (Fig. 4a). The eccentric consists of a circular wheel (A), mounted off-centre on the crankshaft (C), and rotating inside a metal shroud (B) which is connected to the rod (D).

If the eccentric were set 90° in the opposite direction to the main crank, the engine would

run the other way—and this is the principle of the simplest of all reversing gears—Stephenson's

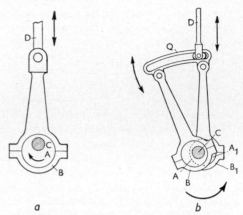

a   b

FIG. 4. a. SIMPLE ECCENTRIC. b. STEPHENSON'S LINK MOTION
A, A_1. Eccentrics. B, B_1. Eccentric straps. C. Crankshaft.
D. Valve rod. Q. Quadrant

Link Motion, invented by George Stephenson himself. In this mechanism, the crankshaft has two eccentrics—one (A) 90° ahead of the main crank and the other (A_1) 90° behind it (Fig. 4b). Either may be arranged to move the rod (D) according to the way a sliding mechanism called the 'quadrant' (Q) is adjusted. In Fig. 4b eccentric A_1 is moving the rod (D), while A is merely oscillating the other end of the quadrant. Some locomotive reversing gears work on this principle, though the details may vary.

In modern steam engines, the box-shaped slide-valve is usually replaced by a piston valve that does exactly the same job, and in locomotives the reversing gear is also used to alter the point of cut-off so as to make the most economical use of the steam power.

Ideally, steam should be admitted to the cylinder at full blast at the start of the stroke and then shut off with a snap. On the huge horizontal engines of the 1890's, elaborate mechanisms were devised so that the cut-off could be regulated very exactly. Again, for maximum efficiency the steam should be expanded to the lowest possible pressure, so as to make the fullest use of the energy put into it in the boiler. Accordingly, the exhaust from a very efficient steam engine is usually led to a 'condenser'—a large metal box kept cold by cooling water circulating through tubes—which condenses it, the condensed water being pumped back into the boiler. An engine with a condenser need not exhaust steam into the atmosphere, and the final pressure in the cylinder may be considerably below atmospheric.

In a single cylinder engine, to expand a useful quantity of steam to a sufficiently low pressure,

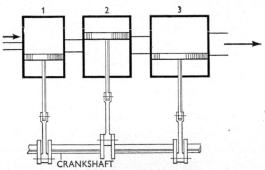

FIG. 5. COMPOUNDING CYLINDERS

Steam is led into the high-pressure cylinder (1), from thence into the larger intermediate cylinder (2), and finally into the still larger low-pressure cylinder (3)

the cylinder must have a stroke too long to be practical. Two or three cylinders are, therefore, often used, the pistons all being connected to the same crankshaft (Fig. 5). Exhaust steam from the first, high-pressure cylinder is passed to the inlet of an intermediate-pressure cylinder of larger diameter, and its exhaust to a low-pressure cylinder of still greater diameter. This method, known as 'compounding', is also used on locomotives, even though they have no condenser, for three cylinders, for instance, of reasonably short stroke can more conveniently handle a given mass of steam with less heat losses than one long-stroke cylinder.

See also STEAM; HEAT ENGINES; ENGINES, HISTORY OF; STEAM TURBINE.

See also Vol. IV: LOCOMOTIVES, STEAM; STEAMSHIPS.

STEAM TURBINE. A turbine is a rotary engine which is driven by a stream of fluid (liquid or gas) directed on to the blades of the rotor shaft. In a steam turbine this fluid is steam. The power, or energy, is derived from the change of momentum of the steam as it enters, passes through, and leaves the blades (*see* MECHANICS). The speed of the flow of the fluid, which in water turbines is produced by a fall in level, in steam turbines is produced by the pressure of steam from the BOILER (q.v.).

The great advantages of the turbine are freedom from vibration and noise, smooth and uni-

form rotary force, and ability to handle large quantities of fluid—in this case steam. Its simplicity and reliability make it a suitable type of engine to use for driving pumps, blowers, and other equipment. In these cases the turbine's most efficient speed is usually much higher than that of the machine it is driving, so a speed reduction gear usually has to be used. Steam turbines do not work very efficiently in small sizes.

Very large steam turbines in conjunction with speed reduction GEARS (q.v.) are used for driving ships: in fact, a steam turbine is the only practicable kind of engine for driving a ship such as the QUEEN ELIZABETH (q.v. Vol. IV), where the total power developed by sixteen steam turbines is about 200,000 horse-power. It is in large electrical POWER STATIONS (q.v.) that the steam turbine reaches its highest development, and many power stations in Great Britain contain turbines of more than 80,000 horse-power each.

Fig. 1 shows a simple form of impulse turbine. In this the steam issues from a stationary nozzle (or nozzles) which is curved so as to direct the jet on to a ring of blades attached to a rotating wheel or disk. These blades are shaped to 'catch' the steam from the nozzle smoothly, and they are curved so that they change the direction of the jet and in so doing receive an impulse which pushes them forward.

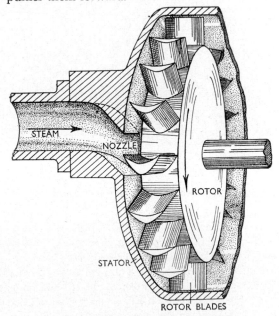

FIG. 1. DIAGRAM OF AN IMPULSE TURBINE

The steam, directed on to the blades, gives them an impulse which rotates the rotor

If, instead of using a separate wheel with guide blades, we were to mount the nozzle itself on a wheel, the reaction of the issuing jet would drive it in the opposite direction to the impulse wheel. The very first steam turbine, made 2,000 years ago by Hero of Alexandria, was a pure reaction turbine of this type, but for various reasons it is never used nowadays (*see* p. 151).

There is another kind of turbine (Fig. 2) which combines the principles of impulse and reaction but is usually referred to simply as a 'reaction' turbine. An essential characteristic of a nozzle is that the passage narrows from the inlet onwards, and consequently the fluid which enters at a

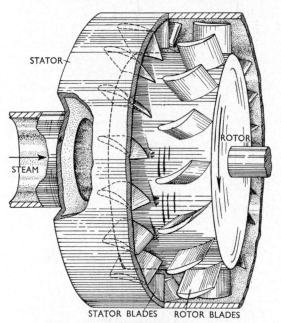

FIG. 2. DIAGRAM OF A REACTION TURBINE

The stator blades form nozzles through which the steam is accelerated and directed on to the nozzles formed by the rotor blades

relatively low speed must come out at a much higher speed. The increase in speed is produced by a drop of pressure, the pressure of the fluid being higher as it enters the nozzle than as it leaves. The casing in Fig. 2 carries a complete ring of nozzles which, as in the impulse turbine, are curved and direct the steam on to the moving blades at the most effective angle. The moving blades are also nozzles, similar to the stationary nozzles but facing the other way, and in addition to catching and deflecting the steam issuing from the stationary nozzles, they also accelerate

it, the drive coming half from an impulse and half from a reaction force. The jet speed in this type of turbine is half what it is in an impulse turbine having the same blade speed. In either case the steam leaves the moving blades more or less at right angles to the direction of motion of the blades.

To obtain as much power as possible from each pound of coal burned in the boiler it is necessary to work with a high steam pressure and temperature at the inlet to the turbine and as low a pressure as possible at the exhaust (*see* HEAT ENGINES). By condensing the exhaust steam in a separate condenser, using a large quantity of cooling water, a very low exhaust pressure can be maintained and the condensed steam pumped back to the boiler as pure feed water. If the steam were allowed to expand from boiler pressure to condenser pressure in one step, the jet velocity from the nozzle would be more than 5,000 feet a second (about 3,500 miles an hour). It is impossible to build a turbine to run fast enough to utilize such a high jet speed efficiently —indeed, a single stage steam turbine normally has a very low efficiency. To obtain a convenient jet speed and enable a high efficiency to be achieved, both with impulse and reaction turbines, the pressure drop from boiler to condenser is divided over a large number of stages. In these multi-stage turbines there are alternately rows of stationary blades carried in the casing and rows of blades attached to the rotor, arranged so that the steam is directed to enter each row of stationary and moving blades at the proper angle. The stationary blades are always nozzles: the rotor blades are also nozzles in the case of a reaction turbine but only guide channels in the case of an impulse turbine.

The successive stages are normally arranged side by side along a horizontal axis, constituting what is called an 'axial flow' turbine. The steam enters at one end and leaves at the other, or, if the flow is very big, the steam may enter at the middle and leave at both ends, an arrangement called 'double flow'. The casing consists of a bottom half, which carries the bearings that support the rotor, and a top half, which is bolted to the bottom half at the horizontal joint after the rotor has been placed in position.

When the stages are very numerous it has proved most practicable to use two or more casings or cylinders, usually arranged in line and with the shafts coupled together. Fig. 3 shows a

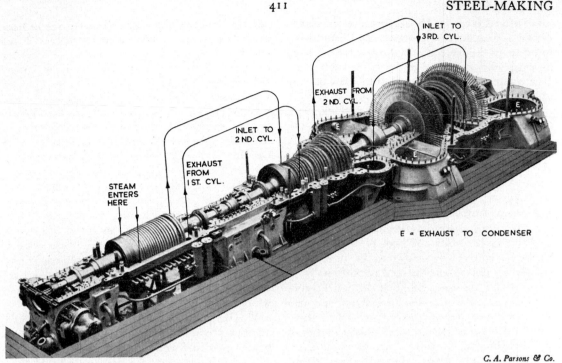

INLET TO
3RD. CYL.

EXHAUST FROM
2ND. CYL.

INLET TO
2ND. CYL.

EXHAUST
FROM
1ST. CYL.

STEAM
ENTERS
HERE

E = EXHAUST TO CONDENSER

C. A. Parsons & Co.

A TWO-CYLINDER STEAM TURBINE WITH THE TOP HALF OF THE CASINGS REMOVED

two-cylinder turbine with the top half casings removed and the rotors in position.

Modern turbines are supplied by the boiler with steam that is highly superheated (*see* STEAM). As the steam passes through the turbine, its pressure and temperature fall until at a certain stage all the superheat is lost, and thereafter drops of water are formed by condensation of some of the steam. These drops damage the blades and reduce the turbine efficiency, and this is one reason why the steam, after passing through the high-pressure turbine, is sometimes re-superheated before entering the medium-pressure turbine.

See also HEAT ENGINES; GAS TURBINE.

STEEL-MAKING. This consists of melting down bars of pig iron which have come from the BLAST FURNACE (q.v.), refining them, and extracting the impurities, which may comprise as much as one-tenth the weight and one-quarter the volume of the iron. Scrap iron and steel are also used as raw materials, and are melted down with the pig iron. In nearly all modern works the blast furnace and the steelworks stand side by side, and the molten crude iron is taken straight to the steel furnace in liquid form.

The key to steel-making is to reduce the carbon content of the metal very considerably, and to get the precise amount of carbon in the finished steel alloy. The steel-maker normally produces his metal within a two-thousandth of the specified content—that is, to within about 3 ounces of carbon in every hundredweight of steel. The steel-maker also reduces the silicon and manganese in the steel below a certain safe level, and extracts the sulphur, and above all the phosphorus, as far as he can.

Impurities vary widely in pig iron. Some iron is so free from phosphorus that the steel-maker can afford to ignore it, in which case he uses a so-called 'acid' lined furnace, built of silica bricks which have very good heat-resisting properties. But if he has to remove phosphorus, his furnace is lined with 'basic' bricks of dolomite or magnesite (*see* FIRECLAYS AND REFRACTORIES) because the lime which has to be used to reduce the phosphorus attacks silica at high temperatures and would soon wear out a silica-lined furnace.

The steel-maker works his process at a tremendously high temperature. If pig iron is melted and brought to a temperature of about 1,650° C., then the carbon in the iron, and also the silicon and manganese, will combine with any oxygen they come in contact with, and will float off as gas. So the steel-maker has to run a furnace at this very high temperature in order to melt and heat his raw materials, and then he has to bring his molten metal in contact with oxygen in some way to draw out the main impurities. In a 'basic' furnace he has also to draw out the phosphorus by the use of lime.

There are three main ways of making steel: (*a*) the open hearth, (*b*) Bessemer, and (*c*) electric arc methods.

(*a*) *Open hearth furnace.* Four-fifths of the 200 million tons of steel made in the world each year is made in open hearth furnaces, invented in England in 1867 by the Siemens brothers (*see* IRON AND STEEL INDUSTRY). An open hearth furnace is perhaps most easily imagined as a shallow tank surrounded by walls and roof of heat-resisting bricks. Along one side, known as the 'front wall', are sliding doors, and in the opposite or 'back wall' is the taphole, plugged with heatproof clay, except when the molten steel is being run off. In each of the narrow end-walls are three holes, the detailed design of which is a matter of great importance, and there are many different methods of planning and arranging them. Through the centre hole hot gas or oil is blown into the furnace, and through the others hot air. They mix and burn with a very hot flame over the top of the bath.

Through the doors in the front wall are charged the raw materials, mainly the pig iron and scrap, in their carefully regulated quantities, order, and compositions. The pig iron may be charged to the furnace either molten or in solid pigs. It is clearly more economical if it is possible to charge molten iron already heated, as it is when the blast furnace and steelworks are near together.

On each side of the bath containing the metal are two heating chambers (Fig. 1), one of each pair pre-heating air and the other fuel gas. These chambers are filled with open brickwork on a chequerboard pattern. The gas and the air are led through one pair of chambers to the furnace, which they enter through the holes in one end wall. While the hot gas and air unite and burn fiercely over the bath, the very hot spent gases leave through the holes in the opposite end of the furnace, and pass through the second pair of bricked chambers, which are thus heated. When the chambers heating the incoming gas and air have begun to cool, the direction of the flow is reversed—a reversal which takes place about every 20 minutes and results in a steadily increasing temperature. This temperature has to be carefully controlled as the furnace roof's normal working temperature is within perhaps 50° C. of the melting-point of the materials from which it is made.

Where oil fuel is used instead of gas, the air alone is preheated at the furnace, and the oil is heated only to a slight degree outside the furnace and is then pumped to a pressure nozzle. With oil an even greater temperature is obtained, causing a quicker melting of the charge and therefore a higher output from the furnace.

Once the charge is melted, the steel-maker starts to refine the metal—that is, to extract the impurities. Oxygen is introduced in the form of iron ore (containing iron oxide) or millscale (an oxide film which flakes off the hot steel during later rolling or forging operations). These materials, when well mixed into the bath of metal, join up with the carbon to form carbon monoxide which bubbles up through the metal and burns off in blue flames.

The silicon and manganese are also oxidized to a large extent, but phosphorus has to be worked out into a slag, a thick surface scum, to prevent its returning to the metal after it has oxidized. This slag, if made rich in lime, attracts most of the phosphorus in the metal into it and holds it there (*see* Colour Plate, opp. p. 416). Phosphorus-rich slag is, incidentally, a valuable ARTIFICIAL FERTILIZER (q.v. Vol. VI).

An average open hearth furnace holds 80 to 100 tons of steel. There are giants of 300, 400, and even 500 tons, but smaller furnaces are more common. A typical 'heat' of steel takes

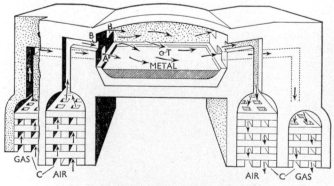

FIG. 1. DIAGRAM OF OPEN HEARTH FURNACE
A. Gas or oil port. B. Air ports. C. Heating chambers. T. Taphole

B.I.S.R.A.

FIG. 2. 'FETTLING' AN OPEN HEARTH FURNACE AFTER ONE CAST HAS BEEN TAPPED AND BEFORE THE NEXT CHARGE IS MADE

from 7 to 15 hours, according to the size of the furnace, the raw materials and fuel used, and several other things.

When the metal reaches the right composition and temperature, the furnace is tapped. The metal is run off through the taphole into waiting ladles, like huge buckets, from which it is 'teemed' into moulds to cool into ingots, ready for the next stage of the manufacturing process (*see* METALLURGY, Section 3).

As soon as the furnace is tapped the furnace crew, usually numbering four, assisted by crews from all other nearby furnaces, start 'fettling'— that is, repairing the furnace by first cleaning it out and then throwing dolomite (magnesium limestone) or silica sand into any holes in the bottom or the walls, particularly at the slag line. This is an exceedingly arduous and skilful task: in the glare of the bright, red-hot bricks of the furnace, man after man advances to the open door and swings his great shovelful into the furnace with astonishing accuracy, grace, and speed (Fig. 2).

(*b*) *Bessemer process.* This process, called after its inventor, Sir Henry Bessemer, works in an

entirely different way from the open hearth process, though it makes use of the same chemical principles. All the oxygen used in the Bessemer process comes from air which, as it is blown violently through the molten iron, combines with the silicon, manganese, and carbon in the iron and carries them off. When phosphorus has to be removed, a lime slag is built up, and the 'blow' extended by a few minutes.

The Bessemer converter is shown in Figs. 3 and 4. It is a gigantic brick-lined metal vessel, the shape of a pear that has been cut off a little below the base of the stalk. The base of the converter lining is pierced with holes (Fig. 3*b*), through which air is blown during the process at a pressure of some 20 lb. per square inch. This is sufficient to penetrate the molten metal, and also to keep it clear of the base of the converter.

The converter is pivoted on very simple bearings, or trunnions (Fig. 3*a*). Laid on its side, it receives its charge of 20 tons or so of molten iron; the air blast is turned on, and the vessel is swung to an upright position, where it emits a spectacular flame and showers of sparks for about 20 minutes. At the end of this time the metal is

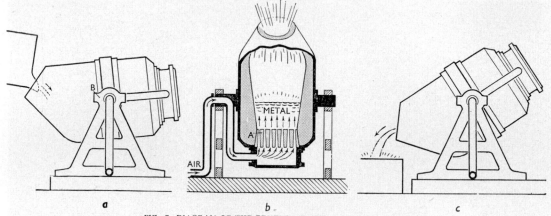

FIG. 3. DIAGRAM OF THE BESSEMER PROCESS OF STEEL-MAKING

a. Converter on its side being charged with molten metal. *b.* Air blown through metal. *c.* Metal being poured into ladle. A. Hearth. B. Trunnions

reduced to comparatively pure iron. The operator learns by long experience to recognize by the shape and colour of the flame exactly when this takes place.

The effect of blowing air into the hot metal in the Bessemer converter is to increase the heat, for the same reason that air blown on to a coal fire with bellows causes the fire to blaze—the oxygen in the air combines with carbon and other elements to release heat (*see* COMBUSTION). The metal at the end of a Bessemer 'blow' is usually about 300° C. hotter than it was at the beginning.

The necessary elements to make steel, such as carbon and manganese, are then added in the form of molten 'ferro alloys'—special irons rich in these elements. The converter is then swung down to pour the metal into its ladles.

The Bessemer process has the advantage that it is very quick; but it is not so controllable as the open hearth process, where the steel maker can make precise adjustments to his composition over a matter of hours. Moreover, the Bessemer process cannot make use of as much scrap as can the open hearth furnace, and this is an economic disadvantage. However, they are both useful for different purposes.

(*c*) *Electric-steel-making.* A furnace may also be heated by an electric arc, a form of spark or discharge across a gap in an ELECTRIC CURRENT (q.v.), which creates a temperature higher than 3,000° C. A conducting point, or electrode, made of graphite, protrudes inward from the roof of the furnace, and the spark leaps from this to the metallic substances with which the furnace has

been charged. Most electric furnaces have three electrodes; such furnaces are used for making special steels like those for motor-car or aeroplane engine parts or stainless steel. They use only scrap metal in their charges and not pig iron, and the refining is carried out as in open hearth furnaces. Electric furnaces range from small $\frac{1}{2}$-ton furnaces to those of 60 tons or even 100 tons capacity.

Electric heating is also used in small furnaces (up to 2 tons capacity) for very special steels, such as those used for machine tools or for gas-turbine parts. Here there is no arc, but high frequency alternating current is used to induce a current (*see* TRANSFORMER, ELECTRIC) to melt and mix the charge of iron and certain alloys. No refining is carried out in these furnaces, which only mix metals.

See also IRON AND STEEL INDUSTRY; METALS; ALLOYS; METALLURGY; STRUCTURAL STEELWORK.

STEREOSCOPE. This is an optical instrument for giving photographs an appearance of solidity or relief. Pairs of photographs in a stereoscope, if viewed through low-power magnifying lenses, one in front of each eye, as shown in Fig. 1, blend together to form a single picture which has a three-dimensional appearance. The illusion depends on the fact that, because of the distance (about 3 inches) between the eyes of a normal human being, the image formed by the eye-lens on the retina of the right eye differs slightly from that formed on the retina of the left eye.

A pair of stereoscopic photographs is taken by a pair of identical CAMERAS (q.v.), side by side

BESSEMER CONVERTERS DURING THE PROCESS OF BLOWING

The metal in the converter on the left is ready to be poured into a ladle

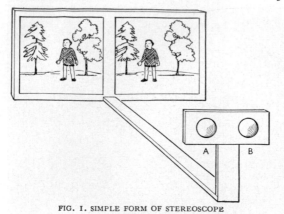

FIG. 1. SIMPLE FORM OF STEREOSCOPE
A. Left-eye lens. B. Right-eye lens

and about 3 inches apart, with shutters released simultaneously by a single trigger. The two photographs are then mounted side by side. The photographs are not exactly the same, as can easily be seen by using transparencies and placing one on top of the other so that the distant objects on each coincide. Nearer objects appear farther to the right in the left-hand photograph than in the right-hand photograph. This effect is known as parallax (see ASTRONOMY, MODERN, Section 2, Vol. III). For example, in the sketches which represent photographs in Fig. 1, the figure of the child in the foreground who is actually standing mid-way between, but in front of, the two trees, appears nearer to the right tree in the left picture, and nearer to the left tree in the right picture.

An appearance of depth is given to the picture seen in the stereoscope because the eyes automatically direct themselves so that the backgrounds of the two photographs are 'blended', that is, seen as a single picture. Fig. 2 shows how the stereoscope works. The right eye sees the card c_1, on which is mounted a photograph,

through a converging lens D_1. The left eye sees the card c_2, on which is mounted a similar photograph, through a similar converging lens D_2. The photographs have been taken with a double camera consisting of two identical cameras mounted side by side, c_1 carrying the photograph taken by the right-hand camera, and c_2 that by the left-hand camera. The right eye, viewing c_1 through D_1, sees a virtual image of it at a great distance, and the left eye similarly sees a virtual image of c_2. The eyes automatically direct themselves so that the two backgrounds of the imaged photographs fall on corresponding parts of the two retinas at the back of each eye. They are then 'blended'—that is, seen as a single picture. In order to blend the two images of the child, the eyes need to turn inward slightly; and because of this the viewer sees the child nearer than the trees, as shown in the diagram. This system is made use of by one method of making stereoscopic or 3D films (see CINE-CAMERAS AND PROJECTORS).

STONEWORK, see MASONRY.

STRENGTH OF MATERIALS, see ENGINEERING DESIGN; STRESS AND STRAIN.

STRESS AND STRAIN. 1. When an engineer designs a building or piece of machinery he needs to know the strength of the various materials he is using (see ENGINEERING DESIGN): how much they will stretch when a load is applied to them; how much they will expand if the temperature changes (see EXPANSION AND CONTRACTION), and so on. A number of these questions can be answered by tests performed on the materials.

If a rod of any material is pulled on one end with a force, it is obviously necessary to pull on

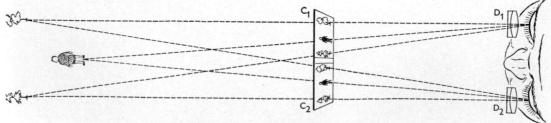

FIG. 2. HOW THE STEREOSCOPE WORKS
On the left are the virtual images of the objects in the photographs, which are blended to give a stereoscopic appearance. c_1, c_2. Photographs. D_1, D_2. Lenses

'SLAGGING OFF' AN OPEN HEARTH STEEL-MAKING FURNACE

The steel has been tapped from the furnace into the ladle in the centre, the floating slag spilling over into slag pans. On the left, the last of the slag is being run from the furnace into a slag pan

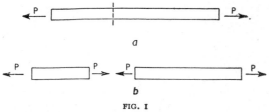

FIG. I

a. Forces (P) applied to the ends of a bar. *b.* The bar is cut, and the forces shown are applied to keep it in equilibrium

the other end with an equal and opposite force to prevent the rod from moving (Fig. 1*a*). If the rod were cut it would be necessary to apply an extra force to each part also to stop it from moving (Fig. 1*b*).

If the two pieces were then to be glued together, the joint would have to carry the force which was resisting the forces at either end. In fact, in the uncut rod also there must be an internal force resisting the pull. This internal force, divided by the area of the cross-section of the rod, is known as the 'stress'. If two rods, one thin and the other thick, have the same pull applied at the end, the thin one will be at a higher stress than the thick one, because the stress is concentrated into a smaller area.

It is possible to have two kinds of direct stress; if the ends of the rod are pulled apart, the stress is known as 'tensile', and if the ends are pushed together the stress is called 'compressive'. In Britain it is usual to measure stress in either pounds per square inch (lb./in.^{2}) or tons per square inch (tons/in.^{2}). The stress is completely independent of the material and depends only on the force or 'load' applied and on the area of the cross-section.

If a piece of elastic is pulled at either end it stretches, and the two ends move apart. Exactly the same thing happens in a metal rod, although the movement would be very small. If this movement, called the 'extension', is measured, and the result divided by the original length of the rod, a ratio is obtained which is called the 'strain'. Unlike the stress, the strain depends on the material of which the rod is made.

2. STRESS–STRAIN DIAGRAMS. These can be drawn in the form of a graph (Fig. 2). Corresponding values of both the stress and the strain are measured. In many cases, the material is tested under tension, the two ends of the specimen being gripped in a test machine that gradually pulls them apart, and the amount of pull, or load, applied by the machine being measured.

The strain is often very small, and is measured by a very sensitive instrument called an 'extensometer'. The loads are converted into stresses, and the strains obtained by dividing the extensions by the distance taken between two fixed points before the stress is applied.

The stress–strain diagram shown in Fig. 2 is for mild steel. The first portion from A to B is straight. Even if the specimen is loaded and unloaded (that is, the force is applied and taken off) a number of times and the extensions are measured, the results will always lie on the same straight line. The slope of this line will vary from one engineering material to another (*see* METALS and ALLOYS). The stress divided by the strain at any point is a constant, called Young's Modulus, and the specimen is said to be behaving in an elastic manner. If the specimen is in the elastic range (from A to B in the diagram), the extension will always be zero when the load is removed. If the value of Young's Modulus is known, it is possible to calculate how much a piece of material would extend under a given load, without having to carry out a special test.

Beyond the point B on the graph, known as the 'elastic limit', the curve is no longer straight but bends over slightly as the strain begins to increase more rapidly. If the load were taken off, the specimen would no longer regain its original length, but would have a small extension left in it called a 'permanent set'. For mild steel the elastic limit occurs at a stress of about 14 tons/in.^{2}

At point c the strain starts increasing very rapidly, and the specimen is said to yield, c

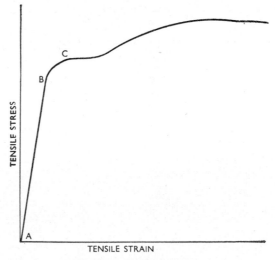

FIG. 2. STRESS–STRAIN GRAPH

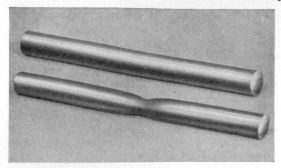

FIG. 3. THE EFFECT OF STRESS ON A STEEL BAR
Before being loaded the lower rod was the same length
and diameter as the upper one

being known as the 'yield-point'. From now on, the curve is partly elastic and partly plastic, and very large increases in strain are obtained for small increases of load. During this stage it is possible to see a change in the specimen, and a neck starts to form at some point along the length (Fig. 3). This means that the cross-section of the specimen has got smaller and finally a break occurs at this section.

3. PLASTIC MATERIAL. It has been shown that elastic material regains its original length when it is un-loaded. On the other hand, a true plastic material when loaded extends and, when the load is removed, stays extended so that there is a permanent increase in its length. For instance, a steel ball and a ball of plasticine dropped from the same height on to the floor produce two entirely different results. The plasticine, being a plastic material, will hit the floor and stay there, permanently flattened. The steel ball will rebound with no detectable change in its shape; probably it was slightly flattened when it hit the floor but, being an elastic material, it regained its original shape. Compared with these two, a drop of water poured from the same height would spread out as a pool. It is generally said that the steel ball was strained, the plasticine was deformed, and that the water flowed. The study of these various properties is called 'rheology'.

4. COMPRESSION AND IMPACT TESTING. In addition to being tested under tension, specimens can be tested in compression by putting them in a machine that presses the two ends together. Short cylindrical specimens are generally tested in this way. In the case of concrete, a cube of either 4 or 6 inches is used, and the test is continued until the concrete is crushed to pieces.

The strength of the concrete is specified as the maximum stress reached in the test.

A material may come fully up to standard in a tension test, but when it receives a sudden blow it is subjected to a shock wave and may break very easily. A piece of cast iron, for example, often breaks if it receives a sudden blow from a hammer. It is therefore necessary to have a means also of deciding how strong a piece of material is under impact. In one of the standard impact tests a V-notch is cut in a round rod of the material to be tested, and the rod is held vertically in a vice at one end with the V-notch at the top of the vice. The rod is broken by one blow from a heavy striker which acts as a pendulum pivoted above the specimen (Fig. 4). The pendulum is pulled back to a certain reading on the scale at A and is then released. The rod is broken off, and the pendulum carries through its swing taking with it a small movable pointer. As a certain amount of energy was used up in breaking the specimen, the pendulum swings only to a point B instead of to a point A'. The amount of energy used in the impact can be determined by subtracting the reading on the scale at B from that at A'.

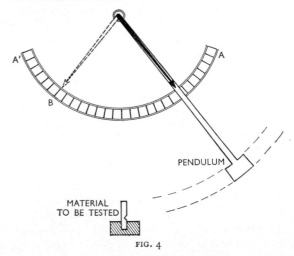

FIG. 4

5. DEFLEXION IN BEAMS. If any rod or other material is supported at either end, and a weight put on the middle of it, it will bend into a curve (*see* p. 90). The degree to which it will bend depends on the load applied, the length of the rod or beam, the cross-section, and the material itself. These are related in particular ways, and the engineer can calculate the deflexion to be expected from a beam without having to carry

out a test. When a beam is loaded, the material of the beam bends, the fibres in the top part being compressed and those in the bottom part being stretched. The beam is consequently deformed, the top part becoming shorter than the bottom part (*see* BUILDING, PRINCIPLES OF).

The deflexion of the beam also depends on the way in which it is supported at each end. If the ends are built into a wall, an 'encastré beam', the beam does not bend as much as it would if the ends were merely supported. This is because the ends are fixed rigidly in direction and are not free to move. This is of great importance in BRIDGE BUILDING (q.v.), for the engineer designing beams to carry the carriage-way of a bridge must be sure that they are strong enough to carry the loads, and that the deflexions are not too great. A truss bridge is made up of a number of different members connected together by rivets, the loads being transmitted through the various members to the ends of the bridge where they rest on the foundations. Thus each member has a force induced in it, in some a compressive force shortening them and in others a stretching force extending them. The engineer can calculate the effect of these various forces, and so can tell what will be the deflexion at any point on the bridge.

See also ENGINEERING DESIGN; EXPANSION AND CONTRACTION; BUILDING, PRINCIPLES OF.

STRUCTURAL STEELWORK. 1. Steel (*see* IRON AND STEEL) is perhaps the most widely used building material in the world today. It is used not only for the framework of large structures of every kind and of smaller, prefabricated buildings (*see* PREFABRICATION), but for such things as radio masts, towers for electric transmission lines, large dock and lock gates, and for many other engineering structures.

Steel has an advantage over other building materials, because, as it is so strong for its weight, a comparatively light steel structure can be used to carry very heavy loads. Unlike CONCRETE (q.v.) it can withstand equally well forces pulling it apart ('tension') or compressing it (*see* STRESS AND STRAIN); and, unlike wrought and cast iron from which it was developed, steel stretches instead of breaking suddenly when a heavy load is applied.

The first experiments with cast-iron or wrought-iron structures were made during the late 18th and 19th centuries, particularly in building BRIDGES (q.v. Vol. IV). In 1801 cast-iron floor beams were used to build a Manchester cotton mill, and in 1851 the first iron-frame building, the CRYSTAL PALACE (q.v. Vol. XII), was built to house the Great Exhibition. This building consisted of cast-iron columns and girders combined with wrought-iron bracing and roof trusses. After 1856, when Henry Bessemer invented his steel-making process, iron gradually gave way to steel for building: the FORTH BRIDGE (q.v. Vol. IV), opened in 1890, contains 54,000 tons of steel, and by 1895 many buildings were carried by columns of steel instead of cast iron. The first steel-frame building in Britain, a warehouse at Stockton-on-Tees, was built in 1898.

In a large modern steel-frame building, such as a block of offices or flats, all the loads are carried by a hidden skeleton of steel (*see* BUILDING, PRINCIPLES OF). The floors and walls are supported by horizontal girders, and these in turn are supported by vertical steel posts, called 'stanchions'. The steel stanchions, which not only take up much less space but are much lighter than BRICKWORK or MASONRY piers (qq.v.) of equivalent strength, reduce the total weight of the building and make possible the erection of great SKYSCRAPERS (q.v. Vol. XII), reaching up to thirty, forty, or even fifty storeys.

A steel-frame building can be put up more quickly than one of concrete, masonry, or brick, for the framework can be made in a factory, while the site is being cleared and the foundations prepared. Again, the lower storeys can be finished off and decorated inside while the framework is still being erected for the upper storeys (*see* BUILDING CONSTRUCTION).

Steel is much used for building heavy engineering workshops with overhead CRANES (q.v.), where the load on the crane may be as much as 350 tons; comparatively slender girders and stanchions carry the tracks upon which these cranes run, some 50 feet up in the air. Steel is also particularly suitable for BRIDGE BUILDING (q.v.) and for constructing aeroplane hangars and similar buildings which must span considerable distances with a clear floor space beneath, unbroken by internal supports. The roof of the Brabazon hangar at Bristol, for example, which covers an area of $7\frac{1}{2}$ acres, is in three sections, each of which has a clear span of more than 330 feet. The roof also carries a most elaborate system of cranes each carrying a load of 12 tons, and one of the windows, also supported by the steel framework, is nearly 350 feet long and 50 feet high.

2. *Preparatory work.* In planning a large steel-frame building, designs are first prepared which show what shapes and sizes are required for the various parts of the framework. These designs are then translated in the drawing office into 'shop drawings' for the workmen in the stock-yards and on the building site (*see* ENGINEERING DRAWING).

Steel for building is made in rolling mills in many shapes and sizes, the most common being

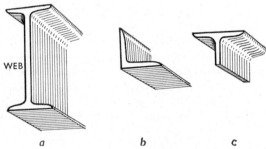

FIG. I. SECTIONS OF STEEL GIRDERS
a. I-section. *b.* L-section. *c.* T-section

'plates', 'slabs' (very thick plates), and 'sections' —lengths of steel with their cross-sections in the shape of the letters I, L, and T (Fig. I). I-sections, which are the most common, are rolled in a number of standard sizes ranging from 3 inches deep by $1\frac{1}{2}$ inches wide up to 24 inches by $7\frac{1}{2}$ inches wide, and in lengths up to 50 feet. This I-shape is particularly suitable for heavy beams and stanchions, as most of the metal is concentrated in the two 'flanges' at the top and bottom of the 'web' which connects them. Angles, or L-sections, which are used for connecting beams and stanchions together and for carrying lighter loads, such as roofs, are also made in standard sizes ranging from 2 by 2 inches up to 8 by 8 inches. T-sections are used only for special purposes, such as roof 'trusses' and as stiffeners for the sides of steel bunkers.

The steel, on arriving at the stockyards, is cut to the exact lengths needed for a particular job: plates and slabs are cut by a 'guillotine', a vast pair of mechanically operated shears, or by melting the steel with an oxy-acetylene flame (*see* WELDING, Section 2*b*); large sections are cut by circular saws, while small sections are 'cropped' in a special machine with jaws and

blades which fit the shape of the section. Ends of steel parts which have to be square are machined in an 'ending' machine—a revolving head carrying steel cutters which is run to and fro across the part. The edges of the plates can be squared by great planing machines, large enough to take plates up to 50 feet long, on which the operators ride in a special travelling carriage. When the pieces of steel have been cut, they are marked with instructions for drilling or shaping. When a number of pieces of identical shape are needed, 'templets' are used to ensure that each hole is in the same place on each piece (*see* JIGS AND FIXTURES). Holes are drilled by a DRILLING MACHINE, and the pieces joined by RIVETING or WELDING (qq.v.).

3. *Constructing the framework.* When the foundations of the building have been prepared, the stanchions are set accurately in position, 'plumbed' to ensure that they are vertical, and then anchored to the foundations by 'holding-down bolts'. Each stanchion has at floor level a 'seating cleat', or bracket, which supports the end of the horizontal beam when it is lowered in place. The beams are themselves fitted with 'end cleats', which are riveted or bolted to the stanchions to make the joint (Fig. 2). The steel skeleton grows higher and higher as work proceeds, great cranes being used to lift beams and stan-

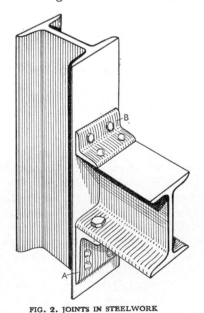

FIG. 2. JOINTS IN STEELWORK
A. Seating cleat (angle section) riveted to stanchion and bolted to beam. B. End cleat (angle section) riveted to beam and bolted to stanchion

THE CONSTRUCTION OF THE BOILER HOUSE AT GOLDINGTON ELECTRIC GENERATING STATION
In the foreground is the travelling crane used for erecting the horizontal beams and vertical stanchions. At the right, lattice girders can be seen

chions to the men working high up on the building. Parts which are too long to be carried to the site or handled in one piece are brought in two halves and then 'spliced' together during erection. The splices consist of steel, bolted, riveted, or welded over the joint.

Though entire buildings can be erected by using standard ⊥-sections jointed together in this way, more complicated construction is used to carry very heavy loads or to span a considerable distance. To carry the heavy floor load of a warehouse or factory, for example, ⊥-sections have to be strengthened by plates riveted or welded to their flanges. These are usually called 'compound girders' (Fig. 3a). For carrying still larger spans and heavier loads, as, for example, when building the balcony of a cinema, stronger girders, called 'plate girders', are used (Fig. 3b). These are ⊥-sections, doubly strengthened by angles, or L-sections, riveted to the top and bottom of the 'web' plate, and with heavy flange plates riveted on to the angles. Such girders can

be built to very large sizes, and exactly proportioned for the work they have to do; a balcony

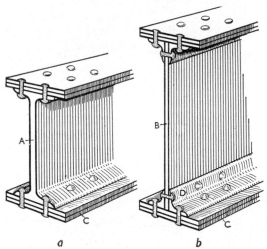

a   *b*

FIG. 3. *a.* COMPOUND GIRDER. *b.* PLATE GIRDER
A. Web. B. Web plate. C. Flange plates. D. Flange angle

girder may be 120 feet long and 15 feet deep and weigh up to 70 tons. Plate girders are frequently used in newspaper printing works, because the enormous printing presses, usually installed in the basement, prevent closely spaced internal supports being used, and so the entire weight of the building above is carried by plate girders.

For roofs, and other parts of a building which carry comparatively light loads, a much lighter 'frame' method of construction is used, with 'trusses' or 'lattice girders'. The basis of the

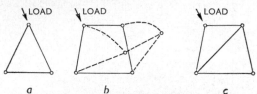

a   *b*   *c*

FIG. 4. RIGID AND NON-RIGID SHAPES
a. Triangle: rigid. *b*. Quadrilateral: non-rigid.
c. Triangulated: rigid

frame is a triangle, as this is the only shape which is rigid (Fig. 4*a*). A triangle, even though loosely jointed, will withstand a load without collapsing, whereas a four-sided figure is not inherently rigid, however strong the corner joints may be (Fig. 4*b*). Thus, trusses and lattice girders are built up from a succession of triangles (Fig. 5*a*). The sides of the triangles are usually L-sections, bolted or riveted to connecting plates, called 'gusset-plates'; each part can be proportioned to suit exactly the work it has to do. Roof trusses can span from 20 to 120 feet or more.

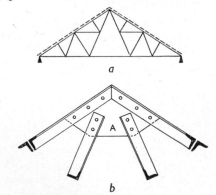

a

b

FIG. 5. *a*. TRIANGULATED ROOF TRUSS. *b*. JOINT AT APEX
OF ROOF
A. Gusset plate

Lattice girders are triangulated frames of rather heavier construction (Fig. 6). They are used, for example, in building cinema balconies where openings for stairways prevent the use of plate girders; or they can be used with trusses to

SUPPORT   SUPPORT

FIG. 6. TRIANGULATED LATTICE GIRDER

support the roof of a factory, where internal columns would restrict the floor space available for machines.

See also BUILDING, PRINCIPLES OF; BUILDING CONSTRUCTION; IRON AND STEEL; IRON AND STEEL INDUSTRY, HISTORY OF; CONCRETE CONSTRUCTION.

SUN-DIAL, *see* TIMEKEEPERS, ANCIENT.

SUPERHEATER, *see* BOILERS.

SUPERSONIC SPEED, *see* Vol. IV: SUPERSONIC FLIGHT. *See also* Vol. III: SOUND.

SURFACE TREATMENT. Nearly all metals and alloys in common use, and especially iron and steel, are attacked by substances in the air and are eaten away by CORROSION (q.v.) unless protected by a layer of grease, paint, chemical, or another less corrodible metal. The most serious form of corrosion, though not the most common, is an 'inter-crystalline' corrosion, where the corroding substance acts between the crystals of which the metals are composed. Surface treatment aims at preventing this substance from reaching the crystals.

A simple coating of oil or grease, being soft, is easily damaged so that the air can find a way in. But a really tough and sticky grease such as lanolin, obtained from sheep's wool, can be a very useful way of keeping iron and steel articles free from rust for periods of temporary storage.

Large structures are generally treated with several coats of paint (*see* PAINTS AND VARNISHES, Vol. VII). If the metal surface is shiny, it is difficult for the paint to get a good grip; so the metal is given a chemical treatment first, by dipping it into a solution of phosphoric acid and other salts which attack the metal and produce a thin coating of phosphate crystals, making a rough surface which helps the paint to stick. If the paint is accidentally scratched later, the coating beneath helps to stop the rust spreading from the scratch mark and causing severe damage.

An important way of protecting metal surfaces is ELECTROPLATING (q.v.)—that is, depositing on the metal by electric current a very thin film of a non-rusting metal. A familiar example is chromium plate—a very thin film of chromium metal applied over a coating of bright or polished nickel. When a bright and shiny surface is not so important, zinc, cadmium, tin, or an alloy of tin and zinc are generally used.

The surface must be absolutely clean so that the thin metal coating can stick on firmly; even the grease from a finger-mark is enough to spoil the treatment. Grease or oil is first removed with paraffin or a similar solvent; then a boiling alkali solution such as washing soda is used to remove the last traces of grease; and finally the metal is 'pickled'—soaked in dilute acid to take off any rust.

Iron or steel articles can be coated more thickly by being dipped into a bath of melted zinc or tin. Coating with zinc in this way is called 'galvanizing' and is very often applied to such things as dustbins, buckets, and wire netting. Tinning is the process used in the making of TINPLATE (q.v.) and is also applied to mincing machines, cast-iron saucepans, and similar domestic articles. To give a zinc coating to small iron or steel articles such as nuts and bolts the articles are put into a box full of zinc dust and heated in a furnace; the zinc then combines with the surface of the iron or steel to form an ALLOY (q.v.). This process is known as 'sherardizing'. In a similar process, 'chromizing', chromium is used instead of zinc, giving an alloy coating similar to stainless steel.

A coating which is used on such articles as domestic gas cookers, baths, and steel saucepans is vitreous enamel, sometimes called porcelain enamel. This enamelling, not to be confused with hard gloss paint, often called enamel, produces a smooth, shiny surface, nearly as hard as glass and difficult to scratch. The method of applying it is described in the article ENAMEL (q.v. Vol. VII). Vitreous enamelling needs a very clean metal surface. Steel can be easily cleaned by acid 'pickling', but this is not possible for cast iron, which is cleaned by a process called shot blasting. Small, broken pieces of hardened steel shot are thrown forcibly against the article to be cleaned so that their sharp edges knock and scrape off all the rust and dirt. The bits of shot are blown across the surface of the article by a blast of compressed air or are spun round in a wheel so that they are flung out across the surface. Sand used to serve this purpose instead of steel shot, but the dust from the sand damaged the workers' lungs.

One protective process known as 'anodizing' can be applied only to aluminium and certain of its alloys, and was much used in the Second World War to protect the structure of aircraft. In some ways the process is similar to electroplating, in that the article is immersed in a solution and an electric current is passed through it; but the direction of the flow of the current is reversed. The oxygen gas produced by the current converts the surface of the aluminium into a tough film of aluminium oxide. When the article is put into service the oxygen in the air cannot attack it further, as it already has a thin oxide coating all over it. This process cannot be applied to iron or steel, as the oxide coatings do not adhere well and are porous, so that air can get through them and still attack the metal underneath.

Surface treatments can be given to iron, steel, and other metals by immersing them in chemicals which produce an oxide coating—usually black, dark blue, or brown. The familiar blue colour of a gun barrel is produced by such a process. These coatings do not give great protection as they are usually somewhat porous, but they can be made more effective if they are oiled.

See also CORROSION; METALS; METALLURGY.
See also Vol. VII: PAINTS AND VARNISHES.

SURVEYING. 1. This is the art or science of finding out the exact shape of any part of the earth's surface as well as the relative positions of surface features and buildings. It is done by measuring the distances between chosen points, the directions of the lines connecting them, and the heights of the points one above another. The horizontal measurements can be used to make a map to any scale (see MAP PROJECTIONS, Vol. IV), and the vertical measurements (the measurements of heights), combined with horizontal distances, can be used to draw contours or to make a cross-sectional diagram showing in profile the heights of hills, depths of valleys, and gradients. Other information, such as the position of towns and the heights of mountains, can be shown by signs and figures (see MAP-READING, Vol. IV).

The same methods of measurement are used to mark out on the ground from scale drawings the position of large civil engineering projects,

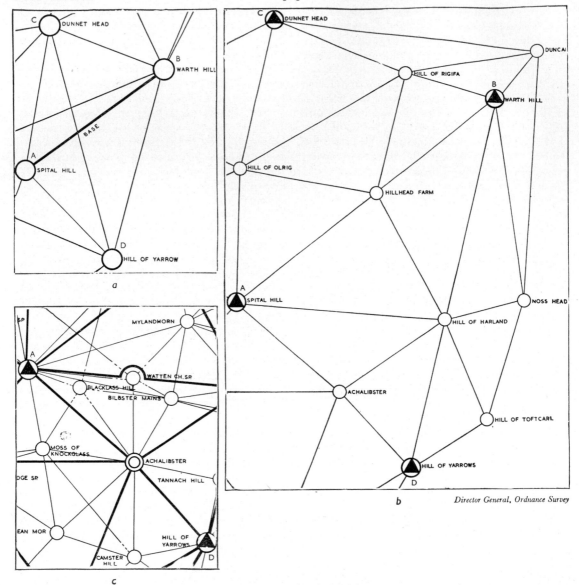

FIG. I. DETAILS OF A TRIANGULATION

a. Primary. *b.* Secondary. *c.* Tertiary. In *b* and *c* the scale is twice that of *a*

Director General, Ordnance Survey

such as DAMS (q.v.) or the track of a new road or railway (*see* ROAD BUILDING).

2. *The framework.* The surveyor begins by measuring the relative positions of a number of points covering the whole area to be surveyed. The instruments he uses are described in the article SURVEYING INSTRUMENTS (q.v.). With some of these he can measure distances and with others angles, either horizontal or vertical. He relies as far as possible on the measurement of angles,

because they can be measured more accurately and more quickly than distances. He begins, however, by measuring the distance between two points, A and B (Fig. I). Then he chooses a third point, C, which can be seen from both A and B, to form a triangle, and measures the angles ABC and BAC. If the length of one side of a triangle and two of its angles are known, the lengths of the other two sides and the third angle can be calculated by TRIGONOMETRY (q.v.). So the surveyor now has the data from which he can plot to any scale, or calculate, the relative positions of these three points, A, B, and C.

Next he chooses another point, D, outside the first triangle, and measures the angles BAD and ABD. As the length of BA is known, all the measurements of the triangle BAD can be calculated, and the position of D is fixed. So he proceeds, by measuring further angles, to construct a network of triangles, every measurement of which is known, covering the whole area to be surveyed. This network is called the 'framework', and the method is known as 'triangulation'. (As a check, the surveyor also measures the third angle of each triangle and, occasionally, the length of one of the sides.)

If the area to be surveyed is very large, the first framework is made with points about 30 miles apart: this is called the primary triangulation. Then the gaps are filled in by a more detailed framework with points about 10 miles apart, called the secondary triangulation. Finally a tertiary triangulation is made with points 3 to 5 miles apart. In the primary triangulation any mistake in fixing one point would affect the whole framework; for this reason, and because of the greater distances involved, only the most accurate methods and instruments are used: these keep the margin of error down to about 1 in 300,000. The later stages do not need quite so much accuracy, because there is always a check from a primary triangulation point about 30 miles away.

In flat or densely wooded country simple triangulation is not always possible. Fig. 2 illustrates the difficulty. Points A and B have been fixed. The next chosen point is X, but X is hidden from A by a forest. The surveyor overcomes this problem by a 'traverse'. He chooses a point C which can be seen from B and fixes it by measuring the angle ABC and the distance BC. The next point, D, visible only from C, is fixed in the same

Director General, Ordnance Survey

FIG. 3. OBSERVING WITH A THEODOLITE ON A TRIANGULATION PILLAR

There is a bench mark on the face of the pillar

way and the traverse is continued until X is reached.

When the framework is complete, it must be fitted into its correct position on the earth's surface. The surveyor does this by fixing the latitude and longitude of one or more chosen points in his framework by ASTRONOMY (q.v. Vol. III): he observes some stars, measuring the vertical angles between each star and the horizontal, and records the exact time. Because the earth is almost a sphere, these angles cannot be the same at any two places at the same time. In the same way he measures the horizontal angle at these points between another visible framework point and a star, recording the exact time. From this he can calculate the true bearing (or angle with true North) of the line observed, and then the framework may be correctly oriented on the earth's surface. In each case it is sufficient in principle to observe two stars, but, in order to be as accurate as possible, between twenty and thirty stars are usually observed each night for four to five nights.

3. *Measuring heights.* By the above methods the

FIG. 2. A TRAVERSE FROM A TO X

Crown Copyright: Air Ministry

FIG. 4. AIR PHOTOGRAPH AND MAP OF LITTLEMORE, OXFORDSHIRE

Reproduced from the 6-in. Ordnance Survey map, 1922, with the sanction of the Comptroller of H.M. Stationery Office

surveyor fixes the positions of points on the earth's surface. He also has to measure the differences in height between these points. This is called 'levelling', and can be done by measuring the vertical angles above or below the horizontal. As the surveyor knows the horizontal distance between any two points, he can then calculate the vertical distance—the difference in height between them —by trigonometry. Another and more accurate method by which differences in height are

measured directly and not by angles is by using a 'level' and 'staff'. This is described in Section 3 of the article SURVEYING INSTRUMENTS.

If the area is large the surveyor begins, as in triangulation, with a primary framework of levels very accurately measured, and then fills in his secondary and tertiary framework, which need not be quite so accurately measured. In levelling over long distances he has to make calculations to allow for the curvature of the earth and the bending of rays of LIGHT (q.v. Vol. III) by the atmosphere.

All these heights are related to mean sea-level. This is calculated at points on the coast by special tide recorders (*see* HYDROGRAPHY); from these the heights of other points inland are fixed by levelling. At some of these points permanent marks, called 'bench marks', are fixed on buildings or on triangulation pillars (Fig. 3). By levelling either from mean sea-level or from a bench mark the surveyor can fix all the heights in his framework.

4. *Plotting detail*. Having completed his framework, the surveyor fills in the various details which are needed for his map, such as buildings, the outlines of woods and lakes, and the lines of roads, railways, and rivers. He can fix the position of these points with reference to the points on his framework, either by using a 'plane table' and 'sight-rule', or by a traverse and 'offset' using a compass and measuring chain (*see* SURVEYING INSTRUMENTS, Section 4).

5. *Air survey*. Surveying by the methods described above, and especially the plotting of detail, is very laborious; the surveyor has to work over all the ground step by step. A great deal of time is saved by modern methods of photographic air survey. Air photographs may be taken with the camera either pointing vertically downwards or obliquely at an angle. Vertical photographs are preferred for map making, especially when heights and contours are required (Fig. 4).

By flying on a straight and level course with the camera set to take exposures automatically at fixed intervals, a series of overlapping photographs are taken. Each pair of photographs can then be arranged in a STEREOSCOPE (q.v.), by means of which an apparently solid image of the ground is obtained, and the relative heights and positions of the various points can be calculated and plotted. In making maps from air photographs it is still necessary to fix the framework by triangulation or traverse, the points on the framework being called 'ground control' points, and their positions and heights being measured by surveyors working on the ground. In large and undeveloped countries, surveyors with their instruments are sometimes carried from place to place by helicopters.

RADAR (q.v.) is sometimes used in modern surveying. In air survey it is used to keep the aeroplane on course while photographs are taken; in a ground survey over a large and undeveloped area it enables the surveyor to fix a framework with sides of up to 300 miles, but less accurately than by primary triangulation.

6. *Application*. The maps and data produced by surveyors are used by the civil engineer in many ways. In choosing the site for a dam, for instance, he can study on a map the courses of all the rivers and streams in the area. By reading the contours he can calculate the amount of water which can be stored by building a dam of a given height in a certain place. In the same way the results of a soils survey (*see* SOIL MECHANICS), clearly marked on a map, will give the engineer vital information about the foundations (*see* BUILDING, PRINCIPLES OF). When deciding the route of a railway or road, the gradients, radius of curves, heights of embankments, and depths of cuttings can be calculated from data supplied by the surveyor.

Before construction begins, the exact position of the various parts of the dam, or the track of the railway or road, are fixed on the ground by using normal surveying methods in reverse—that is, by transferring measurements from the plan or map to the ground. This is called 'setting out'. In TUNNELLING (q.v.), which is usually carried out from both ends simultaneously, a base line (part of the triangulation) is set out on the ground at each end, and the course followed by the tunnellers is continually checked by measuring both levels and angles with reference to the base line. By this means it is possible to make the two 'drives' meet accurately to within 1 or 2 inches over a distance of a mile or more.

See also SURVEYING INSTRUMENTS; HYDROGRAPHY.

See also Vol. IV: MAPS, HISTORY OF; MAP PROJECTIONS; MAP-READING.

SURVEYING INSTRUMENTS. For accurate SURVEYING (q.v.) many different instruments are needed to measure distances, angles, and heights. Their cost varies from a few shillings to several thousands of pounds for some instruments used in air survey. The following are some of the most common instruments in use today.

1. MEASURING DISTANCES. The most accurate instrument for this is a metal tape, which may be up to 400 feet long. In long tapes every tenth foot, and sometimes every foot, is marked with a brass stud; 100-foot tapes are engraved in feet and the first and last feet in decimals of a foot. Some tapes are graduated in metres, or in both

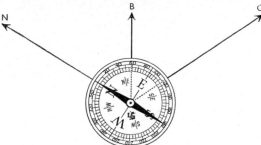

Hilger and Watts

FIG. I. PHOTOGRAPH AND DIAGRAM OF A PRISMATIC
COMPASS

The bearing is read (through the back sight on the left) on
the graduated circle, to which the magnet in the bar is
attached

feet and metres. For very accurate work tapes
are made of 'invar', an alloy of steel and nickel,
which expands or contracts very little with
changes of temperature. For measuring short
distances, where great accuracy is not required,
100-foot linen tapes are used.

Another instrument is the 'engineer's chain',
which is 100 feet long and composed of steel links
joined to each other by rings, every tenth foot
being marked by a brass 'tally'. The 'Gunter'
chain, 66 feet long and with 100 links, may be
used for measuring areas (1 acre = 10 square
'Gunter' chains). Both instruments are used in
rough country and are accurate to within about
1 in 500. Ranging rods are used for measuring

very short lengths and for marking points on the
ground so that they can be seen from a distance.
They are 6, 8, or 10 feet long, with each foot
painted alternately in red, white, or black.

2. MEASURING ANGLES. (*a*) *Horizontal angles*.
The simplest instrument for measuring horizontal angles is the prismatic COMPASS (q.v.
Vol. IV). This is held in the hand, or set up on a
tripod, over the surveyor's first point, A, and
sighted on his second point, B (Fig. 1). As the
compass needle points to the magnetic north, the
surveyor can read the angle between the line AB
and the magnetic north; this is called the 'magnetic bearing' of the point B. Then he sights the
compass on his third point, C, and reads its
bearing in the same way. By comparing these
two bearings he can calculate the angle BAC.
By this method he can measure angles to within
about 1°.

For measuring angles more accurately the
surveyor uses a theodolite, one of the most important instruments in surveying (Fig. 2). This consists of a TELESCOPE (q.v.) (A) fixed to a vertical

Hilger and Watts

FIG. 2. A THEODOLITE

A. Telescope. B. Vertical circular plate. C. Horizontal circular plate. D. Point from which plumb bob hangs. E. Spirit
levels. F. Eye end of telescope. G. Magnifiers for reading
horizontal plate. H. Magnifiers for reading vertical plate

circular plate (B), which are together mounted on a horizontal circular plate (C). Both plates may be rotated, and they are marked with a scale of degrees, minutes, and sometimes seconds. There are many kinds of theodolite, depending on the method of reading the angles and on the diameter of the horizontal plate.

The theodolite is set up on a tripod exactly over a chosen point, usually by means of a 'plumb bob'—a weight suspended by a cord from the centre of the instrument below D. If this point is a triangulation point it is usually marked with a pillar (*see* p. 425), and the theodolite is set up on this. It is adjusted until a spirit level (E) attached to the horizontal plate indicates that it is level. The telescope is then sighted on a mark set up at the second chosen point. In the barrel of the telescope, near the eye end (F), is fixed a 'diaphragm', or glass plate, on which is engraved a pattern of horizontal and vertical lines. The telescope is turned until the central vertical line comes exactly over the mark; then it is clamped to keep it steady, and a reading is taken on the horizontal plate through magnifiers (G). The telescope is unclamped, swung round and sighted on the next chosen point, and another reading is taken on the horizontal plate, which must not be rotated during this operation. The difference between the two readings is the angle between the two points corresponding to BAC in Fig. 1.

(*b*) *Vertical angles.* The theodolite is also used to measure vertical angles, that is, angles above or below the horizontal. To do this the telescope is tilted until the central horizontal line on the diaphragm falls exactly over the mark set up at a chosen point. A second spirit level (E), attached to the index of the vertical plate, indicates the horizontal, so a reading on the vertical plate, through the magnifiers (H), gives the angle of the point above or below the horizontal.

Another instrument, the Abney level or clinometer, which consists of a sighting tube fixed to a semicircular vertical plate marked in degrees, with a spirit level attached to its index, is also used to measure vertical angles. It is held in the hand, and is less accurate than the theodolite.

3. MEASURING HEIGHTS. The vertical distance of one point above or below another can be measured directly, instead of by angles, with a 'level' and 'staff' (Fig. 3). The level, which consists of a telescope with cross-lines (like a theodolite telescope) and a spirit level, is set up on a tripod, at point A, and is adjusted until it is per-

fectly horizontal in whichever direction it is pointed. Then the telescope is sighted on a levelling staff which is held upright in the ground by an assistant, at point B. The staff is marked in tenths and hundredths of a foot (or of a metre), so that the point on the staff which is cut by the central horizontal line on the diaphragm can be easily read. The staff is then moved to point C, the level is swung round, and another reading is taken. The difference between these two readings is the difference in height between the points B and C.

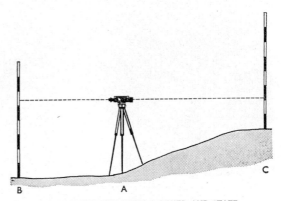

FIG. 3. LEVELLING WITH A LEVEL AND STAFF

The heights of the staffs at B and C are read on the level at A. The differences between the readings gives the height of C above B

4. PLOTTING DETAIL. There are several ways of doing this once the surveyor has fixed his framework. One way is to make a traverse (*see* SURVEYING), using a compass and chain, between two points of the framework. This line is then used as a kind of base-line from which to measure detail points, such as a tree, or cottage, or a cross-road. A line called an 'offset', running at right angles to the traverse, is drawn to each point, the distance being measured by a chain or linen tape. Another method is to use a 'plane table' and 'sight-rule' (Fig. 4). A plane table is a drawing-board mounted on a tripod; a sight-rule is a ruler with sights attached to it. A point on the ground may be fixed on the plane table by sighting it from a framework point and drawing a line to it, the distance being measured along the ground by a linen tape. Alternatively, the point can be sighted from two different framework points; the position at which the two lines of sight cross one another on the plane table corresponds with the position of the point on the ground.

Surveyor General of India

FIG. 4. A SURVEYOR USING A PLANE TABLE SIGHT-RULE

5. AIR SURVEY. Many types of CAMERA (q.v.) are used for air survey. Fast exposures (generally 1/100th or 1/200th of a second) are needed to take clear pictures from a moving aircraft, so that the LENS (q.v.) must be of very high quality. The film, which should be held flat to within a thousandth of an inch or less, is wound on by an electric motor, exposures being made automatically at constant intervals.

Most of the instruments used to plot detail from air photography are stereoscopic (*see* STEREOSCOPE). In one method of stereoscopic plotting, reduced positive copies are made of the negatives. Two overlapping photographs are then fixed in their correct relative positions in projectors, one of which has a red and the other a blue filter; the operator wears glasses with one red and one blue lens. A pin-point of light can be made to move over the ensuing stereoscopic image of the ground, following the track of, for example, a road, river, or contour. At the same time a pencil, moving over a sheet of paper fixed on a drawing board, follows the movements of the light. All detail can be traced on a map in this way.

See also SURVEYING.

SWITCHGEAR, ELECTRIC. The term 'switchgear' is usually given only to large electric switches of the kind used to make and break the connexions between the generators of a POWER STATION and the main power lines, or to control the connexion between two power lines in the GRID SYSTEM (qq.v.). There is also, however, a great variety of small electric switches used to control electric currents.

The output of electric power from each generator in a power station can be switched to a group of three heavy copper bars called bus-bars. These bus-bars serve to connect the generators together and to connect them through other switches to the main power line and also to the auxiliary machinery in the power station, such as cooling fans, water pumps, and coal elevators.

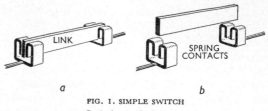

FIG. 1. SIMPLE SWITCH
a. Switch on. *b.* Switch off

The very large switches used for such purposes, called 'circuit-breakers', operate in exactly the same way as the small switches used to control an electric light. Both the large and the small switches interrupt the flow of electric current by removing a copper link that joins two fixed spring contacts when the switch is 'on' (Fig. 1).

When an electric current is interrupted by a switch, an electric flame or arc flashes across the gap between the link and the fixed contacts. In switches controlling small amounts of electric power the arc is small enough to be easily extinguished, but in switches for large powers the arc is large enough to cause considerable damage to the link and contacts by its intense heat. The arc, therefore, has to be extinguished as quickly as possible, and this is often done by blowing it out with a violent blast of air. More usually in Britain, however, oil-filled circuit-breakers are used. The link and contacts are immersed in a bath of oil, so that when an arc is produced, it heats the oil immediately near it, causing some of it to vaporize. The fixed contacts are surrounded by specially shaped 'oil blast-pots' which cause the pressure exerted by the oil vapour to force streams of cool oil to flow through the arc and extinguish it.

English Electric

FIG. 3. 132,000-VOLT POWER STATION SWITCHGEAR

The very large oil-filled circuit-breaker shown in cross-section in Fig. 2 is used to switch one wire of a 132,000-volt supply; three such circuit-breakers are used to control a three-phase A.C. power system (*see* ALTERNATING CURRENT). Each circuit-breaker stands about 16 feet high.

The fixed contacts are in the 'oil blast-pots', and the moving link is carried by a rod operated by remote control, using an electromagnet. This type of switchgear is mounted in the open air, and is surrounded by a framework of steel girders that carry the cables joining the switchgear to the overhead power lines.

In power stations situated in towns where there is not sufficient room to have outdoor switchgear, circuit-breakers for indoor use are manufactured as a unit. Their bus-bars and cable connectors are enclosed in a stout steel case to reduce the risk of fire should anything go wrong. Several of these metal-clad units are fixed side-by-side to form a switchboard for one section of the power station's bus-bar. The risk of fire is reduced still further by placing each such group of circuit-breakers in a separate switchroom. All these circuit-breakers are remotely controlled from a central control board, which is placed in a room well away both from the switchgear and

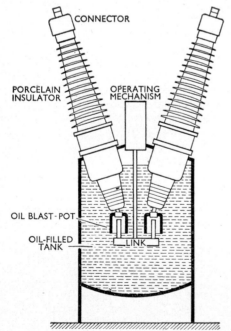

FIG. 2. CROSS-SECTION OF A LARGE CIRCUIT-BREAKER

The operating mechanism moves the link upwards so that the contacts fixed to it connect to the fixed contacts

from the boiler and turbo-alternator houses, so that the control engineer is not distracted by noise or dirt.

Small switches all depend on having a movable metallic link and two fixed contacts, as in Fig. 1. The metallic link is almost always made of copper or a copper alloy, though in some special switches liquid mercury is used. The mercury is contained in a sealed glass tube fitted with two fixed contacts, and when the tube is tilted so that all the mercury runs down to one end, the circuit is broken and the switch is off. With a mercury link it is easier to obtain a clean metal surface at the contacts; dirty contacts have a high electrical resistance which wastes power and may damage the contacts by heating them.

Ordinary switches using a moving copper link are arranged so that the link rubs or 'wipes' across the fixed contacts when they come together and so cleans the contact surfaces. To make good low-resistance contact the fixed and moving contacts are pressed firmly together and the fixed contacts are made of a springy material. Small switches, such as those that control household lighting, also contain springs in order to obtain a 'snap action', so that when the switch is turned off, the fixed and moving contacts fly apart so rapidly under the action of the spring that the arc that tries to form is quickly extinguished.

A bell push is a common example of a simple switch of the non-locking type—one that stays on only while it is pushed. Another such switch is the 'dead man's handle' switch in the control cabin of an electric train (see UNDERGROUND RAILWAY, Vol. IV), which cuts off the power, and so stops the train, if the driver releases his grip on the control handle. Time switches operated by clockwork mechanisms are used to switch street-lighting on and off.

Many different kinds of small switch are operated by an electromagnet; this arrangement is known as a relay (see MAGNETS), and hundreds of thousands of relays are used in TELEPHONE ENGINEERING (q.v.).

T

TELEPHONE ENGINEERING. 1. This is the technique of turning human speech into electric currents, sending those currents along copper wires for long distances, and then transforming them into speech again (*see* TELEPHONE SERVICE, Vol. IV). The basis of the telephone is the MICROPHONE (q.v.), which converts speech into an electric current, and a receiver with electromagnets and an iron diaphragm which turns the current back into speech.

In a modern telephone, the microphone and receiver are fixed in a handset of convenient shape which is connected to the base of the instrument by three wires forming a flexible cord. The base contains a TRANSFORMER (q.v.) which links together the microphone, the receiver, and the line to give the most efficient transmission both ways. The instrument also contains a bell, operating when the subscriber is rung; this is worked by sending from the telephone exchange an ALTERNATING CURRENT (q.v.) of low frequency (usually 16 to 25 alternations per second) along the line. When the handset is taken from its rest, electrical SWITCHGEAR (q.v.) inside the base is moved, so giving signals to the exchange

at the beginning and end of a call. The battery for supplying current to the microphone is, in modern telephone systems, located at the central telephone exchange.

2. TELEPHONE EXCHANGE. Two wires run from every telephone in a locality to a central place, or exchange, at which any telephone can be connected to any other. In the early days all connexions were made by hand at 'manual' exchanges; but these are being replaced by automatic ones, and more than three-quarters of British exchanges are now automatic.

In a manual exchange, each telephone line is connected to a pair of small metal contacts in a socket or 'jack', the jacks being fixed to a large vertical switchboard in front of the operator (*see* Vol. IV, p. 449). When a subscriber lifts his handset to make a call, a lamp glows next to the jack. On seeing the light, the operator inserts a plug (bearing two brass contacts) into the jack of the caller's line; when the two pairs of contacts thus meet, the telephones of the operator and the subscriber form a single electrical circuit. The operator asks what number is required, and then puts a second plug, which is connected to the first plug by flexible cords, into the line jack of the subscriber who is being called. This brings three parties (the operator and both subscribers) into one circuit; when the second subscriber has answered the call, the operator can switch his own microphone and receiver out of the circuit by a hand-switch.

In an automatic exchange, the connexion to the required line is made by mechanical selectors which are controlled by electrical signals sent out from the dial on the instrument of the calling subscriber. Fig. 1 shows a typical automatic selector with 100 fixed metal contacts arranged

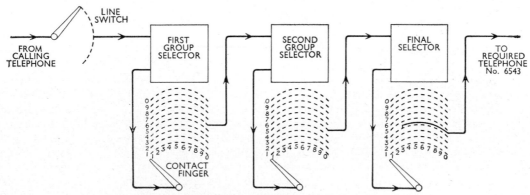

FIG. 1. DIAGRAM OF AN AUTOMATIC TELEPHONE SELECTOR

in 10 rings, each with 10 contacts. There is also a movable contact-finger which can be touched on to any one of the 100 fixed contacts, for the finger can move in two ways—up and down with its shaft and also circularly. Thus to reach the sixth contact on the third ring, the contact-finger is moved three steps vertically and then six steps around. The finger is moved by two electromagnets (*see* MAGNETS), one moving the finger up and down and the other moving it round. These electromagnets are operated by the signals from the telephone dial, and so the numbers that are dialled decide which of the fixed contacts is selected by the moving contact-finger. Each subscriber has the use of a selector, and his telephone is joined to the moving contact-finger. The telephones of 100 other subscribers are joined to the fixed contacts, and he can be connected to any one of them by moving the contact-finger to select the wanted line.

The selectors of an automatic exchange have to do a large number of complicated things which in a manual system are done by the human operator. The electrical signals have to be directed from the dial to the correct electromagnet for the controlling of the switch, the selected line has to be tested and, if engaged, a distinctive 'engaged' signal sent back to the caller. If the line is free, the selectors must make it 'engaged' to all other callers, must ring the bell of the required subscriber, and must then 'switch through' the two subscribers for conversation. When the called subscriber answers, the circuit must automatically record the call so that the caller can be charged with the cost. These and other jobs are done by devices known as relays, which can be seen at the top of the selector in Fig. 2. The relays are small electromagnets which, when energized by an electric current, open and close a number of electric switches.

A single selector will connect to only a maximum of 100 lines, and since exchanges are very often considerably bigger than this, it is necessary for an exchange to use several selectors. Fig. 1 shows typical arrangements in an exchange with, say, 7,000 lines. A subscriber, wishing to make a call, lifts his handset from the rest, and this switches in the telephone instrument to the electrical circuit of the exchange. An electric current flows through the subscriber's line from the exchange battery (a large stock of accumulators or storage batteries), and causes a small rotary 'line switch' at the exchange to turn until

G.E.C.

FIG. 2. TWO-MOTION SELECTOR SWITCH USED IN AUTOMATIC TELEPHONE EXCHANGES

A. Rings of fixed metal contacts to which the various telephone subscribers' lines are joined. B. The moving contact fingers that select the line of the subscriber whose number has been dialled. C. Spindle carrying the moving fingers. D. Electromagnets controlled by the telephone dial which drives the spindle

it connects the line to a free 'first selector'. A clicking 'dialling tone' is then sent to the subscriber, who, when he hears it, dials the first figure of the number that he wants, say 6. When he releases the dial, a spring drives it back to its normal position. The motion of the dial is controlled by a mechanical governor, which can be heard whirring, and as it moves it regularly opens and closes a small switch. This switch is connected to the telephone line, and when the number 6 is dialled, it opens and closes six times, causing six brief signals to pass over the line to the exchange. Each time the switch opens, the electromagnets in the selector move the finger up one ring, or around one contact. In our example the signals from the dial cause the contact-finger of the selector to rise up to the sixth ring of fixed contacts, and then some of the relays at the top of the selector cause the finger to step around the ten contacts in the ring. Each of these contacts is joined to another selector, so that if the first one is already engaged, the second one may be free. When the finger finds a free selector it stops. All this occurs in a fraction of a second, before the subscriber goes on to dial the second figure, say 5. The second selector is now stepped up to the fifth ring, and its finger again searches, this time to find a disengaged final selector. When the subscriber dials the third figure, say 4, the contact finger of the final selector steps up to the fourth ring, and when, finally, the subscriber dials the last figure, say 3, the finger moves round the ring to the third contact. Thus, by the use of three consecutive switches the caller selects first the group of the six-thousand numbers, then the fifth hundred within that group, and finally the forty-third number within the fifth hundred.

In large cities, such as London, Birmingham, and Manchester, the switching systems are much more complex. It is, for example, necessary to dial seven numbers, the first three of which select the exchange to which the required line is connected. For ease in remembering, the dial is engraved with letters as well as numbers, and the three first numbers are made to correspond with the three initial letters of the exchange's name. At the caller's exchange, a complicated piece of equipment known as a 'director' changes the three initial letters dialled by the subscriber into appropriate signals to direct the call through a series of selectors to the required exchange.

Recently, so much progress has been made in designing ELECTRONIC equipment (q.v.) that telephone engineers are looking forward to exchanges where all the switching may be carried out by THERMIONIC VALVES (q.v.) or other electronic devices, instead of by mechanical selectors and relays. This would obviate, for one thing, the wear inevitable in mechanical devices.

A telephone subscriber who wishes to make a trunk call dials a code (usually TRU or O) to obtain the trunk exchange operator. The trunk exchange is similar to a manual local exchange, but has long-distance lines to other trunk exchanges. In the past the trunk operator used to ring the operator at the distant trunk exchange

and ask him to dial the required number. Special automatic trunk exchanges are, however, now being installed so that a call may be put through to any subscriber in Britain simply by dialling a 'routing code' and the number of the required subscriber without any help from an operator at the distant end.

3. LINES, CABLES, and WIRELESS. Two wires are needed to connect each telephone instrument with the local exchange. In the early days all wires were run overhead on poles fitted with cross arms and porcelain insulators. But the large number of telephones in use today makes this impracticable, and most telephone lines in towns and cities are now carried in underground cables. It used to be necessary to provide very thick copper lines on telephone poles in order to obtain a satisfactory volume of speech on long-distance trunk circuits. On some long trunk lines the wires were almost as thick as an ordinary lead pencil. The invention of the thermionic valve, however, has made it possible to amplify the speech currents at regular intervals along the line, so that underground cables can be used for trunk circuits. Nowadays each pair of wires in a long-distance trunk cable is made to carry a large number of separate telephone conversations by a method known as 'carrier telephony' (see CABLES, ELECTRICAL). The invention of submarine valve amplifying equipment has also made it practicable to use submarine cables to carry several separate telephone conversations.

RADIO (q.v.) is being more and more used in modern telephone systems, especially for long-distance international telephone calls. Compact radio apparatus now provides telephone services for small and inaccessible communities—such as the islands off the coast of Scotland.

See also MICROPHONE.

See also Vol. IV: SPEECH, TRANSMISSION OF; TELEPHONE SERVICE.

TELESCOPE. 1. *Refracting telescopes.* An ordinary refracting telescope consists optically of a long-focus LENS (q.v.), called the 'objective', which forms an image of a distant object, and a short-focus magnifying lens, called the 'eyepiece', through which this image is seen by the eye (Fig. 1). When the telescope is properly focused, the rays emerging from the eyepiece are parallel, and the eye sees an inverted and apparently magnified object at a great distance.

In Fig. 1 a distant arrow AB, with its head pointing upwards, sends rays to the objective.

The rays from the head A of the arrow are converged by the objective to meet in A'. The rays

lens of the same diameter and focal length, and an image obtained which is sufficiently sharp,

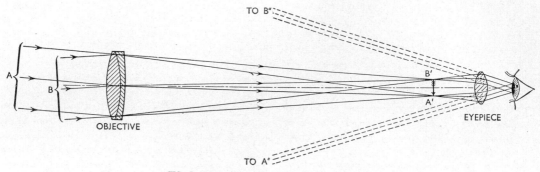

FIG. 1. HOW THE REFRACTING TELESCOPE WORKS

Rays are shown coming from the distant object AB, A'B' is the image formed by the objective, and A"B" the virtual image seen by the eye through the eyepiece

from the tail B of the arrow are converged to meet in B'. The rays from A, after converging to A', continue as far as the eyepiece, and in passing through it are made nearly parallel. The eye sees them as if they came from the distant point A". Similarly, the rays from B, after passing through both objective and eyepiece, enter the eye as if they came from the distant point B". Thus the eye sees the arrow upside down at a great distance and magnified. The relative sizes are magnified in the ratio f_o/f_e, where f_o is the focal length of the objective and f_e that of the eyepiece. Since the image A'B' is to be viewed through a powerful magnifier (namely the eyepiece), it must be very sharp and clear. If an objective consisting of a single lens is used, it is not possible to obtain sufficiently sharp images in a telescope of useful dimensions and magnifying power. This is because a simple lens suffers from optical aberrations (that is, the spoiling of the quality of the image), and that prevents it, however perfectly it is ground and polished, from producing sharp images, free from coloured fringes or halos, over a reasonably large field of view (*see* LENS).

Therefore the objective of a good refracting telescope is never a single lens, but usually consists of two lenses cemented together. The front lens is a double convex lens made of crown glass, and the back lens a plano-concave, or sometimes a meniscus (crescent-shaped section) lens, made of flint glass. By choosing suitable curvatures of the surfaces, the aberrations of the doublet lens can be reduced far below those of a single

and sufficiently free from 'false colour' (as the coloured fringes are sometimes called) to bear a high magnification. Such a lens is called an 'achromatic doublet'.

The eyepiece also does not consist of a single lens, but usually of two separated plano-convex lenses spaced a short distance apart, as shown in Figs. 2a and 2b. When the curvature of the lens surfaces and their distances apart are properly chosen, this arrangement magnifies the image

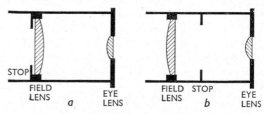

FIG. 2. EYEPIECES OF A TELESCOPE

a. Ramsden eyepiece. *b*. Huyghenian eyepiece

without spoiling it by introducing large 'aberrations'. It has other advantages, also, which are described in the article on LENS.

2. *Terrestrial telescopes.* The fact that objects appear upside down in telescopes of the type just described does not matter when they are used for looking at the mountains of the moon, or the rings of Saturn, but is inconvenient when they are used for making out distant objects on the earth's surface. By adding two additional lenses to the telescope (Fig. 3), objects can be made to appear the right way up. The two added lenses are placed so as to re-image the image A'B' formed by the objective, turning it the right way up without changing its size.

is polished off in such a way as to produce a desired form of surface (very nearly spherical), is

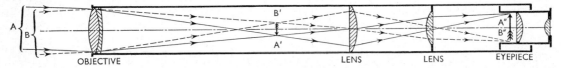

FIG. 3. DIAGRAM OF A TERRESTRIAL TELESCOPE

Rays are shown coming from the distant object AB. A'B' is the image formed by the objective. This is re-imaged at A"B" so that it is seen the right way up

3. *Reflecting telescopes.* A concave mirror will also form an image of a distant object; the nearly parallel rays reaching the mirror from a given point of the object are reflected from the mirror as a converging pencil of rays which come together, almost exactly, in a single image point I (Fig. 4). Each object point sends out rays which produce an image point in this way, and the different image points build up the image, which can then be examined with an eyepiece. Unless the mirror is very large, it is necessary to move the image, by reflection with a flat 'diagonal' mirror, to a position where the observer's head does not block the light on its way to the concave 'primary' mirror.

If the surface of the concave primary mirror is spherical in shape, the rays will not converge accurately to a point. Rays from the outer parts of the mirror will be reflected inward a little too

called 'figuring'. In a Newtonian telescope (Fig. 4) the paraboloidal 'figure' of the primary mirror ensures that when the telescope is pointed directly at a star all the rays converge accurately to a point, and the sharpness of the image is only limited by the effects of the finite wavelength of LIGHT (q.v. Vol. III).

All the very large telescopes needed for photographing objects in distant parts of the Universe are reflectors, because lenses more than about 40 inches in diameter distort under their own weight so badly that the images are spoilt. Large mirrors can be supported from behind by elaborate counterpoise systems of weights and levers. The giant telescopes are nearly all Newtonians, though the largest of all, the Hale telescope (*see* Vol. III, p. 25), with its main mirror 200 inches in diameter, does not use a diagonal mirror, but encloses the astronomer and his

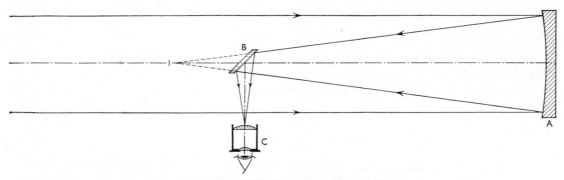

FIG. 4. DIAGRAM OF THE NEWTONIAN TELESCOPE

I is the image formed by the concave primary mirror A (paraboloid). This is reflected by the flat diagonal elliptical mirror B into the eyepiece C

steeply, and the image will be blurred by 'spherical aberration'. This can be avoided by very slightly 'turning back' the outer parts of the mirror in such a way as to convert its spherical surface into a paraboloid, by polishing the surface in a special way after it has been ground spherical. This special polishing process, in which glass

photographic apparatus in a cylinder in the middle of the entering light beam (*see* ASTRONOMY, HISTORY OF, Vol. III).

Modern telescopes are used almost entirely for long-exposure photography, which makes possible the study of stars and nebulae which are much too faint to be seen through an eyepiece.

This means that instead of pointing the telescope directly at a particular object, it is pointed at an area of the sky which may be 4 or 5 degrees in diameter, and all the objects in this area are recorded on the photographic plate, where they

glass, cut into disks or squares, and held pressed against a spherical backing surface, concentric with the mirror surface. When released, the plates spring flat again. The corrector plates of large Schmidt telescopes bend slightly under

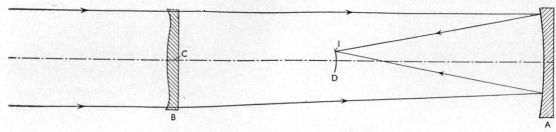

FIG. 5. DIAGRAM OF THE SCHMIDT TELESCOPE

c is the centre of curvature of the spherical mirror A. The 'figuring' on the corrector plate B is very much exaggerated. I is the image formed on the curved photographic plate D

are studied with a low-power microscope after the plate has been developed.

Now although the Newtonian telescope gives a 'perfect' image (in the sense explained above) of a star situated on the axis of the paraboloid mirror, the images of stars slightly to one side of this position are not perfect. When the telescope is used photographically, therefore, only the images close to the centre of the photographic plate are of the highest quality; the others are smudged by an optical aberration known as 'coma'. It follows that the 'useful field' of a Newtonian telescope is very small.

A new type of telescope, devised and first constructed by Bernhard Schmidt in 1930, overcomes this difficulty in a very ingenious way. A spherical mirror is used, and instead of 'turning back' the curve of the mirror near its edge by polishing off glass there, a nearly parallel glass plate is placed at the centre of curvature of the mirror (c in Fig. 5) and the 'figuring' is done on this plate. After 'figuring', the central parts of the plate act like a very weak converging lens, and the outer parts like a diverging lens. The result is to deviate slightly the rays passing through the plate so that after reflection at the mirror they come to a sharp focus.

When a corrector plate of this kind is placed at the centre of curvature, c, of the mirror, it corrects the rays from a star in the outer part of the field of view almost as well as those from a star on the axis. Thus the images are extremely sharp all over the photographic plate. Curved photographic plates have to be used to obtain the sharpest images; these are made of thin

their own weight, but because the two sides of the plate are so very nearly plane and parallel, this sagging does not spoil the sharpness of the images.

See also LENS; MICROSCOPE.

See also Vol. III: ASTRONOMY, HISTORY OF; LIGHT; WAVE MOTION.

TELEVISION ENGINEERING. Television is a system for transmitting moving pictures over long distances by means of radio (see RADIO ENGINEERING). This is done by changing the variations of light and shade in the picture into variations of electric current, which can then be transmitted by radio and picked up by a receiver to be changed back into variations of light and shade on a screen.

The light and shade in the picture are changed into a corresponding electric current by an electronic tube called an 'iconoscope', which is a rather complicated kind of PHOTOCELL (q.v.) fixed inside the television camera. The scene to be televised is focused with an optical LENS (q.v.) on to a thin mica plate mounted inside the air-free glass bulb of the iconoscope. This plate is entirely covered on one side with hundreds of thousands of tiny specks of an alloy made from the metals silver and caesium, so fixed to the plate that they do not touch each other. When light falls on these specks, their caesium atoms vibrate, some of them shaking off one or two of their outer electrons (see ATOM, Vol. III) and leaving the specks with an excess of positive electricity. The stronger the light, the greater is the number of detached electrons and the greater the resulting excess of positive electricity. Thus, the specks in the bright parts of the image on the plate carry more positive electricity than those in the darker parts, and since they do not touch each other they each preserve their own amounts of positive electricity.

The iconoscope also contains an 'electron gun' (*see* CATHODE RAY TUBE) which produces a fine thread-like stream of electrons; this stream can be moved about, as in the cathode ray tube, by the magnetic fields of electric currents in two pairs of deflecting coils fixed to the outside of the iconoscope. The electron stream is directed at the metallic specks on the mica plate, and by means of currents in the deflecting coils it is made to sweep across this plate from left to right in a succession of lines, moving steadily towards the bottom, just as we read a book—a process known as 'scanning'. When the electron stream falls on a speck in a bright part of the picture, just the right number of electrons are drawn from the stream to make good those that are missing from the speck. Consequently, as the picture is scanned, varying numbers of electrons are taken from the stream according to the varying light and shade in different parts of the picture. This varying flow of electrons from the stream causes a varying electric current to flow in the electron gun circuit, and this current forms the required electric 'signal' which the television camera creates for transmission. The scanning electron stream having restored the missing electrons as it passed over the plate, the plate is ready to respond to the next picture.

In the British television system, the screen is divided into 405 horizontal 'lines', across which the scanner sweeps one after the other for each complete scanning. The entire 'picture' is scanned in this manner twenty-five times a second, which is fast enough to give the appearance of continuous motion when the picture is reproduced. In fact, in order to reduce flicker, the complete scan is divided into two successive half-scans, each one selecting alternate lines, and the two half-scans are interlaced to form a complete 405-lines picture. The rhythmic sweep of the scanning electron stream is controlled by ALTERNATING CURRENTS (q.v.) flowing in the deflecting coils, and these currents surge to and fro in step with the 50-cycles-per-second alternating currents in the ordinary power mains.

The electric signal produced by the camera is amplified by THERMIONIC VALVES (q.v.) and

B.B.C.

TELEVISION TRANSMITTING AERIALS AT THE TOP OF THEIR 750-FOOT MAST

then used to modulate—that is, to vary the strength of—a radio wave which is generated by a powerful radio transmitter and radiated into space by the transmitting aerial. The 'sound' part of the television programme is broadcast by a separate transmitter, radiating on a different frequency from the 'vision' transmitter. The sound and vision signals may be separated at the receiver by 'tuning', just as two or more sound programmes may be separated by tuning an ordinary sound receiver. Though separate transmitters for sound and vision have to be used, modern television stations use only one transmitting aerial for both signals.

The radio waves from the sound and vision transmitters are picked up by a receiving aerial and led to the television receiver. The weak signals are first amplified, then passed to two separate receivers, both contained in the one cabinet. The sound receiver is similar to an ordinary broadcast receiver. The vision signal is converted back into variations of light and

SCENE IN A B.B.C. TELEVISION STUDIO AT LIME GROVE, SHOWING ANNOUNCER AND ACTORS ON SEPARATE SETS WITH
LIGHTS AND CAMERAS

shade by a CATHODE RAY TUBE (q.v.). Within this tube a stream of electrons scans a viewing screen in exactly the same way as the electron stream scans the image in the iconoscope. The viewing screen is made of glass coated with a fluorescent substance called a 'phosphor', which, when struck by electrons, emits a small spot of light at the point where they land, the brightness of the spot depending on the number of electrons. The signals from the vision receiver control the number of electrons as the stream scans the screen, and the variations of light and shade in the original scene are reproduced by corresponding variations in the brightness of the rapidly moving spot of light. The speed of scanning is so high compared with the speed of the human eye that the viewer does not see the spot of light, but only the whole pattern of light produced by it during a complete scan. In order to keep the variations of light and shade on the screen in their correct positions, the electron streams in the camera and the receiving cathode ray tube must keep exactly in step. For this purpose special synchronizing signals are produced

when the iconoscope scanning stream reaches the end of a line and also when it reaches the end of a complete picture, rather like the bell that rings when a typewriter reaches the end of a line. These signals are electric currents produced automatically by the electric circuits which generate the scanning control currents for the iconoscope, and after transmission as part of the vision signal, they act upon the corresponding scanning circuits in the receiver and hold them in step.

All the variations of light and shade in the television picture have to be transmitted in $\frac{1}{25}$ second, so the electric signal which 'describes' the picture must be able to change very rapidly: for the British system as fast as 3 million times a second. These rapidly changing signals occupy a much wider band of wavelengths than the sound broadcasts, and it is not possible to fit them into the 'long' or 'medium' wave bands because they take up too much room. There is room, however, in the band of very short waves, and television signals are broadcast in Britain on a wavelength of about 6 metres (18 feet). The electrified layers of air high above the earth which reflect longer waves (*see* RADIO ENGINEERING) are transparent to these very short waves, which are therefore not reflected around the curved surface of the earth. In fact, it is only by placing the transmitting aerial on high ground that television programmes can reach viewers 50 miles away. In Britain special coaxial cables (*see* CABLES, ELECTRICAL), or alternatively a radio 'link' service operating on extremely short wavelengths, carry the television signals from the cameras in the studios to the main high-power transmitting stations throughout the country.

It is possible to transmit and receive television pictures in colour, and colour-television pictures have already begun to be broadcast in America. One method of doing this is to have three separate television cameras in the studio all pointing at the same scene. The first camera 'looks' at the scene through a piece of red glass, the second through a green glass, and the third through a blue. The television signals from the three cameras are then broadcast together. The colour-television receiver has three separate cathode ray tubes, one for each of the signals from the three cameras. The cathode ray tube that takes the signals from the red camera also has a piece of red glass in front of it, and similarly for the green and the blue signals.

The camera behind the red glass 'sees' only the red parts of the scene, and so its cathode ray tube in the receiver shows only the red parts of the picture. Similarly the green and blue cathode ray tubes show the green and the blue parts of the picture. The viewer does not see the red, green, and blue pictures separately, but by a system of mirrors sees all three combined. As all colours can be made by mixing red, green, and blue lights in the right amounts, so the combined picture shows all the colours in the original scene. There are several different ways of sending and reproducing colour-television pictures, but they all depend on combining separate red, green, and blue pictures.

The fact that very short waves are used for television broadcasting influences the design of the receiving aerial. One of the simplest of all aerials is the 'dipole', which has two straight metal rods, each one quarter of a wavelength long, fixed end to end, with some insulating material between them at the centre to prevent contact. The aerial is mounted as high as possible, often on a chimney, with the rods vertical,

and the signal is conveyed to the receiver down a pair of wires, one wire being connected to each rod. The wires are screened with a covering of light woven metal or foil to reduce 'interference' from other electrical apparatus in the neighbourhood.

Another common aerial is the H-type; this has a horizontal non-conducting cross-bar carrying a dipole at the end nearest to the transmitter; at the other end there is a straight metal rod, which reflects the radio wave and increases the amount of signal picked up by the dipole. At great distances from the transmitter, where the signal is weak, more complicated aerials may be necessary; these have two or more extra rods, which enable the aerial to receive a stronger signal from the direction of the transmitter, and so protect it against interfering signals coming from the opposite direction.

One of the most troublesome forms of interference to television comes from motor-car ignition systems. The HIGH-FREQUENCY CURRENTS (q.v. Section 4) which flow in these produce radio waves which may be picked up by the television receiving aerial, and cause bright spots of light to appear on the screen and clicking noises to come from the loud-speaker. To prevent this,

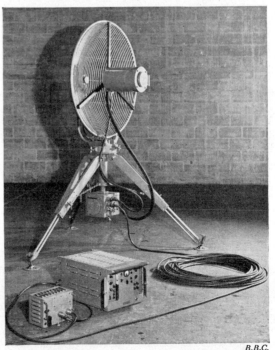

B.B.C.

RADIO EQUIPMENT USED TO SEND TELEVISION PICTURES BACK TO THE STUDIOS DURING OUTSIDE BROADCASTS

resistances, known as 'suppressors', can be fitted in the wires leading to the car's sparking plugs; these reduce the strength of the high-frequency currents and cause them to die away quickly.

See also CATHODE RAY TUBE; RADIO ENGINEERING.
See also Vol. IV: TELEVISION.

TEMPERATURE, MEASUREMENT OF.
Temperature (*see* HEAT, Section 2, Vol. III) affects us at every point in our lives; it controls our bodily comfort, the growth of the food we eat, and almost every industrial or technical process. The citizen, the engineer, and the scientist are all, therefore, concerned with the ways in which it can be measured.

1. SCALE OF TEMPERATURE. To be useful, different THERMOMETERS (q.v.) must give the same reading at the same temperature; and there must be an agreed scale against which the reading is to be taken. It is usual to choose two 'fixed points' (standard temperatures which can be easily repeated in any laboratory) and a number of 'degrees' into which the scale is divided between and beyond these points. As originally suggested by Hooke in 1681, the melting-point of ice and the boiling-point of water (at a standard pressure of 760 mm. of mercury—the average PRESSURE (q.v. Vol. III) of the atmosphere) are always taken for these fixed points. Between them Fahrenheit in 1714 chose 180 degrees; though, as he wished to call the coldest thing he could find (a mixture of ice and salt) zero on his scale, he had to fix the melting-point of ice as 32°, and consequently the steam-point became 32°+180° = 212°. The great Swedish physicist, Celsius (1701–44), preferred to call the ice-point 0°, and to divide the interval into 100 parts, so that the steam-point became 100°. The Celsius or Centigrade scale (written °C.) is nowadays used all over the world in scientific and technical work. In this country the Fahrenheit scale (written °F.) survives in domestic and meteorological measurements and in some branches of engineering.

2. ABSOLUTE SCALE. Unfortunately it is not sufficient just to fix two points of temperature and to divide evenly a number of degrees between them. If we were to compare three thermometers, one an ordinary mercury thermometer, one measuring the resistance of a piece of platinum wire, and one measuring the electromotive force of a thermocouple (*see* THERMOMETER), all agreeing, of course, at 0° and 100° C., then we should

find that 50° on the mercury thermometer was approximately the same as 50·3° on the resistance thermometer and 52·3° on the thermocouple—in other words, from the point of view of the mercury thermometer, the resistance of platinum does not increase 'uniformly' with temperature. But we could equally well say that from the point of view of the resistance thermometer, the volume of mercury does not increase uniformly with temperature. Which thermometer are we to choose? The practical reader may well ask 'What does it matter, as long as we all agree to use the same thermometer?' If, however, a particular thermometer was chosen in this arbitrary way, there would be confusion in many important measurements such as of the efficiency of a steam engine, or the heat lost from a glowing body—which are closely connected with the ideas of 'work' and ENERGY (q.v.). For scientific work, we must somehow check our thermometers against an 'absolute' thermometer, that is, one which measures the 'average energy of motion of its molecules' which is the scientist's definition of the meaning of temperature.

It can be proved that if a gas consisted entirely of molecules that were infinitely small, perfectly elastic, and which did not attract or repel each other, then the average energy of motion of its molecules would be proportional to its pressure—and that, of course, can be measured by direct mechanical means. Such a gas is known as a 'perfect' gas, and, if it existed, we could make an 'absolute' thermometer simply by attaching a pressure gauge to a fixed volume of a perfect gas, in, say, a globe of non-expanding material.

Though there is no gas which is entirely 'perfect' in this sense, gases such as hydrogen and helium are very nearly 'perfect' over a large range of temperature, and by special experiments their small deviations from perfection can be determined. The gas thermometer is thus the standard against which the scientist ultimately compares the other types of thermometer which are used in practice.

The idea of the 'perfect' gas leads us also to the idea of an 'absolute zero' of temperature. For, as we abstract HEAT (q.v. Vol. III) from a substance, the energy of motion of its molecules becomes less and less; there must eventually come a point at which the molecules are at rest, and the substance is as cold as it is possible to be.

By actual experiments with a gas thermometer, we can find out where this 'absolute zero' is. If, for example, the simple thermometer we have described showed a pressure of 373 lb. per sq. in. at the boiling-point of water, it would be found to show 273 lb. per sq. in. at the melting-point of ice. By simple proportion, therefore (Fig. 1), it would show zero pressure (that is, zero temperature) at a temperature of −273° on the Celsius scale; and so we call −273° C. the absolute

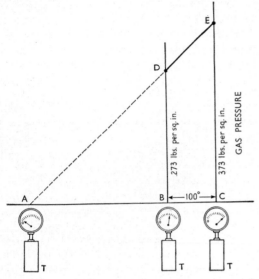

FIG. I. THE ABSOLUTE ZERO

A. Absolute zero. B. Melting-point of ice. C. Boiling-point of water. T. Gas thermometers. If we call BC 100°, then by proportion AB must be 273°, because the measured pressures CE and BD are in the ratio 373:273

zero, at which the molecules have lost their energy of motion, and no further cooling is possible. More exact measurements, taking into account the differences between real gases (helium, nitrogen) and the 'perfect' gas, identify this temperature as −273·15° C. In modern laboratories, temperatures within a few thousandths of a degree of this zero can be reached in special experiments; and measurements at the boiling-point of liquid helium (4° from the zero) are fairly common. For many scientific purposes, the absolute zero is taken as the zero from which to reckon the temperature scale; ice then melts at 273° and water boils at 373°. Temperatures reckoned thus are called 'absolute', and written °K.—the 'K' standing for Lord KELVIN (q.v. Vol. V), who was closely concerned with the introduction of this scale.

3. INTERNATIONAL TEMPERATURE SCALE. The absolute scale is not practical for everyday use; the perfect gas, of course, does not exist, and even the real gas thermometer can be used accurately only in very specially equipped laboratories. In order that the Celsius scale which we use in practice can be checked without difficulty, and its exact relationship to the absolute scale defined, the temperatures of a number of fixed points on the Celsius scale have been internationally agreed. The precise methods and types of thermometers to be used, to measure temperatures between or outside these fixed points, have also been chosen. Thus, besides the ice-point (0°) and the steam-point (100°), the boiling-point of sulphur is defined as 444·60° C. and the melting-point of gold as 1,063° C. When a good thermometer of any type is sent to the National Physical Laboratory to have its scale checked, it is in effect checked at these fixed points, and at intermediate points, using comparison thermometers which accord with this international agreement.

4. HIGH TEMPERATURES. A mercury thermometer cannot be used at much above 500° C. —the glass softens; nor a thermocouple above 1,600° C.—the platinum melts. For measuring high temperatures, we use a 'radiation pyrometer', which is really an optical instrument for measuring brightness. The brightness of the interior of a hot body, such as a furnace, for a particular colour (as seen, for example, through a dark red glass) is proportional to the 5th power of the absolute temperature (that is, 'multiplied together 5 times', thus $2^5 = 2 \times 2 \times 2 \times 2 \times 2 = 32$). If, for example, a revolving shutter, with an aperture 1/32nd of its circumference, placed in front of a furnace hole, makes it look exactly as bright through a red glass as a crucible of melting gold seen without the shutter (temperature 1,063+273° K.), then the temperature of the furnace, in °K., is exactly double ($2^5 = 32$) that of the gold—that is, it is 2,672° K. or 2,399° C. The 'disappearing filament pyrometer' used for this measurement is described in the article THERMOMETER.

5. SOME OTHER POINTS IN MEASURING TEMPERATURE. It is not only the thermometer itself, and its scale, which matters. The thermometer takes time to reach its reading; it also conducts heat along its stem and abstracts heat from its surroundings, so altering them; and it takes in heat by radiation as well as by direct contact. For example, an ordinary mercury thermometer placed in a cup of tea might well give a reading some $\frac{1}{10}$° C. lower than the original temperature of the tea—the difference represents the heat which has gone to warm the thermometer. Also a thermometer, hung in a room to give the air temperature, will not give the right answer unless it is shielded from direct radiation from fires, hot-water pipes, and so on. Measurements of the temperatures of a surface, of flame, of anything rapidly varying or moving, are all special problems, needing special solutions by the scientist.

See also THERMOMETER.

See also Vol. III: HEAT; PRESSURE.

TEMPERING, *see* HEAT TREATMENT, Section 4.

TENNESSEE VALLEY AUTHORITY. The Tennessee Valley Authority Scheme—known throughout the United States as 'T.V.A.'—began as a plan for LAND RECLAMATION, and developed into one of the greatest experiments in combined social and economic planning and CIVIL ENGINEERING (qq.v.) yet made. It has given a new direction to the life of a large area, and has influenced the economy of the greatest industrial country in the world.

The Tennessee—a tributary of the Ohio, which itself is a tributary of the MISSISSIPPI (q.v. Vol. III)—is a great river some 900 miles long, flowing across several southern States of America. Its valley, covering about 42,000 square miles,

was once surrounded by wooded hills and was richly fertile. But the early settlers, in their greed for more land, felled the trees until the hills were bare. What happened then has happened in other parts of the world also. The rains, instead of soaking into the earth, ran down the hillsides, forming torrents and carving channels as they went. The good soil, no longer held by roots, was washed down or blown away as dust (*see* SOIL EROSION, Vol. III). The river, the valley's chief means of transport, became choked with silt and liable to flooding. This once prosperous and happy valley became a district of country slums; and, as poverty spread, racial hatred broke out between its white and Negro inhabitants.

In the 1920s the United States Government realized that something must be done to help the area, and a practical scheme of reclamation was drawn up. For years there was bitter dispute as to whether the scheme should be carried out by the Federal Government or by private enterprise, and not until 1933, when Franklin D. ROOSEVELT (q.v. Vol. V) became President, was the necessary legislation passed by Congress. This Act created the Tennessee Valley Authority, and entrusted to it the task of restoring the valley's prosperity by means of land reclamation, FLOOD CONTROL, HYDRO-ELECTRIC POWER

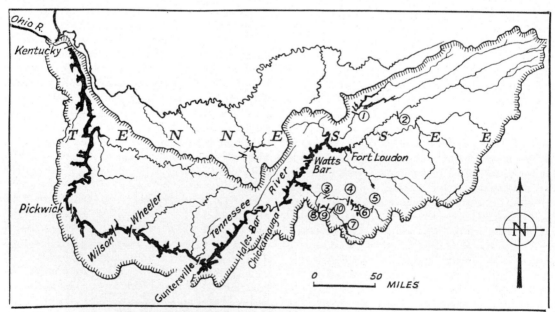

MAP OF THE TENNESSEE VALLEY NAMING THE MOST IMPORTANT DAMS

1. Norris. 2. Cherokee. 3. Appalachia. 4. Hiwassee. 5. Chatuge. 6. Nottely. 7. Blue Ridge. 8, 9, 10. Ocoee Nos. 1, 2, 3

INDUSTRIAL DEVELOPMENT IN THE TENNESSEE VALLEY. A NITRATE PLANT NEAR WILSON DAM

U.S.I.S.

(qq.v.), AFFORESTATION (q.v. Vol. VI), and modern farming methods, and by making the river navigable once again.

An important part of the scheme was the construction of nine large multi-purpose DAMS (q.v.) and reservoirs along the course of the main river, and of eleven more on its tributaries; altogether thirty-five dams now command the valley of the Tennessee (see Map). This chain of lakes has made it possible to control the flow of the river so that fleets of lighters are able to carry heavy industrial cargoes from the Deep South via the Mississippi and Ohio as far as the GREAT LAKES (q.v. Vol. III). Though the main purpose of the reservoirs is to prevent flooding and to irrigate the river valley, they also provide a head of water for many power stations. These generate sufficient electricity to repay the whole cost of construction.

At the same time hills were terraced and planted with new trees to check erosion, and expert advice was given to the farmers to help them restore the productivity of the land. In addition, a number of pleasant holiday resorts have sprung up on the shores of the artificial lakes which help to bring money into the district.

The whole of the original project is now nearly complete, though expansion still continues. New steam power stations, for example, are being built to increase still further the output of electricity—largely to meet the immense demand of the United States Atomic Energy Commission. Indeed, the T.V.A.'s operations as a producer of electric power have now overshadowed its other achievements. It has built up one of the largest power systems in the world, supplying over $1\frac{1}{4}$ million users in seven States.

Up to June 1944, about 750 million dollars had been spent on this vast and many-sided scheme. Great courage was needed to undertake so heavy an expenditure, and it is impossible to reckon in terms of money the benefits that have been derived from it. It is fitting that on all dams and mechanical plants of the T.V.A. are inscribed the words: 'Built for the people of the United States.'

See also CIVIL ENGINEERING.

TESTING MACHINES, see STRESS AND STRAIN; DYNAMOMETER.

THEODOLITE, see SURVEYING INSTRUMENTS, Section 2.

THERMIONIC VALVES. These devices are essential to RADIO, RADAR, and all ELECTRONICS (qq.v.). Their invention in 1904 by the British physicist, Ambrose Fleming, has revolutionized electrical science and proved of great importance to the development of physics and to our knowledge of the ATOM (q.v. Vol. III).

The term 'valve' is used in engineering for a device which allows something—whether air, a liquid, or an electric current—to pass through in one direction only. Thermionic valves are based on the phenomenon of 'thermionic emission'— the escape from any heated metal of extremely small particles of electricity. When a metal is heated, its atoms vibrate vigorously and collide

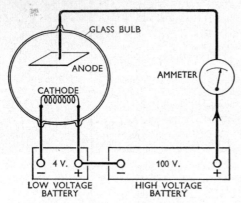

FIG. I. A SIMPLE THERMIONIC VALVE

with one another. The outer parts of the atoms contain minute particles of negative electricity, called electrons, some of which are knocked off their atoms by the collisions and tend to escape. This happens, for example, to the end of a poker whenever it gets red hot. If the hot metal happens to be in a vacuum (a wire, for example, inside an electric light bulb), the escape of electrons from the hot metal is very great.

The simplest kind of thermionic valve looks very much like an electric light bulb, with an extra tab of metal sticking into it at the opposite end from the socket. If this tab (known as a 'plate') were given a slightly positive charge of electricity, the electrons which are being shot out of the white-hot wire in millions would be attracted to it, and would flow to it, forming a kind of bridge or additional electric circuit through the lamp. The stream of electrons is the 'thermionic current'; each piece of metal entering the valve is known as an 'electrode', the hot filament being distinguished as the 'cathode' and the plate as the 'anode' (Fig. I). The valve will allow current to flow through itself in one way only, from anode to cathode (always in the opposite direction to the thermionic current or

stream of electrons). Thus, with a current which is regularly changing its direction by oscillating or alternating (see ALTERNATING CURRENT), the valve will accept only half of each cycle, represented by the upper half of the wave in Fig. 3b. No current will flow if the filament is not heated, or if the anode is not positively charged.

The purposes which thermionic valves serve depend partly on the number of electrodes with which they are fitted. The simplest is the diode (two-electrode) shown in Fig. I; other important forms include the triode (three-electrode) and pentode (five-electrode). In each kind the heated cathode and the anode plate carry out the functions described; the extra electrodes, generally known as 'grids', are interposed between these two; and, since they stand in the path of the stream of electrons, can be of great importance. A very small electrical effort applied to a grid will have a very strong effect in controlling the amount of current that passes through the valve.

The operation of a valve in, say, a domestic wireless set would be upset if the cathode were heated directly from the high-voltage mains. The cathode, therefore, takes one of two forms: either a directly heated cathode, consisting of a hairpin filament of tungsten wire coated with an exceedingly thin film of the rare metal thorium to increase the emission of electrons (Fig. 2a), and heated by a small accumulator—that is, by D.C.; or an indirectly heated cathode, consisting of a small nickel cathode tube covered with a thin layer of mixed oxides of barium and strontium, which emits electrons very freely when heated. Inside this tube, but not touching it by

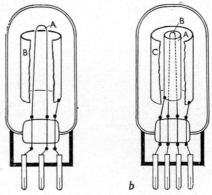

FIG. 2. DIODE VALVES

a. Direct heating. A. Cathode. B. Anode. b. Indirect heating. A. Cathode. B. Cathode heater. C. Anode. Anodes are cut away to show cathodes

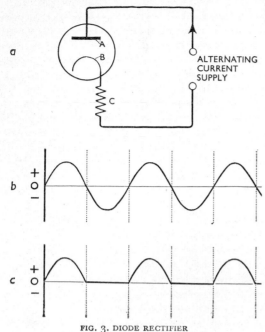

FIG. 3. DIODE RECTIFIER

a. Connexions of rectifier. A. Anode. B. Cathode. C. Resistance. *b*. Flow of alternating current. *c*. Flow of rectified current

When a battery's negative terminal is joined to the control grid and its positive to the cathode, the grid repels some of the electrons emitted by the cathode, thus reducing the stream of electrons which had formed a bridge between anode and cathode and also reducing the current flowing from the anode. By varying the grid voltage the anode current can be controlled, a small change in grid voltage causing quite large changes in anode current. These changes in anode current produce changes in the voltage across a resistance in the anode circuit. In Fig. 5, for example, a change in grid voltage of 3 volts (from −6 volts to −3 volts) produces a change in the voltage across the anode resistor of 120 volts—that is, from 30 volts to 150 volts.

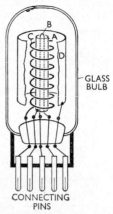

FIG. 4. TRIODE VALVE

A. Cathode. B. Cathode heater. C. Control grid. D. Anode (partly cut away)

a fraction of an inch (Fig. 2*b*), is a filament, which is usually heated by A.C. from the mains through a transformer, making the tube glow. The anodes are nickel cylinders closely surrounding the cathodes.

Diodes are mainly used as RECTIFIERS (q.v.) for converting alternating current into direct current. Fig. 3*a* is a diagram of the connexions of a diode rectifier. The cathode is connected through the load (that is, the electrical job of work to be done, represented in this diagram by the symbol for a 'resistance') to one terminal of the 50-cycles-per-second alternating current mains, and the other mains terminal is joined to the anode. The alternating voltage between the anode and the cathode is shown by the wavy line of Fig. 3*b*. Anode current flows only when the anode is positive as shown in Fig. 3*c*, and the alternating current supply is converted into a fluctuating one-way supply: the fluctuations can be reduced by passing the current through choke coils wound on iron cores (*see* INDUCTION, ELECTRIC). Diode rectifiers are used in all-mains radio sets to provide the high-voltage direct-current supply, and also as detectors of radio signals.

A triode, with a wire spiral control-grid between its anode and cathode, is shown in Fig. 4.

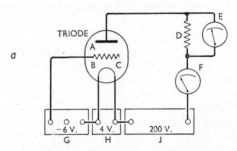

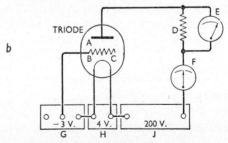

FIG. 5. PRINCIPLE OF VALVE AMPLIFIER

a. When the grid voltage is −6 volts the voltmeter reads 30 volts and the ammeter reads 1 milliamp. *b*. When the grid voltage is −3 volts the voltmeter reads 150 volts and the ammeter reads 5 milliamps. A. Anode. B. Control grid. C. Cathode. D. Anode circuit resistance. E. Voltmeter. F. Ammeter. G. Grid bias battery. H. Low tension battery. J. High tension battery

In this way a small alternating voltage applied to the grid can cause a much larger fluctuating voltage to appear in the anode circuit—which is the principle used in valve amplifiers.

Amplifiers in modern radio sets multiply thousands of times the extremely small electrical signals from distant stations until they are big enough to operate powerful loud-speakers. Fig. 5 shows how a feeble signal led to a grid can be reproduced forty times more strongly on the anode, with the use of local supplies of power; magnifications of 100 times or more are possible with some valves. Amplifiers are arranged in groups, each strengthening the signal passed on from its neighbour, so that a 'hundred times' amplification would have this result: one amplifier, 100 times; two amplifiers, 10,000 times; three amplifiers, 1,000,000 times.

Triodes can also be used as detectors (see RADIO ENGINEERING) and to generate oscillating HIGH-FREQUENCY CURRENTS (q.v.).

Pentodes are used to amplify high-frequency radio currents. For generating the very high-frequency oscillations used in RADAR (q.v.), special valves are made, which are tuned by making their anodes in the shape of small boxes or cavities of the correct size and shape for the oscillation frequency required.

The thermionic valves in miniature radio receivers are no larger than an inch of lead pencil, but the valves in a powerful radio transmitter may be bigger than a man. These large valves have to be cooled by powerful blasts of air or by pumping cold water through a copper jacket placed around the valve.

Thermionic valves are always referred to as 'tubes' in American books and magazines. In Britain the term 'tube' for an electronic glass bulb is mostly confined to X-RAY and CATHODE RAY apparatus (qq.v.), but is applied to thermionic valves in a few special cases.

See also PHOTOCELL.

THERMOCOUPLE, *see* THERMOMETER.

THERMODYNAMICS, *see* HEAT ENGINES.

THERMOMETER. To most people the word 'thermometer' (heat measurer) means a glass tube containing mercury, which tells how hot the oven is or how ill we are. In fact, almost any effect which heat produces on matter—change in volume, colour, shape, electrical resistance, and so on—can be used to measure temperature and so to make a 'thermometer'; so there are many different kinds of thermometer. In practice we choose one for a particular job for its convenience, cheapness, simplicity, and accuracy, according to circumstances.

1. BIMETALLIC STRIP. This is the simplest of all the thermometers. Different materials—such as brass and steel—expand by different amounts when heated. Consequently if a thin strip of brass is riveted or soldered to one of steel, the combined strip, when heated, will expand more on one face than the other, and so will tend to curl up. One end of the strip may be fixed, and the movement of the other end magnified by some lever device, and used to move a pointer over a scale reading in degrees of temperature. Bimetallic strip is made in all shapes and sizes, and is used in simple thermometers of all kinds, and in thermostatic controls (see THERMOSTAT). But this kind of thermometer is not suitable for very exact measurements.

2. MERCURY-IN-GLASS. This thermometer is perhaps the most generally useful of all. For each 1° C., mercury expands by almost 1 part in 5,000, and glass by only 1 part in 100,000. Therefore, if a glass bulb is connected to a fine glass tube (the 'capillary'), filled with mercury, and heated, the mercury will expand much more than the glass, and will rise in the capillary. Such a glass tube, graduated in equal divisions and sealed up at the end to keep out dirt, is a thermometer; and millions of such instruments are made every year.

To obtain a thermometer of a given sensitivity and range, the maker has to choose the diameter of the glass tube, or capillary, very carefully to match the volume of the bulb (usually a cylinder, rather than a sphere, so that the heat flows more quickly into the thermometer when taking a reading). The thermometer is filled with mercury, the end sealed up (after boiling some of the mercury to drive out enclosed air), and the reference points on its scale (see TEMPERATURE, MEASUREMENT OF) are marked by immersing it in well-stirred baths at known temperatures. The distance between the 'pointing' marks is then subdivided into the correct number of degrees. The glass of a thermometer bulb is specially selected, so that after being heated it will come back exactly to the same volume again—otherwise the thermometer would be inaccurate. Even so, a precise mercury thermometer always shows small changes of zero for some time after use at high temperatures, and this has to be allowed for in accurate work.

Mercury thermometers can be made for use from nearly —39° C. (the freezing-point of mercury) to perhaps 500° C. (a limit set by the strength of the glass of the bulb). For temperatures above, say, 100° C. the space above the capillary is filled with a gas such as nitrogen

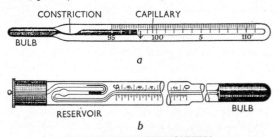

FIG. 1. MERCURY THERMOMETERS

a. Clinical thermometer. *b.* Beckmann thermometer

under pressure, to prevent evaporation of the mercury. Lower temperatures to —80° C. can be reached by using a liquid such as alcohol instead of mercury. Many special types of mercury thermometers are made. The ordinary 'clinical' thermometer and the meteorological 'maximum' thermometer, for example, have a fine constriction or narrowing in the bore of the capillary close to the bulb. The mercury moves up the capillary, passing the constriction in separate spurts, as the bulb is heated. On cooling the mercury thread stays above the constriction, and the maximum reading is preserved until the thermometer is 'shaken down' again (Fig. 1*a*). The 'Beckmann' thermometer has a large bulb and a fine capillary, covering a few degrees only, and divided in, perhaps, $\frac{1}{100}$°; the amount of mercury in the bulb can be altered by running it over into a subsidiary reservoir (Fig. 1*b*), so that the same thermometer can be used for accurate difference measurements ($\frac{1}{1000}$°, perhaps) over small ranges, at various different initial temperatures.

3. THERMOCOUPLE. This is another very useful type of thermometer. If two wires of different metals are twisted together and the free ends connected to a fairly sensitive millivoltmeter, the pointer will move when the twisted ends of the wires are heated (Fig. 2). An electromotive force is produced (*see* MEASUREMENT, UNITS OF, Section 3*c*), which depends on the difference of temperature between the heated ends

of the wires and the ends at the terminals of the millivoltmeter. This combination of dissimilar metals, called a 'thermocouple', is most useful in industry and in the laboratory for the measurement of temperature. For ordinary temperatures, copper and constantan (a nickel alloy) work very well; for higher temperatures, precious metals such as platinum and its alloys must be used. Fig. 3 shows a quick-immersion thermocouple, protected by a silica sheath, measuring the temperature of molten steel in a steelworks. A simple thermocouple (for indicating, for example, the temperature of an oven used for hardening tools or melting metals) would be connected directly

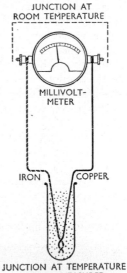

FIG. 2. PRINCIPLE OF THE THERMOCOUPLE

National Physical Laboratory

FIG. 3. MEASURING THE TEMPERATURE OF MOLTEN STEEL WITH A QUICK-IMMERSION THERMOCOUPLE

to a pointer millivoltmeter, with its scale graduated in degrees. The junction of the couple at the voltmeter would be assumed to be at room temperature; but for more exact measurements, it would be kept at 0° in an ice-bath, and the electromotive force would be measured by a network of resistances, used to balance it against a known electromotive force from a standard cell.

Thermocouples have many advantages. They are compact, and read the temperature almost at a point (a thermocouple junction with fine wires can be smaller than any mercury bulb). They can cover a very large temperature range (perhaps 1,600° C. down to −200° C.), and many thermocouples can be arranged to read

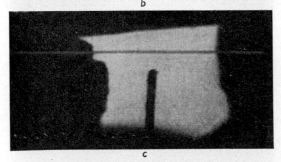

FIG. 4. DISAPPEARING FILAMENT PYROMETER MEASURING THE
TEMPERATURE OF MOLTEN STEEL

The glowing horizontal filament of the pyrometer is seen through the eyepiece against the liquid steel in the background. In *a* the filament is too hot, in *c* too cold, in *b* just right. The vertical black line is an index to help in sighting

on a common dial and if necessary to give a continuous record of the temperature at many points.

4. RESISTANCE THERMOMETER. This is another electrical thermometer. A copper wire increases in electrical resistance by 1 part in 250 for each 1° C. rise in temperature; and so a piece of wire can be used as a thermometer. Its resistance is measured by balancing it against a known resistance by a special device called a 'Wheatstone bridge' (*see* ELECTRIC CURRENT, Section 3). In fact, the most sensitive and precise thermometers in existence work on this principle, using a fine wire of platinum, very clean and pure. To get high accuracy, the resistance of the connexions between the thermometer wire and the Wheatstone bridge has to be allowed for by special circuits, and the bridge itself has to remain very constant in behaviour. At the National Physical Laboratory the resistance thermometer can be used to an accuracy of $\frac{1}{10000}$° C., which involves measuring changes of electrical resistance of only 1 part in 10 million.

5. RADIATION THERMOMETERS. The thermocouple and perhaps the platinum resistance thermometer can be used up to a bright yellow heat; but above the melting-point of platinum, we must look for some form of thermometer which does not itself have to be raised to the high temperature we are measuring. The answer is implied in the words 'bright yellow'; if we can measure accurately enough the brightness or colour of an incandescent body, we can tell its temperature.

The most usual instrument for doing this is the 'disappearing-filament optical pyrometer'. This is a low-power TELESCOPE (q.v.) at whose focus is placed a small electric lamp, the filament of which can be heated to varying brightness by a measured current. Through the telescope (which includes a deep red filter to confine the light to one colour) we see the lamp filament silhouetted against the furnace or hot object of which we are finding the temperature; we increase the current until the filament is just as bright as the furnace—at which point it 'disappears' (Fig. 4). Measurement of the current then gives the temperature if we have already fixed the scale of the instrument, using hot bodies at known temperatures (*see* TEMPERATURE, MEASUREMENT OF).

6. OTHER THERMOMETERS. We have described the most important types; but there are many

FIG. 5. SEGER CONES FOR MEASURING TEMPERATURE

others in use. For example, in the 'vapour-pressure' thermometer (used for oil and water temperatures in cars and aircraft), some liquid (such as alcohol or water) in a bulb is connected to a gauge which measures the pressure of the vapour; in the 'mercury-in-steel' thermometer, the expansion of mercury operates a pressure-gauge directly. In kilns for pottery and ceramics small cones of mixtures in varying proportions of clay, felspar, and other constituents, called 'Seger cones', are much used; after a certain time at a certain temperature a cone of a certain composition will soften and its tip fall over. A row of differently composed cones, therefore, is used to indicate the temperature of a particular firing (Fig. 5). There are some materials which change colour with temperature; paints containing these materials can be used—on parts of machinery, for example—to serve as an indication of dangerous temperatures.

See also TEMPERATURE, MEASUREMENT OF.

THERMOSTAT. This is a device for keeping a temperature steady: for example an enclosure, such as a water-tank, a refrigerator, a room, or an oven, can be kept at a desired constant temperature. The thermostat of an oven, for example, is a temperature-sensitive element which controls the supply of heat to the oven. When the temperature rises above a fixed point, the thermostat operates a switch or valve to cut off the heat; when the temperature drops below the

fixed point the thermostat turns the heat on again. The temperature, therefore, in the enclosure varies only a few degrees above or below the desired level. The thermostat of a refrigerator works in the same way, turning on and off the REFRIGERATOR mechanism (q.v.).

A simple and frequently used temperature-sensitive device is the 'bimetallic strip'—that is, a thin strip of steel and another of brass riveted or soldered together. Since brass expands when heated (or contracts when chilled) about twice the amount that steel does, the combined strip will expand (or contract) more on one face than the other, and will consequently tend to curl up. This curling movement can be made to work a suitable control system within the enclosure, turning it on or off.

In private houses, simple thermostats are common—in electric irons, gas cookers, refrigerators, and central heating and hot-water installations. In industry, more elaborate devices control the temperature of cold storage rooms, baths, ovens, and furnaces of all kinds. In the laboratory, still more sensitive instruments maintain constant temperature, perhaps to $\frac{1}{1000}°$ C., for precise measurements.

Fig. 1 shows the temperature control of a modern electric iron. When switched on, current flows through the resistance R, and the iron begins to get hot. When the bimetallic strip s is hot enough, it snaps open the switch M, which stops the current, and the iron begins to cool.

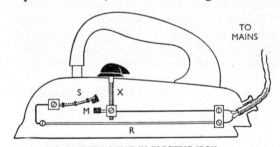

FIG. I. THERMOSTAT IN ELECTRIC IRON
R. Resistance. S. Bimetallic strip. M. Switch.
x. Screw to control temperature

When it has cooled enough for s to close M again, the process starts over again. The average temperature is controlled by an adjusting screw x, which alters the position of the contacts, that is, the temperature which s must reach before it opens the switch.

Fig. 2 shows the mechanism of a more precise thermostat, such as might be used to control a

Sunvic Controls Ltd.

FIG. 2. THERMOSTAT FOR CONTROLLING TEMPERATURES
ACCURATELY

A. A knob on this spindle controls the position of the fixed
contact D, and so alters the temperature of control.
B. Arm moved by bimetallic spiral. C. Flexible arm.
D. Fixed contact.   M. Magnet

well-stirred water-bath in an industrial process
to ±1° C. To give this sensitivity, a long bimetallic spiral, fixed at one end, carries at the other
the moving contact C on a flexible arm. The
normal position of the other contact D can be
adjusted, so that the thermostat can be set to
control at different temperatures as required. A
tiny magnet M carried on the contact arms gives
a 'snap' action when the contacts open or close.

In many industrial processes a thermostat will
have to control the flow of steam, hot water, or
ventilating air, instead of an electric current;
and something more elaborate, such as an electronic amplifier, may become necessary to
enable the small power obtainable, perhaps from
a thermocouple (*see* THERMOMETER, Section 3),
to control the opening or closing of a large
mechanical valve or ventilator. In such cases,
the crude 'on-off' control of the domestic iron
may not give sufficiently good results. Just as a
skilled driver guides a motor-car in a straight
line by anticipating the effect of bumps or holes
which would move it from its course, so more
elaborate thermostats alter the flow of heat by
an amount depending on the difference of temperature from the proper value and make up
for the time-lag between supply of heat and
alteration of temperature by anticipating these
alterations.

The control of gas-heated appliances, such as
a gas oven, depends on supplying a variable
amount of gas to the burner rather than turning
it on and off. A brass tube is fixed to the side of
the oven, its free end projecting into the oven.
A rod of material (invar) less sensitive to changes
of temperature than brass, is attached to the free
end and runs through the tube to a valve outside
the oven, which controls the supply of gas (*see*
p. 16). When the temperature in the oven rises,
the brass tube expands, and the rod, which expands very little, shuts the valve. A by-pass tube
ensures that the gas is not completely cut off
when the valve is shut.

THREE-DIMENSIONAL FILMS, *see* STEREO-
SCOPE; CINE-CAMERAS AND PROJECTORS.

TIM, *see* TIMEKEEPERS, MODERN, Section 3.

TIME AND MOTION STUDY, *see* PRODUC-
TION ENGINEERING, Section 4.

TIMEKEEPERS, ANCIENT. Methods of
measuring time and finding out the hour of the
day existed long before mechanical clocks and
watches were invented. The earliest time-
measuring instruments we know of are the sundials and water-clocks of Ancient Egypt about
1500 B.C. The Egyptians of this period did not
divide the whole day-and-night period into
24 equal hours as we do: instead they divided
the daylight period, from sunrise to sunset, into
twelve equal parts and the night period, from
sunset to sunrise, into twelve equal parts. The
length of a 'day-hour' was, therefore, not the
same (except at the equinoxes, in spring and
autumn) as that of a 'night-hour', and each type
of 'hour' varied in length according to the season

Crown Copyright, Science Museum

FIG. I. COPY OF EGYPTIAN SHADOW-CLOCK
IOTH–8TH CENTURY B.C.

FIG. 2. CAST OF EGYPTIAN WATER-CLOCK FROM KARNAK
TEMPLE, 1415–1380 B.C.

of the year. Their sundials and water-clocks were accordingly devised to indicate hours of this type.

One of their earliest sundials, dating from about 900 B.C., consists of a horizontal bar with a short upright and cross-piece mounted at one end (Fig. 1). In the morning, the bar was set in an east–west position, with the upright at the east end, and the shadow of the cross-piece fell on the bar. There are six hour-marks on the cross-piece, and the time was shown by the position of the shadow in relation to these. At noon the length of the shadow on the bar would shrink to nothing, and the bar would be reversed for use during the afternoon.

In a somewhat later type of Egyptian sundial, a shadow fell upon a flight of steps, the time being known from the number of the step on which it fell. These types of sundial gave a rather rough indication of the time—which was probably all that was needed.

For finding the time by night, the Egyptians would either make observations of the stars or use water-clocks. An Egyptian water-clock consists of a stone vessel with a small hole at the bottom through which water can slowly trickle out (Fig. 2). Scales of hours are marked on the inside of the vessel. At sunset, water would be poured into the vessel up to the topmost mark, and the slow outflow from the bottom would begin. If the Egyptians had used a cylindrical vessel, the level of water would have dropped rapidly at first under the greater pressure, and more slowly later; but with the shape of vessel they actually used the water-level falls at an almost uniform rate, since the more rapid outflow when the vessel is nearly full is compensated by the fact that there is a greater volume at the top, and so a greater outflow is needed to produce a one-inch fall in level than when the water is flowing out from the narrower part of the vessel near the bottom.

A separate scale of 'hours' is marked inside the vessel for each month, to allow for the changing length of the 'hours' according to the season.

Sundials and water-clocks were the only types of time-measuring instruments used throughout the periods of the Greek and Roman Empires, from about 500 B.C. to A.D. 500, though there were many improvements in design. A favourite type of sundial was the 'hemicycle', said to have been invented by Berosus, the Chaldean astronomer, about 300 B.C., and a number of these have survived to the present day. One (Fig. 3) consists of a hollowed-out block of stone on which are engraved eleven hour-lines and two curves cutting these nearly at right angles. The gnomon, or pointer (which is missing), was a short metal rod, projecting horizontally from the point where all the hour-lines intersect, and the time was shown by the position of the shadow of the tip of this gnomon. The dial was mounted facing due south, and in mid-winter this shadow would follow the upper curved line, starting from the left at dawn, reaching the centre at midday, and the right-hand edge at sunset. At midsummer the shadow of the gnomon tip would pass along the lowest edge of the hollowed-out part of the dial, and in spring and autumn it would follow

FIG. 3. A ROMAN HEMICYCLE OF ABOUT 1ST CENTURY A.D.

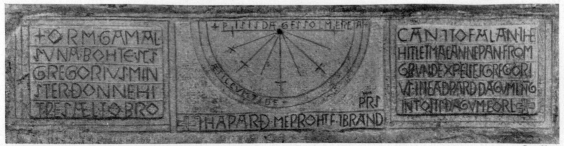

Peter Hood

FIG. 4. SAXON SUNDIAL AT KIRKDALE CHURCH, YORKSHIRE
The inscription records that Orm the son of Gamal rebuilt the church in the reign of King Edward

the middle curve. This dial divided the period from sunrise to sunset with fair accuracy into twelve equal parts.

No water-clocks of the Greek and Roman periods have survived, but judging from contemporary descriptions, some of them must have been quite elaborate, possibly even controlling systems of geared wheels and operating alarms.

Some primitive Saxon sundials, from the few hundred years preceding the Norman Conquest, are still to be seen in England. The Saxons

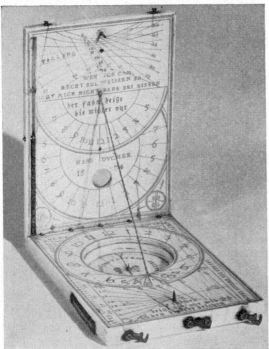

Crown Copyright, Science Museum

FIG. 5. IVORY POCKET SUNDIAL, 1574
The Sundial is set in the right direction by the compass. Hours are marked round this, and on the upper semicircle on the lid. The other scales are used for telling the time in any latitude

divided the daylight period not into 12 'hours' but into four 'tides', and their sundials are designed to indicate these. One on the south side of a Yorkshire church has lines for the four tides and intermediate lines between the main ones (Fig. 4). The gnomon casting the shadow, which is missing, would have stood out horizontally from the point from which the lines radiate.

Rather cruder sundials of this type are found on the south sides of many somewhat later English churches—their lines being intended to show the times of offices or services of the church rather than of the day.

Europe during the second half of the 14th century changed over from the old systems of hour-reckoning to the present-day one, in which the whole day-and-night period is divided into 24 equal parts, with the numbering 1–12 starting from midday and midnight. This change coincided with the introduction of mechanical clocks (*see* CLOCKS AND WATCHES). The new system called for a quite different kind of sundial, in which (Figs. 5 and 6) the edge of the gnomon was parallel to the earth's axis (so that it pointed to the North Pole of the heavens), and its shadow was usually cast on a horizontal or vertical south-facing plate on which hour-lines were engraved.

Dials of this type, which can show solar (sun) time to an accuracy of a minute or two, were used for checking clocks and watches for hundreds of years before telegraphic and radio time-signals became available. When a clock is checked against a sundial, a correction called the 'equation of time' has to be applied, to allow for the fact that the sun's apparent motion round the earth's axis is not quite uniform (*see* ASTRONOMY, MODERN, Section 4, Vol. III), so that sun time and the time recorded by an accurate clock differ by an amount which can be calculated; in November it is as much as 16 minutes.

Crown Copyright, Science Museum

FIG. 6. GARDEN SUNDIAL, 1718

The hour circle is on the outside; inside, a circular table gives
the equation of time for various dates throughout the year

Crown Copyright, Science Museum

FIG. 7. SHIP'S FOUR-HOUR SAND-GLASS FOR TIMING THE WATCHES, 18TH-CENTURY

From quite early days a great variety of most ingenious portable sundials have been devised, which can be folded up and carried in the pocket. Some of these embody a small compass for setting in the right direction, but others, dispensing with this, measure time from the sun's 'altitude' in degrees above the horizon. Some can be used only in the latitude for which they were designed; others are 'universal', that is, adjustable for latitude over a wide range. They were much used in Europe from the 16th to the early 18th century when watches were scarce, expensive, and not very accurate.

Two other forms of primitive timekeepers are sand-glasses and lamp and candle-clocks which show the time by the depth of oil in a lamp reservoir or the length of candle unburnt. King Alfred is said to have used candle-clocks, and a few 18th-century oil-clocks still survive. Sand-glasses have been used since about the 15th century for measuring definite intervals of time: the time taken for the sand to pass from one half of the glass to the other. Sand-glasses have been used to time the four-hour 'watches' in a ship (Fig. 7), the speed of a ship, or the length of a sermon, and they are still convenient for timing the boiling of an egg.

See also Vol. III: TIME; CALENDAR.

TIMEKEEPERS, MODERN. 1. ELECTRIC CLOCKS. The 20th century has seen remarkable progress in precision timekeeping and also in ways of broadcasting time by telegraph, telephone, and radio. In 1900 the most accurate timekeeper available was a pendulum clock with mechanical escapement and compensating pendulum which would keep time to an accuracy of about $\frac{1}{100}$ second per day (*see* CLOCKS AND WATCHES).

The Shortt free pendulum clock, perfected by W. H. Shortt in 1921, is about three times as accurate as this, its errors being only a few thousandths of a second per day. It has a 'free' pendulum, swinging quite free of interference except for a fraction of a second every half-minute when it receives a small impulse released by a separate 'slave clock'. The slave clock, which is electrically connected with the pendulum, is automatically corrected by the pendulum to enable it to release the impulse at the correct time after the next

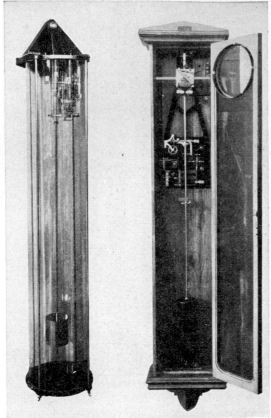

SHORTT FREE PENDULUM CLOCK

This consists of two clocks coupled together electrically. The free pendulum, on the left, is the timekeeper; it receives an impulse every half minute and swings freely between impulses. The slave clock on the right releases the impulse for the free pendulum and receives a synchronizing signal from the pendulum after the impulse is over. The slave clock has a dial on which the time is shown

corresponds to the power transmitted to a pendulum through a mechanical escapement. By means of an electrical 'gearing' the very rapid oscillations from the valve amplifier can be made to control another circuit oscillating at only a thousand vibrations per second. These can be fed into a 'synchronous motor' which rotates exactly once for each thousand vibrations, that is, one revolution per second, and can be mechanically geared to second, minute, and hour-hands. The rate of revolution of these hands is thus directly controlled by the vibrations of the quartz crystal through a system of GEARS (q.v.), partly mechanical and partly electrical.

Under carefully chosen conditions, the vibrations of a quartz crystal can produce a clock which is accurate to at least one-thousandth of a second per day. The time-signals transmitted by radio in Great Britain today are derived from the quartz crystal clocks of the Royal Greenwich Observatory, from electric contacts on their motors. The sixth 'pip' of the time signal represents the exact hour, or quarter-hour, as the case may be.

2. DISTRIBUTION OF TIME. While the 20th century has seen this remarkable achievement in precision timekeeping, advances have also been made in ways of making accurate time easily available to many people.

Soon after the invention of the electric telegraph in the 1830s (*see* TELEGRAPHY, HISTORY OF, Vol. IV) it was realized that electric currents might be used to transmit time-signals from a central master-clock to distant points. In the 19th century many systems were invented, but few were really reliable. From 1904 to 1907, however, the 'Synchronome' and 'Pulsynetic' systems were developed in Britain. In these, a master-clock sent out a pulse of electric current every half-minute to distant 'impulse dials', that is, clock faces with hands controlled by the pulse; in both systems the pulse was reliable and well-defined, and the master-clock was so designed that in transmitting the impulse its time-keeping was not affected. Both these systems are still employed in many factories and offices where it is essential to have a uniform, reasonably accurate time-system throughout.

A somewhat different system is used on the underground railways of London, where the individual clocks, electrically driven or clockwork driven and electrically wound, operate indepen-

half-minute. Shortt clocks were used as standard timekeepers at the Royal Observatory, Greenwich, from 1925 until 1942, when they were superseded by quartz crystal clocks.

In a quartz crystal clock, the oscillating and timekeeping element is a small plate or ring of quartz to which electric wires are attached; the quartz plate or ring is tuned by adjusting its shape and size until its 'natural period' of VIBRATION (q.v.) is exactly one-hundred-thousandth of a second. When a quartz crystal vibrates, it develops small electric charges at each vibration, and these charges can be led to the grid of a radio valve and amplified (*see* ELECTRONICS). Part of the amplified charge can be fed back to the crystal to keep it vibrating continuously—this

dently but are automatically corrected every hour by a time-signal transmitted electrically from a central point. The system of the International Time Recording Company, developed mainly for controlling their time-recorders, is a combination of the impulse and hourly correction systems, for the distant clocks or time-recorders are advanced a whole minute at a time and they are automatically 'checked' and corrected every hour.

In the 1920s and 1930s, with the spread of the GRID SYSTEM (q.v.) of electric alternating-current power supply, it was realized that time could be distributed through the 'grid' by employing clocks with their hands geared to 'synchronous' motors driven from the mains. The speed of such motors is regulated by the frequency of the mains' A.C. The ordinary electric clock used in the home works on this principle. The idea, though an excellent one, unfortunately proved not altogether reliable because the power-stations found it in practice impossible at the 'peak' periods of winter mornings and evenings to keep their frequency always up to the standard rate; consequently clocks connected to the supply ran slow—though they could be and were brought back to correct time after the peak demand was over. Possibly, as new power stations are constructed, this disadvantage will be overcome.

3. 'TIM.' Paris was the first city to have an automatic time-service: a telephone call to an appropriate number produces an automatic voice stating the time. A 'speaking clock', designed for Great Britain at the Research Laboratories of the G.P.O., was put into service in the London area in 1936. To call the speaking clock, TIM is dialled, and immediately a voice is heard saying, for example, 'At the third stroke it will be three fifty-nine and twenty seconds—pip, pip, pip. At the third stroke . . .', &c. Announcements are made every 10 seconds.

This clock works on a similar principle to that used for reproducing sound from sound-films. The actual photographic records from which the speech is reproduced, instead of being on a reel of film, are on circular glass disks 12 inches in diameter, which rotate once every two seconds, several records being arranged concentrically on each disk. The speed of rotation of the disks, on which depends the accuracy of the timing of the announcements, is controlled by a pendulum clock: the pendulum transmits light signals

Crown Copyright, Science Museum

THE QUARTZ CRYSTAL CLOCK
By permission of the Engineer-in-Chief, G.P.O.

which are received by a photo-electric cell, converted into alternations of electric current, amplified suitably, and used to drive the disks carrying the sound records. The whole system is checked against Greenwich Mean Time, and kept to within one-tenth of a second of this time.

See also CLOCKS AND WATCHES.

TINPLATE. 1. The average household in Britain uses about 250 food tins every year, and at least as many tins for other purposes—tobacco, shoe polish, throat lozenges, and lubricating oil, for example. Although these containers are called 'tins', and though it is this metal that gives them their chief characteristic, there is, in fact little tin in them—the tin forms a coating only about $\frac{1}{15000}$ in. thick on a steel sheet about $\frac{1}{100}$ in. thick. Tin accounts for only 2% of the weight, its function being to protect the steel against CORROSION (q.v.) from the substances inside the tin and from the atmosphere, water, or soil outside the tin. The steel provides the strength and the tin the resisting surface.

The tin-coated steel sheet from which tin cans are made is called tinplate. South Wales is the traditional home of its manufacture, and in 1952 some 908,000 tons of this and other sheet was made there, and about 301,000 tons was exported. Tinplate was first made in South Wales in 1665, using iron from the Forest of Dean and tin from Cornwall. Today the tin is imported from abroad, and so is the greater part of the iron ore used to make the steel.

The two parts of tinplate manufacture are rolling the steel sheet and coating it. There are two main ways of doing each of these tasks.

2. STRIP ROLLING. In modern plants, the steel for tinplate is produced as long lengths of steel strip. This may be rolled as a continuous action on 'tandem' mills, which are a series of individual groups of rollers arranged in a long line and geared to work at different speeds to cope with the elongation of the strip as it passes the roll 'train'. The speed at the first stand may be only about 300 ft. per minute but at the final stand it may be about 1,700 ft. per minute (say, 20 m.p.h.). These large units need a great deal of room to operate, and the capital cost is high,

Steel Co. of Wales

A HOT STEEL STRIP EMERGING FROM THE LAST ROLLS IN A CONTINUOUS ROLLING MILL but they produce a large output of good-quality plate very economically and effectively.

In a continuous mill the hot-rolling starts with a slab 3 to 6 in. thick, 20 to 40 in. wide. The slab is hot-rolled down to a thickness of about $\frac{1}{12}$ in. It is finished coiled in strip form, the width of the strip being roughly the length required for the finished tinplate.

It is then 'pickled' in sulphuric acid to remove the scale on the surface, washed, and passed through a cold reduction (thinning) mill. At one modern plant at Tostre, near Llanelly, this consists of five massive sets of rolls, each weighing about 100 tons and each with its own electric motor, developing a total of 18,250 horse-power —about ten times that developed by an express locomotive. The strip emerges from the last rolls $\frac{1}{80}$ in. thick (or whatever gauge is ordered) at 4,500 ft. per minute—that is, over 50 miles an hour. This giant mill, in fact, takes in steel strip about as thick as the back of a pocket-knife blade, and crushes it to the thinness of paper, without heating, all at the speed of a fast car.

After it emerges from the rolls the strip (still in coils) is cleaned of all traces of oil and then softened by annealing (*see* HEAT TREATMENT). Then it is 'temper' rolled, that is, it is passed through two sets of rolls which do not greatly reduce the thickness of the strip but, since no lubricant is used, produce the strip with a dense surface suitable for tinning. The efficiency of a continuous strip-mill is so great that ten men can produce 500 tons of strip in an 8-hour shift.

3. PACK ROLLING. The older rolling mills usually consist of two pairs of steel or chilled iron (hard cast iron) rollers, like large mangles, driven by steam or electricity. The 'sheet bar' with which the tinplate workers start is the same width as the finished sheet will be, but about $\frac{1}{2}$ to $\frac{3}{4}$ in. thick and some 15 or 16 ft. long. The bar is heated in a furnace and passed twice through one set of rolls, being shifted back over the top of the rolls between each pass. After being reheated in the furnace the metal gets three more turns of two passes in the other set of rolls. Before each reheating the plate gets 'doubled' or bent over on itself, like folding a piece of cardboard in two, then in four, then in eight. The procedure is varied according to the thickness (gauge) and the lengths required. After the pack has cooled, the sheets are cut to the size needed.

After being pickled in dilute sulphuric acid to

Richard Thomas and Baldwins Ltd.

A HAND PACK MILL

The operator is feeding a pack of sheets into a 'stand' of rolls through which they must pass many times to reach their final thickness

remove the skin of scale, they are annealed, and then the plates are passed singly through a series of three pairs of chilled cast-iron rolls under great pressure; this cold-rolling gives the sheets a high polish and a dense surface which will not absorb too much tin.

In one of these pack mills six men produce $3\frac{1}{2}$ to 4 tons of plates in an 8-hour shift—a very much slower rate than in the strip-mill.

4. TINNING. Sheet is given its coating of tin, either by being passed through an electrolytic bath on the principle of ELECTROPLATING (q.v.) or by being dipped in a bath of molten tin.

Long strips from the strip mill are uncoiled and pass through the electrolytic tinning plant before being cut into sheets, or, if they are hot-dip tinned, they are cut up into sheets before going to the dipping plant. There are several types of dipping plant, varying in the degree to which they operate automatically. The plates are pickled and washed, and then put through a solution of zinc chloride which acts as a flux (*see* SURFACE TREATMENT) to absorb impurities, before being dipped in a bath of molten tin. After going through a second bath of tin, they pass through three pairs of hard steel rolls running in a bath of molten palm oil. In these rolls the amount of tin on the plate is controlled, the oil keeping the tin on the sheets molten, while the rolls take off surplus tin from the plate surfaces and drop it back into the tinpot.

See also STEEL-MAKING; METALS.
See also Vol. VII: TIN; CANNING INDUSTRY.

TRACK MECHANISM. This is used for certain mobile engineering units and TRACKED VEHICLES (q.v. Vol. IV) to enable them to carry heavy loads over very rough or soft ground. The vehicle runs on an endless belt or track, usually made of flat steel plates, which is laid out along the ground underneath the vehicle and, after the vehicle has passed, is picked up and carried over the top of its loop to the front again. It is used among other purposes for heavy cranes, bulldozers, and other EARTH-MOVING EQUIPMENT (q.v.), military TANKS (q.v. Vol. X), and some farm tractors (*see* POWER FOR FARMING, Vol. VI).

The tracks run over two or more sprockets or pulleys (Fig. 1), one of which is driven from the engine and moves the track round and round. Each time it completes a round it covers a distance which is the length of the loop. The track actually on the ground remains stationary in relation to the ground, another piece of belt being continually laid down in front of it, until the vehicle has passed over it, when it is picked up.

The steel plates of the track are held together by hinges, the joints between the links being formed by hardened steel pins, which fit closely in hardened steel 'bushes' (*see* BEARINGS) so that the track is flexible. For very heavy work, each

plate sometimes bears a flange sticking out at right angles to it, which digs into the ground to improve the grip.

Tanks usually have a fairly long length of track in contact with the ground, requiring a line of several track rollers arranged along the bottom run of the track to help carry the weight of the vehicle. The track itself has short links suitable for a vehicle which may have to run at a high speed on a hard surface, for the shorter the links the more flexible is the chain and the smoother is the running of the vehicle.

Tracked vehicles are steered by slowing one track in relation to the other. One way of doing this is to have a separate clutch and brake for each track. For a gentle turn, all that is necessary is to declutch the track on the inside of the curve the vehicle is to take. The other track then tends to overtake the track which has been declutched, and the vehicle turns a corner. For a sharp turn, it is necessary also to apply a brake to the track which has to be slowed down.

Another method of providing for steering is to incorporate differential GEARS (q.v.) in the transmission, so that when a brake is applied to the shaft on one side of the differential gearing the driving sprocket of the track on that side is slowed down, while the other track speeds up. This system needs no separate clutches to provide steering.

Means are provided to keep the track at the right tension the whole time, and each of the two tracks can move up and down independently of the other so that they can both follow the contour of the ground even when it is very uneven. Occasionally a light track is made of rubber-coated canvas belting instead of steel plates. This is often used where a short track is fitted to the rear of a vehicle which runs on ordinary front wheels, as with the 'half-tracked' military trucks sometimes used in desert warfare.

See also Vol. IV: TRACKED VEHICLES.
See also Vol. VI: POWER FOR FARMING.
See also Vol. X: TANKS.

TRACTOR, *see* EARTH-MOVING EQUIPMENT; TRACK MECHANISM.

TRANSFORMER, ELECTRIC. This is a device by which the voltage (pressure) of an ALTERNATING CURRENT (q.v.) is increased or decreased, sometimes to an enormous extent. Transformers now play an essential part in the

FIG. 1. TRACK OF A CRAWLER TRACTOR

A. Driving sprocket. B. Idler pulley. C. Grousers to give good grip. D. Track rollers to keep bottom run of track on ground. E. Track rollers carrying weight of top run of track
F. Buffer spring

industry, transport, and communications of the modern world.

The transformer is based on the principle of 'induced' currents, by which an electric current flowing through a wire throws out a magnetic influence which causes other currents to start up and flow in any other wires which are near the first one (*see* INDUCTION, ELECTRIC). The wires must not touch one another; each is, therefore, encased in a thin sheath of some insulating material, which may be no more than a coat of varnish or may be very thick indeed. Furthermore, to strengthen the magnetic effect the wires concerned are wound into numerous coils.

A simple kind of transformer consists of two separate coils of insulated copper wire wound

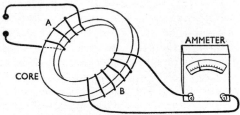

FIG. I. DIAGRAM OF A TRANSFORMER
A. Primary winding. B. Secondary winding

on an iron ring (Fig. 1). When the coil A is joined up to a supply of alternating current, this current, flowing in the coil, sets up in the iron ring an alternating magnetism—that is, a magnetism the direction of which is constantly reversing itself at great speed. The magnetism in the iron ring causes an alternating current to flow in the coil B, by induction. Coil A, which has the original current in it, is called the primary winding of the transformer; coil B, in which a current is induced, is called the secondary winding. The purpose of the piece of soft iron, which is called the 'core', is to increase and concentrate the magnetic effect of the current flowing in the primary winding.

If the number of windings in both coils is the same, then the strength (amperes) and pressure (volts) of the primary circuit will be passed on practically unchanged to the secondary circuit, except for a very slight loss or waste in the transformer itself. But if coil A has, for example, 100 turns, and coil B only 10 turns (that is, ten times fewer), then the voltage of the current induced in coil B will be ten times less than that in coil A. In this way all transformers change, or transform, the alternating voltage applied to

them in proportion to the number of turns on their two windings.

A transformer with more turns on its secondary than on its primary winding increases the voltage applied to it, and is called a 'step-up' transformer; one with fewer secondary turns than primary turns reduces the applied voltage and is a 'step-down' transformer. The amount of power in an electric circuit is equal to the strength of the current (amperes) multiplied by the pressure (volts). A step-up transformer, however, by increasing the voltage does not increase the power, for the transformer is a purely passive device with no source of power of its own. If the voltage in the secondary winding is, for example, stepped-up by 10 times, then the strength of the current is also reduced by 10 times, and the amount of power remains the same.

A common example of a small electric transformer is the bell transformer (Fig. 2). This steps-down the 240-volt mains supply to 6 volts for working an electric doorbell. The primary winding consists of a great many turns of very thin insulated copper wire, and the secondary winding has only $\frac{1}{40}$th as many turns of thicker wire—that is, 6 volts divided by 240. Small transformers are also used in radio receivers and television sets, both to step-down the 240-volts mains current to 6·3 volts to heat the valve filaments, and to step-up the mains voltage to, perhaps, 700 volts to provide the high-tension supplies for the anodes of the valves (*see* RADIO ENGINEERING).

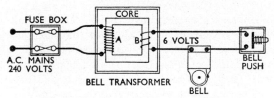

FIG. 2. DIAGRAM OF BELL TRANSFORMER
A. Primary winding with 40 times as many turns as secondary winding B

Very large transformers are used in the GRID SYSTEM (q.v.) to step-up the voltage of the current generated in power stations to 132,000 volts for distribution over the power lines, and then, at the far ends of the power lines, other transformers are used to step-down the pressure to much lower voltages to supply local public mains. The voltage used locally differs in various parts of the country, but it is gradually being standardized to a voltage of about 220 to 240 volts

English Electric Co.

275,000-VOLT HIGH-POWER TRANSFORMER SHOWING
RADIATOR FOR THE OIL-COOLING SYSTEM

for domestic uses. As these large transformers are made very hot by the powerful electric currents that flow through their windings, they are cooled by being placed in a bath of oil, and the oil itself is kept cool by being circulated through radiator pipes.

Besides the transformers used in circuits connected to the ordinary public supply mains, which have an alternating-current frequency of 50 cycles per second, small transformers are also used in circuits carrying currents that alternate much more rapidly. Transformers are used to step-up the voltages of the tiny electric currents generated by MICROPHONES (q.v.), such as those used to make announcements at railway stations. These microphone currents have frequencies as high as 5,000 to 10,000 cycles per second, and the voltage is stepped-up to make them more

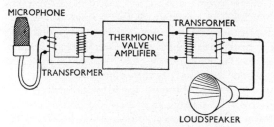

FIG. 3. DIAGRAM OF SOUND AMPLIFIER

suitable for working the THERMIONIC VALVES (q.v.) in the amplifier, and then stepped-down again to make the current which comes from the amplifier suitable to work the loud-speaker (Fig. 3). Small transformers of much the same kind are used to handle speech and music currents.

Electric transformers are also applied to the extremely high frequencies used in RADIO ENGINEERING (q.v.). These radio-frequency currents alternate as rapidly as a million or even 100 million times (cycles) per second. Such transformers differ in construction from power transformers, although they work on exactly the same principle. Radio-frequency transformers simply consist of two coils of wire placed close together so that current in the primary coil has a strong magnetic effect on the secondary coil. They have no iron core, for when radio-frequency currents flow through a coil of wire surrounding a metal core (Fig. 4), the core becomes very hot, and most of the electrical energy is wasted in heating it. This kind of heating is put to good use, however, in melting steel in a high-frequency induction furnace (see STEEL-MAKING, Section 4).

Radio engineers use quite large transformers, without iron cores, to connect together the

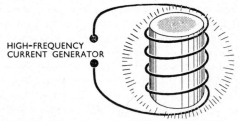

HIGH-FREQUENCY
CURRENT GENERATOR

FIG. 4. METAL CYLINDER HEATED BY INDUCED CURRENTS

different parts of a radio transmitter and to connect the transmitter to its aerial. Much smaller transformers are used for similar purposes in radio receivers.

See also ELECTRICAL ENGINEERING; ELECTRIC CURRENT.

TRIGONOMETRY. This is a branch of mathematics which makes use of certain fixed relationships existing between the parts of a triangle.

The shape of a triangle (but not its size) is determined by the size of its three angles. Since these angles must always add up to 180 degrees, equivalent to two right angles, once two of its angles are known the other can also be calculated. If one angle is a certain size—say 90 degrees, or one right angle—the shape of the triangle will be entirely determined by the size of one of its other angles. Trigonometry is based on this fact.

Suppose ABC and DEF (Fig. 1) are two triangles with right angles at c and F and the

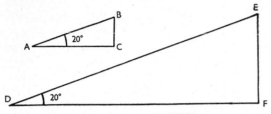

FIG. 1. SIMILAR TRIANGLES

angles at B and E each of 20 degrees, then the triangles must be the same shape, one (DEF) being an enlargement of the other. Each side of DEF will be in a certain fixed proportion (or ratio) to the corresponding side of ABC. Let us suppose that the sides of DEF are three times as long as those of ABC. Then $DF = 3 \times AC$ and $EF = 3 \times BC$. So the ratio of DF to EF, namely $\frac{DF}{EF}$, equals $\frac{3 \times AC}{3 \times BC}$, which equals $\frac{AC}{BC}$, which is the ratio of AC to BC. Thus the ratio of these

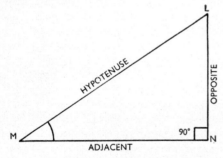

FIG. 2. THE SIDES OF A RIGHT-ANGLED TRIANGLE

corresponding sides is the same in the two triangles; and we can show that this is true for any corresponding pairs of sides in ABC and DEF.

There is a standard method of naming the sides of a right-angled triangle with reference to one angle—in Fig. 2 the angle M. The side opposite the right angle, the longest side, is called the 'hypotenuse'; the side opposite the given angle the 'opposite side', and the remaining side the 'adjacent side'.

The six trigonometrical ratios (that is, proportion of one thing to another) are found by taking

the lengths of the three sides (hypotenuse, opposite, and adjacent) and dividing them by one another. The six ratios (with their abbreviations in brackets) are:

SINE (sin) M	Opposite divided by Hypotenuse	$\frac{LN}{LM}$
COSINE (cos) M	Adjacent divided by Hypotenuse	$\frac{MN}{LM}$
SECANT (sec) M	Hypotenuse divided by Adjacent	$\frac{LM}{MN}$
COSECANT (cosec) M	Hypotenuse divided by Opposite	$\frac{LM}{LN}$
TANGENT (tan) M	Opposite divided by Adjacent	$\frac{LN}{MN}$
COTANGENT (cot) M	Adjacent divided by Opposite	$\frac{MN}{LN}$

Thus 'cos 20°' means 'the length of the adjacent side divided by the length of the hypotenuse of any right-angled triangle, when the angle at M is 20 degrees'. In statements in which that angle is unknown, the Greek letter *theta* (θ) replaces the figure; thus 'cos θ' represents the cosine of the unknown angle θ.

Books are published containing tables of the values of these six ratios, usually to four places of decimals, for angles between 0 degrees and 90 degrees, at intervals of one-sixtieth of a degree (one minute).

Here are two simple problems to illustrate the use of these ratios. In Fig. 3, the top, A, of a tower is at an elevation of 38 degrees as measured from a point P level with its base, B, 70 feet away. We want to know the height of the tower. The ratio $\frac{AB}{PB} = \tan 38°$. So $\frac{AB}{70} = 0.7813$ (from trigonometrical tables). So $AB = 70 \times 0.7813 = 54.691$ feet $= 54.7$ feet, to three significant figures.

In Fig. 4, the legs of a tripod, XY and XZ, are

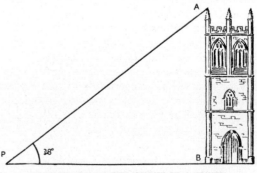

FIG. 3. MEASURING THE HEIGHT OF A TOWER

each 4 feet long, and they are 2 feet apart at their tips. We want to find the angle YXZ. We form two right-angled triangles (the shape needed for calculation) by drawing XW perpendicular to YZ.

We then calculate sin YXW $= \dfrac{YW}{XY} = \dfrac{1}{4} = 0.25$.

We find in the tables that the angle whose sine is 0.25 is an angle of 14° 11′. Since YXW = 14° 11′, YXZ must be just twice as great, or 28° 22′.

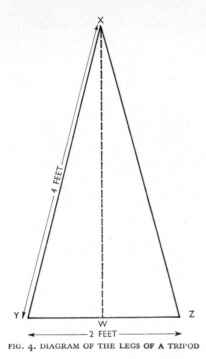

FIG. 4. DIAGRAM OF THE LEGS OF A TRIPOD

We can calculate from a more advanced form of trigonometry the other two sides of a triangle if we know one side and its angles. Surveyors use this fact in mapping the countryside, which they divide into a large number of triangles (*see* SURVEYING).

Most applications of trigonometry, for example when GRAPHS of variations in ELECTRIC CURRENT (qq.v.) are drawn, require far more complicated calculations than the simple illustrations given above. Many problems of MECHANICS (q.v.) are solved by trigonometry, while trigonometrical 'functions', such as sine and cosine, play an indispensable part in much scientific theory.

See also GEOMETRY; ALGEBRA.

TUBES. A tube, sometimes defined as a long, hollow cylinder, may, in fact, be square or oval or one of many different shapes. It can also be of any size, ranging from very large tubes or pipes for various engineering purposes to the extremely fine tubes used for laboratory and medical work—the 'needle' used in a doctor's hypodermic syringe, for example, is a very fine tube made in the form of a hollow needle.

Tubes and pipes are made from a wide variety of materials such as metals, glass, rubber, plastics, concrete, earthenware, and even wood. This article is mainly concerned with metal tubes, which are the kind most commonly used in engineering.

Metal tubes can be used to carry liquids or gases, sometimes under very great pressures, and they can also be used for structural parts. For example, the frame of a bicycle is made of tubing which, being hollow, is much lighter than a solid frame would be, and yet provides the strength needed: the hollow tube uses the metal in its construction to supply the strength only where it is wanted. Tubular SCAFFOLDING (q.v.) is also mainly used in the building industry.

Most common metals and alloys can be made into tubes of one of four types—cast, mechanically joined, welded, or seamless. Cast-iron pipes are made by melting the metal and pouring it into a cylindrical mould, which is spun on its own axis at such a speed that the molten metal is flung on to the wall of the mould, where it solidifies as it cools. This method is known as centrifugal CASTING (q.v.). Suitably protected from rusting, such pipes are often used for conveying water.

A mechanically joined tube is made by bending metal into the required shape and then riveting the overlapping edges or folding the metal so that the edges interlock. A welded tube is made in the same way, the edges being heated to a high temperature and welded together; alternatively they may be brazed or soldered.

A seamless tube, which has no join, can be made in various ways. For example, a hot bar of steel, say 5 inches square and 18 inches long, may be put into a vertical round container into which

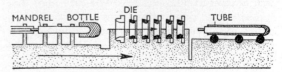

FIG. 1. DIAGRAM ILLUSTRATING THE MAKING OF A TUBE BY THE PUSH BENCH PROCESS

it will just slide, and a round punch bar (say 4 inches in diameter) forced down into it centrally; this presses the steel against the side of the container and produces a bottle or thimble with a closed end. This is then elongated by being pushed horizontally by an internal bar through a series of dies of gradually decreasing diameter. The bar determines the inside diameter of the tube, and the last die the outside diameter (Fig. 1). Another way is to pierce a round bar right through by a spinning operation, known as rotary piercing, between barrel-shaped rolls set at a slight angle to each other (Fig. 2); the pierced bar is then elongated in a mill having rolls with tapered grooves, thus reducing the thickness step by step while the bore is maintained by an inserted horizontal bar (Fig. 3).

Yet another method is extrusion (*see* FORGING AND PRESSING, Section 4) in which the metal is squeezed out hot through a die and over a bar (or mandrel) which determines the inside diameter of the tube. This method is used for softer metals, such as copper, aluminium, and lead, but it can be applied to steel, and also to non-metallic materials such as plastics. After the hot

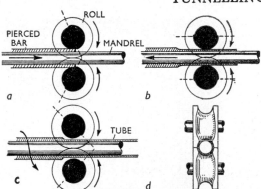

FIG. 3. DIAGRAM ILLUSTRATING THE OPERATION OF THE PILGER MILL FOR TUBE MAKING

a. The pierced bar on the mandrel is driven between the rolls. *b.* The tapering rolls forge the tube and push the mandrel back. *c.* The mandrel moves forward and turns when the gap between the rolls widens. *d.* End view of rolls

processes the metal tube may be made more accurate in size, and smaller, by passing it cold through a die or dies with or without internal support.

See also FORGING AND PRESSING.
See also Vol. VII: GLASS-MAKING.

TUNNELLING. TUNNELS (q.v. Vol. IV) are built to provide direct road or rail routes through mountain ranges or under or over rivers; they can also provide underground channels for water, sewage, or oil. The Romans used tunnels to bring water to their cities, and a rock tunnel which they made near Jerusalem is still in use today. Modern tunnels are often very long and deep: the SIMPLON TUNNEL (q.v. Vol. IV) on the France-to-Italy railway, for example, is $12\frac{1}{4}$ miles long, and in one place the peaks of the Alps rise over 6,000 feet above it. Some tunnels are over 50 feet in diameter. Many are circular in cross-section. Others are horseshoe-shaped, with a level floor on which it is easy to lay permanent roads and railways.

The difficulty, and therefore the cost, of tunnelling is affected mainly by the nature of the ground. Before work begins, careful geological studies are made, usually by boring down into the ground in a number of places. If the project is a large and important one, and the ground doubtful or difficult, a tunnel of smaller diameter, called a pilot tunnel, is often driven first. The course of the main tunnel has to be mapped in advance by surveyors (*see* SURVEYING) with great accuracy to ensure that the tunnelling, which is

Tube Investments Ltd.

FIG. 2. BAR EMERGING FROM THE ROTARY PIERCER

Canadian Ingersoll-Rand

BUILDING THE MAIN POWER TUNNEL IN THE KEMANO HEADING OF THE KITIMAT HYDRO-ELECTRIC SCHEME (q.v.)
Front end of a three-deck drill carriage pulled back while 'mucking' is in progress

usually started from each end, in fact meets correctly in the middle. Difficulties are increased if the tunnel is curved, and still more if it is spiral. Spiral tunnels are especially useful for railways, which must be given a gentle gradient (*see* RAILWAY CONSTRUCTION). With modern methods, however, there is rarely a difference of more than about an inch, horizontal or vertical, between the two 'drives' when they meet. High temperatures, foul air when working deep underground, dangerous gases, and falls of rock or earth are some of the other difficulties that tunnellers have to face.

The rock tunnellers' chief problem is to break up the rock. The Romans heated it with fire and then suddenly chilled it with cold water, which caused it to crack; or they disintegrated it by chemical action with vinegar. Today, powerful DRILLING MACHINES, driven by compressed air, and EXPLOSIVES (qq.v.) are used. The drills, fitted with special hard steel bits, make holes into which explosive charges are rammed. These holes, sometimes over 20 feet deep, are arranged in a pattern, and the charges are fired electrically in a certain order so that the centre of the rock is blown out first (*see* BLASTING). During blasting operations men and equipment must be moved as far from the face as possible, for flying fragments can cause serious injury. During thunderstorms the explosive charges have sometimes been fired prematurely by lightning, causing a number of serious accidents to men working near the face.

A typical time-table of the various operations involved in rock tunnelling is as follows:

Operation	Minutes
Advance of machine for loading broken rock after blasting. (The rock is loaded on to cars for removal to a dump outside the tunnel.) .	10
'Mucking' (removal of broken rock) . .	90
Removal of loading machine . . .	5
Advance of men with rock drills . . .	10
Drilling	100
Charging explosives and blasting . . .	10
Ventilation (blowing out of foul gases) . .	15
	240

This goes on for 24 hours a day, the men working in shifts. In good rock it is possible to excavate an average of about 6 or 7 feet during each cycle.

A tunnel driven through sound rock may need no support; but poor rock, loose earth, or clay must be shored up as the work proceeds. For driving through soft material a special shield was invented by the great engineer Isambard Kingdom Brunel (1806–59), and was first used for building a tunnel under the Thames (*see* Vol. IV, p. 468). Its modern development, known as the Greathead shield, was used in the excavation of the London UNDERGROUND RAILWAY (q.v. Vol. IV). This is a cylinder, perhaps up to 30 feet long and weighing 40 to 80 tons; it contains a vertical bulkhead, with openings which can be quickly shut in case of a fall of earth, and in front of which the labourers work, throwing the dug earth (or 'spoil') back through the openings. Its forward end is fitted with cutting edges which can be pushed into the earth from the rear by hydraulic jacks as the work proceeds.

Underground water is a danger, especially in working under a river, and precautions have to be taken against flooding. If the ground surrounding the tunnel is of sand or silt it may be solidified by injecting chemicals, or in some cases by artificial freezing, until the tunnel has been formed and the lining placed. Another method is to raise the air pressure inside the tunnel above that of the air outside: this prevents water from flowing in. Sometimes air pressure up to three times the normal atmospheric pressure is needed, in which case an airtight bulkhead is used at the tunnel entrance, with double doors for entry and exit. The workmen must not pass too quickly from the high pressure inside to normal atmospheric pressure, for if they do bubbles may form in the blood, resulting in a painful complaint known to tunnellers and divers as 'the bends'.

When building a tunnel beneath a shallow river, sections of the tunnel, of steel or reinforced concrete, are often first constructed on shore, and then, with their ends closed by bulkheads, they are floated out and sunk in a trench dug across the bottom by DREDGERS (q.v. Vol. IV).

Most tunnels, though not all, are lined; this helps to support the roof and walls, to keep out water, and, in aqueducts or water-tunnels, to prevent leakage and give a smooth flow. In poor ground, thick concrete linings may be combined with steel arch rings. The tunnels of the London Underground Railway are lined with cast-iron segments (recent extensions have precast concrete segments), bolted together and backed by concrete. In order to fill up any spaces left between the concrete lining and the rock, and any gaps caused by the shrinkage of concrete in setting, the linings are generally 'grouted'—that is, holes are drilled through the concrete into the rock at or near the roof of the tunnel, and a mixture of cement and water (called grout) is pumped in under pressure.

See also BLASTING.

See also Vol. IV: TUNNELS; SIMPLON TUNNEL; MERSEY TUNNEL; SEVERN TUNNEL; APENNINE TUNNEL.

TURBINE, *see* STEAM TURBINE; GAS TURBINE; WATER POWER.

U

ULTRASONICS. Ultrasonic vibrations are SOUND vibrations (q.v. Vol. III) of too high a frequency, that is, too high pitched, to be heard by the human ear. If sufficiently intense, they can affect the body in other ways, however: they may cause sickness or diarrhoea, and even paralysis if they are powerful enough. Young people can hear sounds of a higher pitch than old people can, and animals can hear sounds of even higher frequencies. Most young people hear sound vibrations occurring as rapidly as 17,000 times a second, while some people can hear much higher frequencies—for instance, the cries of bats which contain ultrasonic frequencies of 30,000–35,000 vibrations a second. Indeed, the BAT (q.v. Vol. II) is a most remarkable user of ultrasonics, emitting short bursts of vibrations which are reflected from obstacles in its path and 'heard' by the bat. Sound is reflected back from an object within a time interval which depends on the distance of the object. An obstacle 15 feet away reflects sound in 0·03 second, and this enables a bat to avoid collisions. A bat can in this way 'hear' the position of obstacles and can thread its way through a maze of wires strung in

FIG. 1. DETECTION OF OBSTACLES BY A BAT
A. Short-wave 'sound'. B. Wire which reflects waves. C. Echoes returning to ears of bat

a room (Fig. 1). Ships now carry instruments which enable them in the same way to detect obstacles in, for example, a fog, and to learn the depth of the ocean or of the channels along which they steam (*see* NAVIGATION, MARINE, Vol. IV).

It is possible to generate ultrasonics by means of tiny whistles, and a properly constructed siren can produce most powerful vibrations of this kind both in air and water. For setting up ultrasonic vibrations efficiently in liquids there are two methods.

(*a*) *The magnetostrictive method.* This depends on the fact that some metals—nickel in particular—contract when placed in a magnetic field (*see* MAGNETS). An electromagnet is made up with a nickel core instead of a soft-iron one and with many turns of wire wound round the nickel ring. When a current is passed through the wire, the nickel core, in addition to becoming magnetized by the magnetic field (just as a soft-iron core would), contracts slightly. If the magnetic field is varied very quickly by passing a high-frequency ALTERNATING CURRENT (q.v.) through the coil, the core will expand and contract correspondingly, and, if dipped into a fluid, will send out a wavelet each time it does so. This device, known as a 'transducer', in fact converts electrical vibrations into mechanical vibrations. The echo-sounding apparatus, with which ships find the depth of the ocean, uses a transducer of this type to send short bursts of high-frequency waves down through the sea to the ocean bed. These are reflected back to the ship, and the time taken for the double journey gives the depth of the sea (*see* HYDROGRAPHY). Usually a parabolic mirror is used to concentrate the waves into a beam.

Ordinary sound waves of lower frequencies cannot be used, for the longer wavelengths of ordinary sound would become so spread out that no practical mirror would be large enough to concentrate them into a beam. In consequence they would be lost before they reached the ocean bed, and even in shallow water would be difficult to separate from the transmitted sound. Besides measuring the depth of the sea, the beam can be directed to detect rocks, icebergs, submarines, sunken wrecks, or, as used recently with great profit, to detect shoals of fish.

These very rapid vibrations are also used for a quite different purpose—to cut very hard materials such as glass. The cutting tool, vibrated by a magnetostrictive device of the type described and flooded with a wet paste made of abrasive powder, is pressed against the glass; its rapid vibrations cause the abrasive to bite into the glass, which is thus quickly cut.

(*b*) *The piezo-electric method.* This method of generating ultrasonic waves depends on the fact that some materials—quartz crystals in particular—change shape when an electrical voltage is applied to them. A quartz crystal, excited by an alternating high-frequency voltage, besides being

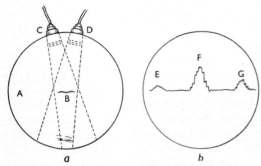

FIG. 2. ULTRASONIC FLAW DETECTION IN METALS

a. The short wave train travels along the path shown by the dotted lines and is reflected to the receiving crystal. A. Specimen under test. B. Crack or flaw. C. Transmitting crystal. D. Receiving crystal. *b.* Trace seen on cathode ray tube when flaw is present. E. Transmitter pulse. F. Echo from flaw. G. Echo from lower surface

able to produce such powerful oscillations in liquids that fountains can be flung many feet into the air, is used in the detection of faults and cracks in metals. Vibrations at the rate of about one million per second are set up in the metal to be tested, and these are reflected from any cracks or flaws (Fig. 2). The reflected vibrations are picked up by complicated electronic equipment, thus revealing the cracks or flaws. Ultrasonic waves are also used to stir up mixtures of liquids into a special, very thorough type of blend known as an emulsion. Intense ultrasonics in gases can separate out solid particles from smoke and fumes in chimneys and so reduce pollution of the atmosphere.

The use of strong ultrasonic power can be dangerous to living things. Germs, for example, can be killed by these vibrations in water, and a mouse can be killed if a powerful beam is directed on it from a high intensity source such as a siren in air. A person could be paralysed if his head were irradiated with strong airborne ultrasonics, and a strongly vibrating quartz crystal in direct contact with the head could even cause death.

See also Vol. III: SOUND.

ULTRA-VIOLET RAYS, *see* Vol. III: RADIATION

V

VALVES, CRYSTAL. These consist of thin disks of crystalline silicon or germanium mounted on a metal base, with one or two sharpened wires pressed firmly against the opposite side. A mounted silicon crystal with a single tungsten wire point touching it acts as a RECTIFIER (q.v.), and can replace a thermionic diode valve (*see* THERMIONIC VALVES). Another kind of crystal valve, known as a transistor, has two phosphor-bronze wire points about $\frac{1}{300}$th of an inch apart pressing against a thin germanium disk, only $\frac{1}{8}$ inch in diameter. When electric BATTERIES (q.v.) are connected to the transistor, the electric current that flows through one of the points is affected by the voltage of the battery connected to the other point. Because of this the transistor can be used in the same way as a thermionic triode valve to amplify weak electric currents. Crystal valves are much smaller than thermionic valves and do not require electric current to heat their cathodes. They are expected to last longer than thermionic valves, which they may one day largely replace in radio receivers and other electronic equipment. The present types of crystal valve can handle only small amounts of power.

See also THERMIONIC VALVES.

VENTILATION. This is the method of supplying the interiors of buildings with fresh air in good condition. Air consists of about one-fifth oxygen and four-fifths nitrogen. Carbon dioxide is also present to the extent of 4 parts in 10,000. Normally, an adult breathes in about 20 cubic feet of air per hour, extracting the oxygen from it, and exhales about half a cubic foot of carbon dioxide. In an unventilated room, therefore, the oxygen gets used up and the proportion of carbon dioxide and moisture, which is also given off, is increased. The amount of carbon dioxide in the air inside a building used to be taken as a standard of ventilation; but it is now known that the moisture content of air can have much more influence on health and comfort than can the presence of carbon dioxide.

Air at any given temperature can hold a definite maximum amount of WATER VAPOUR (q.v. Vol. III): a cubic foot of air can hold 2 grains at 30° Fahrenheit, and 11 grains at 80° F. (7,000 grains = 1 lb.). Air holding the maximum amount of water vapour is said to be 'saturated'. Any amount less than this, expressed as a percentage of the saturation amount, is called the 'relative humidity'. Thus, if air at 80° F. has a moisture content of 5·5 grains per cubic foot, its relative humidity is 50%. At normal indoor temperatures, relative humidity can vary between about 30% and 70% without causing discomfort, but a combination of high temperature and high humidity can be very unpleasant.

Even when not working, an adult gives off as bodily heat about 300 British Thermal Units per hour. (A British Thermal Unit is the amount of heat required to raise the temperature of 1 lb. of water through 1° F.) Also about 800 grains of water vapour are given off by breathing and evaporation from the skin. It is obvious, therefore, why crowded and ill-ventilated spaces rapidly become hot and oppressive. For the absorption of excess water vapour, among other

Alldays & Onions Ltd.

FIG. 1. CENTRIFUGAL FAN

reasons, the quantity of fresh air supplied to an occupied space must be much greater than the amount actually breathed.

For schools and offices, ventilation rates depend on the cubic space per occupant. If this is 500 cubic feet, 400 cubic feet per hour of fresh air is needed for each person, and if it is only 200 cubic feet, the ventilation rate should be at least 1,000 cubic feet per hour. In London and other large cities, by-laws require that in theatres and cinemas at least 1,000 cubic feet of fresh air per hour shall be supplied for each member of the audience. The ventilation of industrial premises is under the jurisdiction of the Government's factory inspectors: in some factories, where harmful fumes are dispersed, the air must be changed thirty times or more per hour.

Rooms can be ventilated by natural or mechanical means. Natural ventilation depends on windows or other openings or, in the case of halls and other large spaces, on cowls and turrets in the roof. Natural ventilation cannot be easily controlled or measured; therefore, where definite ventilation rates are required, some mechanical system is necessary.

The simplest mechanical system extracts the stale air. A propeller fan, for example, in the outer wall of a kitchen prevents kitchen fumes from pervading the building. For forcing air through air ducts propeller fans are not efficient enough, and a fan of radial-flow type is used (*see* COMPRESSOR). When the fan or 'runner' inside a scroll-shaped casing (Fig. 1) is rotated by an electric motor, air is drawn in at the centre of the runner and discharged at the outlet of the casing. A modern 'axial' type fan is made for direct insertion in a length of circular air ducts (*see* p. 87). Axial fans run at very high speeds, but as they are somewhat noisy they are mainly used in industrial work.

Fig. 2 shows a system of 'extract ventilation' in an office building. A radial-flow fan in a chamber on the roof is connected to ducts formed in the ceilings of the corridors, and draws air from the rooms into these spaces. Fresh air to replace the stale air is admitted through inlets behind radiators, thus avoiding cold draughts.

Instead of being mechanically extracted, air may be forced into a building. This is known as 'plenum' ventilation. Often, both plenum and extract systems are installed, this being called 'balanced' ventilation.

With plenum ventilation, the incoming air

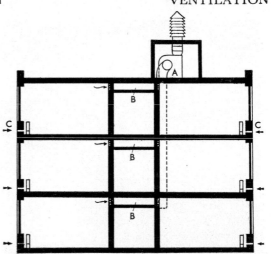

FIG. 2. DIAGRAM OF EXTRACT VENTILATION SYSTEM
A. Fan. B. Air ducts. C. Air inlets

must be cleaned of dust—particularly in densely populated areas, where the amount of dust deposited from the atmosphere may exceed 400 tons per square mile per year. The air is passed through a filter, of which there are many types; one consists of panels covered with cloth, arranged in zigzag form to provide a large area of surface. Dust accumulated on the surface of the panels is removed by a vacuum cleaner.

Incoming air must be warmed in cold weather, and this is usually done by passing it over a battery of pipes through which hot water or steam is flowing. The pipes are usually 'gilled', that is,

Davidson & Co.

FIG. 3. AN AIR WASHER
A. Water pump. B. Primary filter screen. C. Secondary filter. D. Water sprays. E. Scraper plates for removing dirt. F. Eliminator plates for removing excess moisture

Davidson & Co.

FIG. 4. VENTILATION DUCTS IN A MODERN FACTORY WHERE TEMPERATURE AND HUMIDITY HAVE TO BE CAREFULLY
REGULATED

thin metal disks are threaded on the pipes to increase the area of contact between the air and
the hot surface.

In many industries, the best results are obtained if the air is conditioned, that is, is maintained at constant values of temperature and
humidity. The essential component of an air-
conditioning plant is the air washer—a chamber
in which the air passes through water in the form
of fine spray (Fig. 3). If the incoming air is too
humid, a refrigerating plant keeps the spray at a
low temperature, with the paradoxical result
that the air is partially dried by passing through
the washer as some of its moisture is condensed.
Conversely, if the incoming air is too dry, it
takes up moisture by evaporation in passing
through the washer. Both the temperature and
the humidity of the air leaving the plant can be
automatically controlled, in spite of wide fluctuations in outside conditions. The conditioned
air is delivered to the rooms in large ducts
(Fig. 4).

See also Vol. III: WATER VAPOUR.
See also Vol. XI: VENTILATION, DOMESTIC.

VERNIER. This is a small scale added to instruments designed to measure lengths or angles,
such as callipers or theodolites. An approximate
measurement is first made by noting the position
of a pointer which moves along the main scale
and is the zero of the vernier scale (*see* Fig. 1a).
The purpose of the vernier scale is to read more
accurately the position of the pointer without
the aid of more sub-divisions on the main scale.
The main scale in Fig. 1 is graduated in centimetres and millimetres (tenths of centimetres).

James Chesterman & Co. Ltd.

VERNIER CALLIPERS

The vernier measures to an accuracy of $\frac{1}{1000}$ in. on the
lower scale and $\frac{1}{50}$ mm. on the upper scale

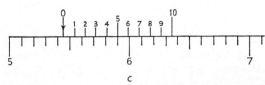

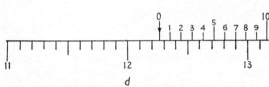

FIG. 1. DIAGRAM OF A VERNIER SCALE

The divisions on the main scale represent centimetres and millimetres

The length of the vernier scale, which has 10 intervals, is 9 millimetres, each interval being 9 tenths of a millimetre long. When the zero of the main scale and the zero of the vernier scale are opposite each other (Fig. 1a), 1 on the vernier scale is 1 tenth of a millimetre to the left of the 1 millimetre mark on the main scale, 2 is 0·2 mm. from the 2 mm. mark, and so on. 10 on the vernier scale is 10 tenths of a mm. from the 10 mm. (1 cm.) mark on the main scale, that is, it is opposite the 9 mm. mark. If the vernier is moved 0·1 mm. to the right, 1 will come opposite the 1 mm. mark on the main scale (Fig. 1b). No other mark on the vernier will now come opposite a mark on the main scale. If, as in Fig. 1c, the 5 mark on the vernier is exactly opposite a mark on the main scale we know that 0 on the vernier is 0·5 mm. to the right of the mark on its left on the main scale. (The reading is 5·45 cm.) Similarly the reading in Fig. 1d is 12·27 cm.

The first vernier scale, invented by Pierre Vernier in Belgium about 1630, was used for measuring angles. This scale was made 1 unit longer than the corresponding number of divisions on the main scale, so that the zero came at the other end from our example, reversing the order of the

numbers on the vernier scale. The principle is the same.

See also LENGTH-MEASURING INSTRUMENTS; METEOROLOGICAL INSTRUMENTS; SURVEYING INSTRUMENTS.

VIBRATION, MECHANICAL. This is the movement of material to and fro past some intermediate position. It is of great importance in engineering. Sometimes, as in CLOCKS AND WATCHES (q.v.), it is essential to the working of the mechanism; sometimes, as in the rattling of bus windows at particular speeds of the engine, it is unpleasant; sometimes, as in the vibration of aircraft propellors, it can be dangerous.

One of the simplest vibrations is obtained when a spring with a weight at one end is hung up by the other. If this is done carefully and the weight allowed to hang steadily, the spring is stretched. This position of the weight is called its equilibrium position. If the weight is pulled down slightly from this position and then let go, it will move up and down regularly for some time, slowly coming to rest again in the equilibrium position. While the distance travelled on each up and down journey continually gets smaller, the time for each journey does not alter.

This is a simple example of what engineers call a vibrating system. The repeated motion is called vibration or oscillation. It is the result of disturbing a system which has mass (the weight) and stiffness (the spring). The degree of vibration is described by the distance travelled by the mass on each side of the equilibrium position, and this distance is called the amplitude of vibration. One complete vibration (up and back and down and back) is called one cycle.

In this example the amplitude gradually diminishes, and when a freely vibrating system acts in this way we say the vibration is damped. A lightly damped vibration executes many cycles of oscillation before coming to rest, but a heavily damped vibration completes only a few cycles before ceasing to move; in fact, it may not even complete one. The cause of damping is FRICTION (q.v.), and in the example given the damping is due to friction between the moving weight and the surrounding air.

The time taken by the system to complete one cycle is called the period of oscillation, and the number of cycles per second is called the frequency. Any vibrating system has one or more particular frequencies at which it will oscillate if first disturbed and then released, and these are called its natural frequencies. In the example given there is only one natural frequency, because the system can vibrate in only one fashion. More complicated systems, containing more than

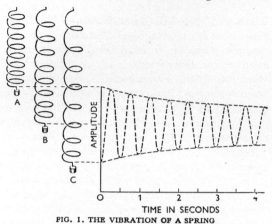

FIG. 1. THE VIBRATION OF A SPRING

A. Spring in compression. B. Equilibrium position.
c. Spring in tension

one spring, can oscillate in several different ways, each of which is called a mode of vibration, and each mode has a different natural frequency. For instance, a stiff plank supported on two equal springs could vibrate so that either both ends went up and down together or so that one end went up while the other went down. Even such a simple structure as a thin plank has a great many modes of vibration and a great many distinct natural frequencies.

The vibrations described so far, which slowly diminish, are called free vibrations, because the weight on the spring, once started, was left alone. If the top end of the spring had been forcibly moved up and down for a time, the motion of the weight would soon have settled down to a regular vibration at the same frequency as the disturbance of the top of the spring, and this sort of motion is called forced vibration. Close observation would show that the top and bottom ends of the spring were not moving quite together; when the top was just reversing the direction of its motion, the bottom would be either a little in front or a little behind. We describe this by saying there is a difference of phase between the ends.

The most important feature of forced vibration is resonance. When a vibrating system is forced to vibrate at or near its natural frequency, it will build up a vibration of very great amplitude, even though the forces causing the vibra-

tion are quite small. This is called resonance, and is very dangerous, because it means that a bridge, or an aeroplane, or a car, or a turbine in a power station might suddenly break, even though quite small forces were making it vibrate. It is said that the singer, Caruso, would cause a wine glass to break into little bits by singing a note of the same pitch (frequency) as the natural frequency of the glass. At the other end of the scale of size, a suspension bridge at Tacoma in the U.S.A. became resonant at the frequency of the eddies in the wind blowing past it. It vibrated slowly up and down for two or three days, after which half a mile of it fell into the river below. The rattling of a bus window at certain engine speeds is caused by resonance of the window with the vibration from the engine.

Materials that are subjected to vibration for a time may crack although they have not experienced any load heavy enough to break them on one application. What breaks them is 'fatigue', and its study is important in deciding how long it is safe to go on using certain parts of machines.

Vibration engineers are concerned with measuring the frequency and amplitude of vibrating structures in order that their designs may be modified to avoid the worst effects of vibration (see ENGINEERING DESIGN). The engines of vehicles, ships, and aircraft are normally run at speeds where the effects of resonance can cause no damage. For instance, although the windows of a bus often rattle considerably when the engine is running slowly, as soon as the bus gathers speed the rattling may stop.

Not all vibration is dangerous or useless. The vibration of the balance wheel and hairspring of a watch is essential to its working. A sloping and vibrating tray is used in the printing works for stacking the sheets of paper which make up this book. CONCRETE (q.v.) is compacted by means of a vibrating rod placed in it while it is wet. The sound which comes from a loudspeaker is a vibration of the air caused by the mechanical vibration of the cone of the speaker following as exactly as possible the electrical vibrations from the output of the RADIO set (q.v.).

See also STRESS AND STRAIN.
See also Vol. III: SOUND; WAVE MOTION.

VOLTAGE, see ELECTRIC CURRENT, Section 7; MEASUREMENT, UNITS OF, Section 3.

VOLTMETER, see ELECTRICAL INSTRUMENTS.

W

WATCHES, *see* CLOCKS AND WATCHES.

WATER POWER. For centuries, men have built water-wheels to use the energy of falling water: indeed, until the introduction of the steam engine in the late 18th century, all industry depended on water power and WIND POWER (q.v.).

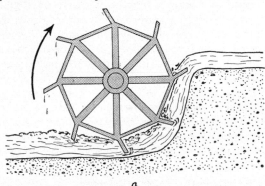

a

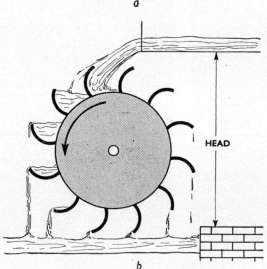

b

FIG. 1. DIAGRAM OF WATER MILLS

a. Undershot mill. *b.* Overshot mill

The earliest water-mills of which we have record are described by a Greek writer about 85 B.C. The familiar mill-wheel, still to be seen in old English water-mills such as the one at Guy's Cliff, near Warwick, was introduced to England about A.D. 760, but was used on the Continent much earlier. What may be called the 'old' water-wheels (to distinguish them from the modern water turbine) were of two basic types— the 'undershot' mill, in which the speed of the stream was the important factor (Fig. 1*a*), and the 'overshot' mill, in which the important factor was the 'head' (or height of fall) of water (Fig. 1*b*). The two different types correspond roughly to the two important types of modern water turbine described below. The undershot wheel uses the energy of motion or kinetic energy of the water, while the overshot wheel uses its energy of position or potential energy (*see* ENERGY).

An obvious disadvantage of the overshot wheel is that, since its diameter has to be nearly as high as the head available, it cannot make the best use of a big head of water—for instance, in a high mountain lake.

These old types of water-mill could usually supply all the power that was wanted on the spot, and until it became possible to generate electricity there was little demand for anything more powerful. With electricity came the possibility of harnessing vast amounts of water power and of generating electrical power for distribution over a wide area (*see* HYDRO-ELECTRIC POWER), and so the modern water turbines were developed.

The modern water turbine has to convert as much as possible of the total available energy in the water into mechanical power for driving machines. The amount of power available depends on the weight of water that flows in a given time and the 'head'—the vertical distance through which it falls. Thus the higher the head and the larger the quantity of water which can be used, the greater will be the power developed.

In modern water-power developments the head is normally obtained by holding water back behind a DAM (q.v.) in an artificial reservoir, or sometimes in a natural lake. Sometimes the dam is on the lower reaches of a river, in which case the flow is relatively large but the head small. A dam built on a higher reach of the river holds back less water, but the water can be taken from the reservoir by means of a tunnel driven through the adjacent hills, and then through one or more steel pipes to turbines in a power station lower down the river (*see* p. 220). In such a scheme the head, not being dependent on the height of the dam, can be much higher—indeed, it may exceed 5,000 feet. In the first case the power is derived from a large quantity of water and small head, and in the second from a larger head with less water. Only in a few cases, such as at NIAGARA FALLS (q.v. Vol. III), can a fairly high head and large flow be obtained together.

Modern water turbines are divided into two classes—impulse turbines for high heads, and reaction turbines for low heads but much larger volumes of water (*see* STEAM TURBINE). In an impulse or Pelton turbine the water passes through one or more nozzles which discharge it in the form of very fast jets; these jets strike a number of specially shaped buckets fixed to the rim of a disk or wheel (Fig. 2). The total available potential energy due to the head of water is converted into the kinetic energy of the moving water; thus, the energy in the water as it enters the Pelton wheel is wholly kinetic. The water strikes the buckets at their middle and emerges from their sides. In doing this it loses most of its velocity, and hence its kinetic energy, which it imparts to the wheel as it is rotated. But not all the water's kinetic energy is used in rotating the wheel; some goes with the water as it leaves the bucket and some is lost in FRICTION (q.v.). Thus the mechanical energy obtained is less than the

equivalent of the initial total energy in the water. The ratio is known as the turbine efficiency, which for a large modern Pelton turbine may be about 90%. The wheel is normally surrounded by a metal casing to collect the water as it leaves the buckets and to discharge it clear of the machine.

In the reaction turbine, the water runs into a steel or concrete casing of spiral shape, which surrounds the wheel, or 'runner'. Unlike the impulse turbine, the casing and runner are under pressure and must be sealed to prevent the water from escaping. Only part of the available energy is converted into velocity before the water enters the runner, and on striking the runner the water loses both potential and kinetic energy, which are transferred to the runner. The reaction turbine may be of the 'Francis' type, which has a runner with blades so curved that the water enters radially towards the shaft on which the runner is fixed and is discharged from it axially (Fig. 3). Alternatively, it may be of the 'propeller' type which has a runner similar to a ship's propeller with fixed blades. The Kaplan turbine is of this type but has movable blades (Fig. 4). The angle of the blades relative to the direction of flow of the water can be automatically adjusted so that the turbine passes the least amount of water necessary to produce the required amount of energy. The efficiency of a large reaction turbine may be of the order of 92% to 93%.

Sté des Forges et Ateliers Creuso   *Ets. Neyrpic*

FIG. 2. CASING (LEFT) AND RUNNER (RIGHT) OF PELTON WHEEL

Water under high pressures enters at A and A_1 through jets controlled by needle valves, and the impulse of the jets on the buckets B drives the runner

Sté des Forges et Ateliers Creusot

FIG. 3. FRANCIS WHEEL AND CASING

The water enters the spiral casing at A and leaves through
a pipe bolted to the studs B, surrounding the turbine C

As the maximum power which a turbine can
give is not always needed, provision is made for
adjusting the quantity of water which is passed
into the runner. In an impulse turbine, the flow
is varied by opening and closing the nozzles with
spear-shaped needles contained inside them. In
a reaction turbine, metal gates or guide vanes,
similar to a venetian blind, which can be opened
and closed, are inserted between the spiral casing
and the runner. These also serve to guide the
water into the runner.

Although the speed of modern water turbines
is much higher than that of the old mill-wheels,
they are still relatively slow-speed machines
compared with the STEAM TURBINE and INTER-
NAL COMBUSTION ENGINE (qq.v.). Speeds of
between 75 and 1,000 revolutions per minute
are the most usual, the speed depending on the
power of the turbine and the head available.
The higher the head and the smaller the power
output of the turbine the faster it can rotate. For
a given output, the higher the head the smaller
has to be the size of the turbine, since it needs to
pass less water. Consequently its weight and cost

are less. The higher the speed the smaller, and
usually cheaper, is the machinery which it
drives; therefore as high a speed as possible is
aimed at. For the same hydraulic conditions and
required power output a propeller turbine runs
faster than a Francis, but it cannot generally be
used when the head exceeds about 150 feet.
Similarly the Francis runs faster than the Pelton
turbine, but its limit of head is at present about
1,400 feet. There is no theoretical limit to the
head for a Pelton turbine, and such a machine
has been made for a head of 5,700 feet.

The modern development of water power
ranges from small installations on tributary
streams, giving a few horse-power for private
domestic purposes, to large projects on major
rivers, with individual machines up to about
160,000 horse-power and weighing more than
1,000 tons, for contributing to the requirements
of extensive public electric power systems.

Much study has been given to the possibility
of making use of the power from the rise and fall

Ets. Neyrpic

FIG. 4. A KAPLAN RUNNER

The runner works rather like a ship's propeller in reverse.
The pitch of the blades can be automatically adjusted to
deal with different heads of water according to the power
output needed

of the TIDES (q.v. Vol. III). The general principle involves the construction of a dam across a river basin or estuary where there is a large tidal range. During the period of flood the sea is allowed to pass through gates in the dam and build up behind it. The gates are closed at the time of high tide, and during the period of the ebb tide the water is released through turbines to generate power. No major tidal project has yet been constructed, but one of the most favourable is on the River Severn, where it is calculated over one million horse-power could be developed. The principal difficulty is that the tidal range of the sea varies with the phase of the moon, and the amount of power which can be obtained is therefore variable. Also, as high tide occurs at a different time each day, the period during which the power can be generated is continually varying, and so variable and intermittent a supply of power is not adaptable to any ordinary industrial purpose.

See also HYDRO-ELECTRIC POWER; ENERGY.

WATER SUPPLY. 1. A regular supply of clean water is of the first necessity to any community. In early times villages grew up close to a river, spring, or well, from which water could be taken by water-cart or human water-carrier. Today, in most developed countries, a constant supply is delivered through mains to every household in towns and in many villages, and, in contrast with the past, the water is purified when necessary. To provide an efficient supply system for a city or industrial area is a major engineering task.

Modern towns, with their thousands of homes and big factories, need enormous quantities of water. The NEW YORK WATER SUPPLY (q.v.) system, for example, provides as much as 870 million gallons a day. In Britain, an average of 20 to 40 gallons per head is used each day in the home and between 5 to 40 gallons for trade and manufacture. More water is always used in summer; in some holiday resorts the demand may increase by twice as much during the holiday periods.

2. SOURCES OF SUPPLY. Fresh water is obtained either from rivers and lakes or from underground, both sources depending ultimately upon rainfall. In Britain, the average rainfall varies from about 20 inches a year in Essex to much more than 100 inches in parts of the mountains of Wales. Much rain water, however, is either absorbed by vegetation or lost by evaporation; in Britain, from 14 to 20 inches a year are lost in this way. One inch of rainfall is equivalent to as much as $14\frac{1}{2}$ million gallons of water per square mile.

(*a*) *Surface water.* Water can be drawn off a river or stream by PUMPS, or, in mountainous and hilly districts, DAMS (qq.v.) can be built across the rivers to form reservoirs. These store the winter flood waters and so ensure a regular supply throughout the year. Birmingham and Liverpool, for example, draw water from reservoirs made by building dams across valleys in the Welsh mountains; and Bristol draws water from Blagdon reservoir in the Mendip Hills—a natural lake the resources of which have been greatly increased by a dam.

Water-supply schemes are not allowed to hold up completely the flow of a river, because rivers play an important part in the SEWAGE DISPOSAL system of an area (q.v.), and because many people, such as water-mill owners, farmers, and anglers, are entitled to certain long-standing 'water rights'. Consequently, 'compensation water', usually between one-quarter and one-third of the average flow during the driest 3-year period on record, is allowed to flow on in the stream.

Since most reservoirs in mountainous districts are situated far from the area they supply, a long aqueduct has to be constructed to take the water first to the water-treatment works, which may be sited anywhere along the aqueduct, and then on to the service reservoirs, which are connected with the distribution 'mains'. The aqueducts may consist partly of covered-in channels, partly of tunnels, and partly of large pipelines, according to the nature of the country. The longest aqueduct in Britain, from Thirlmere in the Lake District to Manchester, is 96 miles long. One of the aqueducts in the New York supply system runs for 130 miles.

Where the water is pumped direct from a large river—from the Thames and the Lea, for example, which supply London (*see* METROPOLITAN WATER BOARD), or from the Severn which supplies Worcester—the water-treatment works and service reservoirs are usually near the pumping-stations.

(*b*) *Underground water.* Innumerable cracks and fissures in the rocks deep down beneath the soil often form vast natural reservoirs, where rain water collects after seeping through the soil.

This underground water is brought to the surface from WELLS AND SPRINGS (q.v. Vol. III) and from bore-holes.

A well is a vertical shaft from 3 feet to 10 feet in diameter and 50 to 400 feet deep; it is usually sunk by pneumatic drills. In some cases, particularly in chalk strata, horizontal tunnels, called 'adits', are driven outwards from near the bottom of the well, their purpose being to find water-bearing fissures which will add to the total yield of the well. The tunnels may vary in length from a few feet to a mile or more.

Coventry Corporation Water Undertaking

FILTER BEDS IN THE RIVER SEVERN WATER-SUPPLY SCHEME

A bore-hole is a shaft cut by tools suspended on steel rods, which can either be lifted and dropped (like a pickaxe) or else rotated (like a carpenter's drill). Both types of boring apparatus were originally worked by hand winches, but are now generally power driven. The usual diameter of a bore-hole is between 8 and 40 inches, and the depth is seldom more than 600 feet.

In Britain, underground water is found only in eastern, central, and southern England. In the City of London, many business premises, including the Bank of England, draw water from wells, though reserves are now beginning to diminish. The yield from large wells and bore-holes can be as much as 2 million gallons per day per well.

3. WATER TREATMENT. Natural surface water in uninhabited areas and fairly deep underground waters are usually safe to drink. But in districts with a large population there is a considerable risk of the water being contaminated, particularly by human and animal excreta. In the past many serious EPIDEMICS (q.v. Vol. XI), usually of typhoid fever or cholera, were caused by impure water. Moreover, many natural waters may be too 'hard' or too 'soft', cloudy or discoloured, unpleasant to taste or smell, or liable to corrode or absorb metals. Nearly all public water supplies, therefore, are now treated by various methods to ensure that the water is wholesome.

The oldest method of purification, called 'slow sand filtration', is still extensively used. This consists of passing the water through filter-beds, which are large open basins with a layer of sand about 3 feet deep. The water flows in over the top of the bed and sinks slowly through the sand. In a short time a sticky film forms on the top of the sand, and this holds up any bacteria, as well as any fine clay causing discolouration; the treated water is drawn off through pipes below the sand. When the bed becomes clogged, it is emptied, and the top layer of sand with the film is removed. The dirty sand is washed and put back into the bed.

A more recent method is, first, to add a suitable chemical (such as aluminium sulphate) to the water in a sedimentation tank. This chemical is called a 'coagulant', because it forms large snow-like flakes, called 'floc', in which suspended matter in the water is trapped or absorbed. The floc, with all the extraneous matter it has collected, slowly sinks to the bottom, and the clear water is drawn off near the top. The clear water is then passed to 'rapid filters', so called because they operate very much faster than slow sand filters. The filter material is cleaned from time to time, by reversing the flow of water so that the filter is washed through with clean water, and by using compressed air bubbles to agitate the material so that the accumulated dirt is separated, rises to the top, and can be drawn off.

Coventry Corporation Water Undertaking

SEDIMENTATION TANKS IN THE RIVER SEVERN WATER-SUPPLY SCHEME

If the water has only to be sterilized to kill the microbes in it, a tiny amount of chlorine gas, usually much less than 1 part per million but enough to kill any bacteria, is mixed with the water; this may give the water a slightly unpleasant taste, however. By another method, super-chlorination, an excess quantity of chlorine is added to the water, which is later 'dechlorinated' by mixing in sulphur dioxide so that no unpleasant taste or smell is likely to remain. By a third method, 'chloramination', ammonia is used with the chlorine. In all these methods the amount of chemicals used is too small to have any harmful effect on humans.

Water from chalk or limestone districts is often very 'hard'. Rain water absorbs carbonic acid gas as it falls through the air and as it passes through the soil. This enables it to absorb and hold any salts of lime or magnesia which it may contact as it passes through the sub-soil. Water which has absorbed a large amount of these salts is called 'hard' because of its feel; and the salts prevent soap from lathering properly. Hard **water** may be softened either by removing the **salts** with cream of lime and soda ash, or by changing the characteristics of the salts with granular substances called 'zeolites'. The former method is often used to soften the water used by railway locomotives; the softening plant can easily be recognized by the heaps of chalk (calcium carbonate), left over from the treatment, alongside the railway track. Zeolites are frequently used in household water-softeners (*see* WATER, DOMESTIC, Vol. XI).

4. DISTRIBUTION. After treatment, the water flows or is pumped into the service reservoirs. These are roofed-in to prevent contamination, and are, if possible, situated on high ground so that the water will flow from them by gravity to the tops of the highest houses (*see* HYDRAULICS). They also hold a general reserve of purified water to provide for the variations in demand between day and night and for emergency demands for fire-fighting (*see* FIRE SERVICES, Vol. X) and other purposes.

Where there are no hills, or where water has to be delivered to a village or factory on top of a hill, the water is either pumped at high pressure from the service reservoir, or a water-tower is erected. A water-tower is a large storage tank, often standing out against the skyline, raised on supports so that it is higher than any buildings which it serves; the water is pumped into the tank and then runs down by gravity to the buildings which need it (*see* p. 90).

Water is delivered from the service reservoirs by a system of mains, or pipes, beginning with a large 'trunk' main, which divides into smaller district mains and service mains. Each building has separate pipes connected with the mains, which lead into a cistern at the top of the house or direct to the house taps (*see* HOUSEHOLD PLUMBING, Vol. XI).

Sometimes a considerable amount of water is wasted by leaks in faulty mains. In order to trace losses, the pipe distribution system is divided into sub-districts, the flow into each sub-district being measured by a meter which records the volume of water on a time chart. From readings on the charts faults can be traced to individual mains, and repairs can be carried out without having to open up long lengths of mains for inspection.

Another method is to use a stethoscope or listening rod; this is like a walking-stick with its upper end shaped into an ear-piece. The water inspector places the pointed end on the road, over the main, and listens with his ear against the other end. If the leak is near by, he can hear the sound of trickling water quite clearly. This method is best used at dead of night when there is no interference from street noises.

See also NEW YORK WATER SUPPLY; METROPOLITAN WATER BOARD; DAMS; HYDRAULICS.

See also Vol. XI: WATER SUPPLY, HISTORY OF.

WATER TURBINE, *see* WATER POWER.

WATER WORKS, *see* WATER SUPPLY; METROPOLITAN WATER BOARD.

WATTS, *see* MEASUREMENT, UNITS OF.

WEIGHING INSTRUMENTS. The technique of measuring a quantity by balancing it against a known quantity or weight has been practised since the earliest historical times, and the main principles which are the basis of most modern weighing machines are very ancient, although the methods and the balances and weights have, of course, been greatly refined and improved.

Of all known mechanical instruments for making physical measurements the equi-arm balance

can give the highest accuracy. The principle of this instrument—the simple balanced lever—has been known and used for thousands of years. The earliest known balance beam is Egyptian and is, perhaps, 7,000 years old. This polished limestone beam was supported on a cord at its centre, and the pans were suspended on cords passing through holes accurately drilled at its ends (Fig. 1). Nowadays, the beam of a precision balance is supported on a finely ground knife-edge, usually of agate, resting on a flat agate or sapphire plane, and the pans are suspended on flat planes resting also on agate knife-edges. One of the most highly accurate balances in the world (Fig. 2) was designed and made at the National Physical Laboratory at Teddington for the purpose of comparing the primary standard weights of Britain. Differences between these standard weights can be determined to an accuracy approaching 1 part in 1,000 million. In proportion, this accuracy would represent to a ton of coal a piece the size of a pinhead.

With these highly accurate balances special precautions have to be taken. The mechanism for operating the balance and for changing the weights from one pan to the other, for example, is actuated from outside the room, so that the observer's body temperature does not affect the balance in any way.

The earliest weights were made of stone or black basaltic rock, and many very ancient ones have been recovered almost in their original condition from excavations in Egypt and elsewhere. Later, brass or bronze was most often used for the best weights. Today, the primary standards are made either from platinum or an alloy called iridio-platinum which is more resistant to wear

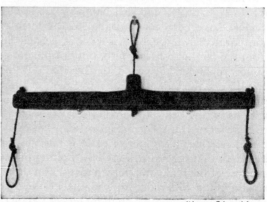

Director, Science Museum

FIG. 1. EGYPTIAN LIMESTONE BALANCE, *c.* 5000 B.C.

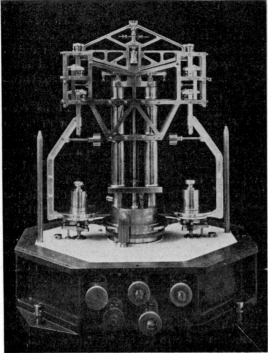

National Physical Laboratory

FIG. 2. NATIONAL PHYSICAL LABORATORY PRECISION
BALANCE FOR WEIGHING PRIMARY STANDARDS

and corrosion; but this material is of such high cost that new materials have lately been developed for high-grade weights. These include nickel-chromium, special stainless-steel, and brass, plated with hard metals such as rhodium or chromium.

The simple lever balance, when adjusted to a sufficiently fine sensitiveness for precision weighing, is a somewhat slow-moving instrument which may oscillate for a long time before coming to rest. But in modern balances 'damping' devices have been incorporated in the form of comparatively large hollow pistons suspended from the pans and fitting into, but not touching, hollow cylinders attached to the main frame or pillar of the balance. The movement of these pistons is slowed down by air resistance, so that they cause the beam to come to rest after one or two swings. Damped balances can be made direct reading; a pointer or scale is fixed to the beam, so that the indication of the pointer or the shadow of the scale on a screen gives, as a direct reading, the difference in weights of the two objects being compared. In more recent balances specially shaped weights can be put on one arm

of the balance by means of hooks attached to dial indicators, so that the sum of the weights needed to balance the article being weighed is shown on the dials without the need for any calculation. A further application of this principle has produced the single-pan constant-load balance, in which a complete set of special weights is supported on the same arm of the beam as the single pan. This balance is 'poised' by removing the necessary weights from their positions above the single pan—the sum of the weights thus removed being shown, as before, on dials.

The accurate balances so far described are used in laboratory work where high precision is essential in the comparison of standard weights, the weighing of scientific specimens, and analyses of various kinds. The large majority of the scales and weighing machines used in commerce incorporate the same knife-edge principles as the scientific balance, but range in type, use, and purpose from the fine balances used by jewellers and assayers for weighing precious stones and metals to the huge weigh-bridges capable of carrying locomotives weighing several hundred tons. Many of the larger weighing machines make use of the principle of the LEVER (q.v.) to enable large weights to be measured by means of much lighter standards. The simplest balance working on this principle is the 'steelyard', known to the Romans and to be seen in many places today (Fig. 3).

Victoria & Albert Museum

FIG. 3. DUTCH STEELYARD, 1673

Where the highest accuracy is not essential, a completely different device, the 'spring balance', can be used. In this, the weight to be measured is made to extend a spring, the extension being measured by a pointer. As a spring stretches by an amount proportional to the force applied, a spring balance gives a reading proportional to the weight bearing on it. Of course, this type of balance is not strictly a balance at all, and it measures weight, not MASS (q.v. Vol. III). It has to be calibrated, or scaled, using known weights in the first place.

The accuracy of all commercial weighing machines is maintained by rigid tests at regular intervals by Weights and Measures Inspectors, using test weights which have been compared with the standard weights of the Board of Trade. These, in their turn, have been tested against the Imperial Standard Pound or the British National Kilogramme, the primary standard weights of this country (*see* MEASUREMENT, UNITS OF, Section 2*a*).

See also MEASUREMENT, UNITS OF.
See also Vol. IV: MEASUREMENT, HISTORY OF.

WELDING. This is a process by which pieces of metal are strongly joined together under heat. There are two main kinds—forge welding and fusion welding.

1. FORGE WELDING. By this ancient process, used, perhaps, for 4,000 years, two pieces of metal (nearly always wrought iron, a soft, tough metal) are joined together after having been softened, but not melted, by heat. The two pieces of wrought iron, having been brought to a red heat in the blacksmith's fire, are placed on the anvil and beaten together with a hammer. Under the blows of the hammer they slowly merge into one another until they finally form one solid piece of metal, with nothing to indicate where the joint has been made and with no greater weakness at the joint than anywhere else.

Chains are often made out of wrought iron bar by forge welding. Each open link is heated, looped around the previous link, and then the two ends are forge-welded together to form a closed loop which is strong, tough, and uniform throughout. A chain of any length may be built up in this way, link by link. The forge welding process has also been widely used for making decorative pieces of wrought ironwork such as gates and trelliswork. Magnificent examples of the forge welders' art are to be found in such cities as Salzburg, in Austria. Today, apart from the manufacture of chains, hand forge welding is largely confined to the blacksmith's shop for general repair work on such articles as farming implements.

Machine forge welding is now used in the manufacture of TUBES (q.v.) and pipes of soft steel, a metal with some of the properties of wrought iron. Such tubes are often made from long, thin, flat strips of soft steel by heating them, bending them to a tubular shape (as if rolling a cigarette), and then passing them, red hot, through a machine which presses the two edges together and makes a forge weld. The smaller the tube, the more easily can this be done, and tubes under $4\frac{1}{2}$ inches in diameter are made by a continuous process in which long lengths of steel strip are heated, bent, and welded into a tube in one operation. 'Pluto', the famous pipeline which carried petrol from England to France under the sea during the Second World War, was made in this fashion.

Most pure metals can be forge-welded, but in practice the process is generally confined to wrought iron and soft steel. This is because many metals, when hot, form a chemical combination with the oxygen in the air, and the oxide thus created (*see* CORROSION) enters the weld and weakens the join.

2. FUSION WELDING. This process, which has become common in the present century, is much more widely used than forge welding as it is successful with stainless steel, other steels of various types, cast iron, copper, and alloys of aluminium and magnesium, which are much used in aircraft construction. Fusion welding relies on melting the metal rather than softening and beating it. To bring about the fusion the two pieces of metal, at the point where they are to be joined, must be raised for a brief moment to a temperature above the melting-point. With steel, for example, this means a temperature of more than 1,600° C. There are three methods of fusion welding— electric, oxy-acetylene, and thermit welding.

(*a*) *Electric fusion welding*. The commonest form is arc welding (Fig. 1). A metal rod is connected to one pole of a circuit carrying a powerful ELECTRIC CURRENT (q.v.), and the two pieces to be welded are connected to the other pole. When the rod is touched for a moment on the metal and then drawn away about half an inch, an electric spark known as an 'arc' is set up where the current leaps across the gap between the end

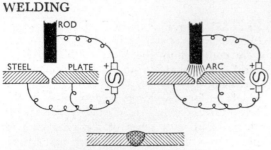

FIG. 1. DIAGRAM OF ARC WELDING

of the rod and the pieces of metal. This arc is intensely hot: it is calculated that the temperature inside it can reach as much as 3,400° C. Therefore, as the welding rod and the arc are passed slowly along the pieces of metal, drops of molten metal fall from the rod and combine with drops of metal melted from the pieces on either side. As a result a 'bead' of metal is formed in the centre of the groove and firmly bonds the two pieces together. The arc welder must hold the welding rod at exactly the right distance from the metal in order to keep the arc alight, and as it slowly melts and gets shorter, he must move it nearer to the groove, keeping it so that neither too little nor too much metal is melted off the two pieces. The ultra-violet rays given off by the arc are extremely dangerous to the eyes and the skin, so the welder watches his work through a dark glass set in a stout shield (Fig. 2).

Arc welding in this manner is a convenient method of joining steel plates and is widely used

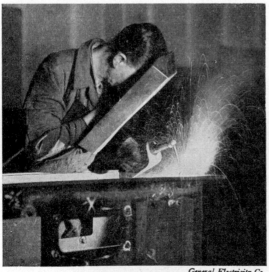

General Electricity Co.

FIG. 2. ARC WELDING

in general engineering work and in SHIPBUILDING (q.v.).

Another form of arc welding, called 'flash butt' welding, uses no rod, the two metal pieces to be joined being themselves directly connected to opposite poles of the electric circuit. By touching together and pulling apart the metal pieces the arc is 'struck' between them for a second or two, just long enough to cause them to begin to melt on the surface. Then they are pushed together under strong pressure, and the weld is completed. This method is useful for securing objects in places where it would be difficult to work with the welding rod.

Thin steel sheet or wire cannot be arc welded satisfactorily, as a light piece of steel would be melted away in the intense heat of the arc before the weld could be made; therefore resistance welding, often called 'spot' welding, is used. The two pieces to be joined are clamped together between strong metal jaws, and an electric current made to flow through the joint. The combination of the heat generated by the passing electric current and the pressure exerted by the clamp jaws is sufficient to weld the pieces very rapidly together.

(b) *Oxy-acetylene welding.* This is similar to arc welding with a rod except that the welding rod and the groove are heated by a flame issuing from an oxy-acetylene torch held close by. Acetylene gas burns in oxygen (*see* COMBUSTION) with a flame sufficiently hot to melt steel. Oxy-acetylene welding is used for securing steel sheets which are rather too thin for satisfactory arc welding. As the size of the flame and the position of the torch can be adjusted to give either hotter or cooler conditions, this method is suited to delicate work which might be damaged by the arc. Copper articles may be welded, or 'brazed' as it is usually called, by this means, using a copper welding rod; and for cast-iron articles either a cast-iron or bronze welding rod is used.

The oxy-acetylene welder uses both hands, one holding the rod, the other holding the torch. A shield is not necessary, but he must wear dark goggles.

(c) *Thermit welding.* This process is used mainly for repairing heavy iron castings and similar large pieces of engineering which have cracked or broken in service. The process makes use of the fierce chemical reaction which occurs when a mixture of powdered aluminium and iron oxide known as 'thermit' is ignited by a strip of

FIG. 3. OXY-ACETYLENE WELDING
The welder has the 'gun' or burner in his right hand
and the welding rod in his left

British Oxygen Co.

burning magnesium. Not only is intense heat caused, but the iron oxides decompose into oxygen (which helps to feed the heat) and molten iron. The broken edges of the iron casting are laid together, and a small clay mould is built around the break. Thermit is then poured into this mould and set off. The heat melts the edges of the broken casting, and the molten iron produced by the thermit joins the edges together.

Welding by arc, oxy-acetylene, and thermit, in the form described here, is used chiefly in joining steel, and to a lesser extent cast iron and copper, but the welding of other metals has been hindered by the tendency of the heated metal to oxidize in the air and the join to be, in consequence, weakened. Recently, however, a method of arc welding aluminium and magnesium alloys has been developed in which the arc and the molten metal are shielded, by means of an inert gas called argon, from contact with the air. Argon is so stable and inert that it will not combine chemically with other substances, and because of this rare quality, it acts as a gaseous 'blanket', keeping the arc and the molten metal out of contact with the air. A gentle blast of argon is projected into the arc, and under these conditions the light but strong aluminium and magnesium alloys, which are used very widely in aircraft construction, may be successfully and safely welded.

See also SHIPBUILDING; AERONAUTICAL ENGINEERING; RIVETING; SOLDERING.

WINCHES, *see* CRANES.

WIND POWER. There are many early records of the use of windmills, such as those coming from Persia in the 10th century. These windmills were quite unlike the familiar 'Dutch' windmill, as the sails revolved in a horizontal plane, like the blades of a helicopter.

The familiar windmill with sails rotating in a vertical plane first appeared in Western Europe (France and England) in the 12th century. In its original form, the whole mill—sail-wheel, gearing, and millstones for grinding the corn—rotated on a vertical post; but in later designs only the sails and the wind-shaft rotated to face the wind, the main body of the mill, containing the machinery, being built of brick. Until 1745 mills had to be turned by hand to face the wind; but in that year a man named Edmund Lee patented the device known as the 'automatic fantail'—a small auxiliary windmill facing at right angles to the main sails and arranged to rotate the windmill by gearing. Under the action of a cross-wind, the fantail would revolve and thus turn the windmill until the main sails once again faced the wind head-on. The only other real improvement made to the windmill between 1400 and 1900 were the various devices for enabling the sails to cope with anything from a light breeze to a gale without overloading the

Harry Meye

17TH-CENTURY POST MILL AT BOURN, CAMBRIDGESHIRE
It was used for grinding corn

K.L.M.

PUMPING MILLS NEAR ROTTERDAM

Joseph Lucas Ltd.

A WIND-DRIVEN LIGHTING PLANT

A generator is directly coupled to the 6-ft. propeller,
and the electricity generated is stored by batteries

machinery. In the original sail-cloth windmills,
a high wind could be allowed for to some extent
by 'furling' the sails. In 1775 Andrew Meikle
replaced the sail-cloth by hinged shutters controlled by springs. A high wind would blow the
shutters open so that some of the wind could pass
through the sails without doing any work. In
1807 Sir William Cubitt replaced the springs by
a hand-control that could be operated while the
mill was running.

In England windmills were used chiefly for
grinding corn and for pumping water for land
drainage in the FENS (q.v.) and Broads. The
power delivered varied from about 20 to 60 horse-
power according to the situation of the mill, the
size and design of the sails, and the efficiency of
the gearing.

Most of the old windmills fell into disuse at
the end of the 19th century because the flour-
milling industry found it better to have a few
big mills, driven by steam or oil engines, rather
than to use many windmills, of small and uncertain power, scattered over the countryside. In
Holland, Germany, and Denmark they are still
used to some extent, and considerable improvements have been introduced.

In the period between the two World Wars
several very big 'wind turbines' (up to 20,000 kilowatts) were designed in Germany, but none was
actually built. Russia set up a Central Wind
Power Institute in Moscow to study wind power
problems after the First World War and, in 1931,
a 120 horse-power machine with a three-bladed
propeller was built for electricity generation at
Balaclava in the Crimea. The Russians intended
to use this machine to gain experience for the
building of a machine of several thousand horse-
power but, so far as is known, such a machine
has not yet been made. In the Second World
War a more modern type of windmill having
two- or three-bladed propellers, something like
those of helicopters but turning vertically, was
introduced in Denmark. Several of these were
installed at village power stations, and some of
them, having blades 40 feet long, generated as
much as 90 kilowatts. Two types of small windmill are quite popular in Britain for providing
power for individual houses and farms. The
first, a high-speed machine developing about
$\frac{1}{2}$ h.p., consists of a simple propeller connected
directly to a small dynamo and arranged to
swivel in to face the wind. The other is the
familiar multibladed farm windmill, which is a

slow-speed machine developing about 1 h.p. This usually operates a deep well pump by means of a long oscillating rod worked by a crank attached to the windmill itself.

The largest wind-driven machine ever built was installed during the Second World War on a 2,000-foot hill called Grandpa's Knob, in Rutland, Vermont, U.S.A. It had a power of 1,680 kilowatts, but after tests over 4 years in which it generated up to 2,000 kilowatts, one of its two blades broke, and the machine was at last abandoned. This American experiment threw much light on the problems to be faced in building and running large wind turbines and encouraged other wind-power studies in U.S.A. One of these outlined a design for a 10,000 kilowatt wind turbine. An unusual new experimental wind turbine of British design consists of a huge two-bladed propeller, with hollow blades connected to a duct leading to an ordinary turbine at ground level. As the blades rotate, the air inside them is flung out through holes in the tips, maintaining a powerful suction through the turbine on the ground, which supplies the power. In the near future, however, the main development of wind power will probably be in the direction of fairly small machines of up to 100 kilowatts for supplying electric power to lonely communities with no other means of getting electricity.

WIND TUNNEL. This is a device for producing a stream of air in which experiments in aerodynamics (*see* HYDRODYNAMICS) may be performed. In a wind tunnel the model of an aeroplane, for example, is kept still, and the air is made to rush past it. The effect on the model is the same as if it were rushing through the air like a full-size aeroplane in free flight.

Fig. 1 shows the arrangement of a typical wind tunnel in which the air moves past the model at speeds less than the speed of sound. A fan (A) driven by an electric motor (B) pushes air continuously down a pipe or duct. After two right-angled bends in the pipe, fitted with 'turning vanes' (c) to help the air pass smoothly and evenly round the bends, the air passes through wire mesh screens (D) which help to remove any remaining turbulence. It then goes through a cone-shaped part of the tube, which is wider where the air enters than where it leaves. As explained in HYDRODYNAMICS (q.v.), this 'contraction cone' accelerates the air so that it is flowing

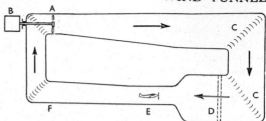

FIG. 1. DIAGRAM OF A WIND TUNNEL
A. Fan. B. Motor. c. Turning vanes. D. Screens.
E. Working section. F. Diffuser

faster when it leaves the cone than when it entered. Immediately after is the working section (E); here the model is placed at the desired angle to the flow of the air. The forces on the model are measured by the tensions in the supporting wires or by a special balance which is sometimes used to support it. When the air has passed the model it goes through another cone (the diffuser, F), which gradually brings the air speed back to what it was before it entered the contraction cone. The air then goes round two more corners and so back to the fan.

Wind tunnels such as this have a working section of a few square feet in cross-sectional area (about 5 ft. by 4 ft.). The air speed is about 160 ft. per second, produced by a motor of about 40 h.p.

In the larger wind tunnel shown in Fig. 2 the return part of the diffuser is arranged around the outside of the working section, so that the external shape is rather like a large boiler. This

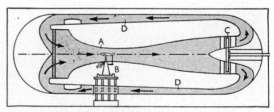

FIG. 2. DIAGRAM OF A LARGE CLOSED-CIRCUIT WIND TUNNEL
A. Working section. B. Balance. c. Fan. D. Diffuser

enables the pressure of the air in the tunnel to be altered according to the type of experiment, since this shape withstands different pressures very well. The area of the working section is 10 ft. by 7 ft., and a speed nearly up to the speed of sound may be obtained, using two motors of 2,000 h.p. each. In such a tunnel, the friction of the air on the walls converts all this power into heat, and hence an elaborate cooling system is required.

The tunnels shown in Figs. 1 and 2 are 'closed circuit' types, the same air circulating continuously around a closed duct. In small tunnels, with a working section of only a few square inches, the air is often taken from the atmosphere and rejected after passing through the fan at the end of the diffuser—an 'open circuit' type of tunnel (Fig. 3). It is sometimes convenient to use an open working section tunnel, in which there are no solid walls to the working section, and the airstream is a free jet.

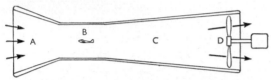

FIG. 3. DIAGRAM OF OPEN-CIRCUIT WIND TUNNEL
A. Contraction cone. B. Working section. C. Diffuser. D. Fan

When an air speed greater than the speed of sound (that is, above about 760 miles per hour) is required, the horse-power absorbed by the tunnel becomes very large indeed, since power is wasted not only by friction between the air and walls but also by the shock waves which inevitably occur. Fig. 4 shows the shock wave pattern around a supersonic aerofoil section (a section of a wing) in a wind tunnel at 1·8 times the speed of sound. Such tunnels are therefore usually rather small: one of the largest in the

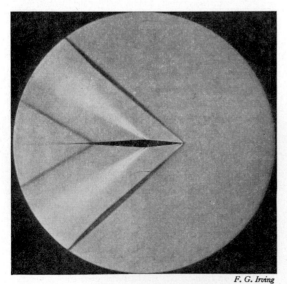

F. G. Irving

FIG. 4. FLOW AROUND A SUPERSONIC AEROFOIL SECTION AT 1·8 TIMES THE SPEED OF SOUND

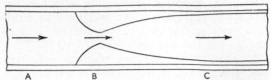

FIG. 5. DIAGRAM OF PART OF A WIND TUNNEL USED FOR SUPERSONIC SPEEDS
A. Speed is less than sound. B. Speed of sound at throat. C. Supersonic speed
(Figs. 1, 2, 3, 5 after Pankhurst and Holder, 'Wind Tunnel Technique', Pitman)

world has a working section of 6 ft. by 6 ft. and is driven by motors of about 20,000 h.p. A single fan could not carry this enormous power, so an axial-flow COMPRESSOR (q.v.) is used instead, rather like that of a gas turbine on a very large scale. Upstream of the working section, a supersonic nozzle is provided which contracts to a 'throat', and then expands (Fig. 5). The air reaches the speed of sound at the throat and then accelerates to supersonic speed in the diverging part. Otherwise the general layout is similar to Fig. 1 except that a more elaborate type of diffuser may be needed. Since large variations of air pressure occur in a supersonic wind tunnel, the construction must be very strong and rigid, and there must be a large cooling plant. The air must be kept very dry to prevent moisture condensing in the working section.

Continuous-flow supersonic wind tunnels of large size consume an enormous amount of power while they are running. The power can be obtained more cheaply by using an intermittent tunnel. One way of achieving very high air speeds is to compress air and store it in a receiver at high pressure; and then, when the tunnel is worked, to allow the air to escape very quickly through the working section. Another way is to connect to one end of the tunnel a large container from which all the air has been pumped out, and then to admit at the other end air from the atmosphere which will immediately flow very quickly through the working section and into the vacuum in the container. This method is more efficient for getting big pressure ratios between the two ends of the tunnel. For the highest speeds of all a combination of both methods can be used—a high pressure receiver at one end of the working section and an evacuated container at the other.

Apart from the types of wind tunnel described here, there are many special types. For example, in a 'free flight' tunnel used for experiments in aeroplane stability, the whole tunnel can be

Crown Copyright

MODEL AIRCRAFT BEING TESTED IN A WIND TUNNEL
Reproduced by permission of the Controller, H.M.S.O.

tilted so that the model glides downhill against the airstream without any support.

See also HYDRODYNAMICS; MODEL ENGINEERING.

WIRE DRAWING. Ordinary wire is made from comparatively thick rods of metal which are drawn, that is, pulled, through a series of wire drawing dies (Fig. 1), each smaller than the previous one. The dies are circular in shape, with a circular hole tapering from the top and bottom surfaces towards the centre, where the hole is slightly smaller than the rod to be drawn through it. It follows, therefore, that as the rod passes through the hole, it becomes reduced in diameter and is elongated. Modern dies are made from an extremely hard material known as tungsten carbide, or, for fine wires, from a diamond having a hole of the required size drilled through the centre of it. Any metal can be formed into wire. Some wires are very thick, while some, made for special purposes, are finer than a human hair.

The rolled rods from which wire is drawn can be as much as 1 inch in diameter. The rod is supplied in coils, each coil containing about 30 ft. The coil is first softened, or 'annealed', by being heated in a furnace in order to give it

ductility; if it were drawn without annealing it would crack in the die (*see* HEAT TREATMENT). Annealing causes a scale to form on the surface, and this is removed by immersing the coil in cold hydrochloric or heated sulphuric acid, a process called 'pickling'. With some metals, however, pickling can cause brittleness unless the process is carefully controlled. In a new alternative process, which is not yet widely used, the rod is alternately bent and beaten mechanically to remove the scale.

The coils are then sprayed with water under pressure to remove all traces of acid. This spraying, known as 'sull-coating', causes an oxide film to form on the wire, and this, together with a further coating formed by dipping the coils in hot lime, makes a base to which soap will adhere, thus forming a lubricant to help the passage of the wire through the dies. After being electrically welded together into continuous lengths according to the length of wire to be drawn, the coils are ready for the drawing machine.

The larger sizes of wire rod may be drawn on a single wire-drawing machine, called a bull-block (Fig. 2); but the finer wire sizes are drawn on multiple wire-drawing machines, in which the wire may pass through as many as twenty dies, being reduced in diameter as it passes through each. The wire is drawn by a motorized block somewhat resembling a miniature ship's capstan, round which the wire is wound before being passed on to the next die.

Since the wire increases in length as it is reduced in diameter, each of the blocks must be made to revolve correspondingly faster to keep the wire taut.

Wire of any metal is made in this way, but the non-ferrous metals, such as copper, can be drawn

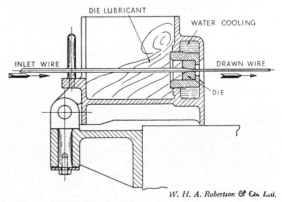

W. H. A. Robertson & Co. Ltd.

FIG. 1. SECTION THROUGH A BULL-BLOCK DIEHOLDER

FIG. 2. A BULL-BLOCK

much finer. For instance, a copper wire rod measuring $4\frac{1}{2}$ inches by $4\frac{3}{4}$ inches by $4\frac{1}{4}$ inches can be drawn into approximately 1,300 feet of $\frac{1}{4}$-inch diameter rod. If this was drawn down to a very fine wire of 0·0024-inch diameter, there would be nearly 2,557 miles of wire. For these very fine gauges, the final drawing stages are totally immersed in lubricant.

The size of wire is measured by the standard wire gauge, known as S.W.G. In this 7/0 S.W.G. (seven noughts gauge) represents a diameter of 0·5000 inch; 0 S.W.G. equals 0·3240 inch; and as the gauge numbers increase, so the wire diameter decreases, until 50 S.W.G. is reached for very fine wires of 0·0010-inch diameter. For easy approximate measurement of wire sizes a gauge similar to a knitting needle gauge is used: it consists of a flat plate in which holes of approximate size have been cut.

WIRELESS, *see* RADIO ENGINEERING. *See also* Vol. IV: WIRELESS TELEGRAPHY, HISTORY OF.

WOODWORKING MACHINERY.

WOODWORKING MACHINERY. All woodworking operations, from TIMBER FELLING (q.v. Vol. VI) to WOODCARVING (q.v. Vol. XII), have been known since very early times, but today most of them can be carried out by machines. The first operation after the trees have been felled, the branches lopped off, and the trunks cut into lengths is to cut up the logs into planks of a convenient size.

The first log-cutting machines were developed on the lines of the hand-saw; that is, they consisted of a thin, straight saw clamped horizontally in a frame and moved to and fro whilst the log was fed slowly into it. Many of these frame-saws can still be seen working in country districts at the present time and producing excellent work.

A variation of the horizontal frame-saw is the vertical frame, in which the saws are placed vertically and move up and down, being driven through cranks by a steam engine or electric motor. As many as twenty or more such saws may be mounted in a single machine so that a log may be cut up into a number of boards during one pass through the machine. This type of machine, though not used much in Britain, is the machine most used in the Scandinavian countries where they have an almost unlimited supply of small diameter SOFTWOODS (q.v. Vol. VII).

In Britain the frame-saw has been almost entirely superseded in the larger mills by the band-saw. Fig. 1 shows what is known as a band-mill. The saw is an endless toothed band, from 4 to 10 inches wide, running on two wheels at a very high speed. The logs are held on a movable carriage by a number of large pincers called 'dogs'. These bite into the log and hold it securely whilst it is being sawn. Once a log has been 'dogged' into position, the operator controls the sawing and all the movements of the log mechanically by means of levers controlling gearing to move the carriage past the saw.

In another type of log-saw, known as the band rack, the logs, instead of being held by 'dogs', rest on a flat table. When the first cut is being taken, the log is wedged so that it cannot move under the thrust of the saw, and then it is turned so that the sawn flat face rests on the table, and is cut up as required. The table is moved by power and is controlled by the operator as in the case of the band-mill.

The circular rack bench, another machine used for 'breaking-down' the logs, is exactly the

T. Robinson & Son

FIG. I. BAND-MILL USED FOR BREAKING DOWN LOGS INTO
PLANKS

As the carriage moves forward the toothed band A cuts
through the log, which is held in place by 'dogs' B

same as the band rack, except that a large circular saw is used in place of the bandsaw.

When the logs have been reduced to planks of a commercial size, the planks often have to be sawn again to still smaller sizes by machines known as 're-saws'. These can be either bandsaws or circular saws—the planks being fed past the saw by means of toothed rollers, or by hand.

All the machines so far mentioned are for cutting the timber straight. For cutting curves a machine like a miniature band-mill is used, fitted with saws of varying widths from $\frac{1}{4}$ to $1\frac{1}{2}$ inches. The operator usually feeds the material to the saw so as to follow closely the required shape, which has previously been drawn on it. Large fretsaws are sometimes used for this purpose, but the narrow band-saw, being very much quicker, is more often used.

The next important operation in woodworking is that of planing. Machine planing is really a misnomer, for it is in fact an adzing or 'chipping' operation (Fig. 2). The plank is placed on the front table, held down by hand and slowly passed over a cutterblock which is revolving at 5,000 r.p.m. or more. These cutterblocks carry two or more knives, and when one cutter has removed a chip, the wood is moved forward slightly before the next one comes round, so that the 'planed' surface is not truly flat but consists of a series of minute regular waves.

The quality of machine planing depends to a large extent upon the smallness of the waves. The slower the plank is moved and the faster the cutterblock revolves, the closer the cuts are together and the better the surface. With cheaper work the feed speed is increased so as to lower production costs, and the waves are more apparent.

The surface planer is used to plane one side of the timber and also the edges if this is required. To reduce the pieces to a uniform thickness a machine known as a panel planer is used. In this case the material is rested on a table and fed underneath the cutters by means of rollers.

These machines are used to a large extent in small shops; but for really high production, machines known as four-cutters are used (Fig. 3), the four sides of the material being operated upon simultaneously as it passes through the machine. The operator feeds the rough-sawn pieces in at one end, whilst his helper removes the finished work as it comes out at the other end. These machines not only carry out square planing but can work the wood to any reasonable moulded shape with equal facility—it is merely a matter of putting cutters of the correct profile on the cutterblocks.

When the timber has to be painted only, it is often used as it comes from the planing machines, but when it has to be polished—as for furniture—it needs a sanding operation to remove the wave marks made by the cutters.

There are many different types of sanding machines, perhaps the most common being the triple-drum sander. This large machine consists essentially of a table over which an endless belt of rubber moves and above which are mounted three drums about 12 inches in diameter. These revolve very fast, at the same time oscillating an inch or so sideways. The first drum is covered

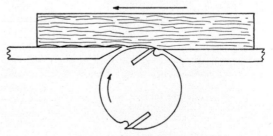

FIG. 2. DIAGRAM OF MACHINE PLANING

The wood is fed past revolving cutters which remove
minute chips (greatly exaggerated here) and so produce a
smooth and practically flat surface

J. Long & Sons

FIG. 3. A FOUR-CUTTER

The rough wood is fed in on the right and finished pieces delivered on the left. A. Hoods covering two of the cutterblocks. B. Rollers feeding the wood through the machine. C. Electrical controls. D. Pneumatic extraction unit for removing the chips from the machine as they are made

Crown Copyright

CUTTING VENEER FOR PLYWOOD

By permission of the Director, Forest Products Research Laboratory

with a coarse sandpaper, the second with a medium grade, and the third one with a fine paper. The height of these drums is adjusted extremely accurately so that each one removes just as much wood as is necessary to produce a smooth surface.

Almost all the other operations of woodwork, such as tenoning, mortising, boring, and dovetailing (*see* CARPENTRY AND JOINERY, Vol. VII) can also be done by special machines. In most cases the tool revolves and the wood is moved under it, but in some cases the wood remains stationary while the tool is moved into it.

See also Vol. VII: TIMBER INDUSTRY; WOODWORK, HISTORY OF; CARPENTRY AND JOINERY.

X

X-RAYS. These belong to the large group of radiations that includes light, heat, and radio waves (*see* RADIATION, Vol. III). All these radiations consist of electromagnetic waves which travel in straight lines at the speed of light—186,000 miles per second. The differences between the various kinds of radiation are due to the fact that their waves have different 'wavelengths'. X-rays, which were discovered in 1895 by the German physicist W K. von Röntgen, have such very short wavelengths that there are about 100,000,000 of them to one inch, about 2,000 times shorter than light waves. X-rays are invisible and can pass through considerable thicknesses of substances such as wood, brick, and steel which are quite opaque to light. They also pass freely through the human body.

X-rays are made by passing a high-voltage electric current through a glass tube (Fig. 1).

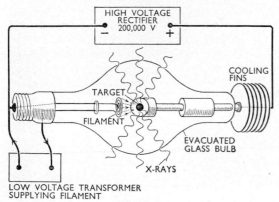

FIG. I. DIAGRAM OF AN X-RAY TUBE

This tube, which is empty of air, contains a flat spiral filament of tungsten wire, which is heated white hot by an ordinary low-voltage electric current. Facing the filament is a heavy rod of tungsten, a metal which can stand enormous heat, and this is cut across at an angle, the sloping face of the rod being called the target. The white-hot filament gives off large numbers of minute particles of negative electricity called electrons. A RECTIFIER (q.v.) producing a very high voltage has its positive terminal joined to the target and its negative terminal joined to the filament. The electrons from the hot filament are accelerated by this high voltage, and strike the target at high speeds, producing X-rays which radiate in all directions.

The X-ray tube is surrounded by thick lead screens which stop the X-rays from escaping, except for a narrow beam in one direction. This screening is necessary because exposure to X-rays for long periods can be very harmful to the health of anyone working with them. The whole apparatus is enclosed in a metal case joined to an 'earth' to protect the operator from receiving electric shocks from the very high voltage supply. The high-speed bombardment of the target by the electrons makes it so hot that in high-power X-ray tubes it is made hollow and is cooled by water or oil being pumped through it.

The wavelength of the rays generated by an X-ray tube depends upon the voltage of the rectifier. The higher the voltage used, the shorter the wavelength, and the shorter the wavelengths the greater thickness of materials the rays can penetrate before they are stopped; short wavelength rays are therefore called 'hard' X-rays, and long wavelength rays, 'soft' X-rays. X-ray machines are usually fitted with a control that alters the voltage of the rectifier and so adjusts the penetrating power of the rays. The quantity of X-rays produced depends on the number of electrons striking the target, and this depends on the strength of the electric current that heats the filament. These separate controls for penetration and quantity are needed in order to produce clear X-ray pictures.

Although X-rays are invisible, a beam of them, if directed at a glass plate coated with zinc oxide, will cause the plate to glow. If a hand, for example, is placed between the X-ray machine and this glass plate, the screen, a light shadow of the hand is cast upon the screen, with the bones casting deeper shadows than the flesh and so standing out clearly. The picture on the screen, therefore, shows not only the shape but the internal structure of the hand. A very thick object placed in the X-ray beam simply casts a dark

AN X-RAY PHOTOGRAPH OF AN AUTOMATIC PISTOL WITH
A BULLET PASSING DOWN THE BARREL

Crown Copyright

X-rays can affect a photographic plate, and X-ray photographs, or 'radiographs', can be used to reveal the internal details even of thick objects.

Radiographs are used by dentists to examine teeth, and by doctors to examine broken bones, to trace metal articles such as bullets in the body, and to detect certain diseases such as tuberculosis of the lungs. Engineers use radiographs for examining metals to ensure that they are free from internal cracks and flaws. Steel plates up to 11 inches thick can be penetrated by the very hard X-rays from a 1,000,000-volt machine. Soft X-rays are used in factories to inspect finished articles such as fountain pens, electric irons, and sparking plugs.

See also Vol. III: RADIATION.
See also Vol. XI: RADIOTHERAPY.

shadow, because the X-rays that pass through it are too weak to make the screen glow. After several minutes' exposure, however, these weak

K.L.M.

WIERINGEN MEER POLDER IN 1931
In the foreground is the old town of Medemblik

Z

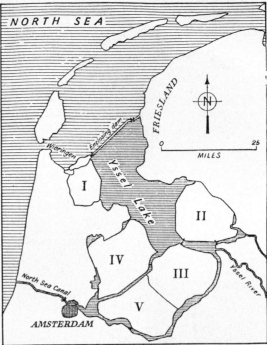

MAP OF THE ZUIDER ZEE SHOWING THE POLDERS CONSTRUCTED AND PLANNED

I. Wieringen Meer polder, 1926–30. II. North-east polder, 1936–42. III. Flevoland-East, 1950–57? IV. Marker Waard, 1957–63? V. Flevoland-South, 1963–69?

ZUIDER ZEE PROJECT (Holland). This is one of the most spectacular schemes of LAND RECLAMATION (q.v.) in the world. When the project is complete, 538,000 acres of fertile agricultural land, some of which is already under cultivation, will have been recovered from the sea. It is the climax of 700 years of toil during which the DUTCH (q.v. Vol. I) have reclaimed over 2,000 square miles from the North Sea and from inland lakes (*see* HOLLAND, Vol. III).

Until the 20th century the Zuider Zee was a shallow arm of the North Sea, driving deeper and deeper into Holland as it washed away the peaty soil. The water was nowhere deeper than 40 feet, and in many places only 8 to 15 feet deep. Its bottom consisted mainly of fertile clay. Between 1887–91 a Dutch engineer, Dr. C. Lely, prepared plans for a tremendous engineering scheme which would rescue this fertile clay for agriculture. Lely suggested that the main area of the Zuider Zee should be shut off from the North Sea, to form a gigantic inland lake, by two enclosure DAMS (q.v.): a small one, about 1½ miles long, from North Holland to the island of Wieringen; and a second stretching nearly 20 miles from Wieringen to the Frisian coast (*see* Map). He proposed that about two-thirds of this lake should be reclaimed; the remaining one-third should receive the waters of the river Yssel, one of the branches of the Rhine delta, to form a fresh-water lake. Water from this lake could then be used for the IRRIGATION (q.v. Vol. VI) of the land to the east and west, which had become seriously affected by salt from the sea. The enclosure dams would themselves have two important advantages: they would provide a short traffic route between the north-west and north-east of the country, and, more important, they would protect the long line of dykes en-

circling the Zuider Zee from the direct attack of gales (*see* FLOOD CONTROL).

Though Lely's plan was approved, the country could not afford such a gigantic undertaking until after the First World War; in fact, it was not until 1920 that work began. The main dam had to be built in the open sea, facing storms and rough seas which often threatened to sweep it away. It took 3 years in all to construct. The sea-bed for the most part was firm enough to carry the embankment, but over a small stretch layers of softer sub-soil had first to be replaced with sand. The embankment was built of boulder-clay—a firm, tough loam, which resists the 'scour' of flowing water and the action of waves extremely well. On the outer side of the embankment a second dam of boulder-clay was built, with its crest at the level of the highest storm-floods and backed by sand covered with a layer of clay or boulder-clay. Below the water-line the earthwork was protected by weighted mattresses of brushwood, and above the water-line by stone and brick.

The boulder-clay and sand had first to be

K.L.M.

THE DAM ENCLOSING YSSEL LAKE IN COURSE OF
CONSTRUCTION

27 large dredgers, 13 floating cranes and belt conveyors, 132 barges, and 60 tugs were at work.

By 1932 the strong tidal currents sweeping through the last gap in the boulder-clay dam were stemmed, and the enclosure of the Zuider Zee had been achieved. Four years later the new Yssel lake was filled with fresh water.

By this time the first polder (area protected by dykes) of some 50,000 acres had already been reclaimed. While the enclosure dam was being built, work had begun on the dyke which would separate and protect this polder from the Yssel lake. This dyke was completed in 1930, and a year later the water had been pumped away, using special high-capacity PUMPS (q.v.) driven by electricity or Diesel engines. Farming started as soon as the soil had been washed clear of salt deposits. In 1942 a second polder of 120,000 acres was reclaimed, about 330,000 million gallons of water being pumped off the land from three immense pumping stations. Work has now started on a third polder, protected from the Yssel lake by a great dyke 56 miles long, and two more polders (each of 125,000 acres) to the south of the Yssel lake are planned. The polders themselves are inter-connected by a network of tunnels and bridges. During the disastrous floods of 1953 the enclosure dam stood fast against the sea and little flooding occurred in that area; the dam itself suffered only slight damage.

The population of this new land will depend mainly on agriculture, though light industries are being developed. The capital, called Lely-stad after Dr. Lely, consisted in 1953 of a group of huts and a pumping station, perched on the dyke, but eventually it will have over 50,000 inhabitants. The total population of the new land is planned to be more than a quarter of a million.

See also LAND RECLAMATION; DAMS; FLOOD CONTROL.
See also Vol. III: HOLLAND.

dredged by bucket and suction DREDGERS (q.v. Vol. IV). The material was then placed in hopper-barges, towed by tugs, and dumped in position. As the depth of water decreased, the boulder-clay was discharged from barges by large floating CRANES (q.v.) fitted with grab buckets. The upper layer of sand was discharged from barges, through the pipes of suction-dredgers, and the clay protecting the sand by floating belt CONVEYORS (q.v.). Before the boulder-clay dam was made, brushwood mattresses were towed into place and sunk in order to protect the sea bottom against erosion. At one time